Hingley, Ronald.

   Rn Writers in Society

Chetin –

Kobuzon –
   Naust. manderion + Rowin
    (1956?)

{ Anderson, Borden
  Cole, Andsley.

SCIENCE IN RUSSIAN CULTURE

Science in Russian Culture

A History to 1860

ALEXANDER VUCINICH

1963
Stanford University Press
Stanford, California

Stanford University Press
Stanford, California
© 1963 by the Board of Trustees of the
Leland Stanford Junior University
Library of Congress Catalog Card Number: 63-19238
Printed in the United States of America

Published with the assistance of the
FORD FOUNDATION

To Dorothy

Preface

Political history, social and religious thought, the arts, and most of the other dimensions of Russian life have been dealt with rather extensively in Western historical literature, but science as a component of Russian culture has been almost completely ignored. This is understandable enough, since science is infinitely less expressive of unique national and cultural values than the arts, philosophy, and—in the case of Russia—religious thought. Lobachevskii's non-Euclidean geometry, Chebyshev's work in the theory of probability, and Butlerov's theory of the structure of chemical compounds tell us much less about Russian culture than Gogol's *Dead Souls*, Lermontov's poetry, and Rimsky-Korsakov's music.

It has also been a deterrent to scholarly interest that science developed rather late in Russia, and that until it began to flourish in the 1860's it was dominated by foreign scholars. Perhaps more important, most Western interpreters of Russian culture have seen the Russian mind as essentially irrational, if not antirational: looking at the work of Dostoevskii, the Slavophils, the Eastern Orthodox theologians, and such leading religious philosophers as Solov'ev, Fedorov, and Berdyaev as representative of the spiritual essence of Russian culture, historians have often concluded that science, at least until the twentieth century, was a rationalist aberration operating on the fringes of Russia's cultural life.

This view is hard to accept. Not only does it offer no help in understanding the great Russian scientists and scientific accomplishments of the nineteenth century; it also fails utterly to explain why Russia was the first, and is now the foremost, nation to embrace what Lord Keynes called the reductio ad absurdum of rationalism, the philosophy of Karl Marx. Above all, it offers no explanation of the present high level of Soviet science and technology.

I began this work in part because I thought a systematic general account of the accomplishments of Russian scientists would be interesting, but perhaps more because I hoped that by tracing the growth of science in Russia I could cast some new light on the dynamics of Russian culture itself. I was eager to deal with the development of science in the Soviet Union, but realizing that I could not fully appreciate that development in a cultural sense without finding its deepest historical roots, I decided to begin at the beginning: this first volume therefore deals only with the formative age of Russian science, which had ended by the 1860's. The growth of science from that time into the Soviet period will be the subject of a second volume.

I am deeply indebted to the Social Science Research Council for a grant that enabled me to devote an entire year to intensive research for this study. A joint grant from the American Council of Learned Societies and the Social Science Research Council allowed me to make the writing of this book a concentrated and uninterrupted undertaking, for which I am grateful. I am likewise indebted to the American Philosophical Society for a grant that enabled me to undertake a final survey of materials available in the great libraries of this country. I also owe thanks to the Hoover Institution for a grant that lightened my teaching duties during the last months of the writing of this volume, and for the generous professional help of its library staff.

I am happy to express my gratitude to Mrs. Shirley Taylor, for her stylistic suggestions and astute criticism; to J. G. Bell, for his many important suggestions for improving the manuscript as a whole and for his untiring search and feeling for precision in fact, style, and logic; and to Gene Tanke, for highly competent and dedicated help during the last stages of preparing the manuscript for publication. I am also grateful to Professor Firuz Kazemzadeh for his careful reading of the manuscript and his helpful substantive criticisms.

A. VUCINICH

Los Altos Hills, California
September 1963

Contents

Introduction

The history of science is an academic label for three complementary branches of historical inquiry. The first and most popular branch is concerned with the evolution of scientific ideas. The historian shows, for example, how one mathematical formula or theorem has led to another, how a hypothesis has been subjected to experimental tests, how a concept has been sharpened or modified, how the scope of scientific inquiry has been broadened, or how the process of fission has produced new sciences. He concentrates on describing the progressive refinement of methodology.

A second branch is philosophic. It is concerned with changes in the logical patterns of scientific explanations, the intellectual sources of scientific knowledge, the relationship of science to other modes of inquiry, and the validation of scientific knowledge. The historian traces, for example, the scientific correlates of Locke's and Hume's empiricism, Kant's transcendental idealism, Mach's and Avenarius's empiriocriticism, or modern logical positivism. He stresses the consequences, whether enriching or disruptive, of individual philosophical orientations.

The third branch deals with the cultural integration of scientific thought. The historian views science not only as a system of knowledge, but also as an attitude and a cluster of values. His concern is with science as a social institution, and with scientists as members of society, with specific social roles. He examines changes in society's valuation of science, and in the scientist's valuation of society. His emphasis is on the social and institutional setting in which the scientist works.

The present study is of the third type. My concern is with the influence of social environment on scientific thought in pre-Reform Russia, and generally with the place science occupied in Russian culture. Ideology, education, and religion are treated as particularly important parts of this environment, but some attention is also given to literary currents, economic and technological developments, political upheavals in Russia and in the West, urbanization, and changing patterns of social stratification. In effect, this book is primarily a study of cultural change as indexed by the development of science and the scientific attitude.

Official ideology everywhere occupies a central position in the social environment of science, but in pre-Reform Russia it affected the very core of scientific thought. The mechanistic "absolutism" of Newton, with its assumption of a perfect, symmetrical, and ahistorical universe, was most agreeable to an autocracy that saw its own privileges and its serfs' burdens in absolute rather than historical terms. The same autocracy was slow to accept the historical orientation of Kant's and Laplace's nebular hypothesis of the origin of the solar system and the evolution of the stars and the planets, Caspar Wolff's theory of epigenesis, Buffon's rudimentary trans- formism in general biology, and Lyell's historical geology. It is worth noting that the first serious efforts on the part of the Russian government to impose a rigid ideological control over science coincided with the emer- gence of the historical view in natural science.

A consideration of ideology inevitably leads to the problem of deter- mining the role of freedom of thought, a complex inquiry not easily closed by categorical generalizations. Crane Brinton reminds us that modern sci- ence developed in a Europe ruled for the most part by absolute monarchs, and that "it owed much to the patronage of these monarchs and their min- isters." Indeed, the sources of freedom are many: a scientist's freedom may derive from the King's favor, from the farsightedness of a state or a patron class, or from the scientist's own ability and determination not to accept restrictions, including the dead weight of custom and authority.

If real freedom of thought prevails, it applies to all types of inquiry, whether scientific, metaphysical, or religious, whether antithetical to pre- judgment or dependent upon it, whether proclaiming the boundless powers of man's rational faculty or insisting upon its intrinsic limitations. But the benefits of free scientific thought may also be offset by the disruptive effects of free thought that is antiscientific, unscientific, or pseudoscientific. Free- dom of thought undoubtedly enriches any culture, but it does not necessarily make for richer *scientific* development.

In describing the complex relationship of science to ideology it is im- portant to bear in mind that science is only one of several modes of inquiry into the problems of the universe; it competes with metaphysical, theologi- cal, aesthetic, and ethical approaches, among others. But science is unique in one important respect: in Max Weber's words, it is "chained to the course of progress." There are no objectively valid criteria to prove the superiority of, say, modern drama over Greek tragedy, of twentieth-century philosophy over the philosophy of Hume or Kant or Hegel, or of our ethical precepts over those of medieval Arabia. But the superiority of modern over Aristotelian physics, of present-day over phlogiston chemistry, of evolutionary over preformist biology, cannot be seriously questioned.

The progress of science—indeed, its very existence—depends on its tolerance of change. Scientific progress is achieved not by sanctifying present knowledge, but by pointing out its inadequacies and seeking to remedy them. To quote Samuel Stouffer, "Science, unlike art and literature, is cumulative, in the sense that a scientific achievement is most successful when it stimulates others to make the concepts and techniques it has used look crude and become obsolete as rapidly as possible." Every scientist is a source of cultural change. He may not be a champion of change; he may even resist it, as scholars of the past resisted the new truths of historical geology, biological evolution, unitary chemistry, and non-Euclidean geometry. But to the extent that he is a true professional, the scientist is inescapably an agent of change. His tools are the instruments of change—skepticism, the challenge to established authority, criticism, rationality, and individuality. And it is here, of course, that the official ideologist raises an eyebrow.

In Russia, particularly after the mid-point in the reign of Catherine II, the guardians of official ideology took up a typically ambivalent attitude toward science: they respected it as a way of attaining practical results, but they feared it as a competing ideology. They especially feared its acceptance as an ideology by intellectuals outside the scientific profession, and above all by schoolteachers.

The school system is another important component of the social environment that bears directly on the development of science and the scientific attitude. The progress of science is basically affected not only by the quality of scientific instruction, but by what various social classes think of education as a formal process and science as a vocation, by what society chooses to have its children taught in school, and by which children get to go to school in the first place. The school is not only an institution dedicated to the dissemination of knowledge; it is also a social agency entrusted with transmitting the official ideology to the young.

Describing the relationship of religion to science is perhaps the most difficult task confronting the cultural historian, for it leads him deep into an age-old conflict between value systems, a social struggle involving all sectors of society in which the battle lines are constantly shifting. In the abstract, the nature of the confrontation seems clear. Both religion and science seek to unravel the riddles of the universe and man's place in it, but their "methods of inquiry" are philosophical opposites. Religion is essentially absolutist, intolerant of change and criticism. Science, by contrast, is relentessly relativist; it thrives on criticism, skepticism, and cultural surroundings amenable to change. Science fits securely into the rationalist tradition; religion is essentially antirationalist. But the actions of men in both camps, and the social dynamics of their conflict, are not so easily categorized. Many impressive reconciliations of religion and science have been put forward—by pious scientists and by scholarly priests—but the battle goes on. In nineteenth-century Russia it raged as fiercely as anywhere.

Three kinds of emphasis appear in this study: biographical, disciplinary, and institutional.

Biographically, I have focused on leading scholars; on champions of new scientific viewpoints, even if they were not scholars of the first rank; and on popularizers of the scientific point of view, whether or not they were involved in original research. Aleksandr Herzen, for example, was not a scientist by vocation and made no contributions to scientific theory, but he was an eloquent and influential champion of science. I have paid particular attention to the cultural role of these scientists and popularizers of science.

No effort has been made to cover every scientific discipline systematically. My concern has been rather with the relationship of individual sciences to the social environment. I have tried also to describe the reaction of Russian scientists to such turning points in the history of modern science as the introduction of the historical view in geology and embryology, the atomistic view in chemistry and anatomy, the configurational view in medicine and physiology, the relativistic view in geometry, and the evolutionary view in biology. Finally, I have tried to identify the ingredients that have gone into building the several great Russian scientific traditions (particularly mathematics), and, conversely, to identify the cultural barriers that prevented a normal development of some sciences in Russia. I have necessarily used a lot of space simply to describe what happened in the various scientific disciplines: what Russian scientists did, what they thought, how their work was received, how it resembled or differed from the work of their Western counterparts.

In deciding which intellectual pursuits should be considered scientific, I have remained largely within the realm of modern science—the scientific thought pioneered by Copernicus, Kepler, Galileo, Newton, and their likes. I have ignored folk science, common-sense technology, and the more recondite sciences and concepts of science. I have given some attention to the humanities, particularly history, but only insofar as the scholars engaged in those disciplines were guided by scientific criteria and were devoted to a search for objective and verifiable knowledge, subject to comparative analysis and generalization. History is emphasized because, to quote Geoffrey Barraclough, "no historian, whatever his dogmatic position may be, can avoid the sort of theorization which is the foundation of a scientific approach."

Institutional analysis—the study of organizations concerned with scientific inquiry—is particularly important for a study that stresses the broader cultural matrix of science. In pre-reform Russia there were four basic types of scientific institution: the academy, the university, the voluntary or semi-independent learned society, and the government agency. Each of these types had its own configuration of standards, academic interests, and attractions for its members; each had its own relationship to the larger community. In particular, the study of these institutions offers interesting insights into the scientist's professional code and the training of future scientists.

This study may be useful as the first more or less comprehensive English-language survey of the most important achievements of Russian scientists and scholars in the century preceding the great flowering of Russian science that began in the 1860's. It is intended primarily, however, not as a chronicle or catalog, but as a historical and sociological analysis of the growth of the *scientific attitude* in Russia—the development of the specific view toward the origin, value, meaning, and utility of secular knowledge that is held today by most intellectuals in Russia and the West.

PART I

THE ROOTS OF RUSSIAN SCIENCE

CHAPTER ONE

The Origins of the Scientific Attitude
in Old Russia

BYZANTINISM

The Byzantine influence on the intellectual tradition of Old Russia was essentially theological, yet it affected every type of search for knowledge and gave a remarkable degree of unity to the moral code and to creative intellectual activity. A special class of Greco-Slavic "teachers" codified theological thought and safeguarded its purity. They were the originators of what came to be known as Byzantinism, an attitude which glorified moral education and for the most part ignored secular studies of nature, society, and man. Basically an antirationalist ideology, it had little use for the labors of Byzantine scholars whose interests did not fall within the rigid limits of official religious philosophy.

The history of Byzantine secular scholarship can hardly be termed a period in the growth of science; yet there were proponents of scientific inquiry during the whole era of the Byzantine Empire—men who, by serving as a link first between classical and Arab scholarship, and then between the Arab heritage and the Renaissance, contributed importantly to the development of scientific thought. The scientific contributions of these Byzantine scholars were, of course, barred from Russia by the power of the Church. Alexander of Tralles (525–605), who left a dozen treatises on pathology and therapeutics; his brother Anthemius, a mathematician, physician, engineer, and architect; and Isidore of Miletus, a mathematician, represented the type of early Byzantine learned men who preserved and elaborated upon ancient scholarship, but the Church blocked all the avenues by which their thought could reach Russia. Alchemy, for example, was one of the particular interests of the Byzantines, yet Russia was noted for the absence of persons engaged in this art.[1]

The direct Byzantine influence on Russia was limited to a theological systematization of religious dogma and to moral-religious education. Most

Church writers were in some measure concerned with a reconciliation of the wisdom of ancient paganism with Christian precepts, and in their writings they brought to Russian soil a few traces—often corrupted—of ancient thought. But the contributions of Hippocrates, Dioscorides, Hipparchus, Apollonius of Perga, and Strato were unknown in Russia until the eighteenth century.

For a long time the Church was guided by Greek metropolitans and priests, whose main task was to render the sacred writings into Church-Slavic and to uphold the approved standards of theological thought. The absolute conservatism of the Church, which consistently opposed intellectual innovations, either Western or native, was dedicated to a perpetuation of the dogma as formulated by early Byzantine writers. Latin, and everything written in it, was for centuries considered the devil's tool and an enemy of Orthodoxy. The budding sciences and skeptical philosophy, with their cumulative challenges to the sacred authority of theological dogmatism, did not find even a feeble echo in Russia.

The two hundred years of Tatar rule are often called a dark age in Russian history, a period of retarded cultural growth, or, at best, of the stagnation of Russian civilization. Under the Tatars, the Church actually suffered very little, if at all. The khans gave ecclesiastical authorities an enviable degree of autonomy and political power. Monasteries flourished: whereas during the four centuries preceding the Tatar conquest 90 monasteries were established, during the centuries of Tatar yoke 150 monasteries came into existence in northeastern Russia alone. Under the Tatars the Church, because of its monopoly on educational activities, became an important political agency poised against the growth of secular cultural forces. The intellectual aridity of this epoch is amply illustrated by the fact that it did not produce a single work with any reference to or use of mathematical knowledge.[2]

For many centuries the writings of John of Damascus, who lived in the eighth century, determined the theological orientation of the Church and its views on philosophy, science, and other secular intellectual pursuits. The chief work of this scholar, *The Fountain of Knowledge,* was translated in the tenth century by John, the Exarch of Bulgaria;[3] subsequently it went through many translations and until well into the eighteenth century provided the Church with all the ammunition it needed in its struggle against heretical movements. Part of this work, entitled "Dialectic," had a definite Aristotelian orientation. It defined philosophy as the highest wisdom, through which man approaches the divine omniscience, and contained elaborate discussions about such antinomial concepts as the essential and the ephemeral phenomena, the similarity and the difference, the quality and the quantity.

In the sixteenth century the still undiminished authority of John of Damascus acquired new strength from the interpretations of Maxim the Greek (1480–1556), who was at first his strict follower. Philosophy, Maxim the Greek asserted, is concerned primarily with God, His justice, and His deeds; it also codifies the moral ideas upon which human societies are built. Yet despite these high qualities, philosophy is inferior to theology because it lacks divine inspiration, and it should be tolerated only to the extent that it generates piety. It becomes dangerous when it crosses the boundaries of the sacred and begins to wander into the slippery bypaths of secular thought. Maxim the Greek admitted that the secular sciences might be beneficial to man, but he was inclined to think that their inherent dangers might outweigh their temporary benefits. Indeed, he was apprehensive of the study of nature because of its tendency to contradict the holy writings. He concluded that "by adhering to the books of John of Damascus you will become both a great theologian and a student of nature."[4] In his opinion, which was shared by the priestly community of sixteenth-century Russia, no writings had been produced since the time of John of Damascus to challenge the truth of his theological thought or the soundness of his appraisal of philosophy and science.

THE RISE OF THEOLOGICAL CRITICISM

With the fall of Constantinople the Russian Church was freed from Byzantine administrative tutelage, but it still clung tenaciously to the Byzantine theological tradition. Maxim the Greek's exuberant reaffirmation of John of Damascus's theological ideas was an index of the Church's unflagging conservatism. This intransigence of the religious hierarchy was solidified by Russia's isolation from Western culture and its gradually developing body of secular and humanistic thought.

The isolation, however, was not airtight, and from time to time flutterings of theological and social criticism emanated from ecclesiastic dissidents of varying opinions. Maxim the Greek gradually became disillusioned with many aspects of religious ideology—particularly with the Church's social and economic orientation—and turned into a powerful and influential critic of the ecclesiastical hierarchy, its absolute powers, and its flagrant deviations from the moral code. Under his relentless criticism,

Orthodox theology and Church philosophy ceased to be a sanctuary of ideas protected from secular influences and the voice of rationalism.

Maxim the Greek was not, in fact, the first critic of the petrified and dogmatic theological and philosophical views of the Church. During the 1470's a strange heresy emerged in Novgorod. Subsequently labeled the Judaizer heresy, it demonstrated clearly the penetration of fragmentary Western ideas through the murkiness of Russia's cultural isolation. The ethnic origin and personal background of Skhariia, the founder of the movement, are tangled in the maze of confusing information; the only well-established fact about him is that he was a representative of Jewish learning. The Novgorod region was not an unlikely place for heretical thoughts to arise, for not only was it accessible geographically to European influence, but also it had escaped rigid Tatar control and had enjoyed a long interim of political autonomy. It had an urban populace open to new views, and even its priests had a measure of independence from the central Church authorities. Within a decade the heretics established themselves in Moscow, and during the reign of Ivan III some of them officiated in court churches. Quietly and slowly, they built a strong, mostly urban, following which refused to recognize the Holy Trinity and the divinity of Christ. They observed the laws of Moses and designated Saturday as the day of rest. They espoused a new ideology which ran counter to the most sacred tenets of Byzantinism. They attacked Church ceremonialism and stressed the essential value of the internal aspects of religion. In their attack on miracles, which formed a substantial part of Orthodox belief, they became the forerunners of a rationalist theological view. They attacked the Church hierarchy and thereby humbled it to the level of a secular institution. They argued in favor of the principle of individuality in religion, stressing the importance of individual religious self-affirmation over the function of the clergy as intermediary agents between the individual and the divine forces. They were even materialistic in one sense: they demanded that the attention of all be focused on the improvement of life in this world.

The Judaizers are of interest to us primarily because their thought contained a significant element of rationalism, incompatible with the official thinking of the Church and sophisticated to such a degree that it could have come only from the West. One work of the Judaizers was a sixteenth-century cosmographic manuscript, part of a larger symposium, which was found in the archives of a former Orthodox fraternity. This work mentions "the wise Klidas" (Euclid), who invented a system for calculating the circumferences and surfaces of circles. It describes the concentric distribution of seventy-eight spheres of planets surrounding the stationary earth, and gives certain details on the sizes of planets and the distances between heavenly bodies. It also contains an unusually large number of mathematical operations. In the same symposium was the so-called "Six Wings," a collection of six tables purporting to show the motions of the moon, which was intended for use in determining the solar and lunar eclipses. "Six Wings" (the title is taken from Immanuel ben-Iacob, a four-teenth-century Jewish writer from Tarascon)[5] may be considered the first document of mathematical astronomy to appear in Russia, and the first to spread the ideas of Arabic and Jewish commentators on Aristotle and Ptolemy. Further research will be needed to explain fully the cosmographic knowledge of the Judaizers as well as the full scope of their intellectual interests.[6] It is certain, however, that even though it was essentially a re-ligious movement, the Judaizer heresy gave religious thought a new, rationalist aspect and brought it into contact with the growing spirit of scientific inquiry.

The Judaizer movement had reached Novgorod by way of the Lithu-anian-Polish state, which at that time boasted of several urban centers in-habited by an ethnically heterogeneous population and exposed to the influ-ences of modern secular ideas. A. S. Orlov identified this heresy as "a kind of Renaissance, transplanted to Russia and dedicated to the emergence of new social forces."[7] A possible Byzantine intellectual influence on the Judaizers should not be ruled out, because it has been established that Immanuel ben-Iacob's writings were known to Byzantine scholars: they were "one of the very few medieval Hebrew writings which penetrated into the Greek world."[8]

Maxim the Greek was undoubtedly aware of the Judaizer heresies, but they do not seem to have been a determining element in his gradual shift from the rigid Orthodoxy of John of Damascus to a more skeptical point of view. He was educated in Italy at the height of the Renaissance and was at first favorably impressed with the philosophy of humanism. However, he came under the influence of Savonarola, spent some time at Mount Athos, and turned with full force against all efforts to revive ancient phi-losophy. To him, Platonic as well as Aristotelian philosophy was essen-tially incompatible with basic Christianity. Although he thus opposed the intellectual legacy of the Renaissance, he may be truly identified as the man who gave Russian culture its first taste of the Western European intellectual currents unleashed by the forces of humanism. His works are devoted mainly to moral and literary questions of his time, but they contain numerous references to events which occurred in Italy during his sojourn there. He mentions the literary movements in Milan, Florence, Venice, Ferrara, and Padua, and takes note of the struggle between the followers of Plato and Aristotle and of increasing attacks on medieval theology. He was personally acquainted with Aldus Manutius, to whose press "Hellenistic studies owed a priceless debt."[9] He knew Johannes Laskaris, from whom he learned about Paris as an educational center which drew young men from all parts of Europe. His keen mind was able to discern the full scope of cultural fermentation in the West. In his writings he refers to many ancient writers, from Homer to Hesiod, Pythagoras, Socrates, Plato, Aristotle, Thucydides, Plutarch, and Menander.

One must not exaggerate the extent of Maxim the Greek's contributions to the blending of the "old Russian writings" with "Western scientific thought." He described experimental science as astrological nonsense contrived to undermine the true beliefs. He speaks of the ancient writers mostly as representatives of corrupt thinking, often misrepresenting their ideas so as to fit them into a theological argument. He made literate Russians cognizant of the intellectual fires lighted by the Renaissance, but he also tried to turn them against much that the Renaissance stood for. In addition to the eighth-century writings of John of Damascus, he found in Cosmas Indicopleustes' *Christian Topography,* written in the sixth century, an authoritative source for his cosmographic ideas. The author of this early work tried to disprove Ptolemy's claim that the earth has the shape of a globe, and to show that it is as square as the tabernacles of Moses.[10]

Despite his bitter opposition to the intellectual momentum of humanism and his refusal to accept any wisdom not incorporated into theology, Maxim the Greek was the herald of a dawning Russian culture. Before him there had been in Russia many religious philosophers of foreign origin—usually Greek or South Slav—who differed from their Russian counterparts only in that they were better acquainted with canonical thought. Maxim the Greek was the first "philosopher" who possessed versatile and profound knowledge, and who, despite himself, reflected some influence of Western education, especially of the Renaissance. He opposed the new ideas, but he had a high esteem for Western schools. He attacked what he loosely identified as "ancient mythology," but he recognized the merits of new philological criticism. He condemned the secular study of nature—the science of his time—but he made his Russian readers aware of its existence. He established a direct intellectual contact between Russia and the West, but he also was among those who were responsible for the fact that, as Berdyaev put it, "Russia had almost no knowledge of the joy of creative abundance which belonged to the Renaissance."[11]

Maxim the Greek pleased the Church with his new translations of old sacred books, but he soon lost favor as a result of his relentless criticism of certain cultural and social aspects of the Russian Church. According to Aleksandr Arkhangel'skii, "He examined and criticized not only particular features of the church or monastic life but the entire Russian social system in all its aspects—religious, intellectual, moral, and even literary."[12] He demanded that theological writings be purged of their numerous fantastic legends and hordes of deified miracle-makers. He expressed his anger at many hypocritical practices condoned by Orthodoxy, including the excessive landholdings of the Church. Thus he became the source of a powerful heresy that grew rapidly and in the middle of the seventeenth century helped create a schism within the Church. Within the framework of the Church, at least, religious dogma was exposed to criticism. When the spirit of criticism began to crystallize outside the Church, the stage was set for the development of scientific thought.

Prior to the seventeenth century most "knowledge" about nature was drawn from the *Hexaëmeron* of Basil the Great, the medieval *Physiologus*, and several less well known symbolic books describing stones, plants, and, mostly, animals as embodiments of various tenets of Christian ethics. From Cosmas Indicopleustes, at least one copy of whose *Christian Topography* was to be found in the library of every monastery, men learned that the sun, the moon, and the stars follow the paths prescribed by angels; John of Damascus informed them about the influence of stars on weather; John, the Exarch of Bulgaria, furnished them with religious proofs that the celestial bodies are but varieties of divine fire. However, in the sixteenth century these Byzantine and South Slav writings ceased to have an exclusive monopoly on the intellectual life of the Muscovite state. Western works in Russian translations became the sources of new ideas, but these works were still few in number and of small influence. Among them the *Lutsidarius* was the most popular. This work was a translation of the *Elucidarius*, a German treatise containing abridged versions of several cosmological works by Honoris Augustodunensis, a twelfth-century Scholastic thinker. It blended the most elementary postulates of Aristotelian physics with character-building advice, and came under attack by Maxim the Greek because of its use of natural explanations to reinforce religious beliefs. This work received fairly wide distribution in Russia and many copies of it were in circulation as late as the mid-eighteenth century.

THE SEVENTEENTH CENTURY: CULTURAL CHANGE

In the West, the seventeenth century was the era of "the scientific outburst," and "the century of the genius."[13] It marked the triumph of reason over religious authority and of the scientific method over the dogmatic exercises of Scholasticism. It was blessed with such a great number of scientific thinkers in mathematics, physics, biology, physiology, and logic that Whitehead was apologetic when he selected for special mention the following twelve: Francis Bacon, Harvey, Kepler, Galileo, Descartes, Pascal, Huygens, Boyle, Newton, Locke, Spinoza, and Leibniz. Scholarship received a healthy impetus from the growth of learned societies, which were a significant index of a broad scientific investigation and scholarly cooperation that surmounted national boundaries. The Accademia dei Lincei in Rome and the Accademia del Cimento in Florence were pioneers of the noblest sort, although they themselves lasted a much shorter time than their influence and spirit. In 1662 the Royal Society of London for Improving Natural Knowledge received its first charter as a private institution, under royal patronage but having no financial privileges and retaining complete independence. The first members of the French Académie Royale des Sciences were appointed in 1666. This institution "was the creation of the first Minister, Colbert, who arranged the appointments and suggested problems in accordance with political interests"; its members received government salaries and, as the need arose, were absorbed by the civil service system.[14]

Seventeenth-century Russia had neither great scientists nor any learned societies dedicated to scholarly pursuits. Historians are divided in their interpretations of the intellectual history of this period. To some the seventeenth century was basically a continuation of the previous century without any appreciable changes; to others it was a grand prelude to the eighteenth century's versatile concern with science. In 1925, on the occasion of the celebration of the two hundredth anniversary of the founding of the Academy of Sciences in St. Petersburg, P. P. Lazarev, an Academician, summed up and endorsed the views of the first group. It was his view that before Peter I, Russia had no scientists whatsoever; moreover, it did not even have any traces of such "beginnings of science" as astrology and alchemy. "If one did meet specialists engaged in practical problems of chemistry and botany," he said, "they were foreigners invited by the tsars to engage in purely practical scientific pursuits: to produce chemicals for apothecaries who were in the service of the Muscovite state."[15] Lazarev emphasized that real scientific development began only after the founding of the St. Petersburg Academy of Sciences in 1725.

Similar opinions are held by such early writers as Shcherbatov, and to a certain degree by Karamzin and several Slavophil critics, who commended the persistence of the ancient ethos and the gradual nature of intellectual change. Miliukov notes in some detail certain changes in the intellectual picture in seventeenth-century Russia; but his conclusion is that Russia was not seriously influenced by the totally alien spirit of modern science, and that during the century there was a gradual substitution of Scholastic thought, which dominated Western European thinking during the twelfth and thirteenth centuries, for traditional wisdom.[16]

The second view holds that the seventeenth century was a period of cultural transformation and gradual expansion of intellectual horizons, particularly of secular thought. It has had many supporters, including such leading historians as S. M. Solov'ev and V. O. Kliuchevskii. Taking note of various cultural forces at work in the seventeenth century, they conclude, implicitly or explicitly, that Peter I did not import science into a cultural vacuum—that, on the contrary, his success in disseminating scientific thought in Russia was the result of the preparatory work done during the previous century. According to Solov'ev, the seventeenth century was so closely linked with the first half of the eighteenth century that it would be an error not to treat them as a unit.[17] During the reign of the first three rulers of the Romanov dynasty, the beginnings of the grand transformation became noticeable: a standing army was established, the first ships were built, tangible efforts were made to modernize commerce, foreigners were granted privileges to build industrial and mining establishments, the need for education began to receive great emphasis, new customs were accepted by the royalty and noblemen, and the relations between Church and State became firmly defined. Peter I received his education in an atmosphere alive with the spirit of general cultural fermentation.

Kliuchevskii follows Solov'ev's line of thought, but his exposition of the intellectual aspects of the social, administrative, and economic transformation is more systematic and penetrating. He puts the grand scale of cultural change in a psychological nutshell: when the Russians first discovered the West they quickly accepted the products of material culture which made life more comfortable but were in themselves no challenge to traditional ideas and mores. Out of a growing intellectual curiosity, however, there came a search into the ideas underlying the Western material creations. In other words, a direct causal relationship lay between the increasing importation of Western comforts and the emergence of intellectual curiosity, the interest in scientific education, and the thinking about a variety of subjects which had not troubled the minds of earlier generations. Up until the first decades of the seventeenth century, Russians thought of Western Europe as little more than "a workshop for military and other articles without regard to how they were manufactured." Only gradually did they begin to realize that Europe was "a school in which one can learn not only various crafts but also how to live and think."[18]

The metamorphosis of Russia during the seventeenth century was far-reaching. The Ukraine and Byelorussia were united with the Muscovite state. Siberia, with its rich resources and new enticements to large segments of a shifting population, was largely incorporated into the Russian Empire. In Siberia appeared the first "cities" and fortresses, to which government representatives, often of high aristocratic origin, were sent in increasingly large numbers. The northern part of European Russia and the steppe in the south absorbed a growing number of refugees from the central areas. The full centralization of political power provided the final crushing blow to the remnants of feudal particularism. The elective *Zemskie sobory,* the representative bodies of all the major estates, lost much of their traditional power. During the second half of the seventeenth century, the military governors (*voevody*), appointed by the monarchs, became the main instruments of the absolute state. The title "autocrat" was officially associated with the tsars.

Thus the institutions of centralized autocracy were blended with those of a feudal social regime. Landholders of various sorts were consolidated into a single estate of feudal aristocracy, upon whom were dependent nine-tenths of the peasants in the central areas. It became legally impossible for the members of lower estates to enter the ranks of the landed gentry. The Church, long a powerful landowner, was forbidden to acquire new holdings. This development marked a revolutionary turn in subordinating the immense power of the religious organization to the institutions of the absolute state and the service gentry. The growth of cities was slow; the seventeenth century was characterized more by a gradual dispersal of population than by growing concentration. Some urban communities even declined in population, as people succumbed to the lure of the wide-open frontier. The rate of urbanization was strikingly uneven: Moscow had a population of approximately 200,000, whereas Iaroslavl', Russia's second-largest city, had only some 15,000 inhabitants.

Metallurgical work began to be done on a fairly large scale, although mainly for the government. Foreign trade expanded significantly, chiefly through the port of Arkhangelsk, which in 1653 handled three-fourths of all the foreign trade. Russia exported mainly furs, skins, resin, pitch, hemp, wax, and wheat; it imported metals, weapons, paper, cloth, silk textiles, numerous luxuries, spices, sugar, and wine. Almost none of the imported goods reached the open market, however; most went to the government or to the aristocracy. The state administration was highly complex, and the increasing needs of the powerful class of service aristocracy (the top echelon of government bureaucracy), together with the rapid growth of internal trade and the expanding industrial and military technology, were a strong impetus to the search for elementary scientific knowledge.

It was a period of empire building, codification of feudal law, consolidated absolutism, industrial beginnings, and the growth of the economic role of the market. It was also a period of conflict, which appeared in many forms and which, by exposing the inadequacies of many traditional values, provided ample room for new intellectual activities. External conflicts, particularly the chronic wars with Poland and Sweden, opened the gates through which a look could be taken at Western Europe. That Russia was eventually victorious in these wars can be attributed primarily to the Westernization of its armed forces, effected by imported technicians and by translations of Western military manuals. The wars brought no new ideas, at least directly, but they had an important effect on industrial technology. Internal conflicts were even more significant, in that they brought to the fore the incompatibility of many old Russian values, values sanctified by religion and embedded in conservative tradition, with the needs and pressures of the new age.

Within the Empire, five conflicts were particularly indicative of changing values and new, secular outlooks. There was, first of all, the conflict between the two leading groups of landholders, the lay aristocracy and the Church aristocracy. This began in the sixteenth century and was at last resolved by the Code of Laws of 1649, which prohibited the Church from acquiring new land.

The second conflict existed within the Church itself. It, too, had begun in the previous century, with the propounding of various heresies. The struggle was essentially one of ideas: the faction led by Patriarch Nikon sought a modernization of canonical religious dogma by ridding religious books of legends about miracles and obvious fables which were no longer useful either for explaining the mysteries of the universe or for teaching moral philosophy. It is significant that Nikon was the possessor of a rather large library that held many works of a nonreligious nature, including those of Aristotle. Nikon's faction was opposed by the Old Believers, who denounced what was in truth "the striving of society to place itself on the open and illuminated path of real knowledge, on the path of enlightening science."[19]

3) The third important internal conflict was between the Church and the State as loci of power, and in this conflict also the Church was the loser. Nikon's protest against the right of the tsar to dismiss patriarchs led to a dispute concerning the basic question of the power of the State and the Church in relation to each other, and in the relation of each to society at large. The solution of this conflict made the Church an agency of the State.

4) The fourth conflict was one which was to lie smoldering for a long time to come: that of the enserfed peasantry on the one hand, and the Church and lay feudatories on the other. It reached its high point in the seventeenth century in the peasant uprising led by Stenka Razin. This conflict was symptomatic of general social disquietude and the crystallization of conflicting value systems.

5) The fifth conflict, of particular interest here, was the somewhat loosely defined battle between the Westerners and the anti-Westerners—or, one might say, between the champions of the old and of the new. This was in fact a struggle between Greek learning and Latin learning. The Greek faction, which was dominant during most of the century and had the support of both Church and State, defended the writings of the Greeks, in corrupt Russian translations, as the only legitimate source of wisdom and as an intellectual bulwark against dangerous influences from the West. Latin writings were regarded with great suspicion because they had first of all been a filter through which Scholasticism had reached Moscow, and then had become a source of unorthodox scientific knowledge. Despite many efforts to preserve the supremacy of the Greek language—and therefore of Greek literature—during the second half of the seventeenth century most Russian translations were done from Latin, which was the scientific language of Poland and Western Europe.

In all these conflicts one sees the failure of the ethos of Russian Byzantinism to meet the demands and challenges of the new era. The crisis of the old ideology stemmed from its unbending opposition to any changes in the time-honored and tradition-sanctified mores and to alien ideas emanating from the cultural centers of Europe. Byzantinism, though founded on medieval Greek religious writings and uncompromisingly opposed to secular philosophy and experimental science, had found it expedient to temper Byzantine theology with a certain number of native superstitions, which eventually amounted to a substantial part of Orthodox thought. Shchapov noted in the 1860's that even in his day most Russians did not understand "the essence of Christianity" and clung to ancient superstitions as if they were "religious truths." In the West, Shchapov observed, Christianity allowed for the exercise of man's intellectual endowments, out of which came an inspired struggle between mysticism and Scholasticism, and, subsequently, between Protestantism and Catholicism; in Russia, on the other hand, Christianity stimulated "neither theoretical nor rational activities" of the intellect.[20]

Thus limited in what it would and would not accept, Byzantinism brought to Russia knowledge only of the peoples who were of interest to the medieval Greek writers: the Russians acquired some knowledge about biblical peoples (and places) and about Byzantium's Asiatic neighbors, but they learned nothing about Western Europe. Byzantinism, in a sense, then, fell into a trap of its own making. And when, for all its virtuosity, it failed in its attempt to keep Russia free of Western ideas, it met its downfall.

In the period of incipient Westernization it was the West that came to Russia, not the Russians who traveled to the West. One should bear in mind, however, that Russia had never been actually shut off from Western influences: its geographical proximity to Western Europe made airtight insulation impossible. As Rainov remarks, the first Russian Church writings contained definite elements of ancient scientific thought, woven into religious dogmas but not completely deprived of their true meaning. "The free wind of world history blew everywhere where thought moved forward, expanding the scope of human knowledge and man's domination over nature. The gusts of wind agitated and shook the minds of our ancestors, chasing away stagnation, inertia, and decadence."[21]

On the other hand, such a recognition of a certain common heritage from the ancient world should not lead us to minimize, as Rainov is inclined to do, Russia's prolonged resistance to ideas outside Byzantine dogma. It was the Renaissance, the titanic revival of ancient thought, that gave birth to modern science. Russia had no Renaissance; modern science came to Russia during the eighteenth century, long after the Renaissance had outlived its great historical role.

Prior to the eighteenth century, Western ideas reached Russia mainly by way of three groups of people: technicians (highly skilled craftsmen, merchants, and military personnel); the Kievan monks, together with an assortment of mostly foreign priests with unorthodox intellectual beliefs; and pro-Western members of the Russian elite.

Western merchants and technicians of all descriptions began arriving in Russia in growing numbers as a result of Ivan the Terrible's concerted efforts to recruit foreign artisans and soldiers. During the reign of Fedor I (1584–98) the number of foreign mercenaries in the Russian military service reached 4,300, and included Dutchmen, Scotsmen, Danes, and Swedes. Boris Godunov (1598–1605) granted special privileges to the Lithuanians who moved to Russia after the pact of Lublin (1569) ceded a sizable portion of their country to Poland. By the beginning of the seventeenth century the influx of foreigners had acquired greater variety—jewelers, painters, tanners, shipbuilders, miners, founders, and coiners. Foreigners opened the first iron, copper, textile, glass, and paper plants in Russia.

In 1631 Tsar Michael (1613–45) requested a Colonel Leslie to recruit 5,000 soldiers, fully equipped, in various European countries. Olearius notes that during Michael's reign more than a thousand foreign families, of different origins, lived in Moscow's "German suburb," and Tanner reports that iron, glass, and paper plants were located near this community. The German suburb was predominantly Calvinist in religious leaning, but adjacent to the community, according to Reitenfeld, there was a suburb of converts—foreigners who had adopted Russian Orthodoxy. The numerous comments by contemporary observers about the Russians' hostility toward the foreigners in their midst suggest that the German suburb was devised as protection against daily ridicule. Olearius mentions that many foreigners adopted Russian dress in order to save themselves from constant verbal abuse, but that on the insistence of the Patriarch, the Tsar issued an order forbidding the practice.[22]

The foreigners did more than provide models of higher craftsmanship; in the pharmacies which they established they introduced elements of chemical knowledge, and in the capacity of Foreign Office employees they were instrumental in collecting for the Russian government previously unknown facts about other countries. The expanding staffs of numerous foreign embassies did much to raise the intellectual aspirations and refine the taste of Moscow's high society. Owing to their interest, many a Western book found its way to Russia and into the hands of a slowly developing reading public.

The role of foreign merchants as a link between the West and Russia was particularly important. After the founding of the port of Arkhangelsk in the second half of the sixteenth century, ships of considerable size arrived to trade with Russia. Foreign merchants used the river routes to reach as far south as the town of Vologda, whence they took to overland routes. "Foreigners, mostly English, appeared in Vologda to purchase goods at more favorable prices by avoiding unnecessary intermediaries. They sailed their own ships from the sea to Vologda, where they erected their own depots."[23] According to S. F. Platonov, "at the end of the six-teenth century the English became fully acclimatized to northern Russia. They spent all seasons trading and working, not only in such busy places as Kholmogory and Lampozhniia but also in such distant and lonely corners as Ust'-Tsyl'ma and Pustozersk on the Pechora."[24] Indeed, North Russia became the first window to Europe. Foreign traders brought in not only different customs and ideas but also new business and techno-logical methods. They were greatly responsible for the building of small shipyards and quite extensive salt industries, and they introduced new and better methods of gathering resin and new tanning and fur-processing techniques.

THE KIEVAN MONKS

The learned monks of Kiev brought to Russia Western ideas of a quite different sort. The Kiev theological school, founded in 1589 by a lay fraternity, was transformed in 1631 by metropolitan Petr Mogila into the Kievan-Mogilan Collegium, and thence became, at the end of the century, a theological academy. The original school was dedicated to ancient "Greco-Slavic learning"; its primary function was to resist the concerted efforts of Polish Jesuits to grasp control of the Ukraine. Petr Mogila reor-ganized the school on the model of Jesuit schools in Poland, but he and his advisers continued to oppose Jesuit expansion in the Orthodox Ukraine, particularly the Jesuit campaigns for unification of the Catholic and Ortho-dox churches. Mogila did much to strengthen the theological unity of the Ukrainian Orthodoxy, but he also introduced a Latin pseudomorphosis of Orthodoxy that ushered in an age of the pre-eminence of Latin thought in Ukrainian Orthodox theology. He founded a "Latin school" of theological thought which profoundly influenced not only the Orthodox believer's ecclesiastical ritual and language, but also his theology, his world view, and his religious psychology itself.[25]

The Kievan-Mogilan Collegium introduced a curriculum which followed the spirit of twelfth-century Scholasticism, with the difference that, unlike the Polish Jesuit schools, the emphasis was on "sciences" subordinated to theology rather than on theology alone. The monks tended to impose the philosophy of Western Scholasticism upon Eastern Orthodox theology, but, recognizing the increasing spirit of scientific thought in Western culture, they were determined to combat its spread in Russia. The extensive writings by learned monks were primarily polemical and were characterized by servile acceptance of all the offerings of Polish Jesuit theologians.[26] It was a new and alien genre, devoted to intellectual exercises within firmly outlined Church authority; all wisdom was subordinated to theology, and theology to absolute truths which needed no scientific verification.

Nevertheless, the contributions of the Kievan-Mogilan Collegium to the intellectual history not only of the Ukraine but of all Russia were substantial. It was the first formal attempt to bring Western ideas, however old, to Russia, and it did much to break down the traditional antagonism toward Western ideas and culture. Not only did it offer efficient training in Latin and Greek, but—even more important—it educated a group of men who played a decisive role in the intellectual and educational developments in Moscow during the second half of the seventeenth century. Incidentally, it contributed to the establishment of a recognized professional status for individuals engaged in pure scholarship. And by its identification with Scholasticism, it kept alive the doctrinal conflict within the Orthodox Church and thus indirectly stimulated the rise of secular thought.

In 1649–50 some thirty learned Kievan monks arrived in Moscow upon the invitation of a leading boyar. Their task at first was that of combing out of church books all deviations from the originals (most of them due to the ineptness of the translators), but gradually their duties were expanded to include a variety of secular pursuits. The work of two of these monks was particularly fruitful. Epifanii Slavinetskii retranslated the New Testament into Church-Slavic, but he went beyond the confines of religious learning, translating the introductory part of Thucydides' history, the concluding section of the *Panegyric on Trajan* by Pliny the Younger, a geographical work on Europe and Asia, and, most remarkably, Vesalius's *De humani corporis fabrica* (1543), a work which laid the foundations of modern anatomy. He is considered to have been the translator of the 1645 edition of Willem and Johan Blaeu's *Atlas novus* in 1661, but since the translation, like that of Vesalius's work, remained in manuscript, it probably reached but a small circle of readers.[27] It was the first writing available in Russian which alluded favorably to Copernicus and the heliocentric theories.[28] Even such later scribes as Simeon Polotskii and Arsenii the Greek treated "cosmological" problems without reference to Copernicus.[29]

It is possible that Slavinetskii's translation of such scholarly works as those of Vesalius and the Blaeus was undertaken on orders from the court of Tsar Alexis (1645–76), who was known for his keen interest in secular learning, particularly astronomy. It was part of the nature of the times to display an intellectual curiosity about secular subjects while adhering strictly to Orthodox theological ideas. Slavinetskii, as a master of both Greek and Latin, was able to extend his interests far beyond holy books to Latin treatises in the developing line of humanistic and scientific thought. His translation of Vesalius' *Fabrica* alone brought to Russia a work of learning from a man who "was a real humanist, conversant not only with Latin and Greek, but also with Arabic and Hebrew."[30]

The second leading Kievan monk who came to Moscow in 1649–50 was Arsenii Satanovskii, who was particularly noted for his translation of *Hortulus regime*, a huge symposium compiled in Latin by "a teacher named Meffret." The symposium consists of excerpts from the books of 120 writers, including philosophers, poets, historians, physicians, and theologians, and is a veritable encyclopedia of all types of knowledge from theology and mystical philosophy to zoology, mineralogy, and medicine.[31] Solov'ev saw in the work of such men as Slavinetskii and Satanovskii a response to the growing demand for encyclopedic knowledge by persons in and close to the court and the Foreign Office.[32]

In 1664 Moscow was blessed by the arrival of another Kievan monk, Simeon Polotskii, a man justly called "a walking encyclopedia." He was charged with establishing a school in the Zaikonospasskii Monastery in Moscow to which the junior staff of the Foreign Office could come for instruction in Latin. In 1666 he took part in the Church Council's attack on the Old Believers; during the proceedings of the Council, with Tsar Alexis in the audience, he delivered a passionate oration on the virtues of knowledge and the need for greater State concern in educational affairs. The following year, in a book addressed to the "thinking flock of the

Russian Orthodox Church," he displayed typical Scholastic rhetoric, with the emphasis on theological erudition and formal precision in the presentation of arguments. This book was too complicated and inflexible in its reasoning to have much real influence on Polotskii's contemporaries, but it is a good record of the necessity among competent theologians to look to the West for new ideas in religious philosophy.

In the year 1667 also Polotskii was awarded the coveted position of tutor to the Tsar's children. This inspired him to complete the *Wreath of Religion*, which is a kind of summing up of Kievan theological learning. The book covers a wide field, borrowing liberally, in a rather encyclopedic fashion, from several "cosmological" fields, with no particular effort to arrange the borrowed ideas within a theological framework. One long section on cosmology contains contemporaneous astrological ideas, which the Old Believers considered quite as dangerous as astronomy.

Antiquated though Polotskii's scientific ideas were, they were an inevitable step forward on the path of scientific development. Polotskii was well versed in Greek, but he preferred Latin and was considered by his contemporaries the most dedicated champion of Latin learning in Russia.[33] His basic contribution was in his eloquent emphasis on the virtues of scientific education, his ruthless attacks on superstition, and his enrichment of contemporary Russian literature by the extensive importing of Western ideas. Indeed, his championship of education brought him many enemies, not only among the uneducated boyars but also among supporters of the Greek orientation.

It cannot be said that the Kievan monks brought any revolutionary scientific ideas to Moscow. The names of Copernicus, Kepler, Descartes, and Galileo were unknown to them, as was, indeed, the great scientific revolution these men had effected. They were primarily dedicated to the preservation of Orthodoxy, committed theologically to a Counter Reformation in a country which was bypassed by the Reformation. It was almost an irony that in this enterprise they chose to rely not on the established theological thought of Orthodoxy but on Scholasticism. They valued knowledge, but only so long as it did not conflict with dogma. Polotskii used his books and sermons to advocate the virtues of "scientific education," but the science that he referred to had no room for mathematics and astronomy or for the experimental method. He and the other Kievan monks did, however, make an indelible imprint on the intellectual history of their age by dealing a mortal blow to the isolation of the Greco-Russian Orthodoxy. To the traditional preoccupation of Church writers with moral precepts they added a new interest in ideas and knowledge. By their attitude toward wisdom rather than by their intellectual erudition and modernity they made a contribution to the growth of the scientific attitude in Russia.

CLERGYMEN OF MANY BACKGROUNDS

The Kievan monks were not the only churchmen who, by introducing new points of view into theological thinking, contributed to the growth of more refined and critical intellectual curiosity and to the advent of secular thought. Priestly scholars of other backgrounds began to perform a similar role. Afanasii, the archbishop of Kholmogory, was a pure product of the Russian Church; Iurii Krizhanich was a Croatian Catholic priest; and the brothers Likhud were representatives of the Greek Orthodox tradition who had the advantages of Italian education.

Archbishop Afanasii, a student of Epifanii Slavinetskii, distinguished himself as a prolific writer with views considerably broader than his office entitled him to hold. In his handbook of medical advice (1696) he gives a systematic description of individual ailments and offers cures, drawn primarily from folk medicine. In his *Hexaëmeron* he tries to blend the biblical story of the Creation with many currently held astronomical notions, with which, aside from an omission of Copernicus' heliocentric system, he shows remarkable familiarity.[34] He had a library containing European-made astronomical calendars, globes, compasses, and telescopes, most of which came to him in Kholmogory by way of the near-by port of Arkhangelsk. The Church, it should be noted, was not opposed to a limited study of astronomy as a means of working out the regularity of holy days. What it opposed was any general exploration of the universe. Thus when Tsar Alexis offered Olearius the position of court astrologist, he was swiftly rebuked by the Church.

Iurii Krizhanich was born in Croatia in 1617 and received his theological education in Zagreb, Graz, and Bologna. Sometime in the middle of the century, for reasons that are not clear, he went to Moscow, where he became an apostle of the unity and national liberation of the Slavic peoples under Russian leadership. He emphasized that if Russia were to assume this leadership, it must first awaken from its intellectual lethargy and overcome the depressing conditions of technological illiteracy, sparse population, and general economic backwardness.

In Moscow he met such representatives of Kievan learning as Slavi-

Pan-Slav

netskii and Polotskii, and also the two leading secular proponents of Western education, the boyars Boris Morozov and Fedor Rtishchev. From conversations with these and other enlightened Muscovites, and on the basis of his own observations, he concluded that ignorance and unwillingness to expand the traditional horizons of knowledge were the main causes of Russia's social ailments. In a certain careful dissemination of scientific knowledge Krizhanich saw Russia's salvation. Despite the open contempt with which he referred to some peoples—particularly the Germans—he deplored Russia's traditional isolation from the West,[35] for "a people learns by borrowing science and scientific results from other peoples."[36] "It is said," he wrote in *The Russian State in the Middle of the Seventeenth Century*, "that learned men are originators of heresies, and that therefore it is not advantageous to seek wisdom. I answer: heresies may also be started by uneducated men."[37] To those who protested that "no heresy was ever started by stupid muzhiks who read no books," Krizhanich replied that "wisdom uproots heresies." "From fire, water, and iron many men die but without them life would be impossible; in the same way man is in need of wisdom." Krizhanich's pronouncements were in full harmony with Bacon's "assured truth" that "a little or superficial knowledge of Philosophy may incline the mind of man to Atheism, but a farther proceeding therein doth bring the mind back again to Religion."

If Krizhanich was opposed to the "Greeks" who insisted that Russia should be cut off completely from Western Europe, he was equally critical of those persons who aped everything Western. He recommended that elements of Western culture be adopted selectively, primarily for their usefulness. He emphasized that science was a broad and versatile field which could benefit all men, in special ways. Philosophy, for example, was indispensable to good government and should be studied by the nobility and a few common men in service of the State. Other social classes should be given practical knowledge about agriculture, mining, industry, and arithmetic.[38]

Krizhanich, unlike most of his fellow priests, was little concerned with theological questions, but he was not an active scientist and seemed unaware of the revolutionary proportions of the growth of science in Western Europe in his time. Yet he was easily the most highly educated person in Russia during his stay there, which included a long exile in Siberia. In his writings he quoted Homer, Plato, Aristotle, Xenophon, Plutarch, Polybius, Cicero, Livy, and Virgil, and showed intimate knowledge of Machiavelli's political ideas. He wrote some thirty books on subjects ranging from *De providentia Dei* to the *Historia de Siberia.* His grammar of the Russian language earned him the title of the founder of comparative Slavic philology.[39]

The brothers Likhud were also exceptional clergymen-scholars who hold a place of some importance in the history of formal education in Russia. From their native Cephalonia they went to Venice for study, and on to the University of Padua, from which they received doctorates. After a long stay in Constantinople and a visit to Poland, they traveled to Moscow in 1685 to become teachers in the new Slav-Greek-Latin Academy at the Zaikonospasskii Monastery. The struggle between the Greeks and the Latins had by this time reached an impasse, and the new Academy was founded in hopes of reconciling the two currents. As Greeks, dedicated to Greek Orthodoxy yet educated in the Western spirit, the Likhud brothers were admirably qualified to teach in the new institution.

Tsar Fedor III (1676–82), in signing the first charter of the Academy, took the opportunity to praise wisdom as "the mother of kingly duties, the invention and perfection of all blessings."[40] The curriculum included such disciplines of Scholastic tradition as speculative philosophy, natural philosophy, rhetoric, logic, theology, pietism, and dialectic, but it also allowed for the teaching of several "civil sciences" not incompatible with the religious point of view.[41] The school's manuals, which the Likhud brothers prepared, followed corresponding Western texts in the Scholastic tradition. The Academy showed less Scholastic rigidity than the academy in Kiev, but, even so, it was sadly out of date. The Likhuds taught physics, but what they gave to their students was a diluted scholasticized version of Aristotle. In their discussion of physics they followed the usual method of first presenting Aristotle's ideas and then refuting those that were unacceptable by invoking the opinion of the Church. They also criticized the ancient "physicists and atomists" Thales, Anaxagoras, and Democritus, and they attacked Campanella's theory that the world is made of four substances—heat, cold, dryness, and moisture.[42] Since no physics whatever was taught in Russia after the brothers left the Academy until the second half of the eighteenth century, it can almost be said that the history of physics in Russia skipped the phase of Aristotelian science.

Under government charter, the Academy was given a number of duties besides that of teaching. It was assigned the thankless task of censoring imported books and exercising vigilant surveillance over the ideas of foreigners employed by the government. It was also supposed to watch teachers in Russian schools, primarily foreigners, who were being hired

N.B.
Precedents!

in ever increasing numbers but could not be trusted as reliable interpreters of Orthodoxy.

The curriculum of the Academy quickly attracted the attention of the Moscow populace, and in the first year the enrollment was seventy-six students—a figure never to be reached thereafter. The students came from all "free estates." In the classrooms, youths from Moscow's highest aristocracy mingled with sons of stablemen and servants in the gentry's employ. Among the Academy's graduates were Lomonosov, Krasheninnikov, and Magnitskii, all of whom were to make notable contributions to science in the eighteenth century.

Closely guarded by the Church, misused by the government, and deprived of the teaching services of men of secular outlook, the Academy could offer hardly more than a somewhat modernized theological education. In time, its main function became that of marshaling theological arguments against the swelling currents of scientific thought. M. M. Shcherbatov, an eighteenth-century historian, said that the students of this institution learned a good deal about Aristotelian philosophy, the hardly intelligible discourses of Plato, and the teachings of Church Fathers, but nothing at all about new discoveries and scientific theories. Physics, chemistry, and mathematics were totally alien subjects, regarded by the Church as heretical.[43]

The Academy had the patronage of several of Moscow's leading pro-Western aristocrats, but the teaching of the Likhud brothers was almost immediately challenged by the anti-Western, pro-Greek elements of the Church. The Latin erudition of the learned brothers proved to be their major liability, even though under their guidance the Academy generally followed the Greek intellectual tradition and was commonly known until the end of the century as the Hellenic-Greek Academy. At the same time, the Likhuds were attacked as "pro-Greeks" by Sil'vester Medvedev, an ardent champion of Western thought and a man known to his contemporaries as "a monk of great mind and scholarly accomplishment." In 1689 Medvedev was considered more dangerous than the Likhuds and was sentenced to death. The Likhuds, however, were the next victims of the Church; in 1694 the two brothers were removed from the teaching staff of the Academy. After an unsuccessful attempt to flee the country, they settled down to dedicate the remainder of their lives to polemics against Catholicism and Protestantism, and, briefly, to the teaching of the Italian language to special classes instituted by decree in 1697 (in the first government-established educational institution in Russia).[44]

The experience of the Likhuds, the Academy, and the "language school" showed that even at the end of the seventeenth century Russia did not welcome secular education. The Church, which had the most powerful voice in such matters, was not yet ready to seek a meeting ground with science and secular philosophy; indeed, it was remarshaling its forces for fresh attacks on scholarship that ventured past the intellectual horizons of Orthodoxy. The establishment of the Academy marked the Church's acceptance of religious *learning* as the most effective weapon in the struggle against the swelling currents of secular knowledge. By the charter, Tsar Fedor authorized the Academy to keep all secular knowledge out of its curriculum and ordered that all teachers caught disseminating natural-scientific knowledge be condemned as magicians and burned to death.[45] Ioannikii Likhud, who was assigned the course in "natural philosophy," made it clear that, owing to his reliance on the "Holy Ghost" and Aristotelian teachings, he could avoid all knowledge incompatible with true religion. The Academy, more than any other seventeenth-century institution, helped to define the lines of battle between two kinds of wisdom—religious and secular, or, as they were called, "free wisdom" and "external wisdom." The example of the Academy made it amply clear that if there were to be any teaching of scientific thought in Russia in the future, it would have to be in schools wholly independent of the Church. It became the task of the succeeding generation, of such leading intellectuals as Feofan Prokopovich, V. N. Tatishchev, Antiokh Kantemir, and Mikhail Lomonosov, to do what they could to overcome the paralyzing effects of the belief in the intrinsic incompatibility of the two wisdoms.

The intellectual dilemma of the end of the seventeenth century is graphically revealed in two contemporaneous accounts by anonymous writers. One account concerns the Greek-Latin question: specifically, which of the two languages should be considered more important in the education of Russian students? The writer answers in favor of Greek, not only because it is the language of the original Christian books but also because it is the language of the philosophy of Aristotle, the astrology of Ptolemy, the geometry of Euclid, the rhetoric of Demosthenes, the medicine of Hippocrates and Galen, and the great poetical creations of Homer. The second account contains a scorching attack on ignorance—"the darkness which blinds the intellect" and prevents man from understanding divine law.[46]

THE PROTO-WESTERNERS

It was not only the imported technicians, the Kievan monks, and other unorthodox clergymen who fostered the first stirrings of a scientific attitude in Russia. A vital role in the cultural transformation of the country was played by a rather small but select group of lay aristocrats who occupied high positions in the government and were associated, in one way or another, with the conduct of Russia's foreign relations. Boris Morozov, the first of the seventeenth-century Russian "Westerners," impressed the sagacious Olearius with his devotion to European educational ideals and his regret that in his youth he had had no access to modern learning. As a tutor of young Alexis Romanov, Morozov made an earnest effort to apply what he thought were Western European educational methods. F. M. Rtishchev, who invited the Kievan monks to Moscow at the end of the 1640's, was among the first to demand that the Church begin altering its traditional rigid stand against foreign ideas. He was particularly vehement in his insistence that the Church cleanse its books of superstitions which provided ready-made answers to questions that in Western Europe belonged to the realm of science.

A. L. Ordin-Nashchokin is rightly considered an early advocate of the reforms of Peter the Great. Born in the Pskov district, adjacent to Lithuania, he grew up with a better knowledge of foreigners and foreign customs than most Russians had, and he was fluent in German and Polish as well as Latin. He became a diplomat, and impressed foreign observers with his sophistication. He was a man who, while respecting Western intellectual achievements, did not ape "Western customs."[47] Samuel Collins, an Oxonian who served as personal physician to Tsar Alexis from 1659 to 1666, described Ordin-Nashchokin as "a great statesman," and "an important and wise minister of the state who took a back seat to no European minister."[48] In the words of Kliuchevskii, he symbolized "a synchronization of general European and national individuality."[49] According to Solov'ev, "he was a forerunner of Peter the Great in that he was aware of the superiority of the West, uttered vociferous public statements to that effect, and sought changes along Western lines."[50]

There were several other early Westerners, such as Grigorii Kotoshikhin, A. S. Matveev, and V. V. Golitsyn, who distinguished themselves either as staunch advocates of modernization or as relentless critics of Russia's cultural inertia, and who by their own styles of life served as models for new ideas, ideals, and aspirations. These men were not all of the same cast; they viewed Western attractions in terms of their own proclivities and backgrounds, and by these differences they diversified the influx of Western cultural traits. Kotoshikhin, for example, rebelled and fled to Sweden, where he wrote a bitter document on the maladies of Russian society, which, he charged, were due mainly to the awesome absence of secular intellectual preoccupations and to a miserable lack of scientific inquiry. Matveev, who was of nonaristocratic origin, wrote several works of a historical nature and possessed a collection of geographical maps and clocks set for different time zones.

V. V. Golitsyn, who wielded great power during the regency of Sophia (1682–89), opened his luxurious and Europeanized home to the elite of Moscow's diplomatic corps and other educated foreigners. Whereas Ordin-Nashchokin, a few years earlier, had been concerned with administrative and economic reforms, Golitsyn was interested in such matters as the spread of educational and religious tolerance, freedom of conscience, and the free admission of foreigners into Russia. As Kliuchevskii has remarked, "Nash-chokin was the ancestor of the practical men of Peter's time," while "in Golitsyn one could discern a liberal and somewhat dreamy lord of Catherine's era."[51]

COURT INFLUENCE

The particular importance of these men, and the others of their kind, was that they were closely associated with and were trusted and respected by the monarchs. Despite the Church's uncompromising and mostly successful struggle against Western languages and science, the Russian tsars began quite early to favor at least some degree of cultural contact with European countries and the dissemination of scientific knowledge in Russia. Ivan the Terrible was the first Russian ruler to make "conscious and systematic efforts to bring Russia closer to the West." He sent a group of young men to Germany to learn "the German language and science"; he encouraged foreign artisans to come to Russia and made the first (though unsuccessful) effort to set up a printing house and a Latin school in Moscow.

Karamzin asserts that Boris Godunov "in his dedicated love for civil education went farther than any of his predecessors." He dreamed of establishing European schools—even a university—in Russia, and he tried to attract learned foreigners to his country.[52] He sent eighteen young men of aristocratic origin to learn "the ways and languages" of foreign countries, dividing them equally among England, France, and Germany. The disinclination of later tsars to repeat the experiment was perhaps due to the fact that none of the young men ever returned. Several died, others ran away from their teachers, and the rest were so intrigued by Western life

England &
Russia.

that they refused to go home after they had completed their education.[53] Boris spent many hours in conversation with his personal physician, an Englishman named Mark Ridley. Ridley was an outstanding follower of William Gilbert's theories of electricity and magnetism, and after Gilbert's death he returned to England, eventually to become a leading authority on magnetism. In a book which he wrote on the subject, he introduced himself as "Doctor in physicke and Philosophie, Latly Physition to the Emperour of Russia and one of ye eight principals or Elects of the College of Physitions in London."[54] Boris, in replying to Queen Elizabeth's request that Ridley be allowed to return to England, expressed a hope that English "doctors, apothecarians, and wise men" would continue to come to Russia either temporarily or permanently.[55]

It was not until the middle of the seventeenth century that foreign books began to appear at the Imperial Court. At the end of the sixteenth century the Court library had fifty-eight books, including forty-one Russian manuscripts, mostly on religious topics, five notebooks of astrological information, and one herbal in German. Under Tsar Alexis (1645–76) many secular books in Latin, Greek, and Polish were acquired.

Alexis was deeply religious and dedicated to Russian traditions, but he also had an interest in medicine, which led him to recruit many foreign physicians to work in Moscow.[56] He founded the Apothecary Department for the compounding of medicines, and, at the same time, the first school for training Russian medical technicians. According to S. F. Platonov, who has studied this period, "We have sufficient documentary information to show that among the persons trained in medical science by foreigners there were also some Russians. In the Azov campaign in 1695 in the Russian armies there were fourteen foreign and seven Russian physicians; several dozen doctors worked in Moscow. In 1682 in the Apothecary Department there were forty-four Russian physicians and students."[57] Alexis was also interested in astronomy, and in 1662 a huge map depicting the distribution and movement of the stars was painted on the ceiling of the state dining room in the Kremlin; it included the signs of the Zodiac, the planets with their orbits, and comets. It was during his reign that Slavinetskii, perhaps at his suggestion, translated Vesalius' *Fabrica* and the *Atlas novus*.

Selenographia (1647), for which its author, Hevelius of Danzig, was given the title Father of Lunar Astronomy, was also translated into Russian during Alexis's reign, twenty-odd years after its original publication, though, like the treatises of Vesalius and the Blaeus, it circulated only in manuscript form. (The only surviving copy of the translation has been preserved not in Russia but in a museum in Vilna.) This work introduced the Russian reader for the first time to the basic knowledge of instrumental optics and added in a fragmentary way to the creation of a Russian scientific terminology.[58]

It is more because of what happened during Alexis's reign than because of Alexis's own interests, contributions, and inclinations in the field of scientific thought that this time was a turning point in the intellectual history of Russia. Interest in the West was aroused not only by the Tsar but also by a select group of officials. This was the period of Ordin-Nashchokin and Matveev, and also of the establishment of unquestionable supremacy of the State over the Church. Westernization ceased to be a desire of ambitious but overcautious rulers alone; it began to receive support from a segment of the Russian elite. This ideal, however, was as yet uncrystallized. It was kept in check partly by the cultural inertia of the majority of boyars and partly by the Church, which managed to control the country's printing facilities until the time of Peter I.

During the last quarter of the seventeenth century, the Church, rapidly recuperating from the wounds inflicted by the Schism, intensified its efforts against the expanding secular wisdom. The slogan of the new campaign was that secular knowledge is equivalent to heresy, and that science is a work of Antichrist. The priests now advised pious persons, if anyone asked them what they knew about ancient Greek science, to give the following answer: "I have not studied Greek philosophy, nor have I read learned astronomers. I have never conversed with sage philosophers, and I have never heard a philosophical debate. I have read only the books of divine law."[59] As the pendulum swung back, the Kievan monks in Moscow began to run into trouble. In 1690 a large number of books which had been published in the Ukraine were publicly condemned; the ablest representatives of Kievan learning were looked upon with renewed suspicion, and Sil'vester Medvedev, an eminent disciple of Polotskii, was condemned to death for having worked against the interests of the State in allowing his soul to be contaminated by "the newfangled books from Kiev."[60] But before the pendulum had swung too far back, Peter I began his intellectual romance with Western Europe. The work of the Kievan monks assumed new importance, but not before the monks had surrendered a large area of their traditional pursuits.

THE PRAGMATIC NATURE OF HISTORY AND GEOGRAPHY

History-writing, about which nothing has so far been said, underwent several notable innovations during the second half of the seventeenth century. Although the traditional chronicle—which made no attempt either to evaluate sources or to deal with complex historical phenomena—continued to be the favorite form of historical writing, several new forms appeared. The new approaches can hardly be compared with the history-writing being done at the same time in the West, but they are interesting as a special kind of writing which shared with traditional chronicles a predominantly theological and teleological orientation, but offered a new comprehensiveness and a more refined narrative technique.

The need for a new, more modern, more comprehensive historiography was heralded by a special study written on foreign models at the request of Tsar Fedor III. An anonymous untitled manuscript—called by Egor Zamyslovskii and A. S. Lappo-Danilevskii "Introduction to a Historical Book" and by S. V. Peshtich "The Historical Learning," in order to accent its "theoretical" orientation[61]—can be considered the first Russian effort to define the cultural and ideological functions of history-writing and to indicate the importance of a "critical" use of ancient sources pertaining to the growth of political, economic, and intellectual traditions. It contains many excerpts from the writings of Thucydides, Polybius, Tacitus, Cicero, and Dionysius of Halicarnassus; Alexander of Macedon, Julius Caesar, and the Emperors Augustus, Theodosius, and Justinian are cited to show the importance they attached to the knowledge of the historical past and to the need to surround themselves with competent historians. History, the anonymous author asserts, is "the best teacher," for its purpose is to establish the truth by relying on accurate documentation and by avoiding the lure of historical fables. Its main objective is pragmatic: it praises good conduct and condemns every evil. It is primarily a source of vital knowledge. The duty of the historian is not only to record events but also to describe various countries and the customs of their peoples. History must be dedicated to the perfection of man. In the accumulation of knowledge the anonymous author saw the best instrument for the improvement of human well-being; he accepted unequivocally the Aristotelian dictum that man's search for knowledge is deeply embedded in his nature. Following Thucydides, he went so far as to assert that the knowledge of history is also important for the prediction of future developments.

The goals and criteria of history-writing set up in the "Introduction" were too high and too rigorous to be emulated by contemporary scholars. As before, most of the histories written in the second half of the seventeenth century were compilations. There was also widespread borrowing from Polish historical studies, with their heavy Scholastic imprint and their tendency to link history with rhetoric.

In 1657 an Office of Records (a department of the Secret Office) was established for the purpose of making a systematic collection of documentary material pertaining to the Russian reigning families from Fedor Ivanovich to the early years of Alexis. The new office was short-lived, but it marked the first serious effort to maintain a centralized record of important events in the history of the country over a period of several generations. It was another proof of the growing awareness in the ruling circles of the psychological, national, and cultural importance of written history; and, not least important, it was the first real attempt by secular authorities to wean themselves from their traditional dependence on Church chronicles.

The third substantial stride in the development of historiography during the second half of the seventeenth century was the appearance of the *Sinopsis,* written by, or at least directed by, Innokentii Gizel' in a Kiev monastery in 1674. This work recognizes "the unity of the Russians" and is based on an extensive use of Polish, Russian, and Ukrainian documents. Although it is mainly concerned with the history of the Kiev principality, it can be considered the first more or less general history of the Eastern Slavs—for it makes an effort to tie this history with that of Moscow, and its interpretations are unmistakably colored by "the Moscow political theory."[62] The author's justification of the unification of Russia and the Ukraine as a re-establishment of ancient historical ties and his lavish praise of Alexis's great wisdom and statesmanship make this work also the first official history of Russia. The *Sinopsis* pleased high government circles not only for its content but also for its graceful style; it went through twenty-nine editions before it was replaced by more comprehensive histories written a hundred years later.

The awakening interest in the historical background of Russia was *Geog.* accompanied by an interest in Russian geography. The study of history was expected to make a psychological contribution, but geography was hopefully envisaged as a source of knowledge which could be utilized in practical ways—for a more efficient administration, for a systematic diffusion of information about foreign countries, and for the scientific assessment of Russia's natural resources. The development of the internal and foreign markets and the accelerated trend toward an administrative centralization of the country required systematic geographical knowledge, and particularly cartography. In cartography there was an obvious blending of the native Russian and Western European traditions. The so-called Great Map, the best example of the native cartographic tradition, was first drafted in the second half of the sixteenth century, but in 1627 many details were added to it, and a special explanatory book was prepared. The map was revised again in 1680. In 1773 N. I. Novikov published a full description of it under the title "The Ancient Russian Hydrography," probably because it gave especially detailed information on rivers, lakes, and oceans.

The Great Map itself has been lost, but we are fortunate in having three copies of the explanatory book. According to a modern interpretation, the map covered the territory from the Arctic Ocean in the north to the Black Sea in the south, and from the Baltic Sea in the west to the Ob River in the east.[63] After Ermak's expedition in 1582, the ruling elite became very interested in the geography of Siberia and looked to maps to answer many of their questions. The explorations of Ivan Moskvitin in 1639 and S. I. Dezhnev in 1648 led Tsar Alexis to order the preparation of a general map of Siberia. After some years, in 1667, such a map—reproduced by the xylographic method from a wood engraving—was published in Tobolsk. It contained certain details of rivers and ethnic groups, but it lacked any geodetic determination and contained numerous gross errors.

The Russians were not unfamiliar with Western cartographic standards, but it is likely that Western atlases were selected for translation and publication more for the amount of information they contained (particularly about Russia's neighbors) than for their technical and scientific excellence. Mercator's *Atlas,* for example, which was published in a Russian translation in 1637, was interesting for the geographical richness of its maps, not for the mathematical calculation upon which it was based. The same was no doubt true of the Blaeus' *Atlas novus.* It is interesting to note that in 1669–70 the Paris Académie des Sciences prepared a *Carte de France* based on the measurement of the arc of a meridian; in Russia the first such measurement was not made until the second quarter of the eighteenth century.

THE ROOTS OF MODERN SCIENCE

By the end of the seventeenth century the scientific attitude held a place, though a tenuous one, in Russian culture. It did not emerge out of a single tradition and it was not the result of a single intellectual process. It was the product of a happy convergence of technical advancement, the adoption of Western ideas and customs by a small but influential group of aristocrats, the introduction of learning into Church writings and Church teaching, and the gradual opening of the country's doors to the intellectual products of medieval and Renaissance Western Europe. There were no scientific books to speak of, but elements of the natural sciences turned up more and more frequently in books—mainly, of course, in translation. In addition to a large body of translations, and the work of the Kievan monks and other clergymen-scholars, there were scatterings of information in chronographies (the most influential being that of a Polish writer named Bielski); in the so-called *azbukovniki,* which were elementary lexicons covering many branches of knowledge and containing a fair amount of botanical, zoologi-cal, and mineralogical information; and in various sorts of medical books. These, too, were for the most part translations, usually of seventeenth-century works. Characteristically, by the time they had gone into several Russian editions they had lost most of their original information on the natural sciences.[64]

Certainly the seventeenth century in Russia produced no true scientists, nor any profound contributors to science, but for the first time in Russia the secularization of wisdom had become an active process. Owing to the needs of the centralized state, and to the intellectual curiosity of a small but powerful elite which was impatient with Greco-Russian learning and Scholastic *eruditio*, Russia gradually threw off its isolation. The interest was not exclusive to the aristocracy. "Prior to Peter I," says Shchapov, "the boyars did not represent an advanced, intellectual class. With few exceptions, the level of intellectual growth was the same for the entire population. The level of the boyars' wisdom was no higher than that of the peasants. Of the 142 best-known writers of Old Russia from the eleventh to the seventeenth century, only four or five were boyars or princes; all the others came from the clergy and, in general, from the lower classes. The writers of noble origin did not stand out by any special intel-lectual characteristics."[65]

But the penetration of Western or classical scientific ideas into Russia was extremely slow. In the seventeenth century—the century of logarithms, analytical geometry, and calculus—Russia's mathematical knowledge did not exceed the most elementary principles of arithmetic contained in the translations of Western European (mainly German) texts written during the fifteenth and sixteenth centuries. V. V. Bobynin noted that the arith-metical manuals, available only in manuscript form, did not go much beyond the principles involved in numeration, the four major calculating operations with integers and fractions, and the square and cube roots.[66] Feofan Prokopovich, a distinguished clergyman of Peter's time, stated that in seventeenth-century Russia all arithmetic and geometry were condemned as magic and were carefully kept out of the school curriculum. It was indicative of the mood of the age that the imprisonment of the boyar Matveev was due in part to his extensive use of numerals in his handbook of medical advice.[67] Petr Pekarskii noted that during the century only one mathematical book was published in Russia and that it contained elementary knowledge needed by merchants.[68]

Furthermore, such Western and classical ideas as did find their way to Russia usually had no perceptible influence and frequently had to be reintroduced at a later date. The Judaizers, for example, were aware of Euclid at the end of the fifteenth century, but during the sixteenth and seventeenth centuries he was wholly forgotten—though in Western Europe at the same time, Euclid's geometry was common knowledge. It was even taught in the select religious schools of Persia, as Olearius noted on a visit there in the 1630's.[69] The Copernican heliocentric theory, which was introduced in Russia in Slavinetskii's manuscript translation of the Blaeus' *Atlas novus* in 1661, was not issued in printed form, or in any detail, until the second decade of the eighteenth century. The rudiments of modern medical science were introduced by the Apothecary Department established under Alexis, but so few Russians were interested that the project was soon abandoned, and medical training was not revived until Peter the Great took the throne.

The reasons for the painfully slow acceptance of scientific ideas are fairly obvious. Russia did not have a leisure class of intellectuals who could pursue scientific work free of Church control, nor were there any secular schools. Furthermore, the limited printing facilities, largely under Church control, were employed almost exclusively in the publishing of government documents and religious literature. The first secular primer was not published until the eighteenth century. The important intellectual figures like Morozov, Rtishchev, Ordin-Nashchokin, Matveev, and Golitsyn made no actual contributions to the study of science, although they contributed enormously to the general advancement of thought by their enthusiastic acceptance of the secular culture of Western Europe. In their way of life and cultural aspirations, they implied a rejection of Russia's traditional isolation and antirationalism, and the end of a millennium of eastward orientation.

At the lower levels, a millennium of empirical science, of accumulated knowledge derived from practical experience and contact with other, Eastern, peoples, had built in the Russian masses a great intellectual potential for scientific thinking. A passage from Shchapov gives some idea of the scope of this potential:

"By colonizing and cultivating the lands situated mostly in river valleys, the toiling folk observed the geological work of rivers, and the gradual changes in the Russian landscape. They learned about erosion and alluvial formations of soil—about land and soil newly formed through river deposits—for which they had many descriptive terms. Government men, merchants, and workers, in their untiring struggle against the Siberian elements . . . , discovered and investigated such striking phenomena of Siberia's nature as the burning and fire-spitting mountains on the Khatanga River, in Taimyr, and in other places. . . . Common people—townsfolk and craftsmen—discovered metal ores, mica, crystals, sulphur, and precious minerals. Self-taught individuals experimented with metal forging and learned about the physical properties of various substances, even though somewhat superficially. . . . Demidov, an ordinary blacksmith who ran away from Moscow's gunnery at the end of the seventeenth century, was the founder of copper and iron works in the Urals. . . .

"Similarly, commercial enterprises and the activities of Russian working men led to the acquisition of a variety of practical knowledge and to the widening of the physical and geographical horizons. Thus, for example, around 1470 the Tver merchant Afanasii Nikitin, together with six persons from Moscow and five from his own town, was led by his commercial interests to India, almost thirty years before Vasco da Gama arrived there. On this journey he collected and disseminated in Old Russia interesting information on physical geography, even though it was limited and superficial. He wrote about the natural products of India, its flora and fauna, and in particular about the monkeys and 'black people.' He also gave information about the hot climate in India and Central Asiatic countries, about many minerals and plants which at the time were unknown in Russia. Ordinary merchants, artisans, and the Cossacks, such as Stadukhin, Buldakov, Dezhnev, the Iakut merchants Shalaurov and Liakhov . . . and many others . . . became famous through important geographical discoveries in the Arctic Ocean and the Bering Straits. . . .

"Furthermore, simple chemical experiments, operations, and products by peasants, townsfolk, and merchants led to certain scientific chemical conclusions. Thus, in approximately 1700 the Arkhangelsk merchant, self-taught chemist, and technician A. Fomin composed his *Description of the*

Industrial Products of the Arkhangelsk Province on the basis of folk chemical knowledge. This work dealt primarily with the folk techniques used in the processing of resin and pitch and the production of turpentine in general. . . . The author obviously undertook a gradual gathering of various kinds of chemical knowledge, and, together with other merchants, experimented with the production of various other chemical products, such as birch oil."[70]

In the sixteenth century, Herberstein and Barberini were much impressed with Russian technical ingenuity.[71] Olearius, as well as Manstein a century later, noted the intellectual curiosity of the uneducated Russian masses. Olearius commented that the Russians were so quick at grasping the complicated skills of foreign artisans that the foreigners were obliged to keep their methods secret in order to save themselves from competition. Manstein was struck by the ability of Russian peasants "to understand everything with which they are confronted" and "to devise and invent remarkably adequate methods for the realization of their ideas."[72] All this was an informal, untutored, and self-guided search for practical knowledge, unaccompanied by any desire for higher education. The resistance to formal education and to secular schools, which cut evenly across all estates and classes, was to remain an undiminished force working against the growth of theoretical science in Russia—a stubborn relic of the Greco-Russian tradition that was scarcely tempered even by Peter's enthusiasm for scientific education or by Catherine's ambitious schemes for establishing a system of public schools.

Russia thus entered the epoch of Peter I with a rich store of technical knowledge and with a choice group of men interested in science, but also with the handicap of a widespread antipathy toward formal secular education. In the West, science was already firmly established as an intellectual pursuit independent of religion. Yet, as Whitehead emphasizes, the scientific revolution was made possible by a dominant aspect of the Christian religion of the West—its faith that the universe possesses an order that can be comprehended by inquiring rational minds. Indeed, it was a religious duty and a mark of virtuous life to employ one's rational faculties in search of a more complete understanding of nature.

Russian Orthodoxy, on the other hand, was dominated by a mystical acceptance of the universe as an entity ruled by miracle-working divine caprice, which could not be comprehended by an inquiring rational mind —only felt, through the medium of awe-inspiring ritual. Russian theology, comments Anton V. Florovskii, never accepted Aristotle and Plato, nor did it find much use for Western European education which had its spiritual roots in the teachings of these ancient philosophers. Instead of the Western "school science," Russian theology emphasized ascetic wisdom, Oriental-Byzantine mysticism, and the writings of the Church Fathers. Most important, it recognized "the supremacy of belief over knowledge, of spiritual integrity and purity over intellectual accomplishments and unnatural school discipline." "The school as such was condemned, or rather rejected in principle, because it contributed nothing to salvation and because humility is more important than the versatility and the aplomb of the 'savant.' "[73] Another writer notes that "Russian Byzantinism was not just a servile repetition but a new and peculiar version of Byzantine culture, in which we can discern a true creative power."[74] Whatever the cultural strength of Russian Byzantinism may have been, it is evident that it was not in the realm of rationalist thought and science. It was a propensity to rationalism that, according to V. S. Ikonnikov, distinguished most Russian heretical movements.[75]

The untempered antirationalism of modern Russian theology and theological philosophy is only a proof that the seventeenth-century abyss between theology and science in Russia still exists. Peter I showed great astuteness when he decided to circumvent the Church in his efforts to found special institutions for the dissemination of knowledge.

CHAPTER TWO

Peter the Great: Science by Decree

THE MAN AND THE TIME

The nineteenth-century Slavophils and their intellectual and ideological allies interpreted the sweeping reforms of Peter the Great as a tragic end of Holy Russia. Peter, they said, disturbed the natural course of Russian life, destroyed the traditional mores and morals, engendered a conflict between the higher and lower social segments, contaminated the country by introducing an alien way of life and a foreign style of government, and thwarted the development of Russian national consciousness. The Westerners, on the other hand, praised Peter for having brought Russia into being by shaking it out of its centuries-old inertia and cultural isolation and opening its doors to the fresh air of Western Europe.

On one point, however, the Slavophils and the Westerners were in agreement: that Peter's reforms were of gigantic proportions and that they laid the foundations of the political organization and secular culture of modern Russia. Easily among the most revolutionary reforms of the Petrine era were those that were concerned, directly or indirectly, with the intellect, science, and secular wisdom in general. The intellectual reshaping of Russia under Peter's dedicated and uncompromising guidance was an arduous assignment and a diffuse process.

The ruthlessness with which Peter's reforms were put into effect is readily admitted by admirers and critics alike. However, he did not operate in a cultural vacuum: the intellectual conflicts of the seventeenth century provided the training ground for the emergence of a small group of admirers of secular inquiry into the mysteries of the historical and natural worlds. True, the Baconian emphasis on objective observation—the inductive method—as the beginning of all scientific knowledge found no echo in Old Russia. Scholasticism, introduced to Russia during the last half of the seventeenth century, adhered strictly to the Aristotelian deductive method. It placed little value on experience and observation as sources of accurate knowledge and limited itself to a manipulation of ideas derived from supersensory and divine truths. Despite the sterility of its content, however, it trained students in the art of precise, logically coherent, and systematic thinking. It also stressed the importance of Latin as the international language of intellectual communication. In the curious it aroused a thirst for knowledge and in the skeptics a search for new orientations and modes of inquiry.

At the close of the century the distribution of secular books, imported mostly from Poland, had greatly increased. Such Polish humanists as A. F. Modrejewski and Jan Petrycy found a receptive audience in Russia.[1] Seventeenth-century rationalism gained a foothold in Moscow's German suburb and from there began to acquire a somewhat broader following. It was in this largely Protestant community that the philosophy of Descartes first appeared in Russia; and it has been claimed that John Locke made his entrance through the same gate early in the eighteenth century.[2]

Young Peter was fortunate in growing up in this atmosphere of intellectual fermentation, although it is doubtful that he ever became familiar with the fine points of Scholastic and humanistic thought or with Descartes' rationalism and Locke's empiricism. He absorbed his father's belief that Russia needed both Orthodoxy, as the basic unifying force, and positive knowledge, as the means to military strength, economic prosperity, and social welfare. Throughout his life he subscribed to the Baconian dictum that scientific knowledge is a utilitarian force that should be employed for the betterment of the lot of human society.

Peter's early education was unsystematic and, by Western standards, conservative. At the age of four he began "playing army" with his own special regiment, made up completely of adults, from whom, as colonel, he received daily formal reports. It was this training, says one of his biographers, that instilled in him a sense of order, precision, and official responsibility.[3] He acquired firsthand knowledge of the modern army as a human organization and a technical enterprise. His formal education was limited mainly to reading and writing and to some acquaintance with the heroes of the past—either real or imaginary—derived from the stories read to him by his teacher. He was taught no science whatever.

But if his formal education was aimless and meager, his intellectual horizons were widened by acquaintance with many educated Western Europeans employed by the Russian government. He was particularly close to the Dutch, who hailed from one of Europe's richest and most progressive countries. From these people the youthful monarch received

an inkling of the great power and usefulness of mathematics, needed by
both the shipbuilders and the navigators at sea. The first Russian ships
built in Pereiaslavl were designed and constructed by ship masters from
Saardam, Holland. Peter's only knowledge of a foreign language was an
elementary acquaintance with Dutch.[4]

PETER I AND KRIZHANICH: A COMPARISON

It would be a gross error to attribute Peter's reforms in the realm of
education and ideas solely to his intellectual alertness and curiosity and to
his good fortune in having personal contact with technical experts from
Western Europe. The temper of his time was his greatest ally, for it
encouraged a search for a way out of the intellectual ruins of a defunct
Byzantinism. Many historians have compared the ideals of Peter with
those of Iurii Krizhanich, the most uncompromising critic of the ideology
of Byzantinism.[5] It is known that Peter's father was acquainted with
Krizhanich, who left the country before the birth of the Great Transformer
but continued to exert considerable influence through his ideas as the
conflicts between the Old Believers and the New Believers recurred. Peter,
like Krizhanich before him, realized that there could be no compromise
between the old and the new and that a drastic break with some of the most
sacred aspects of traditional culture was necessary. It was Krizhanich who
observed that "a good ruler should not be dedicated to the preservation of
old customs" and in so doing openly attacked one of the principal ideological tenets of the Church and Old Russia.[6]

Immediately after Peter's ascent to the throne in 1682 the Old Believers
made a new attempt to regain the ground lost in their struggle with the
champions of change. The dominance of the State over the Church was by
then almost complete, and secular thought had become the basic force
upon which the welfare and the prosperity of the Russian polity were
dependent. The secularization of knowledge, in turn, made cultural contact with the West a historical imperative. The youthful Tsar made
frequent visits to the German suburb in Moscow, where he learned something about the doctrines of Protestantism and its emphasis on the secular
principles of the State.[7] It was here that he became friendly with Franz
Lefort, a Swiss, in whose house he met sophisticated foreigners. From
them he acquired a certain acquaintance with the intellectual ideas of
Western Europe, catching the spirit that permeated their thinking—the
spirit that not only reconciled religion and science but made scientific

inquiry into the order of nature an imperative religious duty.[8] At any rate, he surrounded himself with a group of competent foreigners, as advisers and government administrators. Gradually, he became more convinced of the soundness of his belief that it is wiser and more profitable to introduce new institutions, values, and ideas than to mend the old and decadent ones.[9] Throughout his life, he combined a pragmatic appreciation of science with a firm belief in the compatibility of science and religion, a common orientation among the leading contemporary scientists in the West.

Krizhanich, aware of the broad ramifications of Russia's cultural isolation, intellectual backwardness, and social immobility, suggested a three-point program of remedies for the country's staggering ills. The program provided Peter with the basic principles that guided him throughout his life. First of all, Krizhanich espoused "education, science, and books" as "inanimate but wise and judicious counselors." Positive knowledge and a respect for education were, he believed, the main reasons for the prosperity of the West, and they were the only tools that could help Russia to overcome her economic backwardness, sparsity of population, and general ignorance. He specifically mentioned the study and practice of metallurgy, which would require the establishment of technical schools in all urban communities, the hiring of foreign experts to teach Russians various arts and crafts, and the translation of German technological manuals.[10]

In the second place, Krizhanich was convinced that even though autocracy was the best government for Russia, it must be raised to a higher level of enlightenment, making formal education an integral part of the culture—if necessary, by coercive means.[11] He recommended, for example, that merchants who knew no arithmetic be forced to change their profession. Peter, following the theories of his distinguished forerunner, learned early in youth that both science and education could be introduced in his country only by governmental decrees and unrestrained coercion.

Krizhanich's third point concerned "political freedom," by which he meant official recognition of the rights and complementary social obligations of individual estates as corporate units.[12] He was convinced that the intellectual and material prosperity of Western Europe was the result of a free intercourse among various social strata, and he was equally certain that much of Russia's cultural inertia could be overcome if all groups were given an opportunity to realize their latent potentials. He was particularly alive to the potentialities of merchants and artisans, the middle layers in Russia's complex estate structure, who began to show marked social mobility under the influence of modern technological advances. These were the least conservative of all groups in technological matters, and they figured in many of Peter's educational reforms. Peter departed from Krizhanich's program, however, in almost totally ignoring the peasant.

Krizhanich's program had one predominant and unifying thought: Russia could enter the family of civilized European nations as an equal partner only by means of a rational mobilization of its human and natural resources based on the dissemination of scientific knowledge. To be sure, Krizhanich was not aware of the great achievements in scientific theory made by such giants as Galileo and Kepler and was unfamiliar with Bacon. He was not yearning for the diffusion in Russia of highly abstract astronomical and mathematical knowledge, and indeed did not sense the gathering momentum of the seventeenth century's great scientific revolution. Rather, he had in mind the science of the Renaissance: practical arithmetic, applied geometry, mining technology, and modern agricultural methods.

Peter lived in another age—an age that had gone beyond elementary scientific knowledge and demanded an extensive secularization of both the search for and the distribution of knowledge. Krizhanich recognized implicitly that it was incumbent upon the State to play the leading role in the organization of formal education and scientific inquiry; however, he skillfully avoided taking into account the mounting conflict between Church and State over control of educational and scientific institutions. Peter, as a practical statesman, could not ignore this conflict, and throughout his reign he made bold and mostly successful efforts to strip the Church of its traditional prerogatives in the most important intellectual enclaves. For a while he hoped that the Church would be willing to expand the curricula of its educational institutions to include technical subjects as well as theological ones, but this hope was doomed to disappointment. After his first Western European tour in 1697–98, he made such suggestions to Patriarch Adrian, urging him to convert the theological academies into models of new quasi-secular schools. He was firmly convinced, he said, that ignorance —the inability to harness the power of modern science—only supported the devil in his evil machinations. He reminded the Patriarch that one of the great duties of religion was to dignify work, to make it an essential cultural value. Peter had in mind work based on modern science and dedicated to social welfare when he said that "religion without work is dead, as is work without true religion." He wanted the Church to give its blessings to scientific thought. As the first step, he wanted the students of the theological academies to know not only the gospel, but also such practical matters as how to conduct military operations, how to erect public buildings, bridges, and fortifications, and how to cure the sick. He soon learned that the theological institutions, heavy with the spirit of Scholasticism, had neither the intellectual atmosphere nor the teaching facilities necessary to train technical personnel.

Peter's next step was to ask for help from various Western missionaries located in Moscow, but here again he faced strong resistance to foreign teachers, a formidable remnant of the Russian-Byzantine tradition. Even Feofan Prokopovich, who saw the necessity of hiring foreign teachers, urged that they be closely supervised lest they convert young Russians to "their theologies."

In 1703, at Peter's direct encouragement, a Swedish pastor named Ernst Glück gathered about him a number of Lutheran students and opened a school in Moscow.[13] The institution followed the model of Swedish parochial schools. Its curriculum, as publicly announced, offered introductory arithmetic, geometry, philosophy, ethics, politics, Latin rhetoric, Cartesian philosophy, and the Latin, Greek, German, French, Hebrew, Syriac, and Chaldean languages and grammars. Glück himself translated into Russian Luther's catechism, a prayer book, a German grammar, and brief introductions to the study of the Russian, German, Latin, and French languages. Glück's school is scarcely mentioned in contemporary historical documents; it apparently never gathered momentum, and after Glück's death in 1705 it rapidly faded out of existence. Glück's successor, J. W. Pause, a master of philosophy from Jena, recommended that Turkish and Persian be added to the curriculum as languages particularly important for Russia. The failure of this school, following the disappointments in theological schools, convinced Peter that the only answer to the crying need for modern educational institutions was a system of secular schools, completely free of all ecclesiastical or theological influences.

THE GRAND EMBASSY AND LEIBNIZ'S COUNSEL

During the last years of the seventeenth century Peter had completed his intellectual apprenticeship, and at least the rough outlines of an attack on ignorance were crystallized in his mind. In this apprenticeship two events were particularly important. The first was his active part in the Grand Embassy that took him to several countries of Western Europe; the second was his correspondence with Leibniz. The apparent mission of the Grand Embassy of 1697–98 was to marshal European forces for a gigantic attack on the Ottoman Empire; as it happened, its main achievement was that it provided the youthful monarch with an opportunity to visit European shipyards, manufactories, schools, and centers of scientific inquiry. In Holland he visited dockyards, warehouses, workshops, and lumber mills, inspected modern fire-extinguishing pumps, and arranged a fifteen-year contract giving the printer Johann van Thessing a virtual monopoly on the publication of books for Russia. He inspected the botanical garden in Amsterdam and was shown Professor Ruysch's famous anatomical museum at the University of Leyden, by Ruysch himself. He visited Leeuwenhoek and examined one of his microscopes.

In England Peter had particularly rich and varied experiences. From conversations with the Anglican Bishop Burnet and other church dignitaries he acquired firsthand knowledge of English Church-State relationships. He learned something of the numerous religious sects which were then strong in various parts of England. He visited Parliament and observed its lengthy and tedious operations. At Oxford University he was greeted by academic authorities and granted the honorary degree of Doctor of Law.[14] In the Greenwich Observatory he was initiated into the complex field of astronomy.

It is doubtful that Peter learned much about the art of shipbuilding during his prolonged stay in Holland and England. What he did learn, however, became a colossal historical force in the cultural history of Russia—a turning point in the intellectual growth of the country. He quickly realized that shipbuilding had ceased to be the work simply of dexterous artisans and that it had become an engineering enterprise based on precise scientific blueprints. He understood the importance of modern mathematical knowledge in shipbuilding; and he learned that mathematics was increasingly important also in the development of astronomy. Indeed, this profound appreciation of the importance of mathematics to the growth of modern technology and scientific knowledge proved to be the most valuable lesson learned by Peter during his visit to England.

Before leaving England he acted on his resolve to carry mathematical knowledge to Russia. He secured the consent of Henry Farquharson, "an experienced instructor of mathematics who was educated at Aberdeen University," to come to Russia to teach the Russians "in the knowledge and use of mathematics."[15] Farquharson was joined by Stephen Gwyn and Richard Grice, two young mathematicians who were graduates of Christ's Hospital in London.[16] Peter also ordered a shipment of "mathematical instruments" to be sent to Russia. He authorized a close friend and adviser,

Jacob Bruce—a member of an aristocratic Scottish family which emigrated to Russia in 1647—to receive mathematical instruction from a "well-known London mathematician."[17] Bruce's future career showed that his instructor gave him not only a healthy appreciation for mathematics as a science but a fair grounding in mathematical knowledge as well. He subsequently became one of Russia's early leaders in geodetics and geography and earned great fame through his work on the first Russian almanac with up-to-date astronomical information.

When Peter returned to Russia—no doubt with the introduction of educational institutions in his own country well in mind—he left behind him the physician of the Grand Embassy, Petr Posnikov, so that he might study the organization of English schools. Very little is known about the background, training, and work of Posnikov. In 1692, after graduating from the Slavic-Greek-Latin Academy, he was sent by Peter to Padua University to study "free sciences." In 1695–96 he spent some time in Vienna, Paris, and Leyden "for a more advanced study of medicine." Although engaged chiefly in diplomatic service, he was very active in procuring technical books and scientific materials for various government agencies.

Peter's long contact, through correspondence and meetings, with Leibniz strengthened tangibly his appreciation of the spirit of the new scientific age and of the need for stronger intellectual ties between Russia and the West. It also provided him with the first concrete and comprehensive suggestions for suitable schools and their administration, and for the establishment of conditions conducive to the growth of scientific thought.

Leibniz's interest in Russia was not ephemeral and it had many sources, as is clearly shown in the study by Liselotte Richter. As a young man, he met several Russians who were on special missions abroad and he later corresponded with some of them. There is proof that he tried to learn a Slavic language. In his letters to August H. Francke of Halle University and to a French numismatist, Morel, written in 1697, Leibniz writes of his hopes of persuading Peter to open Russia to the influence of "Christianity and civilization." In his second letter to Morel he explains that cooperation with Russia is needed for the achievement of "the perfection of mankind."[18] His religious ideal was "the glory of God through the growth of knowledge"; he equated the glory of God with a continuous search for rationality. Science, according to him, ensured a gradual unfolding of the *civitas dei*.[19] His particular interest in Russia had a purely secular basis, however. He was responsible for "the general instructions" issued to the members of the Berlin Academy of Sciences in 1700, which emphasized that friendly relations with Russia were indispensable for the general advancement of science. Russia was seen as a source of valuable astronomical, geographical, ethnic, and linguistic information. Leibniz contended that the opening of Russia to systematic study would enrich empirical science and would constitute a major step in the progress of modern civilization. He was attracted to Russia also by his admiration for Peter's courageous and sweeping efforts to fling wide the doors of Russia to modern civilization. Finally, in his scheme, Russia, China, and Ethiopia loomed as gigantic springboards for a grand spread of modern civilization.[20]

In 1697, when the correspondence between Leibniz and Peter began, Leibniz was engaged in building the foundations of the Berlin Academy of Sciences. In a note written in that year, found among Peter's documents, Leibniz outlined the conditions which the Russian government must create as a prerequisite for general enlightenment and scientific progress. The note stressed that Russia must first of all employ foreigners capable of instructing others in scientific knowledge and must also acquire such essential educational materials as books, natural specimens, models, machines, and artistic objects. It urged the immediate opening of libraries, bookstores, presses, museums, and botanical and zoological gardens. Most of all, it emphasized the enormous need for academies and schools, which should concentrate on the teaching of mathematics, languages (primarily Latin), and history. The note viewed education and scientific work in their practical aspects. Scientific research, it made clear, was of value because of its potential usefulness in surveying the country's needs and natural resources and in suggesting improvements in the general field of national economy, such as the expansion of agriculture and the building of canals and factories. The spirit of mercantilism which pervaded the note was to prove of no small influence on Peter's policies of economic development.[21]

In 1716 Leibniz submitted to the Russian Vice-Chancellor, P. P. Shafirov, a number of recommendations for improvements in the systems of transportation and communication. He appended a memorandum on what he deemed to be the logical steps for Russia to undertake in order to emulate the educational and scientific standards of Western civilization. He recommended (1) the systematic collection of "linguistic" material necessary for the advancement of ancient history and ethnography; (2) the encouragement of missionary work by representatives of Western European Christian churches; (3) the study of earth magnetism and the incline of the compass, as an important step toward the improvement of navigation; (4) the organization of astronomical observations; (5) the advancement of geographical knowledge; (6) a systematic survey of the plants, animals, and ores of Russia and her southern neighboring areas; and (7) the translation into Russian of Western scientific and technical books that were known to be useful in the study of modern industrial technology.[22]

Leibniz returned repeatedly to his main theme: the urgent need of a system of public schools. One of the notes written in 1716 projected a three-level hierarchy of educational and scientific institutions as most suitable for Russia: public schools, universities, and academies— the last to be a gathering place for university graduates dedicated to the advancement of scientific knowledge.[23] He stressed that university students must command a knowledge of several foreign languages and must be well trained in the theoretical foundations of modern science.

Leibniz's influence on Peter—and on Russia's intellectual growth—was complex. First, it contributed to Peter's championship of close ties between learned societies (or academies) and educational institutions. In addition to their intrinsic functions, the former were envisaged by both Leibniz and Peter as agencies entrusted with direct administration of educational institutions.[24] Second, it was to a considerable extent responsible for the fact that the Russian word *nauka* (science) acquired the broad meaning of the German *Wissenschaft*, which includes history and philosophy as well as the natural and social sciences. Third, it was largely responsible for transplanting to Russia the notion then prevalent in Western Europe that science, although dedicated primarily to the improvement of human welfare, must not infringe on the sacred domains of religion. Fourth, it reaffirmed Peter's contention that the spread of science and education was the duty of the government and that an academy of sciences should be a government institution, responding to educational and scientific assignments given to it by state agencies. Fifth, it bolstered Peter's tendency to be more concerned with the contributions of science to Russia than to mankind as a whole.

The scientific "nationalism" of Leibniz and Peter was at variance with the Baconian dictum that science must be dedicated primarily to humanity. Leibniz saw in the Berlin Academy of Sciences an instrument for improving the welfare of the German people and earning them an honorable place in the family of nations. In accordance with his ideal, the Academy strove "to unite theory and practice, and to advance not only the arts and sciences but also the country and its people, manufactures, and commerce—

in brief, the means of livelihood."[25] Imbued with the humanist tradition, Leibniz recognized that the ultimate goal of science is to raise mankind to a higher plane of development, with greater control over nature; in this commitment he acknowledged the fact that science must receive its initial momentum from an identification of the search for knowledge with the concrete interests of individual nations. Peter I, like his famous counselor, was aware of the political significance of science; he saw in science the most potent tool for raising the prestige of his country among the nations of Europe. He hoped that a generation of learned men would dispel the widespread notion that the Russians had no respect for science. He also knew that by developing science a modern state strengthens its own power.

Fontenelle, in his famous *éloge* to Leibniz, recognized the great German philosopher's contribution to the growth of scientific thought in Russia in his comment, "In the history of science in Russia he can never be forgotten, and his name will be placed alongside that of the Tsar."[26] Peter did not slavishly accept all of Leibniz's suggestions, but used them to widen the perspectives of intellectual activity and to define the guiding principles of his educational philosophy. Not the least of Leibniz's contributions was that through him Christian Wolff, his most eminent disciple, became Peter's main adviser in the long and tedious preparatory work which led to the founding of the St. Petersburg Academy of Sciences in 1725—an academy born in the spirit of Leibniz's general educational and scientific ideas.

WESTERN TRAINING AND SOCIAL CLASSES

Peter was faced with an abundance of ideas and proposals—some of them emanating from his Russian contemporaries[27]—for the urgently needed educational and scientific reforms. He was at the same time confronted with a drastic scarcity of personnel capable of placing Russia on the path of enlightenment. The country had virtually no trained scholars capable either of teaching science or of pursuing scientific studies of their own. After his unsuccessful efforts to interest Church authorities in adding studies in secular knowledge and arts to the curricula of the theological schools, Peter decided to send young Russians to Western European centers of learning, hoping in that way to form a nucleus around which a class of intellectuals could be developed.

Unfortunately, Russians who traveled in Western Europe left far fewer journals of their impressions than did Europeans who ventured to Russia. In Peter's time three kinds of Russians visited Western Europe: diplomats engaged mostly in trade negotiations, occasional tourists, and students. In 1697 a small contingent of Russian students arrived in the West: twenty-eight young men in Italy and twenty-two in England and Holland. Peter's attempt to create a scholarly class out of whole cloth, so to speak, was interesting, but not stunningly successful. Not simply linguistic difficulties but European customs and mores puzzled and disturbed the Russian students. They were sorely handicapped by their lack of formal education, coming from a country where there was not even respect for education. According to Pekarskii:

"It was during the reign of Peter I that the Russians became acquainted with European sciences through young men who had studied abroad. The brevity of time, the newness of this kind of experience, and the force of old customs and opinions prevented Peter's personal activities and concerns from bearing fruit during his lifetime. At the beginning of the eighteenth century, the persons who went abroad in search of education were employed primarily as translators of scholarly works, mostly in mathematics, navigation, and linguistics. None of these translators became known through independent work and none made scientific contributions."[28]

Peter well understood that nowhere in Russian society could he find enthusiastic and able proponents of modern science. To be sent abroad for education was regarded by the gentry as an insult and a direct attack on what they regarded as the purity and self-sufficiency of their life. I. N. Boltin, who was otherwise sympathetic to Peter's reforms, thought that the sending of young nobles abroad was harmful since the majority of them "returned uneducated, and no wiser, but more vicious and frivolous than before they left the country."[29] Those aristocrats who achieved eminence in intellectual pursuits were atypical of the class, which throughout the eighteenth century was appallingly ignorant.

The Church was no more likely a partner in Peter's campaign for science. Certain changes had been gradually taking place even there, as the storm raised by the Old Believers subsided: prompted by the prelates of the Near East, the Church began to recognize the beneficial role of knowledge in the life of the religious community. But its ideas about knowledge and the institutional mechanisms for its dissemination were far different from Peter's. Earlier, the Church had been preoccupied with questions of morality, and it dispensed with scientific thought by simple declarations of antiscientific character. By the beginning of the eighteenth century the ideology and philosophy of the Church were safeguarded by an alert corps of theologians who, not satisfied with mere dismissals of scientific discoveries, were making elaborate and passionate attacks on them. Learned churchmen condemned philosophical rationalism, Baconian empiricism, and mathematical deduction before they had made any real entry into Russian intellectual life.

To strengthen the Church in its intellectual battle with the secularization of knowledge, Patriarch Adrian insisted—though to no avail—that the spectacle of illiterate priests should be eliminated. Peter, too, would have welcomed a better educated clergy, for his efforts to line up the priestly estate behind his educational plans and scientific aspirations might then have had more chance of success. Priests were even less inclined than the gentry to allow their children to study in the West, fearing that their souls would be contaminated by scientific thought and alien theologies.

Although the lower classes did not figure in Peter's plans for education, they shared with the higher social strata a profound distaste for formal education, as Peter well knew. Lacking any likely candidates, he was determined to create a special class of intellectuals to occupy a middle rung in the total social structure. To what extent he was successful can be seen in I. I. Betskoi's remark, a half-century later, that Russia's failure to produce a middle class with intellectual proclivities was the main reason for her backwardness in the fields of education and science.[30]

The reasons for the general failure of Peter's policy to form a nucleus of teachers and scientists through a systematic education of young men in Western Europe should not be sought only in the disregard for formal education in eighteenth-century Russian society. Students who studied abroad were not subject to proper supervision and, according to J. G. Vockerodt, "did not bring back much more knowledge than they took with them."[31] Influenced by his own experiences, Peter did not require the young men to enroll in any one educational institution; it was his belief that they would derive more beneficial knowledge from travel in France, England, Holland, Italy, and Germany than they would in classes. Unfortunately, upon their return to the homeland, many of the young men were given high administrative posts not conducive to a search for knowledge and educational sophistication, and most of them managed to forget very quickly what they had learned in school or in travel. Probably 150 or so young Russians received Western education during the first two decades of the eighteenth century; sixty of these on their return were employed as official translators. Peter soon understood that the small number of Western-educated Russians would hardly provide an adequate foundation for a sound and efficient educational system, and that other means and methods must be employed.

In Peter's era there were three types of schools in Russia, each representing different traditions and ideologies and dedicated to different curricula. The largest number were the parochial and theological schools, under the supervision of the Kiev and Moscow academies and subject to absolute control by the Church. These schools primarily trained future priests—the pupils were usually the children of clergymen—and were thus largely responsible for the formation of the archconservative priestly estate. Strictly adhering to the so-called Kievan learning, which ignored not only the seventeenth-century scientific revolution but also the intellectual legacy of the Renaissance, these schools permitted no instruction in even the most elementary scientific knowledge. The intellectual monopoly of the Church schools was to be gradually curtailed by the growth of organized scientific inquiry, but the number of people reached by it increased in large numbers, and it was predominant in Russia during the first three-quarters of the eighteenth century. Between 1721 and 1765, twenty-eight seminaries, all modeled on the Kiev Academy, were founded—all, according to Shchapov, providing "empty and sterile exercises of the mind in the Scholastic-logical analysis of supernatural doctrines."[32] During most of the eighteenth century the graduates of the Kiev Academy served as teachers of these seminaries; not until the close of the century was the newer Moscow Academy able to boast of graduates capable of carrying teaching assignments. The promulgation of the Ecclesiastical Regulation in 1721 in some measure strengthened the Church schools by making ordination dependent on a certificate proving the completion of required schooling, but since the Regulation was in practice largely ignored, Peter's hopes of allies in an educated clergy were disappointed.[33]

The second group of educational institutions were the schools sponsored by Western missionaries and devoted both to religious and to secular branches of knowledge, mainly humanistic studies. These schools—of which Glück's Lutheran institution in Moscow was typical—were short-lived and of but slight influence in the history of Russian education. Along with the private tutoring offered by Jesuit monks, they fell victim to the relentless efforts of the Orthodox Church to halt the educational work of rival priests. The missionaries were in any event more interested in seeking religious converts than in disseminating knowledge.

The third type of school during Peter's era was one that had been unknown in earlier times, and indeed was directly the result of Peter's work—educational institutions completely devoid of religious indoctrina-

tion and theological bias, with curricula mainly devoted to elementary
3) mathematics, astronomy, navigation, and several other areas of natural
science. Most of these schools were experimental, and few of them lasted
very long, but they were of great importance as the first general public
schools devoted to the training of personnel for state service. They laid the
cornerstone for the official Russian educational philosophy that has survived
to the present day: a philosophy based on the principle that it is incumbent
upon the state to serve as the indisputable master of the country's educational facilities and curricular orientation, and that religious and secular
education must be separate, although ideologically compatible.

The first secular public school in Russia was the School of Mathematics
and Navigation founded in Moscow in 1701 by the intelligent and enterprising Scotsman Henry Farquharson, brought to Russia by Peter for the
express purpose. The curriculum of this school was dominated by such
sciences as arithmetic, trigonometry, navigation, and elementary astronomy.
In 1715 the school was transferred to St. Petersburg, renamed the Naval
Academy, and given a new curriculum—prepared by Peter himself—which
included arithmetic, geometry, fencing and the handling of rifles, artillery,
navigation, fortification, geography, and drawing. Like other schools of
the same type (the Artillery School, the Engineering School, and the School
of Surgery), the Naval Academy in actual accomplishment fell considerably
short of its title and avowed interests. Its problems were those that were
to plague Russian schools for years to come: a general apathy or animosity
toward formal education, a staggering dearth of native teachers, and the
inability of foreign teachers to cope with the Russian language. Not only
was the language itself a difficult one, but it had as yet absorbed only the
most elementary scientific concepts.

INDIVIDUAL SCIENTISTS

It became the responsibility of rare individuals like Farquharson to
promote the growth of scientific thought in Russia. Only in small part
through secular educational institutions, they struggled to acquaint Russians with scientific ideas from the West—many of them no longer strange
and novel in Europe. On their own, they undertook the first systematic
surveys of the exact sciences, and they added to the Russian language
hundreds of new terms, by means of which Russia could begin to achieve
intellectual rapport with the West. Farquharson set as his standard in
preparing the curriculum of the Mathematical and Navigational School

and acquiring textbooks (many of his own translation) the goal that he thought the students should strive for—not simply what their level of maturity and sophistication might best fit them for. Some idea of the comparatively high level of mathematical knowledge he tried to impart to his students is indicated by the fact that he chose Adriaan Vlacq's *Tabulae sinuum, tangentium et secantium, et logarithmi sinuum, tangentium et numerorum ab unitade at 10,000* for translation into Russian. Directly or indirectly, he helped with the translation of thirty-eight scientific manuals into Russian, and he is credited with a translation of extracts from Euclid's *Elements,* the first effort to popularize Euclid's geometry in Russia.

Farquharson did his own writing in Latin; works chosen as textbooks for his students were translated into Russian. His work contributed to the final victory of Arabic numerals in Russia; henceforth, the Old Slavic letter-numerals, incompatible with modern mathematics, were rapidly discarded. Farquharson was a versatile scholar: he was responsible for the first Russian bronze engraving of Mercator's map of America; he published a table of latitudes to be used by the students of the Naval Academy; he prepared a manual on the use of "mathematical instruments"; he left an unpublished manuscript on trigonometry. Not simply the founder of mathematical education in Russia, he was rightfully considered the first seaman of the Russian fleet; in 1737, twelve years after Peter's death, the government bestowed upon him the rank of brigadier. On that occasion Empress Anne wrote to the Admiralty that he had earned his rank because he was the true pioneer in the teaching of mathematics in Russia, and because all Russian seamen, from the lowest to the highest ranks, were his students.[34] Peter, however, bestowed no particular honors on Farquharson, nor did he apparently feel any obligation to live up to the salary commitments he had originally made to Farquharson in Scotland. Farquharson stayed in Russia until he died in 1739, but he was in financial straits much of the time.

The work of Farquharson should not be considered an index to Russia's scientific achievements during the early decades of the eighteenth century, nor even evidence of a new scientific orientation in Russian society. Farquharson's standards were those of Western scholarship. Both as a scholar and as a teacher he was determined not to dilute scientific knowledge to make it palatable to young Russians who had neither the tradition nor the experience of formal education. Instead, he made scientific education a serious business, and a difficult but rewarding challenge. It was for this reason that the minimum requirements of his curriculum were far higher than those of the other secular schools. Owing to the high quality of his work and to his teaching perseverance, the modern scientific spirit began to find champions among the Russians.

Russia's readiness to travel the path of science, tentative and peripheral at first, was best shown by the intellectual career of Leontii Magnitskii (1669–1739). Originally a student of the Moscow Slavic-Greek-Latin Academy, he pursued independent studies in mathematics, and learned the German, Dutch, and Italian languages. In 1701 he became an instructor in mathematics in the newly founded School of Mathematics and Navigation, and in 1703 he published a two-volume *Arithmetic*, which for a half-century served as the main mathematics textbook in Russia. This work was not a summary of the existing mathematical knowledge in Russia but an encyclopedia of various relevant items mostly translated from Western sources.[35] It was not, however, completely unoriginal, for the author showed much ingenuity in the organization of material, explanatory notes, and selection of examples. There were also some indications that he had a thorough acquaintance with Russia's seventeenth-century mathematical manuscripts—whose meager knowledge the *Arithmetic* far surpassed.[36] The *Arithmetic* was important not only in bringing up-to-date elementary mathematical knowledge to Russia but also in showing the wide range of practical problems—particularly of a military and commercial nature—that could be solved mathematically.[37] As a result of these two volumes, mathematics became the first systematic body of scientific knowledge to acquire a place in Russian culture.

Real recognition did not come to Magnitskii until the next century, however, when historians of mathematics began to reconstruct the story of the growth of this discipline in Russia. In his own time he was almost ignored. He seems to have worked with Farquharson on the translation of the Vlacq *Tabulae sinuum,* but when the School of Mathematics and Navigation was moved to St. Petersburg, he was left virtually stranded in Moscow.

THE CIPHERING SCHOOLS

In 1714, in the hope of building a firmer foundation for a system of elementary educational institutions, Peter ordered that so-called ciphering schools be established in all the provincial capitals. With faculties drawn from graduates of the Naval Academy, the ciphering schools were supposed to provide education for the children of the nobility, the clergy, and certain urban middle-class groups in the basic disciplines of reading, writing, arithmetic, and geometry. Students were slow to come. The fear of unknown subjects and of harsh discipline, and a lack of respect for "written knowledge," were widespread. The tradespeople's children, who were often indispensable to the family's income, were immediately relieved of their educational obligations. The children of the clergy were soon granted permission to attend Church schools instead of the ciphering schools. Owing to these exceptions and to other pressures and circumventions of the law, many ciphering schools disappeared within a few years. Of the forty-seven teachers sent to provincial schools, eighteen returned immediately because of lack of students. As graduates of the Naval Academy, the teachers were subordinate to the Admiralty, which in 1723 tried to rid itself of this unpleasant responsibility and recommended that the teachers be assigned to theological schools and subordinated to the Church. The Church, in turn, was successful in its steadfast efforts to prevent the merging of religious and secular education. With no friends either among the masses of the people or among ecclesiastical authorities, the ciphering schools not surprisingly dwindled. By 1744 only eight of the original forty-two still remained, and these, too, soon ceased to exist or were absorbed by "garrison schools" founded in 1837.

THE GROWTH AND NEW SOURCES OF SECULAR WISDOM

In building the system of secular schools Peter did not have a broad scheme, nor did he pursue clearly defined and consistent educational principles. He first planned to make the School of Mathematics and Navigation, a secondary educational institution, the core of a unified network of training centers, but it became obvious at once that the plan would not succeed because there were no elementary schools to prepare students for secondary training and because there was no institution of higher learning that could train competent secondary school teachers.

With the establishment of the system of ciphering schools in 1714, Peter also began to dream of a center of higher learning. This ambitious idea, at first nebulous and antithetical to the prevalent currents of thought in Russia, gradually appeared more feasible as scientific and secular educational activity began to develop. Many Western secular books were by now being translated into Russian and printed in the new civil script.

Translating and publishing activities had first caught Peter's attention during his visit in Holland in 1697. There he met the enterprising and ambitious Johann van Thessing, with whom he signed an agreement authorizing him to set up a press in Amsterdam for the sole purpose of publishing in Russian and Latin, or Russian and Dutch, selected books in geography, mathematics, architecture, and such other sciences as might help to acquaint Russians with "modern arts and knowledge." The contract stipulated that van Thessing's publishing activity be limited to secular books.[38] To assure van Thessing of handsome profits, Peter ordered that books imported from other sources be confiscated, their salesmen fined, and the money secured transmitted to the Dutch publisher. Alas for van Thessing, he soon learned that Russia had virtually no market for serious books of a secular nature, and the enterprise came to naught.

Translation activity within Russia went on under Peter's direct orders, but since most of the translations remained in manuscript form they reached but a small number of people. The total unfamiliarity with science of most of the translators as well as the inadequacy of the Russian language for scientific expression made many of the works hardly readable anyway. In 1724 Peter, noting that for some sciences there were no competent translators, decreed that in the future all translators be trained in individual disciplines. He stressed the need for translators who were acquainted with mathematics, surgery, civil architecture, anatomy, mechanics, botany, military science, and hydraulics. He ordered that all foreign books be translated into living Russian and not into petrified Church-Slavic, but the order was largely ignored.

As a result of Peter's efforts, the Russian language was enriched by many new words of Western origin. N. A. Smirnov estimated that about one-fourth of all new words belonged to the realm of scientific terminology.[39] The Russian language acquired now for the first time words of Latin or Greek derivation for algebra, anatomy, architecture, physics, optics, botany, humanities, history, ethics, and medicine. Among the newly added scientific terms were also quantity, quality, laboratory, intersection, logarithm, longitude, median, microscopy, observatory, parabola, parallel, radius, university, perspective, and parallax; there were hundreds of others. Many of these terms were subsequently replaced by native Russian words of Slavic origin. The inadequate scientific training of Russian translators and the fact that scientific works were translated from several foreign languages produced considerable terminological confusion at first, but this difficulty was soon overcome.

Although many books translated during the first quarter of the eighteenth century dealt with practical problems, there were also many translations of classics of a theoretical nature involving an impressive breadth of knowledge. Huygens' *Cosmotheros,* translated in 1717, gave the Russians the first exposition of the Copernican heliocentric system.[40] Johann Hübner's *Brief Survey of Old and New Geography,* published in a Russian translation in 1719, popularized the astronomical views of Tycho Brahe.[41] Philipp Clüver's and Bernardus Varenius's general treatises in geography were translated in connection with proposed descriptive surveys of various areas of the Russian empire. Thomas Burnet's *Sacred Theory of the Earth,* showing the gradual emergence of the earth from a chaotic mixture of air, oil, water, and soil, was also translated, as were a section from Pufendorf's philosophy of natural law, Hugo Grotius's *De jure belli ac pacis,* Book III, and Mavro Orbini's *Il regno de gli slavi.* Many extant manuscripts show that the government, probably inspired by Peter, was much interested in acquainting civil employees, at any rate, with foreign countries: they used, for example, several manuscripts on China, and manuscripts on Sweden, Algeria, Persia, and India.

Not primarily as a result of Peter's efforts to this end, but as an indirect outcome of the growing secularization of knowledge and the new spread of scientific ideas, a tiny group of intellectuals began to emerge. They were more important as champions of the modern spirit than as direct contributors to the world of scholarship. Feofan Prokopovich, the first clergyman to support Peter's educational ideals for the Russian people, publicly refuted the primacy of religious knowledge over secular knowledge and pleaded for a free and critical attitude toward all knowledge.[42] As early as 1707 he made an effort to bring arithmetic, geometry, and physics into the curriculum of the Kiev Academy by teaching these subjects in his own classes. A Danish traveler to Russia noted in his journal that in the command of knowledge Prokopovich had no peer, particularly among the Russian clergy, and that, in addition to history, theology, and philosophy, he possessed profound knowledge in mathematics and showed an "indescribable love" for this science.[43] His main concerns, however, were theology, rhetoric, and philosophy—subjects which he approached from a critical point of view. He insisted that a correct understanding of the scriptures required a philological study of full texts and, therefore, a mastery of Greek and Latin. Theologians, he believed, must try to reconcile traditional religious beliefs with modern science. He said the mathematical and physical proofs of Copernicus's heliocentric ideas, for example, required theologians to reinterpret the scriptures "not literally but allegorically."[44]

Two other intellectuals worthy of mention were Antiokh Kantemir and Vasilii Tatishchev. Kantemir, who became a poet and diplomat, wrote to Peter in 1724 about his great thirst for learning and his love of mathematics. After Peter's death he attended Bernoulli's lectures in the Academy of Sciences, and throughout his life he retained respect for "mathematics and ethics."[45] He wrote satires in which he simultaneously ridiculed those who disparaged learning and glorified the virtues of algebra, geometry, physics, astronomy, and medicine. Tatishchev acquired not so much a diversified knowledge as a respect for it. In his historical writing he criticized the superstitions of Old Russia from the point of view of the natural scientist. He was a pioneer in the study of Siberian geography, and he urged that a broad study of the natural history and physical geography of Russia be undertaken.

The awakening of intellectual curiosity, which was slowly making the time ripe for the fulfillment of Peter's dream of establishing a center of higher learning, was further stimulated by the opening of Russia's first public library and first museum (*Kunstkamera*). When the Russians conquered the Baltic provinces they confiscated several libraries and shipped their contents to St. Petersburg, where they were deposited in the Summer Palace. Some 2,500 volumes were confiscated in Mitava alone. These books formed the nucleus of the first Russian public library, founded in 1714. Sizable numbers of books came also from the Moscow Pharmacy and from several private donors. In 1721 Peter dispatched his personal physician, Johann Schumacher, to Holland, England, and France to purchase additional books.[46] The contents of the new library were not carefully selected, but it was adequate for persons engaged in elementary research and for such of the general public as were inclined to make use of it—at first very few indeed.[47] In 1724, for example, there were only five readers, who borrowed a total of 86 volumes.[48]

Russia's first museum was also established in 1714, although it was not opened to the public until five years later. The nucleus of the museum was the famed natural history collection of the Dutch anatomist Fredrik Ruysch, with whom Peter had become acquainted on the Grand Embassy. Ruysch's collection had been built up over a period of fifty years, and in purchasing it Peter thus acquired a representative and intelligent survey of the field of natural history. Although the museum contained in addition numerous instruments for use in the study of mathematics and physics and a small numismatic collection, one early visitor had the impression that it consisted mainly of bottles holding various parts of the human body, many of them examples of pathological phenomena.[49] A whole series showed the growth of the human fetus. In 1718 Peter decreed that all ancient artifacts and fossilized bones of extinct animals be surrendered to provincial or local government agencies and shipped to St. Petersburg.

THE STRENGTH OF GEOGRAPHY AND HISTORY

Peter had a particular interest in geographical expeditions—understandable in view of his pragmatic attitude toward science as a powerful means of achieving a more bountiful and rational exploitation of the country's natural resources. Expeditions were concentrated in the littoral areas and districts said to contain rich deposits of mineral ores. A special party of surveyors, for example, was sent to Astrakhan and Kazan. The surveys of "unknown lands" were conducted at first by a rare breed of men with no formal schooling but plenty of daring, perseverance, enterprising spirit, and sagacity acquired through worldly experience. On an expedition to Kamchatka in 1697–99 Vladimir Atlasov collected a profusion of factual material on the economic and social life of the local inhabitants, the regional topography, and the neighboring islands.[50] In 1719 Peter sent two "geodetists," I. M. Evreinov and F. F. Luzhin, to Kamchatka to study the northwestern shores of the Pacific Ocean and to prepare necessary maps. Many others collected factual material—much of it to rest forgotten in official reports. These men founded a rich and versatile empirical geography, but since they lacked scientific training and the knowledge of Oriental languages, their places were gradually taken by educated foreigners.

In 1720 Peter dispatched Daniel Messerschmidt, a learned Danzig physician, to Siberia for an exploratory mission which lasted seven years. Messerschmidt was assigned by contract to study the area's geography, natural history, medicine, medicinal plants, epidemic diseases, historical documents and antiquities, and "everything deserving attention."[51] He can rightfully be considered the founder of Siberian geography and ethnography. Besides being a trained physician, he knew several Oriental languages and was a talented cartographer. In his travels, he was able to identify rare ores and medicinal herbs, and to undertake a comparative analysis of native languages. Among other accomplishments, he enriched the St. Petersburg museum with valuable objects of scientific and historical interest. Shchapov is of the opinion that the Siberian expedition of Messerschmidt marked the dawn of independent Russian investigation in the natural sciences. The broad scope of the material collected by him is best shown in his survey of birds—*Historia avium*—which consists of nine volumes of sketches and descriptive materials.[52] The greater part of Messerschmidt's work, including ten general volumes of the survey and many collections, was never published, but it proved of much value to Pallas and other naturalists of the second half of the eighteenth century.

Not all geographical and natural history surveys were connected with Peter's mercantilist policies, although they were all essentially pragmatic. Peter's greatest geographical enterprise—the organization of what came to be known as the First Kamchatka Expedition (1725–30) under the leadership of Vitus Bering, a Dane who entered Russian service in 1704—was motivated by a desire to enhance the glories of Russian science. The publicized task of Bering's expedition was to determine whether or not Asia and North America were connected by a strip of land, an exploration that had been previously tackled without much success by several Dutch and English expeditions. Leibniz and Guillaume Delisle, a noted geographer and a member of the French Académie des Sciences, prodded Peter into sending an expedition to the northeastern corner of Siberia to resolve once and for all one of the greatest geographical questions of the time. The richness of America, especially of its gold, was undoubtedly of more than academic interest to Peter, who perhaps envisioned trade relations with the American colonies. It is important, however, that he chose to emphasize what may be called a political rather than an economic role for science, and that he chose geography to be the mirror of Russia's scientific achievements. It was the most logical choice. The empirical substance of the field of geography was most likely to attract the attention of the growing ranks of Western scholars interested in assembling raw data on exotic and little-known countries and peoples.

Thus, incidentally, Peter opened not only the doors of Western Europe to Russia but also the doors of Russia to Western Europe. Largely as a result of the survey, he stimulated a lively European interest in Russia. The substance of Messerschmidt's material on Siberia was used by his fellow traveler Philip Strahlenberg, a captured Swedish officer, who because of his skill and experience was assigned to take part in the expedition. In 1730, after his release, Strahlenberg published a book in German on "the northern and eastern parts of Europe and Asia." This volume was translated into several other languages and became known as the first serious study of Siberia.

There had, of course, been Russian maps before Peter's time, like the Great Map, but they were both scientifically and technically crude—more sketches than maps, involving no use of astronomical knowledge, nor even consistent projections or mechanical measurements. For a while van Thessing printed maps of various parts of Russia which were fairly advanced in conception and design, although hardly reliable in detail. The most impressive product of native cartography of the early phase of Peter's reign was *The Book of Maps of Siberia,* prepared by S. U. Remezov at the request of the Tsar. When it was at last completed in 1701, the *Book of Maps* contained twenty-three maps, all but three of which were of individual towns or rural communities. In 1697 Remezov prepared a general map of Siberia, painted on cotton cloth measuring ten feet long by seven feet wide. The map, inscribed in the outdated Cyrillic, had no latitudes or meridians, and the north and south directions were reversed.[53]

In 1705 the first "civil press" was founded in Russia under the supervision of V. O. Kiprianov, who had studied at the School of Mathematics and Navigation. The director of the press was Jacob Bruce, a man well versed in the astronomical foundations of cartography and the mathematical foundations of astronomy. Under Bruce's direction, the new press became an important geographical and cartographic center. Bruce's interest in cartography was passing in nature, however, whereas Kiprianov devoted his life to the art. He directed the publication of numerous maps based on fairly advanced mathematical calculations and showing a sophisticated knowledge of geographical nomenclature, and he was himself a master engraver. Besides maps of Russian territory, Kiprianov also issued maps of parts of the world beyond Russia, drawn from information contained in foreign atlases.

Closely connected with the preparation of maps were the first Russian geodetic surveys. These were for the most part dominated at the outset by foreign experts (C. Kreis, C. Otto, and others), but in 1715 Peter requested that a selected number of young men be trained in geodetics and sent to the provinces to prepare detailed local maps, which could be used in the preparation of larger maps. In 1721 he issued special instructions calling for the first instrumental surveys on a comparatively large scale. Some thirty geodetic experts were immediately dispatched to various parts of the country.

Peter was, of course, interested in maps to satisfy his personal curiosity and to further the development of one field of Russian scholarship, but he set particular value on cartography and geodetics as sources of practical knowledge.[54] A detailed map of the Baltic Sea, based on foreign sources, contained all known information that would be of use in navigation. In 1717 Peter ordered, and personally supervised, the preparation of a map of all Russia, which he realized would be indispensable for efficient government. This enterprise, however, proved premature. He then undertook the preparation of a map of the Caspian Sea—as part of his ambitious plan to expand trade relations with Persia and other Middle Eastern countries.

The map, completed in 1720 and subsequently submitted by Peter to the French Académie des Sciences, achieved at least one of its major objectives in attracting the attention of Western scholars. Guillaume Delisle, in his treatise on "The Geographical Determination of the Location and the Size of Various Parts of the World," bestowed upon it great compliments and labeled Peter a "prince renowned for his love for science as much as for his great talent in the art of government."[55] In 1721 Fontenelle, the permanent secretary of the Académie, congratulated Peter for his serious concern with the advancement of knowledge and the welfare of science in Russia.[56] That same year Schumacher personally delivered to the Académie a new map of the Caspian Sea, which also received praise from Delisle.[57] These were the first commendations given by Western scientists to Russian scholarly work in science.[58]

Most of the many maps prepared in Russia during the first quarter of the eighteenth century were elementary in their composition and precision because they were based on inadequate astronomical knowledge. According to F. G. W. Struve, it was not until 1745 that the Russians prepared the first map of their country based on the astronomical determination of longitude.[59] Even so, the accomplishments in the fields of geography and cartography far exceeded those in other sciences during Peter's time. Beyond Peter's own enthusiasm, there was the further happy circumstance that they attracted some of the ablest new men of science: V. Atlasov, I. K. Kirilov, V. O. Kiprianov, A. I. Chirikov, and V. N. Tatishchev were only a few of the many men who laid the foundations for the development of geographical disciplines in Russia.

Historiography, as we have seen, had been another part of the intellectual legacy of the seventeenth century. Peter I recognized the value of history, yet none of the different schools founded by him included this subject in its curriculum. The letter of Leibniz to Stefan Iavorskii in which he pleaded for a systematic gathering and publication of documents from ancient Russian history remained unanswered.[60] Peter was more interested in "current history" than in the collection, interpretation, and coordination of documents from the past. The contract by which van Thessing was given a virtual monopoly on the publication of secular books for Russia made specific mention of books dedicated to "the glory of the Tsar"—meaning, of course, Peter I.

Despite the Tsar's own lack of interest, however, there was in the first quarter of the eighteenth century considerable activity in the field of historical investigation. Written histories, though still didactic in tone, lost much of their traditional theological character. It was usual to present the great heroes of the past as paragons of virtue and dedication. In a detailed essay on historiography contained in Feofan Prokopovich's book on rhetoric, the author draws on the wisdom of ancient writers from Dionysius of Halicarnassus to Cicero to show that history must provide models of exemplary behavior and yet be purged of all fables and religious prejudices.[61] History was frequently invoked as a precedent for the government's actions: a military statute, for example, used the experience of Julius Caesar to justify the strategic advantages of the concentration of armed forces in the battlefield. The Naval Charter contained a historical preamble, purportedly written by Peter himself, which gave a brief survey of the growth of the Russian fleet, beginning with the seafaring adventures of the first Kievan princes.

Historiographic activity during the first twenty-five years of the eighteenth century fell into three distinct categories. First of all, there were the translations of well-known Western European histories, including several general historical treatises such as Pufendorf's volume on Western Europe and Baronius' *Annales Ecclesiastici*. Works, some of questionable accuracy, on Alexander the Great, ancient Troy, Jerusalem, and Julius Caesar were also made available to Russian readers. A Russian translation was made of Polydore Vergil's *De rerum inventoribus*, a Renaissance work espousing a rationalist point of view in a bold effort to survey the growth of technology. Although already antiquated, this work was in a sense the first history of science available to Russian readers.

The second category of historical works included general treatises in Russian history, which continued the tradition of Gizel's *Sinopsis* of the preceding century. The most outstanding work in this group was A. I. Mankiev's *The Core of Russian History,* which curiously remained unpublished until 1770—perhaps because it allotted only fifteen pages to the reign of Peter the Great. The author shows his familiarity with earlier work in Russian history, particularly the *Sinopsis* and several works of seventeenth-century Polish historians. Whereas the *Sinopsis* emphasized Ukrainian history, however, Mankiev's work was mainly concerned with the northern areas. And unlike the *Sinopsis,* which covered only the period prior to the Tatar conquest, *The Core of Russian History* dealt with the entire span of Russian history. Mankiev also differed from his predecessors in that he treated Russian history as a part of "universal history." He expressed interesting views on the origins of certain peoples and took note of the impact of the discovery of America, the English Civil War, and the discoveries of gunpowder and the printing press.[62] Solov'ev gave this work an "honorable place" in Russian historical literature and was impressed with its author's careful examination of historical events, particularly in the later periods.[63]

3) Quite the largest category of historical works of the first quarter of the eighteenth century dealt with the reign of Peter I. It is generally agreed that *The History of the Swedish War* is the best of this type. It was a collective work, largely directed by Peter and even edited by him, based on contemporary accounts and official documents as well as on certain more comprehensive histories. The *History* is not a simple war chronicle: it presents rich information on Russian diplomacy of the time and on the organization and growth of the regular army. Not surprisingly, of course, it totally ignores foreign documents and is therefore of limited value.

Censorship Peter was too concerned with the diffusion of positive knowledge to pay any systematic attention to the compatibility of modern secular thought with official ideology. However, the elements of ideological control, particularly in the realm of history and social thought, were not altogether missing. We have seen that A. I. Mankiev's failure to give more space and emphasis to Peter's reign may very likely have been the reason why his historical work was not published before the age of Catherine II. Heinrich von Huyssen's close friendship with Tsarevich Alexis was probably the reason why his *Journal of Tsar Peter I* did not appear in published form. In 1708 Peter threatened to inflict grave punishment on persons caught publishing and distributing literature inciting the people to revolt.

Nothing was published in Russia without Peter's knowledge and approval, but there was little censorship as such under him, and there is on record at least one instance of his opposition to the practice. A translator who was rendering Pufendorf's *Introduction to the History of the Western European States* into Russian decided on his own to omit a statement uncomplimentary to Russia and the Russian people.[64] When Peter learned about the omission, he ordered the statement restored; there was in it, he said, no "denigration of the superior honor of His Imperial Majesty." On the contrary, it implied a justification of the urgency of his reforms.[65]

Though proof is lacking, it is very likely that censorship in the form of imperial disapproval delayed for many years the publication of the advanced works of Ivan Pososhkov, one of the most enlightened Russians of the early eighteenth century. Indeed, the nature of Pososhkov's views no doubt had much to do with the fact that he died in prison. A self-taught man of modest social origins, Pososhkov was not only a talented writer but

also something of an expert in economics and military strategy—a "theoretician" of the social, economic, and political foundations of Peter's reforms and an "applied scientist" with original ideas about reforms. His
Book on Poverty and Wealth (published in censored form in 1842) sought
to outline a plan for a thorough transformation of Russia's social and economic life, based on a dual premise: the growth of the state treasury and
the elimination of social injustice. Pososhkov admired Peter's reforms, but
he believed in improving the social and economic status of the peasants by
assuring them of legal protection against the abuses of landlords.

As a freethinker, unburdened with practical participation in Peter's reforms, Pososhkov projected many broad and courageous—if unrealistic—
plans for a "better life." He agreed with Peter that the aristocracy should
form the backbone of the autocratic government, but he insisted that incompetent aristocrats be removed from high government positions. He
advocated the development of metallurgy with the help of Western scientific knowledge, but he cautioned that this industry must not be allowed
to supplant the work of Russian artisans. He was a spokesman for the
urban middle classes, but he saw in the enlightened and prosperous village
the best guaranty for Russia's progress. Like Krizhanich, he dreamed of a
society in which each estate should have clearly defined legal rights and an
unambiguous place in the division of social labor.

THE SEARCH FOR A CENTER OF HIGHER LEARNING

The vigor and diversity of intellectual fermentation during the last
decade of Peter's reign and the noticeable increase in the thirst for scientific
knowledge resulted in a desire to found a learned society, patterned after
such models as the Royal Society of London (founded in 1660), the Académie des Sciences in Paris (1660), and the Berlin Academy of Sciences
(1700). The idea for such an institution acquired added strength after
Peter visited Paris in 1717, when he attended a meeting of the Académie
des Sciences and became acquainted with some of its distinguished members. He talked to the mathematician Pierre Varignon and to the anatomist
Guichard Duvernoy and made an extremely favorable impression on Guillaume Delisle, the geographer, to whom he showed various maps of Russian regions. He observed chemical experiments made by E. F. Geoffroy
and N. Lémery, and watched an operation performed by a famous English
eye doctor. At an extraordinary meeting under the chairmanship of Abbé
Bignon, the Académie des Sciences elected him a member *hors de tout*

rang. According to Kostomarov, the Académie acted on Peter's request—transmitted through Areskin, his personal physician—that he be honored with membership in the renowned scientific institution. This election was of great personal satisfaction to Peter and a fateful event in Russia's intellectual history; henceforth the ambitious tsar showed a remarkable determination to live up to the great honor bestowed upon him by the French learned society.

In the same year, 1717, Peter received another, more modest, recognition for his enthusiastic support of science. Arnold van der Hulst, a member of a Dutch family which settled in Moscow in the 1770's, dedicated his doctoral dissertation (from Leyden University) to Peter as "an indefatigable investigator and unsparing disseminator of all arts and sciences beneficial to mankind." Hulst's study, in Latin, dealt with the circulation of the blood in the embryo of the chicken, from a strongly preformist point of view.[66]

Peter was not the first Russian to become a member of a ranking foreign scientific institution: Count Aleksandr Menshikov, his protégé and friend of long standing, acquired a similar honor three years earlier. Menshikov, born in a family belonging to the lowest rung of the aristocratic ladder (some say below that), was the first of the so-called "accidental persons" whose emergence was one of the characteristics of the eighteenth century in Russia. These were courtiers of no particular social background whose association with the imperial court helped them to rise to the exclusive group of highest nobility. Menshikov met Peter in the late 1680's, and after 1697 the two were almost inseparable. Before 1714 Menshikov served in the Russian military expeditions in Kurland, Pomerania, and Holstein; subsequently his activities were confined to the country's internal affairs. He was known in diplomatic circles as an intelligent man of doubtful honesty and flagrant insincerity, who espoused Peter's political philosophy and reform plans for purely selfish motives. In a variety of unsavory ways, including the embezzlement of state moneys, he expanded his earthly riches. Peter became aware of the shabby moral character of his friend in 1711, but for three years he did nothing. In 1714 the government appointed a special commission to investigate the extent of Menshikov's dealings, but even after it began to unveil the record of his misconduct, Peter refused to turn against his old friend and supporter.

Menshikov had been apprehensive about his future prospects, being unsure just how Peter would react to his staggering misappropriations of government funds. He therefore very shrewdly set about to impress Peter with his importance by seeking membership in the Royal Society of London. His education was elementary, he had taken no part in Peter's school reforms, and he had not the faintest notion of contemporary science; but he was sophisticated enough to have heard of the Royal Society and to be aware of its great reputation. With the help of English entrepreneurs interested in trade with Russia, he applied for membership, and astonishingly, on July 29, 1714, was elected unanimously.[67] Several months later, Menshikov received news of his election from no less a luminary than Isaac Newton, the President of the Royal Society, who praised him for the help he had rendered Peter not only in the political and military fields but also in the dissemination of "excellent books and sciences."[68]

The extent of Peter's enthusiasm for science did not wane after his enlightening visit to Paris. It was on his return that he sent Messerschmidt and other groups to various parts of the Empire to make scientific surveys of natural riches, and ordered the preparation of the map of the Caspian Sea which was later submitted to the Académie. Now he began to think more earnestly than ever about the founding of a center of higher learning. In a memorandum written in 1718 he stressed the need for establishing an academy to serve as a gathering place for learned Russians and as a center for the translation of scientific works. In shaping this idea, Christian Wolff, who was a professor first at the University of Halle and then at the University of Marburg, exercised great and positive influence. It is not certain when Peter began to communicate with Wolff, or what the scope of their personal correspondence was; it is known, however, that after 1719 there was extensive correspondence between Wolff and Lavrentii Blumentrost—who succeeded Areskin as Peter's personal physician—on the subject of a future academy. (There are some indirect hints of a limited correspondence between Peter and Wolff at this time also.[69]) When word of Wolff's cooperation with Peter reached the West he became the target of the Pietists of Halle University, led by August H. Francke. Francke relied on his acquaintances in the hierarchy of the Russian Orthodox Church to spread rumors of Wolff's alleged atheistic leanings and thus to degrade him in Peter's eyes. Feofan Prokopovich applied all his great prestige and authority in Wolff's defense. Schumacher assured Wolff that all accusations emanating from the West would fall on deaf ears in Russia because the Russian clergy were engaged in the great work of "giving a rational basis to religion."[70] Wolff responded by dedicating his work in physics to Peter.[71]

Wolff was well informed on the extent of educational and intellectual activity in Russia, and thought it unrealistic to establish an academy of sciences. Instead, he urged that a university be established. He contended that an academy must be founded *ad plausum exteriorum,* and staffed by scientists trained in a Russian university.[72] It would be much easier to establish a university rather than an academy because there would be more chance of attracting excellent teachers than established scholars from the West. The Berlin Academy of Sciences, Wolff pointed out, was for a long time a dormant institution because it was founded before Prussia had adequate schools of higher learning.[73]

Although Peter benefited much from Wolff's wise counsel and encouragement, he relied most on his own judgment as well as on the recommendations of his two personal advisers, Blumentrost and Schumacher. He had direct or indirect knowledge of three Western European academies. He personally visited and acquired intimate knowledge of the internal organization, goals, and functions of the Royal Society of London and the Académie des Sciences in Paris, and from Leibniz he learned about the Berlin Academy. The model of the Royal Society did not appeal to him, for it was a free assembly of scholars independent of government control. Furthermore, it exercised minimum control over the scientific interests of its members, and its corporate activities were overshadowed by individual research.[74]

The Académie des Sciences, which grew from informal gatherings of such giants of the seventeenth century as Descartes, Pascal, Gassendi, and Fermat, was conceived as an agency allied with the government and subject to certain governmental controls. Its primary aim, as defined by Colbert, was to provide scientific answers to various questions as they were set forth by the agencies of government. For their service the Academicians became government pensioners and when the need arose were transferred to government departments. According to Joseph Bertrand: "The King has established salaries for the members of the new institution and has placed at their disposal the funds necessary for experiments and for the construction of useful machines."[75] However, at about the time of Peter's visit to Paris the Académie underwent a certain reorganization, and its members turned thereafter more and more to purely theoretical research.

The Berlin Academy, the youngest of the three, differed from its sister institutions in England and France in that it provided room for scholarship in history and linguistics, and, more explicitly than the Paris Académie, was dedicated to the national interests of Frederick I's Prussia. Among other things, it was entrusted with the selection of books to be translated into German and with the general supervision of schools. The three institutions had one thing in common, however: all were dedicated to the search for new knowledge and not the dissemination of existing wisdom. They were pure scientific institutions, with no university facilities whatever. To all three applied what Marie Jean P. Flourens, permanent secretary of the Académie des Sciences, stated in 1863: "The Académie is no University. The barrier which separates them should be eternal. Universities teach, the Académie discovers and improves. This the very terms of its device inculcate: *Invenit et perficit*."[76]

Peter's ideas for a Russian academy of sciences were influenced by two important historical conditions. He realized that a society dedicated to scientific inquiry could exist in Russia only if it had the support of the government, both financial and moral. There was no corporate entity within the Russian polity ready or willing to give its support to such an undertaking. The scientists were few in number and their scholarly skills were rudimentary, to say the least. Therefore, the informal gatherings of great scientific minds which laid the foundations for both the Royal Society and the Académie des Sciences were impossible in Russia. Peter also had to face the fact that Russia did not have a university out of which an academy could be drawn. He was thus obliged by circumstances to combine an institution of scientific inquiry with a university. Before the plan of the new institution was devised, the whole complex problem was studied carefully by Peter and his advisers. In 1721 Schumacher was sent to Western Europe to solicit counsel from many leading scholars. He also tried to persuade a number of scientists to become corresponding members of the future academy.

In the meantime, Peter used the power of law to shrink the orbit of Church control, hoping in that way to break down the spirit of antirationalism. In 1718 he allowed the armed forces to eat meat during the fast; in 1721 special decrees allowed Swedish prisoners in Siberia skilled in mining and other trades to marry Russian women without becoming Orthodox converts; in 1722 a decree prohibited the sale of miracle-working honey and all kinds of charms.

The intention of the Ecclesiastical Regulation of 1721 was not only to stipulate the legal aspects of the subordination of the Church to the State but also to reconcile traditional religious ideology with modern secular rationalism. "It is known to the whole world," states this document, "how meager and impotent was the Russian army when it did not have adequate education, and how its power grew immensely . . . when it learned superior methods from Peter I. . . . The same applies to architecture, medicine, government, and all other activities. The administration of the Church should follow the same path: without the light of learning, the work of the Church can bring no good."[77] The Ecclesiastical Regulation provides ample "ethnographic material" showing Peter's determination to reconcile religion and science by ridding the former of its heavy reliance on superstition and miracles. It was the first official Russian document dedicated to the idea that the future welfare of the nation was contingent on the diffusion and expansion of scientific knowledge and on the extension of the rationalist world view to include the wide domain of religion. As a devout man, Peter did not challenge any of the cardinal beliefs of Russian Orthodoxy; he contended that the Church's antirationalism was anchored to ancillary beliefs and customs which, though given an official Church blessing, were essentially incompatible with the doctrines of Christianity. Peter did very little to elucidate his philosophy of religion; it is certain, however, that his practical goal was to neutralize the Church as a bastion of the conservative forces that opposed science and other manifestations of secular wisdom.

Although Peter sensed that all ranks of Russia's estate system were as one in their lack of interest in education and scholarship, his enthusiasm for an academy of sciences did not flag. The record of a conversation between Peter and Vasilii Tatishchev in 1724 is clear proof of this determination. In that year Tatishchev, as part of a trading mission to Sweden, was commissioned to look for learned men who would be willing to come to Russia as members of the projected academy. According to Tatishchev's own report, he used this opportunity to tell the Tsar that in his opinion an academy alone, without a substratum of educational institutions, would be an extravagant waste of money. Russia, he insisted, had not yet arrived at an intellectual and educational level sufficient to support a learned society of the highest order. Peter replied sensibly that he knew a Russian academy would resemble a watermill without water, but that his beginning would compel his successors to complete the work by digging a canal that would bring in the water. The existing ciphering and parochial schools were, he thought, at least the start of the canal.[78]

Early in 1724 Blumentrost and Schumacher submitted to Peter their detailed plan for an academy of sciences in St. Petersburg. Peter at once approved it, and on January 22, 1724, sent it to the Senate, together with his order calling for the establishment of the St. Petersburg Academy of Sciences and allocating the sum of 24,912 rubles a year for its maintenance. This sum was to be derived from customs duties and license fees collected in several Baltic cities.[79] The plan stated clearly that the new Academy would be charged with the diffusion of knowledge as well as its expansion and would be both a company of scholars and a university.

The new Academy was to concern itself with three "classes of science": (1) mathematics and the sciences dependent upon it (astronomy, geography, and navigation); (2) "all parts of physics" (including theoretical and experimental physics, anatomy, chemistry, and botany); and (3) the humanities (including eloquence and the study of antiquities, ancient and modern history, law, politics, and economics). The university would consist of three faculties: law, medicine, and philosophy. There was to be also a Gymnasium which would prepare young men for university studies.

The first and most difficult task facing Peter and his advisers was that of finding scientists for the new institution. Wolff was reluctant to leave the University of Marburg and for that reason refused the offer made him, but he did consent to help find other scholars who would be more willing. It was no small undertaking. There were still excellent opportunities for scholars in the West, and St. Petersburg was hardly a stimulating prospect, with its cold, its geographical remoteness, and its intellectual vacuity. Europeans had heard, too, about the manner in which foreign scientists were treated by the Russians. The reneging on Farquharson's salary had been reported by John Perry, an English engineer who was hired to survey the possibility of building a canal connecting the Volga and the Don, and who was himself vexed by similar problems. And there was the story of Messerschmidt, who was forced into an obscure existence after he finished the Siberian expedition and settled down in Russia with a Russian wife.

The only lures at Peter's command were promises of high salaries and comfortable quarters. At last, despite all the difficulties, Wolff was successful in signing up a number of eminent scholars to join the new Academy. He took his assignment very seriously. According to Count Aleksandr Golovkin, "he had in mind only a learned society and demanded great achievements and high reputations of those who wanted to join this institution; he did not seek out those persons who wanted to be only professors."[80] The planners of the Academy were faced with another awkward problem: just as the Academy could not be opened until foreign scholars had been found, so the Academic University could not be opened until there were foreign students. None of Peter's numerous experiments in education had really prepared Russian youths for higher studies, because they had not been dedicated to education in the true meaning of the term but rather to the training of semiqualified professionals who were quickly absorbed into government jobs and soon forgot what they had learned. The graduates of the secondary schools knew neither Latin—the international language of science—nor the native languages of the scholars selected to be the first members of the Academy.[81] It was out of necessity, then, that in February 1724 Schumacher wrote to the Russian envoy in Vienna asking him to recruit and send to Russia twelve Viennese students who were versed in "Slavic and Czech languages."[82]

All these preparations went slowly, however, and Peter did not live to greet the first Academicians on their arrival in St. Petersburg. He died on January 28, 1725. In November of that year, Fontenelle delivered a lengthy *éloge* in Peter's honor before a gathering of the members of the Paris Académie des Sciences. He noted that this was the first time in the history of the Académie that such homage had been paid to a monarch. Referring to some of the great mathematicians who were to be the first members of the St. Petersburg Academy of Sciences, Fontenelle said: "These great geometers have brought the sublime geometry of the infinitesimals to a country which twenty-five years ago was completely unaware of Euclid's principles."[83] It was because of Peter's foresight, said Prokopovich in his funeral oration,[84] that "our children are now passionate students of arithmetic, geometry, and other mathematical arts"—disciplines which the preceding generations had regarded as branches of sorcery.

Peter's decision to found an academy of sciences was his last attempt to open the doors of Russia to Western culture. Having failed in this effort with his earlier schemes of sending young Russians for study abroad, of secularizing—even in part—the Church schools, of encouraging Protestant missionaries to open schools, of setting up a system of ciphering schools, of promoting translation activity and the reading of Western secular books, he was in a sense resorting to a last drastic measure in founding an academy. It was an admission of the hopelessness of doing anything at a lower level and in harmony with the gradual secularization of Russian education. It also symbolized his determination to accelerate the influx of Western culture into Russia and his full break with the traditional institutional basis of education.

More than any other person, Peter opened his country to the ideas of modern science—the science of Copernicus, Galileo, Kepler, and Newton.

But this was only a part of his legacy. His historical significance and his most singular contribution lay in the realm of the control and guidance of scientific pursuits: he made science a "government science," a body of knowledge guided and guarded by the state. This legacy has remained unaltered, if not unchallenged, to the present day. Since Peter's time the state has controlled scientific pursuits by choosing the fields requiring scientific inquiry, by imposing ideological limitations on scientific theory, and by defining the educational policies and the social criteria for selecting the men of science. An eminent modern historian of Kazan University has said: "Education . . . was introduced in Russia by the state for its own purposes; it was introduced in the same way as other innovations were introduced during the first quarter of the eighteenth century; it was introduced as coercively, as crudely, and at times as painfully as most of the other designs of the great reformer of Russia."[85]

Peter, we may add, faced the problem of secular education and dissemination of scientific knowledge not only with untempered severity, in the tradition of Russian autocracy, but also with a great dedication and understanding. He appreciated the power of science in unleashing hidden natural forces and placing them at the disposal of man; he was also intrigued and animated by the new and mysterious worlds opened up by science. With his youthful enthusiasm for science, he became a leader of advanced thought. The English engineer Perry noted that Peter was more than willing to explain to "his lords and people about him" the eclipses of the sun and the moon, about which Farquharson kept him specially informed, and the motions of "heavenly bodies within the system of the sun."[86]

In describing Peter's approach to science as generally utilitarian, one should understand the word "utilitarian" in its broadest possible sense. To Peter, mechanics, chemistry, astronomy, and mathematics were the tools with which man could build and navigate ships, improve artillery, and construct canals, manufactories, dockyards, and mining installations. The geographic mapping of the country was to him a requisite for a well-rounded and efficient government. In history he recognized a source of national rejuvenation and political unity. He regarded the secularization of wisdom and the dissemination of scientific knowledge as the only way in which Russia could be freed from the fetters of cultural inertia stemming from the ultraconservatism and antirationalism of the Russo-Byzantine intellectual tradition. He considered the development of science something which "would earn us respect and honor in Europe", and refute the wide-spread belief that "we are barbarians who disregard science."[87] Farsighted in his views on science, as in other ways, Peter appreciated the need for theory and daring experimentation as well as for more practical research. "I do not damn the alchemist who seeks to transform metals into gold," he said, "nor the student of mechanics who, in his search for perpetual motion, looks for the extraordinary, for he unexpectedly discovers many collateral things."[88]

CHAPTER THREE

The Academy: Dilemmas and Triumphs

THE FIRST YEARS OF THE ACADEMY

In the summer of 1725 the first members of the Academy of Sciences began to arrive in St. Petersburg. By the end of the year sixteen scholars, most of them in their thirties, were in residence as the original membership of the new institution. Thirteen of the new citizens of St. Petersburg were Germans, two were Swiss, and one was French. Among the first to reach the distant northern city was the mathematician Jacob Hermann, upon whom his new colleagues bestowed the lofty title of *professor primarius et Matheseos sublimioris,* primarily because he was the oldest in the group. He was a typical example of the high scholarly standards which Christian Wolff demanded from the men whom he recommended for membership in the fledgling Academy. With Leibniz's backing, Hermann had been elected to the Berlin Academy of Sciences in 1701, and subsequently he had taught at the Universities of Bologna and Padua. He was not one of the great mathematicians of his age, yet he was widely known and enjoyed an enviable reputation.

The interests of the members were representative of the great scientific ideas of the time. Joseph Delisle was an astronomer; Georg Bilfinger, who was originally inclined toward logic and metaphysics, worked in the field of "experimental and theoretical physics," while Christian Martini switched from metaphysics and logic to physics. Daniel and Nicolaus Bernoulli came from a distinguished Swiss family, which for over a century produced mathematicians of the first order. The former became professor of physiology and the latter professor of mechanics. Working in mathematics were also Christian Goldbach and Friedrich Mayer. Johann Duvernoy worked in anatomy, surgery, and zoology. Johann Kohl was appointed professor of eloquence and church history; Michael Bürger, professor of chemistry and practical medicine; Gottlieb Bayer, professor of Greek and Roman history; Johann Beckenstein, professor of jurisprudence; and Christian Gross, professor of moral philosophy. Josiah

Weitbrecht was an adjunct in physiology and Gerhard Müller in history.

The first Academic meeting, which took place in November 1725 (actually before the official opening of the Academy), marked the first formal presentation of the great scientific ideas of Newton and Descartes in Russia—but, significantly, the discussion was not in Russian and no Russian scholars were present. The Academicians on this occasion were divided into Newtonians and the proponents of the Cartesian theory of vortices.[1] All members recognized the great scientific future and methodological potentiality of the calculus, pioneered by Newton and Leibniz. A month later the Academy held its first public meeting, at which a lively discussion centered on Leibniz's and Wolff's physical theories.

Catherine I, Peter's widow, moved quickly to help the institution founded by her husband. On December 7, 1725, she sent a decree to the Senate whereby the Academy was formally established. Lavrentii Blumentrost, who had been so important in its planning, was wisely chosen the first president. The son of a German physician who joined the Russian service in 1667, he had been born in Moscow and spoke impeccable Russian. He could also speak adequate Latin and Greek, which he had learned in Glück's school. He studied medicine in Halle, Oxford, and Leyden, and in 1718 became Peter's personal physician and the supervisor of the imperial library and the Kunstkamera, for which he negotiated the purchase of Ruysch's famous anatomical collection. Because of his training and experience, he was undoubtedly the Russian best able to work with the foreign scholars, and he had the further advantage of easy access to the imperial court.

Catherine's decree recognized the Academy's internal organization as specified in the plan approved by Peter in 1724.[2] For some reason, however, it failed to stipulate that the recommended charter be formally ratified. As a result, for the first twenty-two years of its existence the Academy functioned without a statutory definition of the duties and prerogatives of the institution as a whole and of its individual members. Fortunately, the 1724 plan provided a rough guide: it stipulated that Academicians engage in independent research in their respective disciplines, prepare extracts from foreign publications containing valuable scientific information, pass collective judgments on inventions submitted to them for appraisal, provide expert answers to inquiries emanating from government quarters, and prepare Latin and Russian textbooks in their fields. They were to hold weekly meetings for the presentation and discussion of selected scientific topics, as well as three annual public meetings at which individual scholars would speak on topics from their respective sciences.[3] It was understood that each member would also teach in the Academic University.

The immediate prospects for the Academy were bright. Prince Aleksandr Menshikov, who actually ruled the country on behalf of the Empress, was a man identified with Peter's reforms, and the new institution could count on his support at the court. In 1725 a three-story astronomical observatory for the Academy was built on Vasil'evskii Island, and its inventory was enriched with the arrival of Academician Joseph Delisle, a professor at the Collège de France, who delivered the instruments bought by Peter in Paris. The observatory was considered one of the finest institutions of its kind in Europe.

In the same year the personal libraries of Peter I and his son Alexis, the former containing many works in geography and military sciences and the latter an unusual number of religious books, were transferred to the Academy, which soon acquired several other private libraries. In 1728 the Kunstkamera, which had grown into a museum rich in specimens of natural history and ethnography, was placed under the Academy's jurisdiction and was opened to the public. The Academy was also given Peter's collection of instruments used in the study of physics, which became the nucleus of its Museum Physicum. In 1728 the Academy acquired its own press, made in Holland, and immediately embarked on a modest publication program. Within several years the press had not only Russian, Latin, and German typefaces but also Georgian and Arabic types. The system of institutions subordinated to the Academy also included a number of workshops engaged in such "arts" as the production of optical instruments, precision equipment, and drafting tools. These auxiliary institutions of the Academy were erected on firm and lasting foundations.

Although the Academy was expected to perform many duties, it was chiefly dedicated to the dual task defined in Peter's 1724 plan as the search for new scientific facts and the dissemination of existing knowledge. Its essential functions were scientific inquiry, through individual and group efforts, and education, through the facilities of the Academic Gymnasium and the Academic University. Owing mainly to the lack of students, particularly at the university level, during the early years the first Academicians were primarily concerned with scientific research. Their highly sophisticated scholarly activities were a drastic innovation in the intellectual life of Russia, and they entered areas for which no paths had been blazed in the history of Russian science. Bilfinger, G. W. Krafft, and Daniel Bernoulli tackled a whole series of problems in mechanics by combining the method of experiment with mathematical analysis. Delisle produced the first measurements of "astronomical points" as a preliminary to making more reliable geographical maps. The first issue of the Academy's proceedings, *Commentarii Academiae scientiarum imperialis petropolitanae*, in 1728, contained an article by Johann Bernoulli, a professor of mathematics at the University of Basel and the father of Daniel and Nicolaus, on the integration of differential equations, and Christian Goldbach's study on the same subject—a revolutionary jump from the elementary mathematical knowledge popularized by Magnitskii and Farquharson.

These and similar contributions made the Academy almost instantaneously a European institution; paradoxically, considerable time elapsed before it also became a Russian institution in the true meaning of the term. Résumés of several of the articles from the first volume of the *Commentarii* were immediately translated into Russian—with bewildering results, owing to the limited Russian scientific vocabulary and the scientific ineptness of the translators. Besides the résumés, the translations contained brief, simplified (if unintelligible) explanations of some of the important scientific ideas of the day, including the theory of gravitation and the elements of the integral and differential calculus.[4]

The scientific interests of the members covered a wide range—from the most advanced theoretical concepts of mathematical analysis to Scythian history. Mathematics became the forte of the new institution. Nearly half of the original sixteen members were skilled mathematicians who themselves made real contributions to the field. In 1727 this group acquired inestimable new strength with the arrival of the youthful Leonhard Euler, who at first held the chair of physiology, then physics, and, finally, mathematics, but who from the very beginning displayed remarkable mathematical talents. His arrival heralded the start of the Academy's notable interest and success in mathematics.

In carrying out its second major assignment, the diffusion of knowledge, the Academy was not so successful. When the Academic Gymnasium was opened in 1727, it admitted 112 students, predominantly children of foreign families resident in Russia and of a few eminent Russian aristocratic families in St. Petersburg. From this respectable beginning, however, fortunes declined: within two years the enrollment had dropped to 74, and by 1737 it was only 19.[5] This was perhaps inevitable, for several reasons. The teachers, mostly Academicians, knew no Russian, and only a few Russian youths were conversant with foreign languages. The courses were more or less haphazard in plan, since most of the teachers lectured on their particular enthusiasms without trying to make them part of a broader study. The emphasis was heavily scientific, although it was obvious that the students were far more interested in humanistic subjects.

There was in addition a profound sociological reason for the Gymnasium's lack of vitality. Peter's proposed charter had made no class discriminations in regard to enrollment in the Gymnasium and the University, but after Peter died the new regime proceeded to embark on a policy of class exclusiveness in formal education. This was in tune with a whole array of legal enactments which directly or indirectly strengthened the economic and political power of the gentry. The obligatory lifetime service of the gentry to the state was reduced to twenty-five years, and the gentry was given the right to exile disobedient serfs to Siberia. Military service, by which many had heretofore raised themselves, was also redefined along class lines, so as to be prohibited to peasants and other lower estates.

The new trend toward the formation of "estate schools" was closely related to the gentry's animosity toward rigorous scientific education. In the exclusive Infantry School, founded in 1732, an attempt was made to satisfy the gentry's desires by ridding the curriculum of all rigorously scientific subjects—so much so that the government found it necessary to justify the generally undemanding nature of the curriculum with the explanation that "by no means everyone is inclined by nature toward military affairs; the state needs political and civic education as well."[6] By drawing the aristocratic youth away from the Academic Gymnasium into places where mathematics and the natural sciences were alien disciplines, the Infantry School and others like it to a considerable degree impeded the Academy's task of educating young Russians in the spirit of modern science.

The Academic University was in even more dire straits than the Gymnasium. For the first six years, the eight students brought from Vienna— or those who stayed on—represented the University's entire student body. Not a single Russian was enrolled, for none was prepared. The ciphering schools gave only elementary training, and the various naval, military, and engineering schools were too technical and offered little in the way of Latin and the modern European languages. The seminaries which existed in several provincial towns were still dominated by medieval and Scholastic subjects, and in any case students there would hardly have been urged by their teachers to apply for admission to a secular university. By 1731, then, there was not a single student in the Academic University. The following year the Senate tried to do what it could to remedy the situation by sending twelve students from the Moscow Slavic-Greek-Latin Academy to enroll in the University, but most of these were subsequently assigned to the Great Northern Expedition (1733–43) or to the Academy's shops.

During this entire period the professors complained about the small number of students, and the students complained about the poor teaching methods of their professors. It was this situation that the Academy's first charter, issued in 1747, was designed to ameliorate. The charter stated explicitly that the function of the University was to teach not languages but science, and that thirty students who had proved their ability to communicate in Latin should be admitted annually. The aim as defined by the charter was to create an institution no different in its standards from the Western European schools of higher education. Emphasis was placed on the training of young Russians for scientific pursuits. The charter reiterated the established tradition of opening the University's doors to young men "of all ranks." The students received state stipends. At the middle of the century the guidance of the University was entrusted to the first Russian members of the Academy. All these measures were fruitless; by 1783 there were only two students and in 1796 only three. Several years later the University ceased to exist.

The attempted democratization of the University, it should be pointed out, was not an official design to curb the growing class exclusiveness; rather, it was a contingency arising from the fact that the gentry had still shown no interest in advanced scientific training. It is significant that until well into the nineteenth century, the aristocracy—the only estate that could really afford the advantages of higher education—produced only one-quarter of the total membership of the Academy.[7] The overwhelming ignorance of the provincial gentry in eighteenth-century Russia was abundantly recorded by numerous contemporary observers.

Not only the University but the Academy itself was beset by heavy storms, the mounting effects of which threatened at times to weaken it to the point of extinction. That the Academy was in the end able to survive these onslaughts was primarily due to the remarkably high caliber of most of the original Academicians, whose devotion to science helped them to rise above the troubled atmosphere.

Much of the difficulty arose from the fact that although the Academy was conceived to be an agency of the government, it was looked upon by much of the ruling elite with considerable skepticism, and often with open animosity. To most government officials it was an expensive and superfluous institution. With the death of Catherine I in 1727 the Petrine enthusiasm for science and learning had run its course. Peter II (1727–30), under the influence of conservative boyars, moved the court to Moscow, taking the Academy president, Blumentrost, with him. In Blumentrost's absence, Johann Schumacher, the secretary of the Academy, was given limitless powers, which he utilized to divest the Academic councils of genuine authority. Except for a short interval in 1742–43, he was the real director of the Academy until he retired because of old age in 1759, after appointing a relative, Johann Taubert, to succeed him. Schumacher's qualifications for the secretaryship were respectable but not extraordinary: a degree of Master of Philosophy from Strasbourg, and experience under Peter I in planning the new Academy, followed by government service in departments having little to do with science. In his direction of the Academy he followed the bureaucratic pattern. He played the Academicians against one another, gave them purely mechanical and trivial assignments (which, fortunately, they often ignored), and treated them generally as underlings.

When the Court returned to St. Petersburg under Anne (1730–40), the Academicians expected conditions to improve; but unfortunately this was not the case. The conservative boyars were replaced by powerful officials of foreign origin, particularly by Germans from Courland, who, though usually not unsympathetic to Peter's ideals, were more interested in their own advancement than in the public good. The presidency of the Academy was held by a succession of Court favorites. Hermann Karl Keyserling, the descendant of an old Westphalian family which had become transplanted to Lithuania, held the post after Blumentrost, in 1733–34; following him came Baron Johann Albrecht Korf, a *Kammerjunker* at Anne's court. Baron Korf assumed the title of Supreme Commander. He issued orders that Academic records henceforth be written in German instead of Latin, and that business correspondence be carried on in both Russian and German—he even taught Academicians how to write reports and how to sign their contributions! In 1740 he was named Minister to Copenhagen. His successor, Karl Brevern, wrote to Christian Wolff about his determination to help the Academy rise to the noble heights envisoned by its founder.[8] But two months later, on the death of Biron, his patron, he was dismissed.

Under Elizabeth (1741–61) there was a widespread reaction to the

"German rule" and a gradual reestablishment of Russians in the key government positions. Elizabeth herself, uneducated, superstitious, and fond of luxurious pleasures, had no particular interest in the Academy—certainly not in its scientific integrity. Her choice for president in 1746 was a twenty-two-year-old aristocrat, Count Kiril Razumovskii. Young Razumovskii had but a meager education, and no experience, but he was the brother of Elizabeth's closest and most intimate counselor, Aleksei Razumovskii. Like his predecessors, Kiril Razumovskii relinquished most of his prerogatives to Schumacher, who, despite a temporary fall from grace—purportedly for embezzling government funds—and a brief imprisonment, managed throughout this period to retain his control of the Academy.[9] Schumacher's stubbornness, his thirst for power, and his bureaucratic propensities added new fuel to the smoldering conflict between the scholars and the government. As a gesture of compromise with the new "pro-Russian" policies, he allotted some of his powers to G. N. Teplov, a personal friend of Razumovskii.

THE FIRST CHARTER AND COMPOUNDED DIFFICULTIES

In 1747 the Academy was granted its first charter. This document divided the institution into the Academy proper and the University. Scholars were correspondingly divided into Academicians, who were expected to dedicate themselves to scientific investigation and to the training of future scholars by working closely with selected adjuncts and promising students, and Professors, who were to lecture at the Academic University. Contrary to Peter's original wishes, the new document excluded the humanities from the Academy (but not from the University) and grouped all the sciences treated by the Academy into three classes: geography and astronomy; botany, natural history, anatomy, and chemistry; and experimental physics, mechanics, and higher mathematics. A special article made Latin and Russian the official languages of the Academy.

The members of the Academy accepted the new document with alarm and open dissatisfaction. It gave formal recognition to Schumacher's administrative office and indeed represented a most flagrant denial of Academic autonomy. The orders which now began to emanate from the chancellery were arrogant and disrespectful of the scholars as individuals and as a learned body.[10] Working hours were now strictly prescribed and the violators were fined. The Academicians were forbidden to read journals while scientific papers were being delivered at the meetings. The charter and subsequent orders left the Academicians quite at the mercy of the administrators' every whim. This impossible situation lasted well into the 1760's. The mounting grievances and the growing demoralization of the staff were drawn to the attention of Peter III when he ascended the throne in 1761, but in his brief reign he had more pressing problems. Finally, in an attempt to cure the Academy's chronic ailments, Peter's successor, Catherine II, ruled in 1766 that the chancellery be abolished and that it be replaced by a special commission made up of Academicians. For a time it appeared that the Academy might at last acquire the administrative autonomy that Peter I had promised in 1724, an autonomy which had proved in the scholarly world of the West to be an important requirement for scientific work.

The Academy remained rife with dissension. The major conflict lay between the dedicated Academicians and the administrators, who sought to suppress any efforts to make the Academy a "republic" within the system of monarchical absolutism. Allied to this conflict was a bitter quarrel between those who believed that the Academy should be concerned equally with the sciences and with industrial and fine arts, and those who believed that it should be concerned exclusively with scientific investigation. Schumacher and his administrators, as well as the successive presidents, endorsed the first position, but they also had some Academicians on their side.

This conflict was in a sense an early, somewhat unclear, version of the battle between the Westerners and the anti-Westerners. The latter espoused the idea that the Academy should not be an imitation of analogous institutions in the West but a typical Russian organization of a primarily technological sort, in harmony with the native culture. Most Academicians resented this orientation because it drained the funds allocated for pure research and because there was no intellectual meeting ground between them and the hired artisans and artists. During the 1730's and 1740's the number of scholars declined while the number of all kinds of nonscientific personnel steadily increased, threatening to transform the whole tenor of the Academy. The movement favoring intensified work in the arts and crafts received special impetus in 1735 when Empress Anne gave Peter's lathes and other tools to the Academy and President Korf requested the Senate to assign Russia's most skilled mechanic, Andrei Nartov, to the Academy to teach young men how to use them. With the backing of certain elements outside the Academy, Nartov soon became a director of the Academic chancellery (with the title of "counselor"). In that position he emerged as an advocate of a more rigid and thorough administrative control over the research and teaching activities of individual scholars. He refused to appeal to the government for more funds; on the contrary, he thought that the staff should be reduced to whatever level was consistent with the meager subsidies grudgingly advanced by the Senate.[11] As Nartov *vS.* was carried on to new peaks of power, Schumacher abandoned his former position and began to oppose the excessive concern with the arts as something incompatible with the aims of the Academy. Nartov's luck at last turned against him in 1743, and he was rudely removed from his position of power, whereupon Schumacher resumed his old stand.

The infant Academy suffered also from a vicious internal conflict between the so-called Russian and German factions. During the German-influenced reign of Anne—when thousands of Russians were sent to Siberia—the conflict within the Academy was only a smoldering one because the Russians were still numerically weak and occupied positions of secondary importance. The resentment over "German rule" was voiced mostly by lowly students and isolated adjuncts and translators. They were given encouragement by the widespread resentment in St. Petersburg over the dominance of Germans in the key government positions. The foreigners, mostly those invited to Russia by Peter I, represented the main group supporting the Academy, or at least tolerating it. However, they constituted a serious handicap to the growth of indigenous scholarship, for they had little faith in the ability of the Russians to develop their own ranks of scientists and did nothing to encourage it. It was from such men that the idea originated of allowing the foreign members of the Academy to concern themselves exclusively with scientific investigation, leaving the Russians to teach the arts and crafts. The overbearing conceit of some of the foreign scholars rankled. Academician Bayer, famed for his knowledge of various Oriental languages as well as of Scythian and early Russian history, scorned to acquire even the most rudimentary acquaintance with the Russian language.

The foreign Academicians were so closely tied up with the government that the death of Anne, and the subsequent pronouncement of Elizabeth's "pro-Russian" policies, caused grave alarm among many of them. It was at this time that Euler, the most distinguished member of the Academy, decided to leave Russia. It was also at this time that open suspicion was cast on foreign scholars as possible clandestine informers of various Western powers. In 1746, for example, the government ordered that the materials collected by the Great Northern Expedition be transferred from the Academy's premises as a precaution against any possible copying of their contents for the benefit of foreign powers.[12] A few years earlier an order was issued to place guards around the Academy's press so as to safeguard the secret documents printed for the government from possible conveyance to foreign powers by way of potentially disloyal foreign scholars.[13] Government employees were ordered to refrain from passing "any descriptions of provinces, reports, books, maps, and other materials" to Academicians without proper authorization.[14]

During the 1740's the conflict between the two factions came into the open. By this time the Russian ranks were strengthened—and the first Russians had become full-fledged Academicians. The Academy had reached a major crisis, and its critics both in Russia and in Western Europe were legion. The bureaucratic power of the Academy chancellery did not suffer from the radical change in governmental policy; on the contrary, as we have seen, the chancellery acquired sundry new powers. In a number of ways the 1747 charter made it clear that the highly theoretical and abstract work of the most eminent foreign Academicians was considered undesirable; in articles 34 and 35 it emphasized that the Academy was a scientific department of the government—an agency charged with providing answers to practical questions emanating from government departments.

In Russia the most common criticism of the Academy was that it had misdirected its activities—that it did not concentrate on the sort of intellectual activities that would be most beneficial to the country. Christopher Manstein, a German who was in the Russian military service from 1736 to 1744 and who left Russia during Elizabeth's "pro-Russian" campaign, summed up these views:

"Up to now Russia has not drawn any practical benefits from the Academy. The only fruits borne by this institution, at a huge expense, during the first twenty-eight years of its existence are that the Russians now have a calendar based on the St. Petersburg meridian, that they can read newspapers in their own language, and that several German scholars invited to St. Petersburg know enough mathematics and philosophy to earn 600–800 rubles a year, while among the Russians there are not more than one or two persons who would be able to fill the position of professor. . . . The Academy is not so organized as to enable Russia to receive from it even the smallest benefit, because its members are not predominantly engaged in the study of languages, moral sciences, civil law, history, or practical geometry—the only sciences from which Russia could benefit. Instead, the Academy's staff works mostly in algebra, speculative geometry, and other fields of higher mathematics. They also undertake critical studies

of the dwellings and languages of various ancient peoples, and make anatomical observations of human beings and animals. Since the Russians
consider these sciences empty and useless, it is small wonder that they
have no desire to have their children become acquainted with them, even
though the instruction is tuition-free. This is the reason why the Academy
often has more professors than students, why it is compelled to bring young
men from Moscow, to whom stipends are granted, and why often no one
attends the lectures of the professors."[15]

Inside the Academy, however, the students' chief complaint was that the
foreign scholars considered lecturing a burdensome chore which they
avoided as much as possible, and that no effort was made at a systematic
presentation of any science. Russian scholars complained about the arrogance of their foreign colleagues. S. S. Volchkov, the secretary of the
Academy, in 1761 deplored the never-ending feuds among the scholars,
their unwillingness to devote any time to Russian students, and the total
unfamiliarity of some of them not only with Russian but with French.[16]
A translator at the Academy charged in 1742 that it was no accident, but
the result of the discriminatory policies of such officials as Schumacher,
that after eighteen years there was still no Russian professor in the
Academy.[17]

Both government and academic authorities were seriously disturbed
when reports from diplomatic posts began to indicate how widely known
the plight of the Academy was in Western Europe. The government was
not much interested in developments in the field of science, but it was
very sensitive to the failure of the Academy to perform the political and
diplomatic role entrusted to it by Peter I—the role of proving to the West
that the Russians were not barbarians, were not lacking in appreciation of
the intellectual accomplishments of modern Europe, and indeed had contributions of their own to make. How seriously the authorities viewed the
deteriorating international position of the Academy—it was even rumored
in the West that the very survival of the Academy was in question—can
be seen from the following order given to Professor A. Kaau-Boerhaave:

"Since a number of persons wishing ill to the Academy have spread
rumors that her Imperial Highness [Elizabeth] plans to do away with
the Academy . . . and since you have received permission to go abroad
for six months, the following commission is entrusted to you. . . . In
every city that you visit you shall refute the unfounded rumor and try to
convince learned men everywhere that her Imperial Highness has had no
such plans but, on the contrary, has consistently worked for the Academy's

improvement; and that even though the President [Razumovskii] is absent from the Academy he manages it with great success, just as if he were not absent, which is obvious by the number of works published during his absence and by other accomplishments. You will be given a copy of every academic work published during the President's absence so that you can fully refute the false rumors."[18]

The conflict between the German and Russian factions was not an all-embracing one: there were such eminent foreign scholars as Euler who were neutral, and there were also those who crossed national lines. There is some truth in the statement made by a modern Academician that this conflict was more social than national, that it pitted not so much two national groups against each other as two rungs of the Academic ladder.[19] Shchapov is of the opinion that the survival of traditional Russian animosity toward Western culture and the tendency of foreign scholars in the Academy to reciprocate with similar hatred were at the bottom of the bitter conflict.[20] Crisscrossing the larger battle between the Russian and German factions were the continual flare-ups between individual scholars, of whatever nationality, over Academic policies, scholarly jurisdictions, personal proclivities, and participation in informal groups.

The Church, clinging tenaciously to its Russo-Byzantine tradition and distorted Scholasticism, was another powerful force which kept a sharp eye on all activities of the Academy, ready to pounce on any scientific ideas that seemed incompatible with Orthodox theology. It was fear of the Church that kept Delisle's article on the rotation of the earth and Daniel Bernoulli's statement on Copernicus's heliocentric system from appearing in the Academy's Russian publications. During the 1740's Lomonosov was alarmed at the immense number of sermons that were sheer anti-scientific tirades, frequently including attacks on individual scholars. In 1756 the Synod demanded that all manuscripts which claimed the existence of many worlds, and in general any works which contained ideas contrary to the teachings of the holy religion, should be denied publication. By now, however, the Church, having lost its traditional monopoly over the country's printing facilities, did not possess absolute power in repressing the flow of ideas inimical to its ideology. For the first time, many demands issued by the Synod were ignored. The most effective resistance of the Church to the spread of scientific thought was in the new seminaries, all modeled on the Kievan Academy, where the teachers were totally ignorant of the ever-expanding areas of secular wisdom. In general, during the eighteenth century the intellectual interests of the Church schools were a sort of *eruditio* mixed with hazy transcendental-metaphysical ideas borrowed from German Scholastic philosophy. Greek and Latin were taught by persons who themselves had only a rudimentary knowledge of these languages. In all Church schools, both seminaries and academies, the natural sciences were either excluded completely from the curriculum or of very minor importance.

Vasilii Tatishchev, in his classic "Conversations about the Usefulness of Science and Schools," written in 1733 (but not published until the end of the nineteenth century), was critical of the Moscow Theological Academy because, in his opinion, it taught poor Latin and placed too much emphasis on empty rhetoric. He also noted that the teachers knew no mathematics, "the basis of all philosophy," and that their teaching of physics was purely nominalistic, the theories of such giants as Descartes being wholly unknown to them. He noted that logic, as taught in this school, consisted of exercises with empty and often incorrect syllogisms, and that the teaching of jurisprudence ignored the natural law and the works of Grotius and Pufendorf, "which were respected throughout Europe."[21]

The troubles of the young Academy of Sciences were also aggravated by the dilatory granting of funds by the government and its unwillingness to provide funds for additional research and equipment. This situation did not necessarily reflect any deliberate government effort to curb the work of the Academy; rather it was one of many results of a depleted national treasury. Both Anne and Elizabeth made token financial contributions to the Academy, but both failed to carry out their promises of supporting scholarship by sound budgetary methods. These and other difficulties which beset the Academy and placed blocks in the paths of scholarly investigation were partly responsible for the fact that some of the leading foreign scholars were eager to leave St. Petersburg.[22] As soon as they could, they left—men like Jacob Hermann, Christian Martini, Georg Bilfinger, and Daniel Bernoulli.

As the troubles of the Academy mounted, it became increasingly difficult to fill the vacant Academic positions with scholars who measured up to Wolff's high standards. During the 1740's only ten foreign scholars joined the Academy, and a similar situation prevailed during the 1750's. A number of these were able and promising young scholars, but along with them came men with little or no interest in scientific work. Gottlob Juncker and Jacob Stählin, for example, distinguished themselves as writers of festive odes and epitaphs designed to add luster to numerous court ceremonies and Academy celebrations. Friedrich Strube de Piermont and

Peter LeRoy, who entered the Academy with the aid of influential friends, had nothing to do with serious scholarship.

THE ACADEMY'S INITIAL CONTRIBUTIONS

The contributions of the Academy during the first decades of its existence have been subject to various and opposing evaluations. For a long time the negative view was dominant; the new scientific institution was considered too alien to Russian culture and too remote from Russia's needs to perform a historically constructive role. Manstein's comments, quoted earlier, were a typical criticism of the 1730's and '40's. Vasilii Tatishchev, the leading Russian intellectual of this period, was equally outspoken. In the first place, he did not approve Peter's idea of "broadcasting the seed before the soil was plowed," that is, of establishing an Academy before there was an adequate system of lower and secondary schools. Peter's assurance that the Academy—a "watermill without water"—would compel his successors to build a canal so as to bring the water to the mill was ill-founded, according to Tatishchev. Twelve years after Peter's confident statement, great scholars gathered in St. Petersburg, but the quality of the schools was even worse than before, and in the provinces, Tatishchev commented, schools stood neglected and ruined.[23]

In 1925, on the occasion of the two-hundredth anniversary of the founding of the Academy, the physicist P. P. Lazarev, in delivering the main oration, reiterated the old view that because the foreign Academicians were not interested in the needs of Russia the work of the Academy bore an exceedingly abstract character.[24] The same statement was repeated in 1935 in a symposium commemorating the one-hundred-fiftieth anniversary of the death of Euler, the most illustrious member of the early Academy.[25] These negative views, however, have been countered by glowing praise of the Academy's early contributions to Russian culture. At the end of the last century, A. N. Pypin, in a somewhat exaggerated condemnation of the Slavophil rejection of science as a Western import, remarked: "It was not Western science which took us away from the people. Science made it possible for us to develop a broad social and national self-consciousness."[26] Peter I and the Academy, he argued, won for Russia an honorable place in the family of civilized nations; in the eighteenth century no intelligent person saw any incompatibility between science—borrowed from the West "because there was no other place to borrow it from" —and the "national spirit."[27]

In our time the Soviet historians of science emphasize the far-reaching contributions of the early Academy. G. A. Kniazev and A. V. Kol'tsov made a grand reversal of the traditional opinion when they wrote that the work of the first Academicians—particularly that which resulted from group research—"was closely related to the needs of the country."[28] They mentioned especially cartographic work, directed by scholars who established astronomically correct geographical points and worked out more or less original methods of cartography. The contributions of the early Academy have been interpreted in the most favorable light in such major works as the *History of the Academy of Sciences of the U.S.S.R.,* Volume I (1958) and the *History of Natural Science in Russia,* Volume I, Part 1 (1957).

Those who have been skeptical of the contributions of the early Academy have usually been unaware of the wide range of its functions. They tend to remember only the theoretical work of its foreign scholars and its limited teaching facilities. Many of these critics have overlooked the fact that the Academy was for years the only institution in Russia which had a systematic program of translation of foreign works, both scientific and popular. Particularly during the reign of Elizabeth, the translating activity assumed wide proportions and was an important influence not only on the steady growth of a reading public but also on the development of a Russian literary language. The translation department of the Academy, known for a time as the Russian Council (founded in 1735), was even more important historically, in that it represented the first formal gathering of Russian intellectuals. It implied a certain native intellectual self-assertion, and its very existence was an encouragement to the development of a Russian intellectual class. From 1755 to 1764 the Academy published *Monthly Essays,* the first popular literary and scientific journal in Russia.

The Academy placed the study of the country's natural and cultural resources on a fairly systematic basis. It participated in the Great Northern Expedition—often referred to as the Second Kamchatka Expedition or the First Academic Expedition—carried out under the sponsorship of the Admiralty. This undertaking produced valuable scientific and ethnographic material, and it also provided scholarly apprenticeship for a group of young Russian naturalists. The members of the expedition were divided into three groups. The first group was given the task of surveying and describing the shores of the Arctic Ocean from Arkhangelsk to Kamchatka. The second group, headed by Vitus Bering, planned a voyage from Kamchatka to the western shores of America. The third group—made up primarily of members of the Academy staff—undertook to reach

Kamchatka by an overland route and to gather information of value in the study of natural history. Among the members of this group were the astronomer Louis Delisle de la Croyère, the natural scientist Johann Gmelin, the historian Gerhard Müller, the adjunct Georg Steller, and several Russian students, including Stepan Krasheninnikov.

Because of the political and economic importance of geography, the Academy established a special geographic and cartographic department— for many years the only one of its kind in Russia—of which Euler was for a time a distinguished member. Soon after its inception this department prepared Russia's first *Atlas*, based on astronomically determined geographical points and consisting of maps of nineteen different localities and a general map of Russia.[29] Many other practical functions were also performed by the Academy. It issued an annual calendar, relieving both the Church and the government of a chronic headache, and it worked on the problem of establishing a system of standard weights. It published the *St. Petersburg Gazette,* the capital's only newspaper and an important medium through which Western ideas were brought to the attention of the slowly growing reading public. During the first three decades of its existence the Academy was the main instrument in the growing Westernization of Russian culture.

It seems eminently clear today that the Academy's first major contributions were made in the two fields which contemporary critics regarded as least practical and relevant to the country's real needs. These fields were scientific investigation of a highly theoretical nature and the education and intellectual apprenticeship of Russia's first true scholars. All other work of the Academy shrinks in significance when compared with its accomplishments in these two fields.

Because of the generally difficult conditions under which the Academy was compelled to operate during its early years, one might hardly expect it to have accomplished any solid work in science. However, scientific contributions did come, and they received immediate acknowledgment in the West. Paradoxically, the government's skeptical attitude toward the worth of the Academy had one good result: the first scholars, carefully chosen in the West, were seldom troubled by government requests for solutions to practical problems and could thus occupy themselves in comparative solitude with speculative and theoretical work. In this scholarly isolation, not unnaturally, they were less preoccupied with transplanting Western science to Russia than with pursuing original investigations which added to the existing body of scientific knowledge.

From the very beginning, the Academy was a fountain of new knowledge. The publication of Johann Bernoulli's article on the integration of differential equations in the first issue of the *Commentarii* was symbolic of the tenor of the young Academy. It heralded the emphasis which the Academy was to place on mathematical work and its prolonged identification with great mathematical tradition of the University of Basel, which was one of the most formidable scientific attainments of the eighteenth century. Just as the brothers Jacob and Johann Bernoulli distinguished themselves in Basel by their untiring search into the ramifications and refinements of Leibniz's and Newton's mathematical legacy, their St. Petersburg disciples—Jacob Hermann, Daniel and Nicolaus Bernoulli, and Leonhard Euler—gave additional depth to the synthesis of these remarkable attainments. Young Nicolaus Bernoulli, who died in July 1726, immortalized his adopted city by naming a problem in the theory of probability "the St. Petersburg problem." His brother left St. Petersburg in 1733 as a result of his uncompromising opposition to Schumacher, but not before he had completed the first draft of *Hydrodynamica*, a fact stated on the title page of the volume when it was published in 1738. The Bernoulli theorem on hydraulic pressure, postulated in this book, was born in St. Petersburg.[30]

Among the eminent foreign scholars who joined the Academy, three names are of striking importance: Leonhard Euler, Johann Gmelin, and Gerhard Friedrich Müller. These three, each of whom represented a different area of scientific endeavor, were prominent both as scholars of great achievement and as persons who exerted a profound influence on the growth of specific areas of scientific inquiry in Russia. Each was the founder of an important current in the Russian intellectual tradition. All three spent their formative years and reached the peak of their scientific achievements in Russia, and all three spent most of their adult lives as active members of the Academy. Euler and Müller came to St. Petersburg at the age of twenty, Gmelin at seventeen; thus in a way all three may be considered products of the Academy as well as benefactors of the Academy and the Russian nation.

EULER AND THE ACADEMY

Although Euler was barely twenty when he arrived in Russia in 1727, he had already proved his astounding mastery of mathematics. He had been a special student of Johann Bernoulli in Basel and at the age of nineteen he had been honored by having the Paris Academy of Sciences accept for publication two of his papers, one on the masting of ships and one on the philosophy of sound. He decided to go to Russia partly because he failed to get a hoped-for position at the University of Basel and partly because his good friends, the young Bernoullis, were in St. Petersburg. In the Academy he first held the chair of physiology, then of physics, and finally, from 1733, that of mathematics. In the same year he married a daughter of his countryman Gsell, who was brought to Russia by Peter I and who at the time worked in the Academy as a painter. The marriage introduced a personal equation into Euler's relationship with the Academy and with St. Petersburg. An untiring worker, moved by great ambition and devotion to science and quiet and withdrawn in nature, he remained detached from the quarrel within the Academy between the German and Russian factions.

Euler's work was highly diversified, but his enthusiasm for mathematical calculations gave unity to his scholarly labors. In 1727 Schumacher reported to Peter II that Euler's plan of research covered a wide range of problems, from a mathematical analysis of the sounds produced by musical instruments to the designing of mathematical formulas for the flow of water from different kinds of containers and the motion of bodies in fluids. Theoretical though it was, his scientific work was rooted in practical sciences like navigation and cartography. He was consistently interested in the relations among various exact sciences and in the philosophy of science. Almost from the beginning of his career it was apparent that mathematical calculation was his main interest; everything else was material on which he tested his complicated mathematical theories. With Daniel Bernoulli he shared a keen interest in discerning the kernels of general theory in concrete physical phenomena and reducing them to a mathematical formula. Euler did not approach mathematics in a fragmentary fashion; he developed the large fields of mathematics systematically, and he tackled every problem as an integral part of a complex whole. It was Condorcet who made the statement that Euler differed from the other great mathematicians of his age in that he was the only one who "embraced the mathematical sciences in their universality."[31] M. A. Lavrent'ev put it this way: "Euler's genius embraced all the branches of contemporary physical and mathematical sciences—analysis and algebra; analytical and differential geometry; the mechanics of solids, fluids, and gases; optics and the theory of electricity; astronomy; and a number of technical sciences. He laid the foundations for several independent disciplines—the calculus of variations, the theory of differential equations, and the theory of numbers."[32]

Immediately after his arrival in St. Petersburg, Euler began to produce scientific papers which were read at conferences and published in the *Commentarii*. Within a short time he had thirteen published papers to his name. He also delivered public lectures on logic and higher mathematics and contributed popular scientific articles to a supplement of the *St. Petersburg Gazette*. One of his students, V. E. Adodurov—the first Russian to be elected a member of the Academy's scientific staff—translated an arithmetical manual prepared by Euler into Russian for the use of the students of the Academic Gymnasium.[33] Conscientiously and industriously, Euler met the rare requests for counsel on various practical matters which emanated from government quarters. He devoted many hours to preliminary work on five detailed maps of Russia, and in 1735 his intensive astronomical calculations resulted in partial blindness.[34] The main expressions of his scholarly enthusiasm and genius were, however, his papers in *Commentarii*. It was these papers more than anything else that drew the attention of Western scholars to the St. Petersburg Academy. In 1734 Daniel Bernoulli wrote to Euler from Basel: "I have not words enough to describe how eagerly people everywhere inquire about the St. Petersburg transactions."[35]

In 1736, sorely wounded by internal strife and still trying to find its proper niche in Russian culture, the Academy earned itself a place of honor in the main current of Western scientific development. This was the year of the publication of Euler's *Mechanica,* one of those milestones of eighteenth-century science which opened new vistas of inquiry and widened the intellectual horizons of Western man. In the words of Condorcet: "The treatise on mechanics that Euler gave to the world in 1736 is the first great work in which analysis has been applied to the science of motion."[36] Johann Bernoulli greeted the work with great enthusiasm: "Up to now no other book has appeared which has contained such a wealth of important and newly discovered results deriving from the very heart of mathematics."[37] It was not the substantive part of this book that attracted the attention of the world of scholarship; its chief value was that it marked the first systematic use of mathematical analysis in a natural science. Although Newton was an inventor of the calculus, in the *Principia* he chose to present his ideas in a rather conservative geometrical or synthetic fashion. This method, relying on geometrical figures, was cumbersome and required special consideration for each problem. Euler introduced analytical methods—he was the first to offer mathematical analysis as a method for the solution of a number of leading problems in mechanics. The *Mechanica* proved to be only the beginning of Euler's lifelong work on the systematization of the calculus and mathematical analysis; it built a bridge between mathematical abstraction of the highest order and the constantly growing areas of applied science.

Although the Academy was not highly valued by Russian authorities and although Euler, particularly in his early work, addressed himself primarily to the scholarly world of Western Europe, his great reputation did leave a profound imprint on the culture of his adopted country. It contributed to making the Academy a permanent institution and a source of growing Russian prestige in the West. There is no doubt that Euler's reputation in mathematics made this science a special challenge and attraction to promising young Russian scholars. Even in the Russia of the 1730's, Euler succeeded in demonstrating the great dignity of the preoccupation with pure ideas. He showed significantly that applied science was not a matter of work on technical problems, but something far more challenging: the application of mathematical analysis to the phenomena of natural science.

The Academy, despite its drawbacks, made Euler's life on the whole rather comfortable. His salary was increased successively from 300 rubles in 1727 and 600 in 1733 to 1,200 rubles in 1740. His rising star appears not to have provoked Academic jealousy. His colleagues tolerated his friendly relations with Schumacher, particularly because he was not allied with any particular faction in the intramural battle. In his unfinished autobiography he frankly expresses his great debt to "favorable conditions" in the Academy during the early years of his career. Indeed, he says, without these conditions, "I would have been compelled to occupy myself with other sciences, which, by all indications, would only have set me back." He freely acknowledges the importance of those years: "His Majesty [Frederick II of Prussia] asked me where I had acquired my knowledge. I answered truthfully that for all my knowledge I was indebted to my work in the St. Petersburg Academy of Sciences."[38]

Euler talked about the "favorable conditions" in the Academy but not about the generally unfavorable conditions which affected the place of the Academy in the Russian polity—conditions which may have had a great deal to do with his decision in 1741 to leave Russia and accept the invitation of Frederick II to join the Berlin Academy of Sciences. The question

Reasons for Euler's leaving

of what prompted Euler to leave the St. Petersburg Academy has been answered many times and in many different ways. The reasons were probably a combination of interwoven ones, more or less as A. Satkevich has described them.[39] First of all, it must be remembered that Frederick II, who was determined to shake the Berlin Academy out of its chronic lethargy and make it a great institution of learning, promised Euler attractive living conditions and the directorship of the department of mathematics.

It is also to be remembered that during the thirteen years of Euler's stay in St. Petersburg the Academy was without a charter and therefore in a shaky legal position, which left it open to the autocratic propensities of Schumacher and resulted indirectly in the resignation of such eminent scholars as Hermann, Daniel Bernoulli, and Bilfinger. The Academy's finances were also shaky, and no guarantees for their improvement were anticipated. The chronic deficit of the Academy's budget and occasional tardiness in the payment of monthly salaries must have been particularly worrisome to foreign scholars without other sources of income. Euler himself suffered little from these irregularities, especially after his star began to rise, but the threat was always there.

In addition to these more or less personal anxieties, Euler was quite aware of the severe limitations to scholarly work in Russia, largely determined by the attitude of the government. The general suspicion of science, which made the Academicians even potential spies in the eyes of the government, was certainly not conducive to independent thought. Like his distinguished colleagues, Euler lacked the stimulus of an intellectual, or at least sympathetic, environment. By 1740 the atmosphere was on the verge of becoming hostile. A growing anti-foreign sentiment emerged in reaction to Biron's despotism and to the waves of Baltic Germans who swarmed to St. Petersburg in search of employment. Euler was particularly alarmed by the anti-German governmental policy which followed the death of Anne. This is made quite clear in his autobiography, in which he comments that "after the death of glorious Empress Anne, under the regency which followed, the working conditions began to deteriorate."[40] Finally, St. Petersburg's climate was disagreeable, and life in that city was further complicated by frequent fires and by the practice of billeting soldiers in private homes.

In his request to be released from his contract with the Academy, Euler gave poor health as the reason for his wish to leave the country.[41] Perhaps a more important reason was one which he implied in a brief conversation with the Queen Mother of Prussia. Soon after his arrival in Berlin, Euler was introduced to this royal personage, who received him as if he were a prince and proceeded to question him in friendly fashion. Euler, showing extreme reserve and caution, answered all her questions as briefly as possible and volunteered nothing. The dismayed queen asked him to explain his unusual timorousness. "Madam," he replied, "I have just come from a country where people are hanged if they talk."[42]

There is no evidence that Euler ever sensed any ominous reaction to his scientific work in Russia or that during the period of Biron's ruthlessness he was viewed by the authorities with any particular suspicion. It is fairly apparent, however, that throughout his mature life, and particularly after he acquired a family, he felt a strong need for security, for those close to him if not for himself. As a scholar, he had no clearly defined status in Russian society, which was rigidly stratified into estates, all existing as both social and legal entities, but which of course had no category for the intellectual aristocracy. It is not surprising that when, decades later, he was asked by representatives of Catherine II to return to Russia, he expressed a desire to be appointed vice-president of the Academy; in such a position he would have had easy entry into the highest ranks of St. Petersburg society.

In Berlin, where he stayed from 1741 to 1766, a life close to the Court, in the midst of the Enlightenment fervor, gave him courtier status with all its flattering privileges. Although it became harder and harder for him to avoid academic intrigues, he somehow managed, and his stature grew through his mounting scientific contributions. By the time he was forty he was the leading mathematician in Europe. It is interesting that he had still to thank his continued association with the St. Petersburg Academy for a substantial measure of his success. He was made an honorary member of the Academy, and during his stay in Germany he published 109 works in St. Petersburg and 119 in Berlin—the best proof of his continued close cooperation with the St. Petersburg institution.[43] Satkevich makes a cogent statement on the differences between the works published by Euler in St. Petersburg and in Berlin:

"Interesting also is the fact that whereas Euler's Berlin treatises are mostly of an applied mathematical character and are written in French, the St. Petersburg publications are written in Latin and in the pure-mathematical and abstract-scientific spirit. In Berlin he tried to respond to the needs of society, which was closely linked to the Academy and demanded from it solutions for current scientific problems. He regarded the St. Petersburg Academy as a true repository of the most profound scientific knowledge and as a scholarly body which was not compelled to gear its work to the humble interests of the general public. Of Euler's two long works which appeared at that time, one, dealing with navigation (*Scientia navalis*), was published in St. Petersburg, and the other, dealing with astronomy (*Theoria motuum lunae*), was published in Berlin for the convenience of the author's proofreading but at the expense of the St. Petersburg Academy."[44]

The differences between the two academies were not so sharp as Satkevich portrays them, but it is true that the St. Petersburg institution was the more detached of the two from the technical and intellectual needs of the state. This condition was chiefly due to the lack of appreciation for science among the members of the ruling elite rather than to any deliberate emphasis on "pure science." As a further amplification of Satkevich's statement, it may be mentioned that Euler's classic work on differential calculus, *Institutiones calculi differentialis,* was published in Berlin but at the expense of the St. Petersburg Academy,[45] and that the work in which Euler presented the first systematic study of the calculus of variations was written in St. Petersburg (though published in Lausanne in 1744). It should be added, however, that Euler's three-volume study of integral calculus (published in 1768–70) was begun and substantially completed in Berlin.

It was not only in the sponsorship of some of his studies that Euler was actively associated with the St. Petersburg Academy during his years in Berlin. The scope of his assorted tasks was fairly large, and he well earned the 200-ruble monthly stipend which the St. Petersburg Academy allowed its honorary members. Some of the duties performed by Euler throw significant light on conditions and changes in the Academy during the 1740's and 1750's. He was requested to plead with some of the great scholars who had left St. Petersburg to return and resume their academic duties, and in a number of ways to defend the institution in the face of mounting and often malicious attacks coming from the former Academicians. He procured books and scientific materials for the Academy. In 1744 Count Kiril Razumovskii, who two years later was appointed president of the Academy, traveled in Western Europe "to acquire habits of civilized societies" and spent some time in Berlin at the home of Euler. One of Euler's important assignments was that of tutoring selected young Russians who were sent abroad for advanced study. Stepan Rumovskii and S. K. Kotel'nikov, who subsequently became skilled mathematicians, stayed for several years with the Euler family in Berlin. The Russian government did not give these students adequate financial help, however, and in 1755 it decided to recall them altogether rather than increase their monthly stipends.

In 1749, at Razumovskii's request, Euler submitted a list of topics to be used in an essay-writing contest, similar to the ones long sponsored by the Paris Académie des Sciences, and he later acted as one of the judges. He was also asked to suggest candidates for membership in the St. Petersburg Academy.[46] Thanks to these services, and to the continued warmth of his attachment to the St. Petersburg institution, the Russian authorities, in the words of Condorcet, never treated him as a foreigner.[47] In 1746 and again in 1750 he was approached about returning to the Russian capital, and given handsome offers to do so. He refused both times, but he never allowed the door to be closed completely. Finally, in 1763 he himself renewed the question in a letter to Gerhard Müller, secretary of the Academic Assembly. On July 17, 1766, he arrived in St. Petersburg to begin a new phase of his productive scientific career.

Euler's return to Russia was a great victory for the St. Petersburg Academy. It was in a way a first step toward the rehabilitation of this institution, which during the two preceding decades had found it more and more difficult to lure established scholars to St. Petersburg. It also showed that the rays of enlightenment had begun to reach the summit of government, as evidenced by a willingness to meet Euler's rather stiff demands. The eyes of Western scholarship were again turned on St. Petersburg, and mathematics resumed its former honored place in the Academy's expanding domains of scientific inquiry. It is difficult to say whether Euler's original arrival in St. Petersburg in 1727 or his triumphant return in 1766 was the more significant event in the growth of Russia's great mathematical tradition.

GMELIN AND THE SIBERIAN EXPEDITION

Johann Georg Gmelin is important to us not because he was a man of extraordinary intellect and scientific achievements, but because he was the originator of one of the strong scientific traditions in the history of the Academy. This was the tradition of the scientific study of the country's natural resources—a mighty intellectual current upon which much of the Academy's glory rested until well into the nineteenth century. From its very inception this study was only in part determined by the practical needs of Russia's expanding economy. It was equally focused on the goal of supplying the budding natural sciences with a body of empirical data and of organizing the collected data into modern scientific categories. The pursuit of this goal incidentally afforded young Russian naturalists a splendid opportunity for apprenticeship in scholarly pursuits, and it gave the Academy the satisfaction of contributing unique empirical data to the general fund of scientific knowledge.

Gmelin experienced a series of disappointments in St. Petersburg and left Russia after two decades of active membership in the Academy, but his scientific career, at least in terms of scholarly output, did not extend beyond his association with this institution. As an adjunct of the St. Petersburg Academy from 1727 to 1731, he studied the latest theoretical works in chemistry and the biological sciences. In 1731, at the age of twenty-two, he was assigned to the Great Northern Expedition, headed by Vitus Bering, which took him as far as Iakutsk and kept him away from St. Petersburg for ten years. His work in Siberia was not always pleasant. Many of his assistants—mostly persons exiled to Siberia—proved unreliable, and he was plagued by arrogant commanders of government outposts and inadequate support from the Academic authorities. The main fruit of Gmelin's Siberian travels was his *Flora sibirica*, published by the Academy in four volumes (1747–69).[48] This exhaustive study contains descriptions of 1,178 different plants, many of them previously unrecorded. Linnaeus remarked in one of his letters, even before the *Flora sibirica* had appeared, that Gmelin had discovered as many plants as all other botanists put together. Academician Ruprecht wrote in the nineteenth century: "Gmelin was a friend of Linnaeus but not a blind follower of his system. His *Siberian Flora* is organized in terms of Roy's natural families, as corrected by Royer, from which subsequently developed the system of Jussieu."[49]

In 1751–52 Gmelin published his equally famous *Travels in Siberia from 1733 to 1743*, which soon was translated into many languages, but ironically not into Russian. This book is a remarkable document about the life, customs, arts, and commerce of the inhabitants of Siberia during the first half of the eighteenth century, when much of the indigenous culture was still a living force and the antagonism between the conquerors and the conquered was still ablaze. It was because of this book that Pekarskii stated, more than one hundred years later, that Gmelin's decision to leave Russia was a fortunate one: if he had remained in the country his book would have been shorn of many factual data by the censors, who often deleted from manuscripts "even the most naïve and inoffensive" ideas.[50] Sound as he was in his scholarly judgments, Gmelin was not always tolerant or perceptive in his other views, and his unpleasant experiences in Siberia unfortunately influenced his published statements. He enlarged upon the general ignorance and crudities of frontier life in a sweeping criticism of laziness, drunkenness, and other alleged vices of the Russians as a nation.

Georg Wilhelm Steller, Gmelin's colleague in the Siberian expedition, was also a pioneer in the scientific study of Siberia's natural history. Steller joined the Great Northern Expedition in 1739, several years after becoming an adjunct of the St. Petersburg Academy. He was by training a physician, but in the Academy he took up the study of contemporary natural history, and this became his chief interest in Siberia. He was a resourceful and tireless worker, and in Siberia—which he never left—he produced many scientific papers of admirable quality. After his death in 1746 in a lonely Siberian town, the venerable Feofan Prokopovich lauded his utmost sacrifice for the cause of science in a commemorative ode.[51]

On Bering Island, marooned in the winter of 1741–42 by heavy ice and Arctic winds, Steller wrote *De bestiis marinis* (published in 1751), which was to immortalize his name in the annals of natural history. Contemporary scholars were particularly attracted to his description of the lamantin (*Rhytina borealis*), a marine mammal which became extinct before the end of the century. Most of his works were published posthumously—some of them, like the book on the natural and human resources of Kamchatka, which appeared in 1774 in Germany, very carelessly—and they became useful sources for contemporary scholars. Stepan Krasheninnikov relied on them in the preparation of his geographical and ethnographic description of Kamchatka, Gmelin in the preparation of his *Flora sibirica*, and Peter Pallas in his zoological studies. Linnaeus extracted valuable taxonomic information from Steller's herbariums.[52]

GERHARD MÜLLER

Gerhard Friedrich Müller was associated with the Academy for over fifty years. During this long period he identified himself more intimately than any other single person with the pains and fortunes of this institution. He was one of those rare foreigners who adopt Russia as their homeland and so fully immerse themselves in the life streams of its culture that they overcome the dilemma of split loyalty. As Secretary of the Academic Assembly, particularly after 1755, he maintained extensive contact with Western scholars and earnestly sought to restore the prestige of the Academy. He solicited advice from fellow Academicians and honorary members; he tried to quiet the rumors about Russia's being a bad place for scientific work; and he prepared the way for Euler's return to Russia. He was largely responsible for turning the *St. Petersburg Gazette* into a serious literary undertaking.

historiographer

Müller can rightly be identified as the founder of a new kind of Russian historiography, based on a systematic and critical amassing of historical data. From 1735 to 1765 he published the famous *Sammlung russischer Geschichte,* which contained excerpts from medieval chronicles, Byzantine writings, Western European works, and other sources of Russian historical lore.[53] This series—the first systematic publication of important Russian historical documents—proved of enormous value to Western scholars, to whom most of the material had hitherto been inaccessible.

under Censorship

Like many other foreign scholars who settled in Russia, Müller was obliged to seek a certain measure of security for himself and his family in a close adherence to the official ideology, to the point of becoming an apologist for the existing social system. In time, political considerations seriously affected his scope as a historian—particularly after he was prohibited by the government from studying the genealogies of aristocratic Russian families on the grounds that he might shed unfavorable light on certain phases of early Russian history.[54] Despite his protestations of loyalty to the autocratic system and belief in the social *status quo,* his applications for the establishment of a historical department in the Academy were twice refused, in 1744 and 1746. On one occasion he was seriously reprimanded for having lent his personal notebook containing excerpts of foreign visitors' views on Russia to several of his acquaintances. He was officially accused of showing disrespect for the Russian nobility because one of these notes remarked that the great Russian princes were forced to bow before their Tatar masters.[55] In 1745 the government requested Müller to explain why he had prepared a map of a number of "newly discovered" islands. For several years he was not permitted to continue his work on a revision of the Great Map of Russia, being prepared by the Academy's Department of Geography, or to work on any special maps of Siberia.[56] No man, said the historian August L. Schlözer, knew more about Russia's past and present than Müller, and no one learned more thoroughly what he should not talk about.[57]

Müller's main historical contributions were in the field of Siberian history—he is sometimes called "the father of Siberian historiography."[58] With Gmelin, he spent ten years (1733-43) in Siberia as a member of the

Great Northern Expedition. There, he and his assistants collected a vast amount of historical, geographical, and archaeological material, and recorded oral traditions. Müller made extensive use of archival materials as a source of historical information; he searched through and systematized some twenty archives, mostly of private families. The collected materials—the so-called *Siberian Portfolios*—were subsequently used by Mikhail Shcherbatov in his volumes on Russian history, by Nikolai Novikov in the preparation of his *Ancient Russian Bibliophilia,* by Nikolai Rumiantsev in his gathering of "state documents and agreements," and by the "Archaeographical" Commission and many other scientific bodies and individual scholars. They are still not exhausted—perhaps because of their formidable detail and tedious style, including an overfondness for epigraphy. Even as a historian's historian, Müller soon became antiquated. But no one can deny the value of his systematic, thorough, and careful gathering of historical material.

The special methods which Müller devised for the collection of historical, ethnographic, and linguistic data resulted in a rich store of cultural material on a great number of different Siberian societies. Ethnographic descriptions, Müller thought, were not only "pleasant reading for most people" but also of great importance to historians because they showed the common ancestry of peoples with similar customs and languages.[59] Müller himself prepared notable ethnographic descriptions of the Kalmuks, the Buriats, the Ostiaks, and the Samoyeds. In his old age he collected valuable materials having to do with the reign of Peter I, the Russian exploratory voyages in the Pacific Ocean, the Pugachev uprising, and several other vital phases of Russian history.

During the nineteenth century, Müller fell into disrepute because of his adherence to the Variag theory of the origin of the Russian state, which was shared by such other eighteenth-century historians as Bayer and Schlözer. His reputation is still attacked on this account by Soviet historians, even though the question of the origin of the Russian state was hardly central to his scholarly interests. It has been only in the past several decades that the Russians have undertaken to publish the complete *History of Siberia.*[60]

When the Academy began making plans for its fiftieth-anniversary celebration, Müller, who arrived in St. Petersburg in 1725 as one of the first adjuncts, was asked to write a history of the institution. Unfortunately, he managed to get through only the first eight years (Stritter carried it on to 1743). His essay is not a model of impartial study, but it depicts very fully the growing pains of the young Academy and may be considered the first historical essay dealing with Russia's intellectual tradition.[61]

Modern science finally took root in Russian culture thanks to foreign scholars, particularly such men as Euler, Gmelin, Steller, and Müller, who not only made substantial scholarly contributions but also founded great scientific traditions which became an inspiration to future generations of Russian scholars.

The Academy was at first slow in producing able Russian scholars. During the first sixteen years of its existence, only one Russian—V. E. Adodurov—was admitted to membership, with the rank of adjunct in mathematics. Adodurov came of an aristocratic family in Novgorod, where he attended the local seminary just long enough to learn basic Latin and to acquire an interest in natural philosophy. He was one of the first to be enrolled in the Academic Gymnasium in 1727. He was associated with the Academy from 1733 to 1741, and was the only adjunct of his generation who did not advance to the rank of professor, but his departure from the Academy was apparently due to changes in interests and attractive openings elsewhere. He worked for a time with Euler, until the many tasks assigned to him by the Academic chancellery took him away from his chosen field. He is remembered less as a mathematician than as the author of a *Short Russian Grammar* (1731), an abbreviated and simplified version of the extensive grammatical manual written by Meletii Smotritskii.

The first rallying point for the thin ranks of Russian intellectuals who found their way into the Academy during the 1730's was the Russian Council, established in 1735 as a special department of the Academy to expedite the modernization of the Russian language and the translation of modern scientific works into Russian.[62] There was at this time a growing struggle for literary pre-eminence between the Church-Slavic language and the daily language of the people. The Church-Slavic language, the official language of the Church, was employed only in religious and literary works or for the expression of spiritual thoughts. It was a dying language, totally unsuited for transformation into a vehicle of scientific expression or secular culture in general. Peter I knew this and made the wise decision that the secular books of the West should be translated into living Russian. This meant that the Russian language had to be rapidly enriched to meet the challenge of the avalanche of new technical terms and expressions contained in the foreign works. It was a difficult task, the more so since most of the available translators were schooled in the Church-Slavic language of the seminaries.[63]

The Russian Council was the first corporate body entrusted with the difficult work of broadening the Russian language so as to keep pace with modern secular thought. Many of the translations issued by the Academy around the middle of the eighteenth century, when the translation activity was so heavy that a new press had to be added, were for light reading, but they did their part in enlarging Russia's reading public. The Russian Council came to an end in 1743. Two years later its most energetic member, Vasilii Trediakovskii, the author of a "new and short method of Russian versification," was appointed a full member of the Academy with the title of professor of rhetoric.[64]

During the 1740's and 1750's more and more young Russian scholars began to assume high positions in the Academy. All of these were the Academy's own products. Typical of this group was Stepan Krasheninnikov, who as a student participated in the Great Northern Expedition. In 1750, after meritorious scientific work, he was appointed professor of botany and natural history. His *Description of the Land of Kamchatka*, unpretentious in both concept and style but richly detailed, has become a classic of Russian scientific literature. It is the earliest survey of the geography, history, and ethnography of Kamchatka and makes a plea for the application of the methods of science to the study of Russia's natural and human resources.[65] Krasheninnikov was a true pioneer in ethnographic fieldwork among Russia's tribal societies. In his book the Kamchadals of Kamchatka received a comprehensive treatment, adorned with occasional comparisons with the tribal phase of Greek culture. The *Description of the Land of Kamchatka* won almost immediate recognition in the scholarly world. In 1760 it appeared in a French translation, somewhat abridged, in 1764 in English, and in 1766 in German.

MIKHAIL LOMONOSOV

A different kind of scholar was represented by S. K. Kotel'nikov and S. Ia. Rumovskii, who may be considered the first Russian disciples of Euler. Although they did not attain the status of important thinkers or experimenters, they were an important link between Euler and the great Russian mathematicians of the nineteenth century. There were only a few other Russian scientists during this period—notably Mikhail Lomonosov, who, with his great intellectual power, his scientific and philosophical erudition, and his wide academic interests, became a symbol of Russia's readiness and determination to deal with scientific questions of the highest order. None of Russia's many great scientists has been subjected to more praise than Lomonosov by those whose writing has been dedicated to the glorification of Russian intellectual achievements. It is his symbolic role more than his actual contributions that explains the continued growth of his reputation. He represented a turning point in the history of science in Russia; more than any other pioneer, he helped to make science a vital part of Russian culture. Regardless of the intrinsic value of his scientific work, he was the first Russian scholar to whom true science was not a mere collection of empirical data but a theoretically unified body of knowledge.

Lomonosov was born in 1711 in a little village in the delta of the Dvina, not far from the White Sea. His father, a well-to-do fisherman and trader of peasant stock, was known in the village as a man of energy, enterprising spirit, and technical competence. In his pursuit of fish and marine mammals, he occasionally sailed as far as the islands of Novaia Zemlia and Spitsbergen. The young Lomonosov accompanied his father on these voyages, learning the habits of the sea and the intricacies of the fishing and hunting trade and preparing himself for the responsibilities of manhood in Russia's cold and treacherous north. We should recall, however, that the north opened Russia's first "window to Europe," and that in the seventeenth and early eighteenth centuries almost all of Russia's foreign trade passed through Arkhangelsk, the only Russian port visited by foreign merchant ships, mostly English. Foreign traders became regular visitors to the north, and some, seeking bigger profits, built factories, docks, and trading posts. Gradually, they moved from Arkhangelsk to other towns in the north. Thanks to their contact with Westerners, the local population broadened their intellectual horizons and acquired new wants and ideals. Documents show that during the first two decades of the eighteenth century all the Lomonosov males could read and write.[66] Isolated from Moscow and central Russia by swamps and forests, the north had escaped Tatar domination and remained comparatively free of feudal institutions. Its sparse population included a comparatively high number of refugees or exiles from the south, many of them religious dissenters or freethinkers. The culture of the north was therefore in constant flux, which encouraged the search for innovations in both techniques and ideas.

Mikhail Lomonosov quickly went beyond religious works in his search for knowledge, discovering for himself such books as Magnitskii's *Arithmetic* and manuals on grammar and versification. At the age of nineteen he was admitted to the Slavic-Greek-Latin Academy in Moscow, where he was to prepare for the priesthood. According to Boris Menshutkin, his most reliable and detailed biographer, this Academy enabled Lomonosov "to make up to some degree what he lacked"—a general education based on training in logic and philosophy.[67] Here he became acquainted with many problems with which contemporary scientists were concerned, although from a Scholastic or Aristotelian standpoint. The classical education that Lomonosov received in the Academy—including excellent Latin —placed him on "the firm ground of European civilization" and helped him to develop habits of precise and methodical treatment of scientific topics. He read with enthusiasm and careful attention the handful of purely scientific books which were donated to the Academy library by a learned priest. When he was awarded a scholarship to the Academic University of St. Petersburg in 1736, he was ready for serious scientific study. Eleven additional students were admitted to the Academic University in the same year; none of them succeeded in achieving recognized academic status.[68] Lomonosov had the good fortune to be sent by the St. Petersburg Academy to the University of Marburg for advanced study in the scientific fields related to metallurgy. It was a broad assignment, which led him into the study of physics and chemistry under the careful guidance of the aging Christian Wolff.

After a sojourn in Germany, where gay social life combined with the systematic search for higher education, Lomonosov returned to St. Petersburg in 1741 to begin a long and highly diversified academic career. It was exactly this diversity which impressed Pushkin many decades later. "Combining unusual will power with an unusual power of comprehension," Pushkin wrote, "Lomonosov embraced all the branches of knowledge. The thirst for learning was the strongest passion of this passion-filled soul. Historian, theoretician, mechanician, chemist, mineralogist, artist, and poet—he scrutinized and fathomed everything."[69] He even found time to finish the catalogue (begun by Gmelin) of the holdings of the Academy's Mineralogical Section.

Lomonosov was well acquainted with the great scientific questions which confronted the leading scholars of his day; he worked with great devotion, yet never quite consistently, on the "natural philosophy" legacy of the giants who produced the "first physical synthesis" in the seventeenth century. In some of his discourses he was naïve and unscholarly, yet in others he showed signs of genius. With great originality he deduced from Daniel Bernoulli's experiments a theory which differs in no substantial regard from the present-day kinetic theory of gases. He has been recognized as the first chemist to entertain serious thoughts about the difference in chemical properties of elements and compounds. He was well aware of the profound significance of Newton's *Principia* even though he was not proficient in mathematics and in some ideas was a Cartesian. Although he was a profound admirer of the Newtonian scientific legacy, he found himself in disagreement with the great English scholar's identification of mass and weight; he also agreed with Euler in refusing to accept the universality of gravitational attraction.[70]

Lomonosov envisaged and worked out a blueprint for the founding of a new science of physical chemistry, which he believed could apply the methods of physics to the study of chemical problems.[71] He was convinced that the power of combined physics and chemistry would be increased if they could be given a solid mathematical foundation. In his "Discourse on the Uses of Chemistry," which he delivered to the Academy in 1751 in the Russian language, he asserted that in his efforts to enter the hidden world of invisible material particles a chemist must also be a physicist and a mathematician.[72]

In his criticism of Boyle's claim that the weight of metals increases on calcination in air, Lomonosov postulated, in a somewhat crude form, the law of the conservation of matter. This had been hinted at by earlier scholars, but it did not receive its masterly formulation and experimental verification until shortly after Lomonosov's death, in Lavoisier's treatises.[73] Menshutkin was rightfully annoyed that Lomonosov's work on this problem went unnoticed not only by Western scholars but also by Russians.[74] Lomonosov formulated an interesting theory of color based on the assumed existence of three kinds of primary material particles and three kinds of particles of ether; different colors, he believed, were the products of different combinations of these six elements. Although it involves certain archaic notions and confuses the physiological and physiochemical properties of color, Lomonosov's theory shows that he was familiar with some of the advanced scientific ideas of his time. He was, for example, acquainted with scientific efforts to fuse the wave theory and the corpuscular theory of light: he himself favored Huygens' wave theory, despite its current unpopularity.[75]

Lomonosov also studied the elasticity of air and the atmospheric electricity; in all these he combined serious scientific thought with remarkable intuitive insight. Some of his ideas later became parts of the larger complexes of scientific theory.[76] In his "Thoughts Concerning the Causes of Heat and Cold," written in 1744, he attacked the widely held view that "hidden qualities" or mysterious essences explained combustion and claimed that heat consists of "an internal circular movement of the combined matter of the warm body."[77] In his refutation of the phlogiston chemistry he was ahead of his time.[78] In his theory of the origin of the earth's strata he anticipated historical geology.

To Lomonosov, science was not simply a collection of facts explaining the universe or small parts of it; nor was it a system of metaphysical principles based solely on sheer intuition and not subject to experimental proof. Experimentally verified and observed facts were to him the substratum of science, the essence of which lay in general truths—the laws of nature. He insisted that theory, as the core of science, feeds on both empirical facts and general hypotheses. "The best method of studying nature is to establish a theory on the basis of observations, and then to correct the observations on the basis of the theory," he wrote in one of his discourses. Science, he believed, must have an experimental basis and philosophical unity. Experiments produce raw data for generalization; philosophy provides intuitive insights into the riddles of nature which open new avenues of research and call for experimental elaboration and verification. When he was accused by a young German scholar of generalizing beyond the limits allowed by his experiments, he retorted that if the physicist were denied the right to generalize and speculate, he would have no way of rising above the routine of mere observing and recording, no opportunity to subject his findings to the critical scrutiny that opens up new worlds of discovery. He asked his overcautious adversary: "Is the chemist, for example, condemned forever to do nothing else but hold the pincers in one hand and the crucible in the other, and to keep his eyes fixed on the coals and their ashes?"

Lomonosov's insatiable intellectual curiosity, reinforced by his self-assigned role as the champion and defender of Russian culture, led him beyond science into the broad field of the humanities. He wrote a book on Russian history, *The Ancient History of Russia*, published in 1766. In this work he attacked an assortment of Western historians who, in his opinion, were guilty of gross inaccuracies in their studies of Russia's past. He was particularly critical of Müller for recording certain events regarded as unfavorable to Russia, and he criticized Müller's and Bayer's unqualified endorsement of the Variag theory of the incipient Russian state.

Lomonosov introduced a new genre of historical writing in Russia, which placed an equal emphasis on the scrutiny of documentary sources and a literary style. He saw history as simultaneously a scholarly study of the national past, an embodiment of ideology, and a form of literary expression. Solov'ev states that Lomonosov "was not prepared to study Russian history, because for him, as well as for his contemporaries, history was less accessible than any other branch of knowledge."[79] Solov'ev gives him credit for a number of intuitive conclusions pertaining to the earliest period of Russian history which were verified by subsequent research; however, he contends that Lomonosov's historical method amounted to little more than "a lifeless rhetorical paraphrasing of chronicles." Kliuchevskii, less critical, is of the opinion that Lomonosov was reflecting the dominant idea of the Elizabethan age when he held that Russia should live by herself and rely on her own natural and intellectual resources.[80]

In the years following Lomonosov's death his historical work was largely forgotten, and it had almost no influence on the first succeeding generation of Russian historians.[81] In the nineteenth century, however, his attacks on the Variag (Norman) theory of the origin of the Russian state were endorsed by several leading Russian historians.

Lomonosov belonged to the small group of scholars and literati who were concerned with the problem of a standardized Russian literary language. Trediakovskii and Kantemir cautioned against drastic deviations from the Church-Slavic language, which, though long the medium of literary expression, was as ill-suited for modern prose and poetry as it was for science. Lomonosov advocated a blending of Church-Slavic with the living language of the common people, and in his own writing he deliberately substituted living words with unambiguous meaning for Church-Slavic terms with conflicting and unclear meanings.[82] With these efforts, Lomonosov inaugurated the epoch of Russian pseudoclassicism, as Belinskii named it. This linguistic hybrid proved in the end to be too artificial to last as an effective means of expression; no eighteenth-century writer could "breathe life into the dead Lomonosovian forms."[83]

If some of Lomonosov's enthusiasms were short-lived, the value of his contribution to the development of scientific thought in Russia can hardly be exaggerated. None of his eighteenth-century compatriots pleaded more passionately and worked with more dedication for the training of Russia's own scholars than Lomonosov. He made an earnest, if unsuccessful, effort to improve the Academic University, and he played a leading role in the founding of Moscow University in 1755. He strove to create a wider interest in science by translating scientific classics into Russian. In the preface to his abridged translation of Wolff's treatise on experimental physics he declared to his countrymen that "the centuries of barbarism" were over and that "we live in an age in which science, after its restoration in Europe, is growing and making progress."[84] He noted that Peter I had been proved correct in his prediction that "our expansive state would provide a home for the higher sciences and that these would be accepted by the Russian people with love and devotion." He inaugurated public lectures on the natural sciences in the Academy. In 1745, after his first lecture, the Senate authorized him to give a series of Friday afternoon lectures, these to be announced in the Cadets' Corps, the Main Office of Artillery and Fortifications, and the Medical Office. The *St. Petersburg Gazette* reported that the lectures were attended by many aristocrats and persons close to the imperial court. Lomonosov's belief in the eighteenth century as a century of free and experimental inquiry became a popular theme for public speeches by other noted Russian scholars of the time, such as Krasheninnikov, Kotel'nikov, and Rumovskii.

Although Lomonosov was a religious man, he subscribed without reservation to rationalist philosophy. He was able to accept the spiritual legacy of Orthodoxy, yet at the same time dedicate his scholarly studies and poetry to the affirmation of the superior value of scientific wisdom. In defending before his skeptical countrymen the scientific observation of the passage of Venus over the sun's disk in 1761, he cited the Bible, but he also quoted passages from the history of science and Basil the Great. He frequently lamented the deeply embedded Russian disdain for science and took every opportunity to enlighten his countrymen in the spirit of modern scientific inquiry. He claimed that nature in its infinite richness provided ample room for both science and religion: whereas the task of the former was to illuminate divine wisdom, the task of the latter was to understand the colossal manifestations of divine will.[85] He attacked the priests who used the pulpit for scathing condemnations of science, chiefly on the ground that they stepped beyond religion into an area in which they lacked competence. In the spirit of early Protestantism, Lomonosov asserted that "all prudent and good persons are obliged to search for methods to enable them to explain and avert all so-called conflict between science and religion." He went so far as to claim that this advice came from Basil the Great, "the wise teacher of our Orthodox Church."[86] Actually, Lomonosov reinterpreted the theology and philosophy of Orthodoxy to bring them into harmony with contemporary intellectual developments, showing here, as in many of his scientific ideas, an attitude well ahead of his time.

During the first decades of the Academy's existence a variety of reasons combined to keep the study of science in the Academy isolated from all consideration of the practical problems of the country. One of the reasons for this isolation was, of course, the generally distrustful attitude of the government. But there were other reasons, including the inadequacy of the Academy's equipment for studying problems of a nontheoretical nature and the lack of interest in such problems on the part of the overwhelmingly foreign Academy membership. Lomonosov was the first established scholar to petition against the Academy's failure "to disseminate scientific knowledge among the young people," and against its preoccupation "with alien sciences which are of no use to the Russian Empire."[87] Although much of his own scientific work was in the realm of abstract principles of chemistry and physics, he pleaded for a scientific study of the country's natural resources, and he personally inquired into the feasibility of opening a trade route across the Arctic Ocean.[88] He set up Russia's first chemical laboratory and even established a workshop for the production of porcelain. In his paper "Concerning the Conservation and Increase of the Russian People" he raised a scholarly voice against the country's main enemies: ignorance (particularly in sanitation), excessive physical work demanded from enserfed peasants by the Church and the feudal lords, and antiquated customs (he condemned, for example, the marriage of young girls by older men).[89] He fought valiantly, if sometimes inconsistently, to ensure the Academy a vital and honored place in the system of government institutions, seeking in particular official recognition of the cultural importance of science and a precise determination of the social status of the scholar.

Like Peter I, Lomonosov saw in scientific pursuits not only a source of cultural progress but also a powerful means of acquiring for Russia an honorable place in the family of nations. He emphasized Peter's belief in science as an essential condition for the introduction of "just laws, efficient courts, and honest mores."[90] "The honor of the Russian people," he said, "demands that they apply their intellectual abilities to scientific pursuits and other important activities."[91] His own efforts to this end were considerable: he was a fountain of new knowledge, an effective teacher, a champion of secular education, and an outstanding contributor to the development of the Russian scientific terminology.

Lomonosov was a man of fiery temperament, who traveled from field to field looking for skirmishes. His continual battles brought him enemies and distracted him from systematic work in natural science, the field in which he was especially trained and for which he showed remarkable talent. His life was a story of feuds with all comers. He was a thorn in the side of the Academy's German majority, which he fought, sometimes unjustifiably, with great fervor. Once he served a jail term as a result of a petition of five foreign colleagues: he was accused of taking a disrespectful attitude toward discussions at scientific meetings. Despite the bitterness of his feuds, however, he counted some of the Germans among his dearest friends.

Somewhat surprisingly, Lomonosov made no serious effort to befriend Russian scholars associated with the Academy, although here he could have expected to find his natural allies, particularly since his avowed aim was to make the Academy a national Russian institution. He was a bitter foe of Trediakovskii, who shared with him the honor of being the first Russian Academician. Another adversary was Rumovskii, who studied under Euler in Berlin and later, as a member of the Academy, played a leading role in developing Russia's system of higher education. Rumovskii thought Lomonosov lacked scientific depth: in two letters to Euler he writes with unrestrained irony about Lomonosov's inventions.[92] Scholars like Krasheninnikov, Kotel'nikov, and A. P. Protasov managed to avoid any sponsorship that Lomonosov could have offered them.[93]

When Lomonosov died in 1765, no *éloge* was read in his honor. Six months after his death, Andrei Shuvalov published, in Paris, a small book containing his ode to Lomonosov and a French translation of Lomonosov's ode, "Morning Meditations About Divine Majesty." Shuvalov's ode describes Lomonosov as "the Homer of the North" and glorifies his heroic efforts to transform a "primitive country" into a land of "enlightened reason." The first biography of Lomonosov, prepared under the auspices of the Academy, appeared as an introduction to his collected works published in 1784. The biography contains numerous previously unrecorded details about Lomonosov's life and literary efforts, but it says little about his scientific work.

Today, Lomonosov has in the Soviet Union the stature of a Leonardo *the Myth* da Vinci, a Descartes, or a Newton. Soviet historians say that, like Leonardo, Lomonosov was a universal man who explored the whole gamut of human endeavor, and that, like Galileo and Newton, he possessed the genius of being able to grasp the essentials of some of the great mysteries of nature. This appraisal is more a summation of the ringing encomiums that successive generations of his countrymen have lavished upon him than an impartial assessment of his scientific contributions. Lomonosov was a great man of knowledge; as a legend embodying much social significance he has become even greater. In point of fact, he has acquired this eminence slowly. In his own time, Lomonosov seemed to be the only person to consider himself a genius: more than once he commented scornfully on the pedestrian nature of his fellow Academicians' scientific work, contrasting it unfavorably with his own intellectual achievements. There is no question that he stood head and shoulders above most of his colleagues, but it should be remembered that during the 1740's and 1750's the Academy had lost most of its illustrious members. Men like Delisle, Euler, and Gmelin were gone, their chairs either vacant or occupied by men of secondary, and sometimes doubtful, scholarly standing. Many of these, not surprisingly, hated Lomonosov. Trediakovskii's biting ode "Self-Glorifier" was thought by most contemporaries to have been addressed to Lomonosov.[94] The poet A. P. Sumarokov, jealous of Lomonosov's ties with persons influential at court and angered by his arrogance, wrote a whole series of parodies of his literary works.

Unappreciated by his colleagues, and extremely sensitive to the least criticism of his work, Lomonosov sought connections with Russian aristocrats in high places who could help him to secure honorary membership in foreign academies. With the assistance of Count Mikhail Vorontsov he was elected a member of the Bologna Academy, but his appeal to Ivan Shuvalov to recommend him to the Paris Académie des Sciences for honorary membership brought no favorable result. However, he needed no political recommendations for admittance to the Stockholm Academy of Sciences, which elected him an honorary member in recognition of his study of the formation of icebergs in the northern seas. This study, written in Latin, was issued first in a Swedish translation and shortly thereafter in German and Russian translations.

Lomonosov's most immediate praise came from the young Russian professors of the newly founded Moscow University—but it was Lomonosov the poet and grammarian whom they applauded. Lacking the opportunity to hear Lomonosov deliver his papers at Academic meetings, or even to read them, since some of the most important ones remained unpublished until more than a century after his death, these young professors were almost entirely ignorant of Lomonosov's scientific work. Within the first twenty-two years of its founding in 1775, Moscow University published three volumes of Lomonosov's studies, thus doing a great deal to carry his name beyond the scientific centers to the educated public.

During the period of intellectual fermentation stimulated by Catherine II's flirtation with the philosophy of the Enlightenment, the Lomonosov legend began to crystallize. Radishchev, at the end of the eighteenth century, tried to do something to check it, for it threatened to grow out of all proportion. He credited Lomonosov with significant contributions to versification, particularly to the codification of the rules of "Russian prosody based on the harmony of our tongue," but he pointed out the uselessness of his work in rhetoric and the inferiority of his historiographic scholarship in comparison with that of Tacitus, Raynal, and Robertson.[95] Lomonosov's work in chemistry was, he thought, of only secondary importance. "Though this science fascinated him," Radishchev said, "though he spent many days of his life in the investigation of the truths of nature, his course was that of a follower. He walked on ways previously opened up, and in the endless riches of nature he did not find the smallest blade of grass that better eyes than his had not seen, nor did he find any more primitive sources of matter than his predecessors had discovered."[96] Radishchev saw Lomonosov's greatness not in his intellectual achievement but in his successful opening of new vistas in the arts and sciences. In this regard he likened him to Bacon, who made no additions to scientific knowledge but who showed "how to advance learning."[97] What Radishchev thought of Lomonosov as a scientist is not today of any great significance, and we must remember that he did not have access to Lomonosov's complete scientific papers, but his opinion at the time helped to clarify Lomonosov's true place in the history of Russian science. As an opener of vistas, even with few direct disciples, Lomonosov was a man of gigantic stature; he showed in an impressive fashion that science is the *sine qua non* of modern civilization, that scientists are social agents of vital importance, and that the pursuit of science must occupy an honorable place in Russian culture. Indeed, it was largely because he was so far ahead of his time that his direct followers were so exceedingly few.

Pushkin agreed with Radishchev in his low opinion of Lomonosov's poetry, and he no doubt underestimated Lomonosov's work in chemistry, physics, and geology, but he was impressed with the magnitude of his knowledge, his quest for learning, and his devotion to the spread of scientific knowledge among Russian youth. He thought it was wrong to describe Lomonosov as a Russian Bacon. He was a "Russian Lomonosov" —nothing else. Pushkin was right. He recognized that Lomonosov could be justly appraised not in terms of what he had given in the way of original thought but in terms of how he had helped to advance the spirit of science. He was particularly impressed with Lomonosov's ability to reach intellectual heights quite beyond his contemporaries. "Lomonosov was a great

[margin note: Pushkin's appraisal.]

man," Pushkin wrote. "During the interval between Peter I and Catherine II he was the only indigenous champion of enlightenment. He built our first university. One may rightly say that he *was* our first university."[98]

SCHOLARSHIP OUTSIDE THE ACADEMY

During the long period between Peter I and Catherine II, the Academy fought to ensure a respectable and functional place for itself in the Russian polity. By the time of Catherine II's ascent to the throne in 1762 this struggle had ended. For its victory the Academy was indebted to several leaders of science whose careers were independent of the Academy. These men were limited in scientific training, but they were intelligent, dedicated to secular knowledge, and imbued with Peter the Great's scientific spirit and enthusiasm for learning. Two of them—Antiokh Kantemir and Vasilii Tatishchev—deserve special attention.

Kantemir (1708–44) was among the first group of students in the Academic University, where he attended virtually all the lectures given by the most eminent professors. His proficiency in algebra was noted by his contemporaries. His intellectual contributions were made chiefly in translation, writing, and diplomacy. After a few rather experimental translations of minor works, he produced a full translation into Russian of Fontenelle's *Conversations on the Plurality of Worlds*. The translation was completed in 1730, but owing to many difficulties with Church censors, its publication was delayed for ten years. Fontenelle's work, originally published in 1686, was a skillful attempt to draw a comprehensive picture of the heavens on the basis of pre-Newtonian science (its first appearance predated Newton's *Principia* by one year). It contained impressive, if occasionally inaccurate, material on the historical growth of astronomy and its relationship to the neighboring branches of natural science. It was notable as being one of the first successful efforts to popularize science by the use of a vivid style and ingenious expository techniques, and as its author Fontenelle may rightfully be called the man who provided the strongest link between the scientists of the seventeenth century and the *philosophes* of the Enlightenment. Kantemir was not satisfied with merely translating Fontenelle's work; he also wrote an Introduction in which he extolled the virtues and power of scientific knowledge, and he added numerous explanatory notes to the text. For example, in explaining the term "philosophy," he informed his readers that it was a generic term for a combination of logic, ethics, physics, and metaphysics, and he went on to give a simple description of the contents of each of these disciplines. One of the important incidental results of this translation was the enrichment of Russian scientific terminology; many terms introduced by Kantemir are still in use more than two centuries later.

Kantemir was also a writer of satires, in several of which he tackled the question of the cultural significance of science. His Satire I, published eighteen years after his death, was directed against persons who disparaged science. It is a biting attack on groups—lay and ecclesiastical—who had vested interests in ignorance and tried to perpetuate it by leading concerted campaigns against the scholars of the St. Petersburg Academy. Kantemir shows a profound distaste for the social principle which placed the reins of government in the hands of hereditary aristocracy, and he warns that Russian scholarship will continue to lag so long as learning is not recognized as an important means of elevating society. Satire I was in a way Kantemir's expression of the secular philosophy defined in the Ecclesiastical Regulation of Peter I and in the sermons of Feofan Prokopovich; written in the last days of the reign of Peter II, it was also a literary rebellion against the mounting social forces—supported by the Church—that were bent on uprooting the modern ideas instituted by the reforms of Peter the Great.[99] Obviously, it did not have an easy time with the censors. In "Poem IV" (1735), dedicated to "the glorification of science," Kantemir makes an interesting effort to delineate the historical course of scientific growth.[100]

As a diplomat, first in London (1732–38) and then in Paris (1738–44), Kantemir maintained extensive correspondence with various officials and members of the St. Petersburg Academy of Sciences and was of service to the learned society in numerous ways.[101] He helped the Academy to acquire a number of astronomical instruments, and it was chiefly on his recommendation that the Academy elected to honorary membership Hans Sloane, who succeeded Newton as president of the Royal Society of London. Also on his recommendation, Maupertuis, the great mathematician-philosopher who was a member of the Paris Académie des Sciences and subsequently president of the Berlin Academy, was named an active honorary member of the St. Petersburg Academy. Kantemir corresponded with Euler and Voltaire, and he took great pride in ensuring the prompt delivery to St. Petersburg of all the publications of the Paris Académie des Sciences.

Vasilii Tatishchev was easily the greatest non-Academic Russian scholar of this period, and of particular importance because he served as an intellectual link between the era of Peter the Great and the first succeeding generation. In a sense, he symbolized the dilemmas and tribulations of Russian scholars who did not have direct access to Western tutelage. He was aware of the organization and scholarly interests of the Academy and had a certain acquaintance with some of its members, but he achieved his own intellectual stature outside its jurisdiction and without its guidance.

Tatishchev came from a poor family, which, owing to some misfortune in the distant past, had fallen from the highest ranks of the aristocracy. During the first decades of the eighteenth century he was a military officer and took part in several major wars. Subsequently he traveled in Western Europe in the service of the government, finally achieving the post of chief administrator of the Ural mines. In this capacity, and with unfortunately premature hopes, he opened several mining schools. During this phase of his career he was absorbed in the study of the natural sciences, and he acquired a considerable library in these disciplines. His administrative work took him to various parts of the country and brought him into contact with representatives of many ethnic and social groups, and these experiences, supported by his unusually wide reading, led him to develop a rationalist point of view. He became convinced that if Russia was ever to pull itself out of the doldrums of ignorance and cultural stagnation, it must take the path of enlightenment. In the growth of science from the achievements of the philosophers of ancient Greece to the successes of the modern natural scientists of England and France he saw the most convincing index of cultural progress. Tatishchev's familiarity with both ancient and modern scientific ideas was proof that the Academy was not the only channel through which theoretical knowledge about the universe had begun to filter into Russia.

Even as a mining administrator, Tatishchev was keenly interested in Russian history, ethnography, and geography, and he subsequently became a historian and social scientist. He was fully aware of the importance of historical documents and undertook to collect as many ancient chronicles and legal acts as he could. Though he still held the physical sciences in high esteem, now he insisted that the Russians must first of all concentrate on a systematic study of their history and on careful and thorough surveys of the natural and human resources of their country. History became the basis of the whole pattern of enlightenment. As Solov'ev noted: "According to Tatishchev, neither the theologian nor the jurist, the physician, the administrator, the diplomat, or the military commander can successfully perform his duties without a knowledge of history."[102]

Following the philosophy of Peter the Great and Feofan Prokopovich,

Tatishchev stuck firmly and uncompromisingly to the idea of the compatibility of science and religion. In his remarkable "Conversations About the Usefulness of Science and Schools," he insisted on the indispensability of science for religion.[103] Divine omniscience, he argued, was a repository of all wisdom; man's share in this wisdom does not come as a gift but as a result of diligence and search. Rudiments of science had reached medieval Russia only to be suppressed by an alliance of the Tatar conquerors and the Church hierarchs, and it was the Church that was chiefly to blame for the backwardness of contemporary Russia. Like Iurii Krizhanich in the preceding century, he contended that ignorance, rather than positive knowledge, was the fertile ground in which heretical ideas grew.

As an adherent of rationalism, Tatishchev emphasized that history should be a careful and critical scrutiny of the past and a survey of the progressive victories of positive knowledge over superstition and ignorance. To him "science" was a broad term, covering the practical arts, rationalist philosophy, theoretical knowledge of nature, empirical surveys of the natural resources beneficial to man, and even certain spheres of thought intrinsically incompatible with the best interests of human society. He enumerated five distinct categories of sciences: the "indispensable sciences," which include philology, home economics, natural, divine, and civil law, logic, and theology; the "useful sciences," which include grammar, oratory, foreign languages, mathematics, physics, and chemistry; the "entertaining sciences," those of poetry, music, dancing, horseback riding, and painting; the "useless sciences" (most of which are likely to contain false information), which include astrology, physiognomy, chiromancy, and alchemy; and the "harmful sciences," comprising all sorts of divination and sorcery. He emphasized that his classification was not absolute and that social stratification introduced an element of relativity; thus, for example, he considered pneumatology indispensable for theologians, useful for philosophers, and totally without value for historians and politicians. Tatishchev did not apply his wide definition of science in any particular way, and he continued to evaluate science in terms of positive knowledge about nature and human society. Man's strength, after all, was based on his rational faculties rather than on his submissive reliance on the supernatural.

Tatishchev mixed with the country's intellectual elite. One of his intimate friends was the learned Feofan Prokopovich, whom he describes in his major historical work as a man so thoroughly versed in "the new philosophy of science and theology" that he was without peer in the history of Russian culture.[104] The two shared an unreserved admiration for Peter's dictum that education of the people should be one of the leading tasks of the state, and also one over which it should have undivided control. Like Peter the Great, Tatishchev was concerned almost exclusively with the education of the nobility, and, as if apologizing for the Tsar, he stressed that freedom was not a necessary condition of scientific growth. In his "Conversations," written in the form of a dialogue, he puts himself the question whether it is true that freedom is the basic condition for the growth of science. His answer is "No!" If freedom is basic, he argues, then the Lapps and the Tatars, who enjoy "perfect freedom," should have the most advanced science. "And thus we see," he goes on, "that freedom is not an essential and basic condition for the growth of science; the care and diligence of government authorities are the most important conditions for this development."[105] In his major work, *The History of Russia Since the Earliest Times,* he is simultaneously a champion of autocracy, as the best form of government for his country, and science, as the indispensable source of modern enlightenment.[106] Tatishchev was, at the same time, a Christian with deep-seated convictions and a vociferous foe of hypocritical teachings in religious schools.

Tatishchev did not quarrel with the St. Petersburg Academy of Sciences, yet he resented the staggering contrast between its lofty theoretical aspirations and the low educational level of Russia's social elite. He thought that this apparent abyss could best be bridged by the publication of historical, geographical, and legal knowledge in the Russian language. For this purpose he undertook to write Russia's first *Lexicon,* which he succeeded in completing to the letter K. The *Lexicon* describes, with uneven accuracy, items from "the governmental, administrative, and social life of contemporary Russia; historical, geographical, and ethnographic names and titles; as well as items from archaeology and the arts."[107] There is considerable charm in many of the explanations drawn from Tatishchev's own experiences.

Tatishchev submitted his *History of Russia Since the Earliest Times* to the Academy in 1739. It is a monumental work, on which he labored for some twenty years, and it represents the first attempt to write a comprehensive and systematic survey of Russian history on the basis of a critical examination and interpretation of historical documents. In truth, it is not a history of the conventional sort: Tatishchev was concerned in the main with identifying the proper field of Russian history and its basic documentary sources, and the *History* is almost exclusively limited to a survey of the major Russian chronicles (some now lost) and excerpts from foreign

works on the ancient peoples of Eastern Europe. In a lengthy Introduction, he reveals his attitude toward science, religion, and politics, as well
as his familiarity with such great European philosophers as Descartes,
Locke, and Wolff and such political thinkers as Pufendorf, Grotius, and
Machiavelli.

For unrecorded reasons, the *History* was not published during Tatishchev's lifetime; Volumes I–IV were issued between 1768 and 1784, and
Volume V finally appeared in 1848.[108] It may be inferred with good cause
that Tatishchev's contemporaries considered this great work dangerous to
"good habits of society." The long suppression may have been the price
Tatishchev paid for his attacks on the hypocrisy of the teachers of religious
schools,[109] but it is to be noted that his frequent criticism of the role of
foreigners in Russia did not earn him many friends in the Academy—
which, of course, had enough influence to delay the publication.

Although it was unpublished, Tatishchev's voluminous manuscript did
not lie buried in the Academy archives; on the contrary, it was made use
of by many contemporaries, including scholars of the caliber of Müller
and Lomonosov. August Schlözer learned his basic lessons in Russian
history from Tatishchev's work, and Ivan Boltin considered it the most
reliable collection of historical documents.[110]

The *History* has been widely acclaimed by leading historians of succeeding generations. Solov'ev states that modern historians sharpened their
methodological tools by criticizing Tatishchev's scholarship, and that nineteenth-century Russian historiography bore out many of his conclusions.
Solov'ev makes it clear that Tatishchev's contributions in the fields of legal
history and geography were as impressive as those in political history.[111]
According to A. N. Pypin, Tatishchev was the first Russian scholar to introduce the methods of science into historical inquiry by combining a critical examination of the "complex masses of facts" and the presentation of
data in terms of "rational categories."[112] K. N. Bestuzhev-Riumin says
that Tatishchev provided an early model for the careful gathering of historical sources and for the blending of historical studies with various allied
sciences. The same author asserts that although Tatishchev's talents did
not reach the magnificent proportions of Lomonosov's, his contributions
were equally important in the history of Russian scientific thought. "The
natural scientist Lomonosov strove to give natural science general philosophical unity; the historian and popular writer Tatishchev strove on his
part to discover the general principles of man's community life and his
morality."[113] A modern Soviet specialist in historiography expresses the

view shared by his colleagues when he says that Tatishchev was "the first Russian historian in the scientific sense."[114]

Tatishchev died in 1750. He spent the last years of his life in a small village near Moscow, where, as on several previous occasions, he was under court trial for his alleged advocacy of ideas inimical to "the good habits of society." Moments before his death he heard the news of his acquittal.

His biographer, Nil Popov, sums up his historical role in these words: "For us Tatishchev is in many respects a significant phenomenon of his time. . . . He was original in his religious and political convictions, which did not suit the authorities. He was industrious and alert in every position he occupied. Industry and diligence were an outstanding feature of his epoch, for only after the time of Peter's reforms did work, especially intellectual work, begin to emerge as a value recognized by all estates of Russian society."[115] Tatishchev, we may add, symbolized the inner contradiction that characterized his age—an age that was in a way simultaneously aware of the virtues of positive knowledge and the latent dangers of enlightenment to the state, the essence of whose power was dependent on the continued isolation of its subjects from the foundations of modern secular wisdom.

PART II

SCIENCE IN THE AGE OF REASON

CHAPTER FOUR

Science, Enlightenment, and Absolutism

CHANGES IN SOCIAL STRUCTURE AND EDUCATIONAL IDEALS

A fierce ideological conflict dominated Russian society during the last three-quarters of the eighteenth century. The forces pressing for a return to the ways of pre-Petrine Russia gave ground grudgingly before the onslaughts of Peter's intellectual heirs, who championed an even more intensive emulation of the cultural standards of Western Europe. But although the country's social and economic structure changed exceedingly slowly, the effects of the cumulative transformation were clearly discernible before the end of the century.

By 1800 Russia was the most populous state in Europe. From nineteen or twenty million in 1762, the population grew to thirty-four million by 1796. This growth, occurring in the face of protracted wars, occasional famines, and rampant plagues, was primarily due to imperial expansion. Russian domination over the Chukchi territory in northeastern Asia was confirmed. Lithuania and the last remnants of the Ukraine were also absorbed into the Empire, and, after the third partition of Poland in 1795, the Russian boundary stretched westward beyond Byelorussia. In the south, the Crimea was acquired.

Despite these rich accumulations, economic growth remained slow. There was almost no urbanization: in 1800 only three per cent of the people lived in urban communities. In 1765 the country had less than 40,000 workers in establishments roughly classified as industrial. The increased output of basic mineral ores contributed more to the expanding of foreign trade than to fostering domestic industry, although some industrial branches did show tangible progress. At the same time, however, the economic power of the state was further broadened; state income rose from sixteen million rubles in 1762 to over sixty-eight million rubles in 1798.

During the second half of the eighteenth century, Russian society was characterized by the consolidation of estates and a minimum of vertical mobility. At the bottom, the peasant was further depressed by the rapid

loss of a few residual freedoms. Serfdom became a rigid institution in the
midst of a complex legal matrix. In 1760 Elizabeth, eager to settle Siberia,
authorized the gentry to exile rebellious serfs permanently to the distant
eastern lands. Six years later Catherine II empowered the gentry to impose
penal servitude on disobedient serfs. Indeed, during the reign of Catherine
II, serfdom came to be identified with the unqualified dependence of serfs
on their masters. At the same time that the peasants were made wholly the
private property of the landed gentry, the gentry themselves were relieved
of their traditional obligatory service to the state.

By means of large donations of land and "state peasants" to her favorites,
Catherine II created a "super-elite," a new and powerful class within the
ranks of the traditional aristocracy. The majority of Russian aristocrats,
however, gained nothing from their conversion into an economically and
politically idle estate. They acquired a good many local administrative positions, but their "political life" was generally confined to ludicrous conflicts
between individual lineages and a bizarre participation in meaningless local
elections. The drastic difference between rural and urban living split the
aristocracy into two sharply distinct groups, each of which was in turn
divided into upper, middle, and lower layers. The country aristocracy,
which comprised the majority, was particularly opposed to economic and
social change. The appalling ignorance of this privileged class was so
paradoxical that it attracted the attention of many contemporary travelers
from the West.[1]

The enserfed peasants did not accept the loss of their freedom without
protest. In the second half of the eighteenth century, outbursts of unrest
began to assume relatively large proportions. In the seventeenth century
there had been occasional peasant uprisings in protest against injustices
committed by military governors (*voevody*), but in the eighteenth century
the peasant rebellions took on a class character.

The technical inability of the aristocracy to cope with the growing
complexity of state administration and the full isolation of the peasantry
from all opportunities for enlightenment came to be the standard conditions of Russian life. The peasants continued to share the hostility of the
gentry toward formal education, but they had far less chance than their
lords to manifest this hostility in any positive way, since the state made no
provision for their education. George Macartney, who was the British
envoy to St. Petersburg from 1764 to 1767, wrote that in their ignorance
the Russian gentry were unsurpassed in Europe and that the Russian

government found it more difficult to civilize the aristocrats than the peasants.[2]

A powerful satire written by the Russian playwright Denis Fonvizin in the late 1760's excoriated the gentry's ignorance and their almost total lack of interest in formal education in biting and unmistakable terms.[3] N. M. Karamzin, writing at the beginning of the nineteenth century, maintained that educational ambition was lacking primarily because "educated persons up to now have had few advantages, and a very limited sphere of activity."[4] The ideology of which they were the official representatives placed no premium on enlightenment. And yet the need of the unusually complex state machinery for competent administrators, technicians, and military men grew increasingly desperate. → *gentry vs. bureaucracy.*

The gentry's unwillingness to acquire a university education made it imperative for the government to rely more and more on the middle strata. Catherine hoped that accelerated urbanization would lead to the emergence of a third estate dominated by the urban artisan-commercial population. She envisaged this group as the motive force in her schemes to improve national welfare and education. An educated middle class was expected to solve feudalism's gravest dilemma by enabling the state to employ a sufficient number of educated persons to handle the essential functions while preserving the traditional cultural backwardness of serfdom and, generally, the social status quo. The enlightened and forward-looking I. I. Betskoi bemoaned the absence of a third, or middle, estate in Russia. He was convinced that Russia would be unable to build an adequate educational system so long as it lacked such an estate.[5] Catherine also had Diderot's word that "the lower classes" were the real source of future leaders in sciences and the arts.[6] *hope for a 3rd estate*

No society can assure effective conditions for scientific development unless it possesses special institutions dedicated to the transmission of knowledge and to the training of individuals to become searchers after new knowledge. Nor can a society develop educational institutions unless a need for them is profoundly felt by at least one of its major social classes. In eighteenth-century Russia no class or estate felt this need, despite the clear desire of the state for competent civil servants. The desire had a primarily military background, it is true, but it was nonetheless broad in its range and pressing in its urgency. It was met in part by the employment of trained foreigners, but this was in most respects unsatisfactory. The Russian governments of the eighteenth century considered it increasingly urgent to develop adequate educational facilities and to root out deeply embedded prejudices against formal education. In the face of tradition, the state was obliged to carry out its educational policies through a method of trial and error, and almost invariably the results were pitifully small.

Most of the attempts of the immediate successors of Peter I to recruit students for the Academic University and Gymnasium were fruitless. By granting stipends to children of the lower and middle gentry, the government managed to keep the two military schools in operation, but scientific and technical education, so dear to Peter I, was more and more neglected in favor of a new educational fashion patterned on the manners of the European aristocracy.

The few existing schools in Russia were not touched by the new fashion. Indeed, for a long time it was followed chiefly by private tutors, usually foreigners, employed in aristocratic homes. The new education was limited to *belles lettres,* quasi-philosophical and moralistic treatises, and private theatricals. Largely alien to the needs of the state and society at large, it was dedicated purely to the ephemeral interests of a small part of the aristocracy.

The emergence of the new educational philosophy coincided with the switch from German to French as the paramount influence on the cultural life of Russia's leading cities. The switch, which was gradual, began during the reign of Peter I when French nationals, representing all walks of life, began to settle in Russia in increasing numbers—engineers, military experts, merchants, teachers, "adventurers of all sorts."[7] This influx swelled rapidly during the reign of the queens. When diplomatic relations were re-established between France and Russia in 1756, the French ambassador was surprised to find that he was not the only representative of his country in St. Petersburg—indeed, he wrote with distaste, there were "swarms of Frenchmen, who, after some tussle with the law in Paris, have infested the northern region." Twenty years later a French observer noted that Frenchmen "are pouring into Russia like insects into warm lands, and small Russian newspapers are much cheered by the continual arrival of adventurers who are as rich in hopes as they are poor in earthly possessions."[8]

A Swiss national, appointed an instructor in the St. Petersburg Artillery School in 1786, made this observation: "Since colonies of various nationalities live in St. Petersburg, the manners and customs of the local population are highly diverse. It is difficult to know which style of life is predominant. The French language provides a bond which brings together various national groups, but other languages are also spoken. At multinational gatherings communication is usually carried on in Russian, French, and German, but one should not be surprised to hear the Greeks, Italians, English, Dutch, and Asiatics speaking in their own languages.

"The Germans in St. Petersburg are artisans, mostly tailors and shoe-makers; the English are saddlers and merchants; the Italians are architects, singers, and purveyors of paintings; but it is difficult to say what the French are. Most of them change their callings annually; they arrive as lackeys, work as teachers, and then become counselors; they are actors, tutors, merchants, musicians, officers."[9]

It is not difficult to explain why the French influence became dominant in Russia during the second half of the eighteenth century. Used as the *langue du haut monde* of St. Petersburg, the French language opened the gates to wider French cultural influence. Russian diplomats and aristo-cratic travelers had ample opportunity to discover that French was the language of Western Europe's high society. The arrival in Russia of many French nationals, representing the entire vocational spectrum, also greatly contributed to the eventual dominance of French influence. Following the example of the Court, Russian aristocrats at all levels, with a new abun-dance of leisure, were charmed by the urbanity of French culture. France had acquired a reputation throughout the world as "the country of perfect *politesse,* supreme elegance, and gentility of manners."[10] In addition, French culture, as exported to Russia, offered something that the Russian urban gentry was delighted to find. The Swiss teacher in the Artillery School puts it this way: "Under such climatic conditions as are found in St. Petersburg, where there are only several weeks of nice weather, and under such a government as that of Russia, which does not encourage in-terest in politics, ethics, and literature, social pleasures are limited and home entertainment has become a great art. Splendor and exquisite comfort, luxury and aristocratic taste, abundance of food and refinement of table manners, lightness and frivolity of conversation provide a compensation to a gay person for the limitations imposed on his body and soul by nature and the government. Dancing and playing follow each other in succession: every day can be a holiday."[11]

The new emphasis on polished manners, conversational charm, and literary sophistication greatly heightened the demand for teachers of aristo-cratic youth and provided them with enviable remuneration. The demand was so great that even former lackeys and hairdressers found employment as teachers in aristocratic homes.[12] This was particularly true during the initial phase of intensive French influence—that is, during the middle years of Elizabeth's reign. The turning point came with the government decree of May 5, 1757, which ordered that henceforth all foreigners interested in private teaching be required to pass qualifying examinations administered by the St. Petersburg Academy of Sciences and Moscow University.[13]

The Catherinean period witnessed the appearance of the first generation of educated noblemen, who, unlike their immediate predecessors, were sufficiently worldly to see the difference between a tailor and a trained teacher. Many frivolities still passed as true education, but the 1780's could boast of a small group of genuinely enlightened gentry: the *petit-maître* of the Elizabethan period was now replaced by an *homme des lettres,* who was likely to be a "freethinker, a Mason, or a Voltairean."[14]

Typical of this relatively tiny group was Catherine II herself. Catherine, who read mainly light novels as a young girl, accidentally discovered the works of Voltaire and thereby developed a genuine thirst for humanistic knowledge. Soon she had struggled through the four volumes of Bayle's philosophical dictionary and had read Tacitus' *Annals* and Montesquieu's *The Spirit of Laws.*[15] After she had become the ruler of Russia she corresponded with Voltaire, D'Alembert, and Diderot as well as other leading figures of the Enlightenment. French *philosophes* were then putting the finishing touches on a new system which taught that "the education of man begins at birth" and that the acquisition of positive knowledge must be accompanied by a reaffirmation of moral principles. Rousseau spoke for his age when he asserted that the most basic and thorny problem of moral life was how to harness educational techniques so as to produce moral beings and how "to resolve the conflict between . . . [man's] moral ends and his physical nature with its amoral passions."[16] Catherine even had a passing fancy for the work of Buffon. She read his chief production, the *Natural History,* and was sufficiently impressed by it, even though Buffon hinted at a common origin for men and apes, to appoint an Academic commission to translate this monumental work into Russian. In return, Buffon sent the Russian Empress a flattering letter in which he prophesied that the time would come when Russia would save European culture from decadence.[17]

Another graphic example of the influence of humanistic education is provided by Aleksandr Vorontsov, who belonged to one of the most illustrious families of the high aristocracy. In describing his own childhood, he reported: "Our father took us regularly to the court theater, where French comedies were performed two times every week. I remember this experience because it helped us develop a positive inclination toward reading and literature. My father ordered from Holland a well-selected library that contained the works of Voltaire, Racine, Corneille, Boileau, and other French writers. Among these books was also a collection of almost a hundred volumes of the journal *The Key for the Understanding of European Governments*, published since 1700. I remember this collection because it was from it that I learned about the most interesting and most important events that had taken place in Russia after 1700. This publication helped me to develop an inclination toward history and politics."[18]

A NATIONAL UNIVERSITY

Up to the 1760's, the so-called cultural activities of the French-imitating Russian aristocracy were mainly limited to the "artistic decorations of life" —theater and spectacles, with a smattering of interest in literature and philosophy and no really serious educational pretensions. This education was, of course, mainly private, and mainly limited to the arts and the humanities, to philosophy, and to citizenship. It was quite divorced from the technical requirements of the country and from the growing need for dissemination of the fundamental elements of the exact and natural sciences. Doctors, engineers, land surveyors, and military experts were as few as they had been at the beginning of the century. The fashionable search for humanistic education gave the state increasing numbers of enlightened administrators and diplomats, but the shortage of technical personnel continued to be acute.

The pressing demand for technical personnel was made more complicated and more urgent by a rising nationalist clamor for an end to Russia's heavy dependence on hired foreign professionals. Ivan Shuvalov, Mikhail Lomonosov, and a handful of other men of power, knowledge, and patriotic dedication were the leaders of the new movement, which had its first major triumph in the founding of Moscow University in 1755.

In several ways, Shuvalov was the ideal man to inspire and lead the new movement.[19] As a young man, he had shown an unusual facility for languages, which made it possible for him to read widely in the humanistic fields. He became an influential figure in Elizabeth's court. Shuvalov was that rare intellectual of his time who was sympathetic both to the scientific investigations conducted by members of the St. Petersburg Academy of Sciences and to the literary and philosophical ideas imported from France. He showed his respect for the Academy's scientific work by sponsoring

Lomonosov (who reciprocated by dedicating several odes to him). He acknowledged his admiration for the French Enlightenment by commissioning Voltaire to write an *Histoire de l'empire de Russie sous Pierre le Grand* (published in 1759–63 in two volumes) and by paving the way for the founding of the Academy of Arts in 1757.

In his plea for the opening of a university in Moscow, Shuvalov stressed that "it is to the sciences that civilized peoples are indebted for their superiority over the peoples who live in the darkness of ignorance."[20] Elizabeth's decree of January 12, 1755, which formally established the university, stated: "Since every good comes from the enlightened mind, and since the enlightened mind uproots evil, it is vitally necessary to strive to spread in our empire the various kinds of knowledge obtainable by the methods of science."[21] To many Russians the decision to open a new university may have seemed unduly optimistic. The unfortunate experience of the Academic University, located in the country's political and cultural center, demonstrated that young Russians were little interested in higher education. At the time of the founding of Moscow University, the Academic University had very few students. But the new university was not founded because Russian society at large called for it: it was founded by the government to train technical and administrative personnel. The government drew the first students from the seminaries; it also attracted young people to higher studies through stipends, promises of lucrative employment and higher army rank, and recognition of university study as active government service.

The selection of Moscow as a new university city was not whimsical; it resulted from a serious preliminary study of all favorable and unfavorable conditions in Moscow and elsewhere. Although St. Petersburg was much more in touch with contemporary Western European educational currents and possessed more experienced scientists and educators, Moscow represented an older, more Russian, intellectual tradition. The founders of Moscow University wanted this school to be a *national* institution. They realized that the large numbers of the Moscow gentry and urban middle classes (*raznochintsy*) were a rich source of potential students closer to the Russian cultural tradition than were their St. Petersburg counterparts. Furthermore, they maintained, Moscow was a logical place for a university because it was situated at the heart of the Empire. They also emphasized that the cost for the maintenance of a university in Moscow would be appreciably lower than in St. Petersburg.[22] Some of the founders cherished a secret hope that away from the swelling government bureaucracy in

St. Petersburg it would be possible for the new university to achieve some degree of autonomy.*

The founding of Moscow University was a partial admission that Peter's great hopes for the success of the Academy had not been realized. It also indicated a return to the early suggestion of Leibniz and Wolff that universities staffed by persons more competent in the art of teaching than in independent scientific investigation were what was needed for Russia's advancement. Moscow University was also dedicated to scholarship, but this dedication remained secondary for some time, and the emphasis at the start was on good teaching.

Whereas the faculty of the Academic University was, for the most part, restricted to certain narrow specialties, Moscow University began with a broad program in the general sciences. It was divided into three faculties—philosophy, law, and medicine—although it was some time before all three were real working faculties. Following the tradition of the Academic University, the new institution taught no theology; the omission, however, was probably due to a reluctance to enter the educational domain of the seminaries rather than to any fundamental belief in the strictly secular nature of university education.

In the spirit of the Western academic tradition, the Moscow faculty enjoyed a comparatively high degree of autonomy. It was subordinated directly to the Senate, and there was no administrative office of the type represented by the ill-reputed chancellery of the Academy. On the other hand, the University Council, which was made up of teaching personnel, did not have the right to elect high administrative officials. This restriction derived from the fear that foreign scholars, who were expected to be in the majority at first, might elect non-Russian officials.

The new university made a novel effort to reconcile the general national need for education with the pervasive estate principle of Russian society: it opened its classrooms not only to the aristocracy but to the *raznochintsy* as well. Past experience had shown that the aristocracy's resistance to higher education was incompatible with the country's growing demand

---

* Richard Pipes points out that after the founding of Moscow University, particularly during the closing decades of the century, the rivalry between St. Petersburg and Moscow became intense. In St. Petersburg, owing chiefly to Catherine's personal taste, "the French example permeated manners, speech habits, social behavior, and to some extent even thought." Moscow, on the other hand, became the center of widespread forces which resented French influence. In Moscow, Pipes states, "the prevailing foreign influence was German and English, that is, sentimental rather than traditional, mystic rather than skeptical, anti-Voltairean and anti-materialist." Richard Pipes, *Karamzin's Memoir,* pp. 18–19.

for professional manpower. Among the Russians elected to the St. Petersburg Academy during its first fifty years, not one was of aristocratic origin: most of them came from the families of clergymen by way of theological schools. Moscow University satisfied both the estate principle and the urgent need for educated persons by instituting two gymnasiums within its framework. Although both were designed to train future students for the university and had the same curriculum, one was entrusted with the training of aristocratic youth and the second of the *raznochintsy*. Never before had the principle of equal facilities for different free estates been tried in Russia. The Infantry School had had a special department for young men of nonaristocratic origin since the 1730's, but its curriculum concentrated on practical skills.

Ambitious in its organizational plan and idealistic in its goals, Moscow University had, as expected, a very slow beginning. Attracting young men to higher education was difficult, and many of those who were lured into enrolling were quickly discouraged by the difficulties of study. One of the early graduates of the University remarked in his autobiographical notes that "none of the students, with the exception of those enrolled in the Medical Faculty, had a definite goal."[23] Of necessity—and despite the intent of the founders—most of the first teachers came from abroad. They were, as a rule, adept enough in accustoming themselves to their new cultural surroundings and educational duties, but until the nineteenth century the level of instruction was uneven and generally low. The building of the curriculum, instructional facilities, and the teaching staff only inched along. For the first five years, for example, there was no instruction in mathematics, and not until the early nineteenth century did the teaching of this subject go beyond the elements of arithmetic, algebra, geometry, and trigonometry.[24] In 1765 only one student was enrolled in the Faculty of Law, and a few years later the same was true of the new Faculty of Medicine; four years earlier the government had found it necessary to send ten young men to Leyden University for medical study.[25] In the entire reign of Catherine II, not one person was granted the degree of doctor of medicine by Moscow University. For a decade the Faculty of Law consisted of only one professor. Following the proclamation of 1762 which freed the gentry of obligatory service to the state but stipulated that aristocratic youths must attend military schools, there was a mass withdrawal of aristocratic students from the University Gymnasium.[26] According to Kliuchevskii, although the University system (including the two gymnasiums) had 100 students on the day of its opening, some thirty years later it had only

82.[27] (A second gymnasium was established in Kazan in 1758 to help train students for university studies; like its counterpart, it consisted of two parallel institutions, one for young aristocrats and one for the *raznochintsy*. Enrollment was never high, however, and from 1788 to 1798 the school was closed.)

THE SEARCH FOR A PUBLIC SCHOOL SYSTEM

In its conception and design, Moscow University was too far ahead of its time to receive much support from any of the rigidly defined estates which made up Russian society. For the first fifty years, it barely subsisted; yet it showed constant progress, which guaranteed its survival and eventually made it a great institution of higher learning. Catherine II, steeped in the mass of pedagogical thought coming from the West, realized that the University and its Moscow and Kazan gymnasiums would hardly solve the country's vast educational problem, and that a more comprehensive school system must be instituted. With hopes of a future system of centrally controlled elementary and secondary schools in mind, she sought to implant a pattern of education dedicated both to national purposes and to the universal principles of the Enlightenment as these were defined by contemporary French philosophers. She and her advisers conceived an educational system devoted to scholarship, military arts, civic functions, and commerce. Catherine gave much thought to educational matters and corresponded with a group of illustrious Western proponents of the Enlightenment, but she lacked the determination and efficiency to pursue her goals in the face of great odds. The problem of how to promote the philosophy of the Enlightenment while preserving the rigidity of Russia's estate system seemed insolvable. Like her predecessors, Catherine saw no value in educating the enserfed peasantry.

In Catherine's time, moreover, the difference between the so-called free estates fully crystallized. Besides legal, economic, and political distinctions, there was now a noticeable tendency toward moral and psychological distinctions. Refinement was considered a trait of the aristocracy; good manners and love of work were attributed to the urban middle classes; sobriety and diligence were thought to be the virtues of the clergy.[28] These judgments may not have been particularly indicative of the real character of individual estates; what was significant was the growing inclination to consider each estate as a kind of self-contained society with unique attributes and attitudes.

Catherine's admiration for the educational philosophy of the Enlightenment began to give way when she realized what a public school system would do to the estate system, and how it might engender conflicts between various groups and produce challenges to the established political authority. During the 1760's and 1770's she concentrated more on the principles of educational philosophy than on their implementation. During the 1760's the raising of the educational level of the aristocracy was uppermost in her mind. It was in this period that I. I. Betskoi, at Catherine's behest, opened a boarding school for noble girls age 5 to 18. During the 1770's, under Betskoi's influence, Catherine decided that a middle class was the natural source of an educated citizenry and that all future schools must take the middle layers of urban society into most serious consideration; at her request, a commercial school was established in Moscow.[29]

It was not until 1782 that Catherine II appointed the famous Commission for the Establishment of Public Schools, headed by Petr Zavadovskii. The delay was partly the result of the distractions of foreign wars and internal peasant rebellions, but these served to reveal to Catherine the thinness of her liberalism and her enthusiasm for the Enlightenment. The Commission was directed to prepare and gradually to implement a general plan for public schools; to train teachers (for which a school was opened in St. Petersburg in 1783); and to organize a special agency for the translation of textbooks into Russian. The Austrian school system was to serve as a model, and for this purpose F. I. Iankovich-de-Mirievo, an Austrian Serb, was employed as chief consultant. The work of the Commission was of gigantic proportions, despite its lack of proper authority and financial resources.[30] It worked closely with the Academy of Sciences and with many experienced educators, scholars, and public officials. The Academician Franz Aepinus was one of the leading members of the Commission. The Charter of Public Schools, signed by Catherine in 1786, called for the establishment of "main public schools" and "small public schools." The former were to be opened in twenty-five provincial capitals; the latter were to operate on a district level.

Under the influence of the Academy of Sciences, great weight was given to the various natural and exact sciences in the curricula of the new schools. The curriculum of the twenty-five main schools included arithmetic, general and mathematical geography, geometry, mechanics, physics, natural history, and civil architecture, in addition to numerous courses—at Catherine's request—in civics and religion.[31] More than any earlier Russian educational institutions, these schools were designed to give their students a sound preparation for higher studies. Henceforth, the growth of Russia's educational institutions was to be a continuous and cumulative process. In 1800 the country had 315 main and small public schools with 790 teachers and 19,915 pupils (including 1,787 girls).[32]

Although the aim of the 1786 school reform was to produce an enlightened third estate in Russia, it actually set the stage for the education of all free estates, though with a predominance of the children of the aristocracy and urban merchants. That the system was a comparative success was due in great measure to the availability of teachers, trained mostly in the St. Petersburg teachers' seminary, and to the extensive publication of textbooks. It also owed a great deal to the accumulated effects of earlier attempts to create a nucleus of educated citizens, to the expanded opportunities for those who commanded knowledge, and to the youthful enthusiasm for modern humanistic ideas shared by the country's leading citizens, weak in number but strong in devotion to the cause of the Enlightenment. These schools came too late to affect the status of scholarship seriously during the era of enlightened absolutism, but they furnished sound foundations for the gymnasiums and universities established in the early decades of the nineteenth century. Their solid curriculum in the natural sciences became a tradition to which the growth of science in Russia during the nineteenth century was heavily indebted.

It should not be forgotten that Catherine's public schools were founded in an atmosphere of fear of Western ideas. The appeal of a flattering Voltaire or an accommodating D'Alembert or Diderot was seriously counterbalanced by Rousseau's ideas on liberal education, which declared silent war on the institutions of the autocratic system. Catherine was openly disturbed when Rousseau's ideas began to filter into Russia. Among other things, Rousseau's didactic and philosophical attack on the *ancien régime* represented an added threat at the time of Pugachev's rebellion against the inhumanity of serfdom, the institution on which the autocratic regime was built.

The greatest paradox of this age was the recruitment of a legion of Russian Voltaireans, led by Catherine II, from the ranks of an aristocracy steeped in traditionalism and committed to upholding the social status quo. Referring to Voltaire's influence in Russia, Pushkin stated that the great French philosopher was a "leader in thought and fashion," and he implied that the eighteenth-century Russian aristocrats may have overlooked the crux of his philosophy—his criticism of existing social institutions and proposals for their improvement—in their dazzled acceptance of the literary façade. Herzen, using exaggeration for the sake of emphasis, declared that whereas Voltaire's philosophy had freed Frenchmen of old prejudices and transformed them into revolutionaries, in Russia it served as a means for reinforcing the slave-like dependence of the people on the whims of the absolute monarch.[33] Catherine's dwindling enthusiasm for the humanistic thought of the Enlightenment led her to veto the teaching of French in the newly established public schools and to recommend the teaching of Tatar, Chinese, and Greek.

Prior to 1786, the Russian monarchs sought the building of schools as a source of enlightenment and knowledge; after 1786, the schools were also assigned the task of upholding the official ideology through a careful sorting out of knowledge. Peter I was too eager to bring science to the Russian people to be aware of any threat to monarchical absolutism and to a society anchored to the institution of serfdom. But Catherine II clearly recognized this threat, and her dilemma was further complicated by her conviction that the advancement of science was essential to her country's prosperity.

The French Revolution, in which education played so important a role, intensified Catherine's dilemma. Many ideas to which she had subscribed fervently in her youth came to fruition in the atmosphere created by the Revolution. During this critical period, St. Petersburg's teachers' seminary was almost completely neglected, but it managed to survive because teachers were required for the newly occupied parts of Poland. In her old age, Catherine abandoned the idea of opening new universities in Pskov, Chernigov, and Penza, as planned by some influential members of the Zavadovskii Commission; instead, she set up a system of censorship as a means of checking the influx of dangerous philosophical and scientific ideas from the West. During the last decade of the eighteenth century "many books were suppressed, which a little earlier were not only tolerated but distributed to the reading public as models of good literature."[34] The eighteenth century and the grand promises of enlightened absolutism came to an end firmly clenched in the tight fists of a professional system of censorship.

The reverses of Catherine's age left a heavy imprint on the development of scientific thought. But an equally strong and opposite influence came from the irreversible influx of Western ideas and the growing demand for technical knowledge for military and industrial purposes.

More than her immediate predecessors, Catherine undermined the traditional power of the Church by an extensive expropriation of its landholdings and by her personal identification with secular learning. The teaching of religion became an integral part of the public school education, but it was entrusted to lay teachers rather than to priests. Seized by the spirit of the new age, the religious schools also began to teach the natural sciences and mathematics.

Science found new vistas, institutional supports, and champions. The intellectual supremacy of the Academy of Sciences was not seriously challenged, although scientific inquiry began to be a concern of other institutions as well. Moscow University, many government departments, new learned societies, and independent scholars added to the growth of scientific thought. Because of the slow development of the new school system and of a middle-class group dedicated to scholarly pursuits, foreigners continued to dominate the most advanced and pioneering branches of knowledge. Russian scientists grew more numerous and their interests more diversified, but their contributions lay more in making science a functional component of Russian culture than in extraordinary additions to the swelling currents of scientific thought.

THE ACADEMY AND ACADEMIC AUTONOMY

The Academy of Sciences entered the age of Catherine II weakened by internal strife and loss of international prestige, which hampered its efforts to attract scholars from the West. In July 1761, the Senate—in response to bitter complaints by Lomonosov—publicly voiced its dissatisfaction with the Academy, which "while receiving huge donations from the state treasury has not done any useful work for the state for a long time."[35] Prompted no doubt by Lomonosov, it mentioned especially the paucity of Russian professors, assistants, translators, and students in the Academy, and the failure of foreign professors to fulfill their obligations in research and teaching.[36]

When Catherine II ascended the throne the following year, Lomonosov was relieved of his duties as the head of the Academy's Geographical Department, but soon afterwards the president of the Academy revoked the order. Some time later, Catherine ordered that Lomonosov be retired, then changed her mind. In the summer of 1764, she visited Lomonosov in his home, very likely as a way of publicly demonstrating the debt of the state to the man who symbolized Russia's scientific progress. Otherwise, during the first years of her reign, Catherine showed little concern with the Academy's internal affairs. On July 2, 1763, she attended a jubilee meeting at the

Academy at which Academicians Franz Aepinus and Johann Zeiger read learned papers on various aspects of natural history. Both papers were read in German despite the stipulation of the charter that only Latin and Russian be employed in Academic meetings. After that, whether on Catherine's order or not, the use of German in the Academy noticeably decreased, while the use of Latin correspondingly increased. This and other changes of a similar sort helped to allay the fear among Russian scholars that the days of Empress Anne—and German domination—might be returning.

The 1760's were the years of Catherine's passionate allegiance to the pronouncements of the *philosophes* of the Enlightenment; they were also the years that unveiled certain grave inconsistencies within the tangled and uncertain mixture of absolutism and enlightenment. In one of her first communications to the Academy, Catherine complained about the institution's publication of "books which are against law and morals"—among which she included Rousseau's *Emile*.[37] The Academy responded by preparing a plan for the establishment of censorship outposts at all ports of entry. The plan was not carried out, but it was a portent of things to come toward the end of Catherine's rule; it heralded the gradual evolution of the Academy into one of the watchdogs of official ideology.

The return of Euler in 1766, one year after Lomonosov's death, was the greatest single development in the Academy during the early years of Catherine's rule. The Russian government paid an unusually high price to induce the famous mathematician to return to St. Petersburg. "Catherine received the mathematician as if he were royalty, setting aside a fully furnished house for Euler and his eighteen dependents, and donating one of her own cooks to run the kitchen."[38] Besides these material benefits for himself and his family, Euler also obtained a promise from Catherine that steps would be taken to reorganize the Academy so as to ensure more autonomy for scholarly pursuits and eliminate the sources of debilitating internal strife. As the ranking Academician, Euler himself presided over all meetings in the absence of the president, and he was one of those chiefly responsible for the selection of new Academicians.

While carrying on his many scientific pursuits, Euler took time to devise a detailed scheme for the reorganization of the Academy.[39] Catherine thereupon appointed a Commission—of which Euler became an important member—to draft detailed recommendations for a thorough reorganization of this institution. Replacing the chancellery *de facto* and the president *de jure,* the Commission was also entrusted with administering the affairs of the Academy in the interim. Razumovskii continued to serve as president, but his office was shorn of its traditional prerogatives and the Academy was actually headed by a new director, Count Vladimir Orlov, the brother of Catherine's favorite, Grigorii Orlov. The regular members of the Commission nominally represented the Academicians, but its director was an agent of the government, directly responsible to Catherine II; however, since both the Commission members and the director were hand-picked by the Empress, the Commission in reality represented the interests of the court far more than it did those of the scholars.

Count Orlov was scarcely suitable for the task of director. When Count Redern of the Berlin Academy of Sciences visited St. Petersburg he was appalled that a man with so little comprehension of scientific inquiry and so little respect for it could have been chosen to head the Academy. "My God," he said to Euler, "what an extraordinary kind of person you have for the president of the Academy—a person who is against all scholars, who regards the Academy as useless, and who believes, with Rousseau, that science would make the world only more evil!"[40] At first Orlov seemed inclined to assert himself in his new office, but in time he abandoned his duties altogether. He eventually was replaced.

His successor, S. G. Domashnev, a second-rate poet whose reputation was largely due to his having dedicated an ode, composed at the age of sixteen, to Catherine, was more intelligent and better educated but equally disrespectful of the Academy and its scientific staff. M. I. Sukhomlinov gave this assessment of Domashnev's attitude toward the Academy: "With his name are connected some unpleasant memories in the Academy's history. Despite his intellect and education, Domashnev did not fully understand his status in relation to both the Academic Assembly and the Commission which at that time governed the Academy. In his relations to the Academicians who made up the Commission, the director was designated to be *primus inter pares,* sharing with them the same rights and duties in the management of the Academy. But Domashnev sought to expand the authority vested in him by law; he talked to the members in the abusive tone of an overlord and issued orders filled with most biting innuendoes against individual Academicians. The behavior of the overbearing director was condemned by the government and the public and led to his dismissal from the Academy."[41]

Hating Domashnev's arrogance, Euler took no part in Academy affairs except when it became imperative to do so. It was during Domashnev's directorship that the Academy celebrated its fiftieth anniversary. On that occasion Domashnev delivered the main oration, which, in addition to apotheosizing the great virtues of the Empress, pleaded that the scholars study not only the natural sciences but also the moral codes and history—that "most useful of all branches of human knowledge."[42]

In 1783 Catherine with one stroke of the pen appointed her favorite, Princess Ekaterina Dashkova, as director of the Academy and abolished the Academic Commission, which meant the end of all plans for a reorganization. The abolition of the Commission cut off the last formal channel through which the scholars could influence the administration of Academic affairs. Dashkova appointed an army colonel to serve as the counselor for administrative matters. The Academy was thus brought into conformity with the new concept of monarchical absolutism based on a clear legal definition of delegated authority and jurisdiction of bureaucratic units. The spirit of the Petrine law, which made the whim of the ruler an unchallenged authority, worked against giving the Academy a legally defined place within the Russian polity; it did receive, however, a modicum of operational independence and collegial management. The spirit of Catherine's laws curbed the monarch's whims by providing firm legal definitions for the jurisdictional components of the state apparatus; at the same time, it strengthened absolutism by drastically limiting the vestiges of autonomous action which still existed in many political institutions. The abolition of the Academic Commission was a sacrifice of collegial administration—and the areas of comparatively autonomous management of internal affairs—for the sake of conforming to a strict legal definition.

An ambitious, educated, and capricious woman, Princess Dashkova was at first eager to bolster the none too steady structure of the Academy, but her interests wandered and most of the Academy's problems remained unsolved. One of her first actions was to visit Euler; she wanted, perhaps, to show the Academicians that, unlike her predecessors, she openly admired the true pillar of the Academy's intellectual strength. Dashkova helped the Academy's press to acquire additional equipment and to expand its publishing program, and she obtained salary raises for all members of the staff. As evidence of her concern for the popularization of science, she increased the number of public lectures delivered in the Russian language and added three new series—in mathematics, geometry, and natural history. These lectures, she pointed out, were particularly welcome to "the sons of poor aristocrats and junior Guards officers."[43] In 1785 N. P. Sokolov became the first person after Lomonosov to deliver a series of public lectures in chemistry in the Russian language.

Princess Dashkova had only small interest in pure research—or, for that matter, in higher education. She was proud of having raised the number of students in the Academic Gymnasium from seventeen to fifty, but she made no attempt to revive the almost defunct Academic University. *–1796 = end* In 1796 the University had three students, and shortly thereafter it ceased altogether to exist.

During Princess Dashkova's term of directorship, the Academy, like many another intellectual group, felt the force of the French Revolution. Catherine II, well aware that it was men of knowledge who had lighted the revolutionary fires, reacted instantly to the signs of revolutionary spirit exhibited in Aleksandr Radishchev's *A Journey from St. Petersburg to Moscow* (1790) by exiling its author. Radishchev, who was, paradoxically, a product of the Catherinean Enlightenment, quickly became a symbol of the new intellectual forces seeking a change in the political and social order. "Radishchev's crime," says David Marshall Lang, "was not simply that he preached the liberation of the serfs. It was rather that he had stripped the veil from the sacred shrine of Russian absolutism and revealed the sham which lay behind. He had poured scorn on the mystical adoration with which Russians were, and still are, taught to worship their rulers."[44] Aleksandr Vorontsov, Princess Dashkova's brother, was one of Radishchev's great admirers. He was so grief-stricken by his friend's exile to Siberia that he retired in seclusion to his country estate.

The Princess remained in St. Petersburg, determined, in her own words, to pay no attention to the "odious people" who loudly supported Catherine's withdrawal from the philosophy of the Enlightenment.[45] Yet in her official capacity she was compelled to be part of the Academy's first enforced ideological purification, which saw such illustrious men as Condorcet expunged from the list of its honorary members; his crime was active participation in the French Revolution. An old and disappointed woman, Princess Dashkova showed no enthusiasm for the Academy's new course, and her resignation from the position of director in 1794 was welcomed by people close to the Empress. She chose as her replacement P. P. Bakunin, a relative and the son of a senator, who was appointed for a four-year term. *Dashkova resigns.* *1794*

All the services rendered to the Academy by Dashkova, about which she boasted to Catherine, were scarcely enough to outweigh the damage done to the Academy by her chosen successor. Bakunin, a rough, tactless person of little education, made no effort whatever to uphold the honor of the scholars and the dignity of scientific work. He entered the directorship with a surplus of 46,000 rubles in the Academy treasury and left it with a deficit of 22,000. His cousin, S. R. Vorontsov, called him "un étourdi présomptueux et ignorant," who contributed to the Academy nothing but "disorder and confusion."[46] He treated the Academicians with contempt and made decisions of vital importance to individual scholars without consulting them. Academician Stepan Rumovskii, who directed the astronomical observatory, was surprised one day to find that the whole first floor of his building, and all instruments located on it, had been taken over by one of Bakunin's favorites.

During Bakunin's tenure the Academy became part of an elaborate censorship system decreed by Catherine in September 1796, two months before her death. Censorship had not heretofore been unknown in Russia, but it had so far been fragmentary and decentralized. The Academy itself acted as a halfhearted watchdog over secular books, and the Synod over religious literature.[47] Catherine's decree made censorship a wide and centrally controlled operation to combat the ideas flowing out of the French Revolution. It specified two actions: the establishment of censorship outposts at five main customs stations, and the immediate abolition of all private presses in Russia. A Senate decree stipulated that the censorship committees in the customs stations were to consist of three persons each: a clergyman appointed by the Synod, a public official appointed by the Senate, and a "prominent scholar" appointed by the Academy. Bakunin was not required to appoint Academicians to these committees, but his choice fell on two distinguished Russian scientists: S. K. Kotel'nikov and Petr Inokhodtsev.[48] Paul I, Catherine's successor, went one step further. In 1797 he issued a decree which read: "Since various books imported from abroad undermine religion, civil law, and good manners, it is henceforth forbidden to import any volumes from abroad, regardless of the language in which they are written. This will apply also to music."[49] Not surprisingly, this sweeping measure was never fully enforced, but it did disrupt the Academy's exchange of books with the scientific institutions of the West. In 1798 the Academy was informed that in the future it could publish no geographical maps without government clearance.[50] At the same time, Russian youths were prohibited from going to Western Europe for advanced study.

Bakunin was the last to hold the office of director. In 1798 he was replaced by A. L. Nikolai, a person close to the court, who was granted the rank of president and is remembered as a friend of scholarship. He appointed a commission of eminent scientists to prepare a new Academic charter which would guarantee more administrative autonomy. Thus, with Nikolai, the oppression began to lose impetus, and the first years of the nineteenth century were full of optimism for the future of the Academy and the promotion of scholarship.

Despite the difficult conditions under which the Academy worked during the 1790's, the number of studies published in its scholarly journals actually increased slightly over that of the preceding decade. Since the number of scientific publications in the country as a whole decreased during this period, it seems logical to attribute the Academy's record to the fact that its scholarly periodicals were by now sufficiently established to appear with regularity.[51]

THE ACADEMY'S SCIENTIFIC LEGACY: EULER

During Catherine's reign, science ceased to be a poor relation of Russian culture. The colossal stature of Lomonosov, the emergence of promising Russian natural historians, Catherine's early humanism and rationalism, and intensified Western influence at all levels combined to create a social atmosphere favorable to scientific thought and scholarship. But the position of science was more indefinite than ever before; for now the guardians and codifiers of official ideology recognized that it was not only *resource &* the greatest source of economic and military power, but also the most formi- *threat* dable threat to the perpetuation of the social and political status quo. Catherine II, educated and intelligent, was quick to grasp this dual cultural role of science.

With the exception of Peter I, no Russian monarch had shown more admiration and respect for science than Catherine II; yet none had held the Academy in a tighter rein. Despite this crushing inconsistency, and despite Catherine's intellectual twists and turns, her age was one of great fermentation of ideas, of many currents and crosscurrents of thought, and of new ventures in the expanding world of science. By now, even with its administrative shackles, the Academy was a settled institution, in which men continued to do their work and for which, often by sheer luck, new scholars from the West always seemed to be found. In addition to Euler —whose return to Russia in 1766 after a great scientific career in Germany gave added luster to an already impressive mathematical tradition—the Academy was strengthened by the arrival of two outstanding scientists in the mid-eighteenth century. Peter Simon Pallas came to Russia in 1767 not to end but to begin a rich series of scientific efforts to penetrate the mysteries of the earth—its geology, flora, and fauna—and also to give general science additional keys to the understanding of what was then known as natural history. Franz Aepinus, who came to St. Petersburg in 1757, was an important link between the generations of Euler and Pallas. As a physicist, he made the first efforts to place on a mathematical basis certain knowledge arrived at experimentally in magnetism and electricity. During the second half of the eighteenth century, particularly after the return of Euler, the scientific work of the Academy was largely in the field of mathematics, both practical and theoretical, and in the natural sciences, notably Pallas's expeditions of 1768–74, which produced a vast amount of empirical data and astute theoretical insights.

Euler returned to St. Petersburg with strikingly new views on science and philosophy. During the 1750's he saw the intellectual atmosphere of the Berlin Academy much enlivened by a great and enthusiastic debate, led by Pierre de Maupertuis, centered on the relation of science to philosophy. Although he participated mostly as an observer, he became fully acquainted with the great intellectual issues of the time. To his pure mathematical wisdom he had now given a philosophical foundation, tempered by his strong Calvinist point of view. It was perhaps this belief in divine authority, more than his inclination to regard mathematical analysis as the sole method of inquiry in the natural sciences, that led him to inveigh against the experimental method.

In Berlin, Euler had also emerged to some extent from his ivory tower when circumstances placed him as acting head of the Berlin Academy after the death of Maupertuis. During the Berlin period he also became adept at writing of scientific matters on a popular level. His *Letters to a German Princess,* published in French in 1760–61 and addressed to the daughter of one of his aristocratic friends, surveyed contemporary physics in a language full of idiom and wit. His *Elements of Algebra,* which appeared in 1768–69 in a Russian translation (two years before the German original), was also in the popular vein. In his preface to the work, Euler says that his aim was "to compose an elementary treatise, by which a beginner, without any other assistance, might make himself the complete master of algebra."[52] It was during this period also that his scientific investigations gathered great momentum. In the six years before his return to St. Petersburg, Euler published some seventy separate works, including several long volumes. His *Dynamics of Celestial Bodies* was published in Rostock in 1765, the year he decided to return to Russia.

Owing to the diversity and richness of his experiences and accomplishments, Euler easily became the leading figure of the Academy. He demonstrated at once that he had not returned to Russia to retire but was, on the contrary, at the peak of his productivity. During the remaining seventeen years of his life—despite the blindness which afflicted him shortly after his return—he produced almost one-half of the approximately 800 papers which comprise his complete work; more than 300 of these were published posthumously, mainly in the Academy journals. Also immediately on his return, Euler plunged into the arduous task of rehabilitating the administrative organization of the Academy. Unfortunately, this was also the period of the growing contempt for scholarship on the part of the directors appointed by Catherine, and the loss of the last shreds of academic autonomy. Euler's plan for new Academic positions was in part carried out, however: on his recommendation, the Academy elected to membership two outstanding German scholars, Caspar Wolff from Berlin and Samuel Gmelin from Tübingen. It was also Euler's proposal for a chair of natural history which eventually brought Pallas to the Academy. It is unfair to Euler to interpret his failure to recommend any Russians for membership in the Academy as a sign of prejudice against Russian scholars —as was insinuated by Chernov. Rather, it was part of his earnest effort to strengthen the Academy by electing men whose high scholarly standards had been demonstrated in their published scientific papers.

EULER'S DISCIPLES

Because of his blindness, Euler was forced to rely on his younger colleagues and former students in recording and organizing his ideas. Among the scholars who worked with him and who in a sense could be considered his disciples, eight were members of the Academy: his son, Johann Euler, Petr Inokhodtsev, Wolfgang Krafft, Anders Lexell, Nicolaus Fuss, Mikhail Golovin, S. K. Kotel'nikov, and Stepan Rumovskii. In 1783, the year of Euler's death, these scholars constituted exactly one-half of the Academy's learned staff. As happens so often, none of these scientists came even close to the scholarly eminence of their great teacher, even though most of them made noteworthy contributions to various fields of mathematical analysis, astronomy, and physics. Unlike their teacher, they dedicated only parts of their lives to scientific work, which consisted mostly of efforts to amplify or to translate Euler's works. Their real contributions lay rather in teaching, writing mathematical textbooks, and modernizing the public school curricula. By their efforts, Russia acquired a whole generation of men with a comparatively high level of mathematical literacy. It was their work that introduced a broad curriculum in mathematics into the military schools; it was their work that made it possible for the St. Petersburg teachers' seminary to produce such an able mathematician as Timofei Osipovskii. They took mathematics, in all its power and complexity, beyond the narrow confines of the Academy.

Euler's students were a powerful link between Euler and Russia's great mathematicians of the nineteenth century: they gave continuity and necessary vigor to the development of a profound mathematical tradition in Russia. In was because of them that Russia recognized Euler's greatness and paid him deserved homage. While Euler was still alive, the Academy commissioned a recognized artist to execute a mural in the Assembly Hall, representing allegorically the Wisdom of Geometry and including as part of the composition the formulas of Euler's theory of lunar motion. In his eulogy commemorating Euler's death, Condorcet told the Western nations that they could learn from Russia—"a country which, at the beginning of the present century, we regarded as scarcely removed from barbarism" —how to bestow honor on the great men of science.[53]

Euler's most productive and versatile Russian disciple was undoubtedly Stepan Rumovskii, whose astronomical work earned him election to the Swedish Academy of Sciences and high praise from Euler and Aepinus. His tables of geographical coordinates of selected localities in various parts of the Russian Empire showed remarkable precision for his time. When they were published in 1786, Russia was shown to have more determined geographical coordinates than either France or Germany.[54] Rumovskii translated into Russian Euler's *Letters to a German Princess* and Nicolaus Fuss's famous *éloge* to Euler, and he contributed a series of papers on mathematical analysis to Academy journals.

Early in his career, in 1761, Rumovskii headed the Academic team sent to Selenginsk, Siberia, to observe the passage of Venus over the sun's disk. Bad weather kept the group from completing its task, but Rumovskii made a number of local astronomical and meteorological observations which, when published in the Academy's *Novi Commentarii* in 1762, added to his reputation. In 1769 Venus again passed over the sun's disk, and Rumovskii—now established as the Academy's chief astronomer—headed the team of observers sent to Kola. The weather this time was somewhat better, but still far from ideal. Bessel remarked that Rumovskii guessed more than he saw; but, guess or not, the Russian astronomer's findings helped Joseph Delambre to determine the mean horizontal parallax of the sun.

The bubbling intellectual activity in St. Petersburg and the paucity of competent scholars lured Rumovskii into an extraordinary variety of intellectual endeavors. For several decades, he skillfully headed both the geographical department of the Academy and the astronomical observatory; besides his regular lectures in mathematics at the Academic University he also gave special instruction in theoretical and practical astronomy to a selected group of students; he delivered public lectures on topics ranging from his astronomical observations to the history of optics; he served for a short while as editor of the *Academic Bulletin* and the *New Monthly Works*, both published by the Academy in the Russian language for the benefit of the general reading public; and he was for a time the editor of various almanacs, which he modernized and occasionally used for the dissemination of elementary astronomical knowledge. Rumovskii's versatile and inquisitive mind led him far beyond the natural and exact sciences. He contributed an article on the history of Russian law to a French publication, he wrote the explanations of a number of ancient mathematical terms for Russia's first etymological dictionary, and he played a leading role, early in the nineteenth century, in the establishment of new schools of higher learning. He was for a time curator of the Kazan school district, a position which gave him authority over the newly founded Kazan University. In his old age he translated Tacitus's *Annals* into Russian.[55]

It is in no way a belittling of the great role played by Euler's disciples in the diffusion of mathematical knowledge in Russia to point out the importance also of a new and dynamic French scholarly influence during the last decade of the eighteenth century—more or less independent of the French revolutionary influence which so disturbed the government. In such leading institutions as Moscow University the old "German" mathematics—presented in the textbooks of Wolff and Weidler and dominated by seventeenth-century practical orientation—was still strong, and the Eulerians dominated the Academy of Sciences and the public schools; but a French influence had begun to appear, especially in the military schools. This influence represented the new mathematical trend in France, stemming from the tradition of Descartes and Fermat and combined with modern advances in mathematical analysis, which culminated in the brilliant work of Clairaut, D'Alembert, Lagrange, Legendre, Monge, and many others in such disciplines as mechanics, hydraulics, mathematical physics, differential equations, the calculus of variations, and astronomy. Far from being a denial of Euler's contributions, French mathematics was simply a refinement, an expansion, a new and imaginative application. One of the principal counsels of Laplace to younger mathematicians was: "Read Euler, read Euler—he is the teacher of all of us." Although the independent work of Euler and Lagrange on the calculus of variations converged at many points, the work of the younger Lagrange eventually began to take on new aspects and to acquire a new depth. Whereas Euler's *Mechanica* (1736) showed that the geometrical method of Newton's *Principia* could be advantageously replaced by an analytical method, Lagrange's *Méchanique analytique* (1787) marked the full victory of the analytical method, the work contained no geometric figures but only "algebraic operations."

Euler's disciples remained untouched by the work of the new generation of French mathematicians, but at the close of the eighteenth century, with the admission to the Academy of S. E. Gur'ev, the indifference came to an end. Gur'ev, a graduate of the Artillery School, was not only the first Russian scholar to rise to the status of Academician without an Academy education; he was also the first product of modern French mathematical influence to become a member of the Academy.

THE SCIENTIFIC EXPEDITIONS: PALLAS

It has been said that Euler's close working relationship with his students, particularly with Nicolaus Fuss, constituted the introduction of "group research" in the Academy, although it was not formally recognized and was clearly of secondary importance in the over-all scheme of Academic work. Group work under the Academy's aegis received its real test in the scientific expeditions made between 1768 and 1774, and it proved to be highly successful. Fieldwork had not been unknown to the Academy—which had helped, for example, to arrange the Great Northern Expedition (1733–43)—but the expeditions of the late 'sixties and early 'seventies were far more ambitious than any previous ones, not only in size but also in general planning and the mobilization of scholarly interests. They have been justly called the greatest single undertaking of the Academy during the entire monarchical era. The basic contributions of these expeditions are contained in bulky volumes, most of which attracted the immediate attention of scholars everywhere. They were written by individual scholars but often included materials collected by several members of various expeditionary teams. These materials enriched every branch of natural science from mineralogy and botany to meteorology and local geography, including valuable ethnographic and demographic material and useful information on agricultural techniques, human and animal diseases, and local arts and crafts.[56]

These expeditions betokened a fruitful synchronization of the work of the Academy with Russia's acute need for the development of economic potential and foreign trade. One of the participants, Academician Gülden-städt, was correct when he stated in a public lecture that whereas "many discoveries made by Academicians belong to the realm of ideas," still others "have a direct influence on the welfare of the present generation."[57] This dual service of scientific inquiry was clearly demonstrated in 1769 when the Academy sent its leading astronomers to Siberia primarily to study the passage of Venus over the sun's disk but also to establish, on an astronomical basis, the geographical position of certain Siberian localities. The massive empirical materials and daring scientific generalizations resulting from these expeditions raised the study of nature in Russia to the level of Western European naturalist inquiry. They served as the foundations for a strong Russian tradition in the natural sciences which in its compass, vitality of ideas, and scholarly enthusiasm was on a par with the mathematical tradition. "In consequence of these expeditions," wrote the English historian William Coxe, "perhaps no country can boast, within the space of a few years, such a number of excellent publications on its internal state, natural productions, topography, geography, and history; on the manners, customs, and languages of the different people, as have issued from the press of the Academy . . . and it may not be an exaggeration to assert, that no society in Europe has more distinguished itself for the excellence of its publications."[58] The basic works prepared by the leaders of expeditionary teams were immediately published in German, French, or Russian.

The group work of the expeditionary teams brought together men of various levels of scientific sophistication and maturity: each team had, in modern parlance, senior scholars, junior scholars, and aspirants for higher academic degrees. The teams thus represented not only a pooling of knowledge but also an intellectual blending of generations—a sort of university with a fortunate combination of theoretical training and practical research. Such mature scholars as Pallas were given a golden opportunity to exercise their scholarly gifts; others, like Ivan Lepekhin, acquired the experience necessary for becoming mature and accomplished scholars; while still others, as typified by Nikolai Ozeretskovskii, went through a scholarly apprenticeship of the first order. The expeditionary teams were happy mixtures of Russians and Germans; there was very little of the traditional friction and jealousy. Traveling into strange lands where there were virtually no roads, where the weather was normally harsh, and where there were frequent encounters with hostile people—natives and frontiersmen as well as fugitives from the law—all this required a great deal of courage, dedication to scholarship, and plain idealism. Two leaders of individual teams, Samuel Gmelin and Johann Falk, met tragic deaths in the course of duty.

The chief architect and guiding spirit of the expeditionary work of the 'sixties and 'seventies was Peter Simon Pallas, one of the leading figures in the annals of the Academy. The expeditions were primarily a gigantic instrument for obtaining empirical knowledge relevant to a dozen of the natural and social sciences; Pallas was in a way the scientific codifier of the acquired data. Although as a naturalist he was recognized as equal to his great contemporaries Linnaeus and Buffon, Pallas was primarily an encyclopedist; yet he displayed the profound insight of a true specialist in any field to which he gave his attention.[59] One of his biographers describes him as "traveler, zoologist, botanist, paleontologist, mineralogist, geologist, and even agricultural expert and technologist."[60] He was acclaimed by his contemporaries as a naturalist of the highest order and his classic *Travels Through Various Provinces of the Russian Empire, 1768–1773* (written in German) was translated in rapid succession into French, English, Russian, and Italian. After Euler's death, it was Pallas above all who kept the prestige of the St. Petersburg Academy at enviable heights—with the aid of such sound scholars as Lepekhin, Gmelin, Güldenstädt, and Ozeretskovskii.

As a combination of the eighteenth-century naturalist and the nineteenth-century natural scientist, Pallas stood well above his generation. He was a discerning and astute collector of scientific data. In his descriptions of animals, he used exact measurements and took careful note of their geographical distribution. But he was not a narrow empiricist; much of his work was devoted to a search for general laws of nature. In 1777 he read to the assembled Academy a paper in which he postulated an original theory of the structure of the earth. He identified a primitive granite, free of any organic admixtures, as the core or the axis of mountain chains. This core, he claimed, was surrounded or intermixed with a great variety of vertically embedded rocks with no fossil content—the crystalline schists of modern geologists. Surrounding the core and the crystalline schists, Pallas conjectured, were the secondary mountains, composed of calcareous rocks of marine origin, normally rich in fossils. This layer, in turn, was surrounded by the tertiary mountains, made of clays and marls, like those observable in the Urals. Pallas could thus generalize because he had added empirical knowledge about the vast expanses of the Russian state to his familiarity with geological observations in Western Europe and particularly with the main trends in the history of geological thought. It was because of this discourse that Cuvier named Pallas the founder of modern geology.

In another discourse (1780), concerned with the variations in animals, Pallas presented certain theories of his own lying somewhere in the hazy area between the biological ideas of Linnaeus and those of Buffon. His ideas on the hybridization of animals struck Darwin as particularly stimulating.

As a young man, with considerable knowledge and intellectual courage, Pallas postulated that no hard and fast lines separated the plant and animal kingdoms. Early in his career, he saw the possibility of several species' having a common progenitor; he also thought that several species could become one, including many radically different varieties. In the intellectual battle between the proponents of preformism and those of transformism, he first sided with the latter but reversed himself soon after his arrival in St. Petersburg. As a young scholar he envisaged a tree as representing all the animal and plant species.[61] Erik Nordenskiöld concludes his survey of eighteenth-century achievements in his *History of Biology* with an account of Pallas's work, in which he describes Pallas's *New Mammal Species from the Rodentia* as "one of the really sound pieces of work that paved the way for modern comparative anatomy."[62]

Although native to Germany, Pallas received much of his education in Holland and England. His early work dealing with intestinal worms and zoophytes, along with his great promise, earned him election to the Royal Society of London. At the age of twenty-six he went to Russia, already an experienced and widely acclaimed scholar. He accepted Russia as his new homeland and spent his most fruitful years there as an Academician. In 1795 Catherine II gave him two estates and a home in the Crimea. In 1810, after the death of his wife, Pallas left the Crimea for Berlin, where he died the following year.

As a scientist, Pallas received wide recognition; he was eulogized by Cuvier and quoted by Lyell and Darwin.[63] But he was of special value in the intellectual history of Russia. More than any other single person, he impressed upon such leading Russian scholars of the eighteenth century as

Lepekhin, Sokolov, V. F. Zuev, and Ozeretskovskii the high value of scientific exactitude in the study of nature. He also honored some of these scholars by quoting their material *in extenso*.

His prose style, particularly in his *Travels in Southern Russia*, is remarkably limpid and fascinating; it drew wide attention to his work and generated much interest in the scientific accomplishments of the expeditions. Under his influence, the museum in St. Petersburg was enriched with many specimens collected by various teams, and became a lively cultural institution with a rapidly growing number of visitors. This interest was reflected in the public lectures delivered by the professors of Moscow University, in which topics in natural history were the most common. Pallas also impressed his Russian colleagues, as well as foreign scholars in the Academy, with the need for specialized study of individual branches of nature. He may rightly be considered the founder of zoology, botany, and paleontology in Russia. Oddly enough, in response to an ill-directed request by Catherine II that he undertake the compilation of a universal dictionary, he also prepared the way for the development of comparative linguistics in Russia.[64]

LEPEKHIN AND WOLFF

Pallas's star generated the most light and its rays reached farthest. But it was only one of many stars.

Another gifted natural historian was Ivan Lepekhin, who, in the words of one of his first biographers, "was sharp in thought, solid in judgment, exact in investigation, and reliable in observation." After attending the Academic University, he was sent to the University of Strasbourg to study medicine. He returned to St. Petersburg after obtaining his medical degree, and was elected an adjunct of the Academy. In 1768 he was appointed to head the Academic team sent to the lower Volga and Caspian basins for a systematic gathering of material in natural history and geography. This work completed, Lepekhin and his group swung in a northeasterly direction to survey the northern stretches of the Ural Mountains. After some further study in the Arkhangelsk area, they returned to St. Petersburg in 1772.

Lepekhin's valuable findings were eventually published under the title *Journal of Travels in Various Provinces of the Russian State*, which appeared in four volumes (1771–1805). Written in a clear and vivid style, this study is a storehouse of information, much of it previously uncollected. The work contains, for example, precise descriptions of some 600 species of plants and some 300 species of animals.[65] The observations on mineral resources are equally interesting and cogent, enriched by the author's familiarity with mineralogical theory. (Lepekhin stood firmly against the theory that mineral deposits are not found in high mountains.) Again and again, he takes up the complex question of the interrelationship of physical environment, climate, and the living world. The *Travels* are also a rich source of material on the customs of isolated Russian rural communities and on the social and economic problems of the Ural miners, who, as transplanted peasants, moved from one form of feudal bondage to another. Lepekhin also collected invaluable ethnographic material on the Mordvinians, the Chuvash, the Zyrians, the Tatars, and the Bashkirs.

The astounding erudition of Lepekhin's major work reached scholarly circles far beyond Russia and helped draw the attention of the Western world to the work of Russian scientists. The first three volumes of the *Travels* were translated into German and published between 1774 and 1783. Among other great honors which came his way, he was elected a member of the Berlin Society of Naturalists. Two insect species and a rare plant were named after him.

In the encyclopedic sweep of his interests, Lepekhin was also a typical Russian naturalist of his age. He translated the bulk of Buffon's voluminous *Histoire naturelle* into Russian; he contributed twenty-one papers to the Academy's scientific journals published in foreign languages; and he made special studies of such practical matters as cattle raising, silk production, and folk medicine. As the first secretary of the Imperial Russian Academy, founded in 1783, he contributed to the first Russian etymological dictionary.

In their encyclopedism Lepekhin and his colleagues could not match the unusually broad compass of Pallas's erudition, and as specialists in individual sciences they lacked the depth of the great master. Yet they measured up to the standards of eighteenth-century scholarship, which, while requiring rigor and objectivity in scientific analysis, treated science as a part of philosophy. There were some, however, who viewed science and philosophy as a dichotomy. V. F. Zuev, for example, argued that one of the basic duties of science was to determine the origin of organic matter and the processes underlying the formation of natural objects, and to answer similar questions that traditional philosophy, in its "realistic" and "nominalistic" branches, had failed to answer.[66]

Russian naturalists were first and foremost collectors of information. But most of them were also well acquainted with the leading philosophical questions of the day, and all were versed in the theoretical issues of contemporary science. The works of the Jussieus, Haller, Buffon, and Linnaeus were as popular and as profoundly influential among Russian naturalists as they were in the scientific circles of Western Europe. The philosophical and theoretical questions, however, were not central to the interests of the Russians. To be sure, Russians referred to theory in lectures marking special occasions in the Academy or in textbooks when called upon to synthesize various branches of natural science. But their chief concern was always with the compilation and classification of data. Despite this bent and their failure to make significant additions to scientific theory, it would be an error to identify them as outright imitators of Western biological thought, as was done by Shchapov.[67] The expeditionary work of scientists in Russia provided enough empirical material for the publication of 161 independent studies from 1742 to 1822 and made possible exciting and original developments in all branches of natural science.

Aside from the expeditionary fieldwork and certain diversified projects of Euler's disciples, who tended more and more to neglect purely scientific pursuits in favor of other activities, the Academy was chiefly identified with independent scholars. Some of these solitary Academicians were of signal importance in the development of individual sciences during the second half of the eighteenth century.

Perhaps the most outstanding among them was Caspar Wolff, the founder of modern embryology, known in the scientific world primarily through his formulation of the doctrine of epigenesis—that is, the progressive formation and differentiation of organs from a homogeneous germ.[68] As a result of his investigations a shift was made in the interpretation of the nature and significance of species. Whereas Linnaeus and his followers looked upon species primarily as convenient indices for the registration and classification of thousands of animal and plant forms, Wolff regarded them as full-dimensional natural realities. A true species was, he thought, more than simply an aggregate of morphological features; it possessed an internal unity of which the morphological characteristics were only external expressions.[69]

With his conception of *materia qualificata*, Wolff anticipated the modern theory of genes, and with his clearly expressed assertion that heredity is changeable and that new species can and do emerge, he became the eighteenth century's most eloquent precursor of Darwin. His studies of plant metamorphosis were acknowledged by Goethe as indispensable to his own work.

Wolff's original and daring ideas, however, were in no way influenced by Russian scientific tradition; the direction of his theoretical thought had been fully determined before he joined the St. Petersburg Academy. He went to Russia in search of a free atmosphere where he could pursue his scholarly work unhampered by the sort of pressures he had found in Berlin —where his unorthodox views on the transmutation of species had made it impossible for him to teach. Wolff had actually very little to do with the development of scientific thought in eighteenth-century Russia, and his influence was equally inconsequential in Western Europe—until 1812, when his work on the intestinal canal of chicks was translated from Latin into German and led to the demise of the preformist doctrine. This work, though first published in St. Petersburg, was based on data collected and interpreted in Berlin. For alas, in St. Petersburg Wolff did not find the atmosphere so free as he had expected, and he quietly abandoned his embryological studies. He never repudiated his evolutionary ideas, but he did not argue publicly with Pallas, who was an outspoken foe of all anti-preformist views.

Wolff lived so secluded and withdrawn an existence that when he died the Academy could find scarcely any biographical information for the customary *éloge*. He performed autopsies for the police department and spent long hours studying the Academy's large collection of monsters—no doubt as part of his unvoiced attack on preformism, for monsters are hard to account for in any theory of a uniform, predetermined, and static mold for all the members of each plant or animal variety.

Wolff's scientific work formed part of the first grand challenge to the absolute rule of the mechanistic view in the natural sciences, by questioning both its static, ahistorical orientation and its tendency to equate the laws of organic and inorganic nature, biology and mechanics. Wolff did not attack Newtonian mechanics directly; he merely tried to formulate a law which would have the same universality in the living world as the law of gravitation was thought to have in the physical world.

THE GROWTH OF THE SCIENTIFIC ATTITUDE IN MOSCOW

The founders of Moscow University intended it to be both an institution of higher learning and a source of new ideas in the humanities and sciences. As a matter of policy from the very start, scholarly achievements were not of prime importance in the selection of the faculty; most of the instructors were popularizers of science or philosophy, and without fixed specialties. Furthermore, in contrast to the Academicians, who were encouraged from time to time to write textbooks and manuals for their students, the faculty of Moscow University was not permitted to use any textbooks except those prescribed by the head of the University and the Faculty Council, a body made up of the instructional staff of the University.

Among the first professors of Moscow University were two recent graduates of the Academic University, who had so far shown no particular aptitude for scholarship. One of these was hired to teach mathematics but soon switched to the loosely defined field of philology. Of the original eight professors, only the two were Russians; the others were foreigners, all graduates of German universities: Tübingen, Stuttgart, Vienna, Leipzig, and Göttingen. Seven of the eight were in the social sciences, literature, and philosophy. But if Moscow University at first produced little in the way of original scientific work, it led all intellectual institutions in eighteenth-century Russia in stimulating popular interest in science and helping to develop a scientific attitude.

In an extensive program of public lectures, the professors brought to Russians for the first time many of the great philosophical and ethical issues currently absorbing to Western minds. In 1762 one of the professors inaugurated a quarterly entitled *Collection of the Best Works for the Dissemination of Knowledge*, which treated various "physical," "economic," "industrial," and "commercial" matters.[70] The University press published the first collection of Lomonosov's works and issued Russian translations of works by Pope, Locke, Bacon, Bossuet, and others. To be sure, some of these translations were appallingly garbled, and some were so emasculated by the censors of the Synod that they were actually corruptions of the original. Nikolai Popovskii had particular difficulty with his translation of Pope's "Essay on Man." In the first place, he did not know English and made his translation from a French edition of the famous poem; even then, he admitted that there were lines which he did not fully understand. But his main trouble came from the Church censors, who charged him with having disregarded the views contained in religious books. They were most critical of the poem's endorsement of the plurality of worlds and of Copernican heliocentrism.[71]

A learned association which had close ties with the University was the Free Russian Council, founded in 1771 for the purpose of collecting documents relating to Russian history, particularly the evolution of Russian law. One of the ambitious undertakings of the Council was the systematic preparation of an ecclesiastical dictionary and a geographical dictionary, both of which were completed in the first decade of the Council's existence. The Council's *Works* carried articles by eminent clergymen and such erudite laymen as M. N. Murav'ev and F. N. Golitsyn. In the 1780's the work of the Council was gradually taken over by similar societies with firmer financial resources.

Although France was now the source of Russian ideas and fashions, Moscow University had no direct contact with the French intellectual centers. The only foreign teachers in the early years were German, and their employment was looked upon as no more than a temporary expedient made necessary by the acute shortage of competent Russian teachers. It was realized that even the first Russian teachers would have foreign degrees, but it was hoped that in time they would supplant the Germans. In the years 1757–58, only two of the eight instructors were Russians; in 1770–71 the staff of fourteen instructors was equally divided between Russians and Germans. These Russians had received their higher degrees in Scotland, the Netherlands, and Sweden.

S. E. Desnitskii and I. A. Tretiakov were sent by the government to the University of Glasgow to study mathematics, but their interest turned to law and they subsequently introduced a pragmatic-historical element into Russian jurisprudence. At the time of their studies in Glasgow the University was the seat of a great intellectual fermentation, full of audacious ventures into the most complex questions of socio-ethical and economic reality. Tretiakov and Desnitskii thus became the bearers of advanced thought. Tretiakov's essay on "Causes of the Fast or Slow Enrichment of Nations" (1772) was the first Russian presentation of Adam Smith's ideas in political economy. Desnitskii, at the request of the royal court, translated Sir William Blackstone's *Commentaries* in three volumes.

Desnitskii was an outspoken foe of Wolff's and Vattel's version of the theory of natural law, then accepted by the majority of the Moscow University faculty, which claimed that "the law of nations is originally no other than the law of nature applied to nations." This antihistorical point of view placed law above history and nations, which cannot abrogate or change it. Desnitskii was an enthusiastic supporter of the historical-comparative approach to the study of Russian law; this method, he claimed, made it possible to determine how legal abstractions were molded by societies into living realities, and how legal concepts changed from one historical period to another and from one social system to another. He was equally opposed to the students of law who placed no value on theory and to those who tended to attribute the immutability of the laws of Newtonian mechanics to the laws governing human societies. In his middle-of-the-road position, he impressed upon his contemporaries that the study of law must be based on four pillars: moral philosophy, Roman law, natural jurisprudence, and national law.

Werner Sombart has said that the eighteenth-century Scottish moral philosophers, with their humanistic, historical, and comparative point of view in the study of institutions, were the true ancestors of modern sociology. In bringing this point of view to Russia, Desnitskii and Tretiakov became the founders of the sociological study of Russian institutions, even though they only incidentally applied their theories to the study of actual situations. They not only introduced the concept of social change but also equated it with the idea of progress.

S. G. Zybelin and P. D. Veniaminov received doctorates from Leyden University. In 1765–66 Zybelin gave his first lectures in "theoretical medicine" at Moscow University, while Veniaminov took up the teaching of "philosophical botany." Neither of them produced any work of substance, but they were influential as ardent supporters of rationalism, careful research, and the scientific attitude. M. I. Afonin was granted a doctoral degree in 1766 by the University of Uppsala, where he studied under Linnaeus. At Moscow University, he taught botanical classification and nomenclature. Afonin paved the way in Russia for a scientific study of the origin and types of soil, but he had neither the intellect nor the background to match Russia's great soil scientists of the nineteenth century.

During the first half-century of its existence, Moscow University served as neither a source nor a transmitting station for the great and influential currents of modern scientific thought. Suffering protracted birth pains, the University was too weak to gird itself for the ideological onslaughts on the elements of academic freedom. To the government, the St. Petersburg Academy was the display piece of Russia's participation in modern science—the embodiment of Peter's dream of lifting the country out of barbarism into the modern age. It amiably supplied the Academy with the funds it needed, particularly for the salaries of the learned staff—no doubt remembering all too well the rapid deterioration of the Academy's reputation and welfare when the foreign staff resigned during the troubles of the 1750's. Catherine's readiness to pay handsomely for Euler's return marked the start of a period during which the government consistently lived up to its financial obligations toward the Academy.

At Moscow University, however, things were different. From the very beginning, the teachers were so grossly underpaid that most of them were obliged to seek additional employment—usually as tutors in boarding schools or private homes. Sometimes, for a variety of reasons, salaries were not paid for months on end.[72]

The demoralization of the teachers was acute, and drunkenness was common. The burden of the foreign professors was particularly heavy. Their difficulties with the language made it well-nigh impossible to maintain friendly relations with the students, who as a rule had only the most elementary knowledge of Latin, and no knowledge of the modern Western European languages. The miseries of these instructors were aggravated even more by Catherine's order in 1767 that all lectures at Moscow University be delivered in Russian.[73]

The foreign instructors at Moscow University showed far more interest in the cultural life of their adopted homeland than their counterparts at the St. Petersburg Academy. They did earnestly try to learn Russian, and they were enthusiastic in their work on numerous projects designed to advance the cause of science among the Russian public. The audiences which attended their public lectures grew increasingly alert and scientifically aware, eager to hear about the latest philosophical and scientific ideas from the West. Many of the translations published by the Moscow University press were made by the foreign instructors, and by working closely with their Russian colleagues they added significantly to the body of Russian scientific terminology. With their diverse academic backgrounds and training, they directly exemplified the intellectual ferment then characteristic of Western thinking. Thus, while the members of the St. Petersburg Academy were adding more and more to the fund of scientific knowledge, the professors at Moscow University were expanding and instructing the circle of those who wanted to learn about science.

There was another telling difference between the St. Petersburg Academicians and the Moscow professors. The Academicians worked mostly in the natural and exact sciences, which were little affected by the ideological issues of the day, and they wrote in Latin, French, or German, which removed them even further from the eyes of ideological watchdogs. Moreover, no person in the Synod was sophisticated enough to recognize Caspar Wolff's embryological concepts and Pallas's geological interpretation of the origin of mountains as challenges to the biblical stories of the creation. Most of the Moscow University professors, on the other hand, worked in the humanities and social sciences, which were deeply concerned with contemporary ideological questions. As a rule, they wrote for the public at large, not for the scholarly world, and they wrote mostly in Russian. Thus exposed, they were subject to constant pressures emanating from the

Synod and other bastions of conservatism. It is not particularly surprising that they loudly upheld the cause of absolutism, the estate system based on the institution of serfdom, and official theology; nor is it odd that the most noticeably loyal to the status quo were the foreign professors.

In 1769 Dmitrii Anichkov, an instructor in mathematics and philosophy, completed a work on "the natural origins" of religion. He was immediately and unanimously attacked by his colleagues as an upholder of Lucretius's paganism. A devastating denunciation by a spokesman of the Synod followed; he labeled Anichkov's work an open condemnation of "all Christianity" and urged an intensified Church surveillance of all writings, scholarly or not.[74] Professor Mellmann, toward the end of the century, ventured to make the first formal presentation in Russia of the ideas contained in Kant's *Critique of Pure Reason*. He was expelled from the University and from Moscow as well.

During this period, the Moscow professors extolled in books and lectures the superiority of monarchical rule (Schaden), the glory of Russia in contrast to revolution-racked Western Europe (Chebotarev), and the evils of freedom (Hause). In 1799 Professor Hein delivered a speech devoted to "the status of science in Russia under the guardianship of Paul I" in which he greeted the newly instituted censorship, including its sweeping restrictions on the importation of scientific books, as a wise effort to save true science from "pseudo-science."[75] Two Moscow University professors were relieved of their teaching assignments in order to serve as official censors.

At the end of the eighteenth century, Moscow University was an established institution with graduates who occupied key positions in the government, the army, the literary field, and public life in general. But it was to be another thirty years before the University could be called a noteworthy scientific center. Its curriculum was still unbalanced and incomplete, and students were unable to pursue any subject intensively. It offered a respectable number of courses in Greek and Roman history, but none at all in Russian history. One elementary survey of Russian law was the only special course for students who expected to enter the government service. One graduate of the University noted in his autobiography that all he learned about the law of his country was how to fill out the petitions addressed to the highest government authorities.[76]

The young university was further hobbled by the unwillingness of the government to send its graduates to Western Europe for additional studies. Young Russians were assiduously prevented from attending universities in France, which were the blossoming centers of scientific and humanistic research, and for decades only handfuls of students were sent to other European universities. The ten young men sent by the Senate in 1761 to —— Leyden University to study medicine were the largest single group to go to the West in search of formal education. Paul I went so far as to prohibit his subjects from attending any Western European universities at all.

These difficulties, however, did not crush the University—they merely prolonged its infancy. In the meantime, Moscow University was without a peer in Russia as a disseminator of scientific knowledge. During the last decade of the century it finally acquired a small group of professors, including A. M. Briantsev, who were capable of wrestling with highly theoretical problems and had an interest in the general laws of nature.[77] At this time the University press undertook to publish new editions of certain of the mathematical contributions of Newton, Daniel Bernoulli, Euler, and Lagrange.

The effects of Moscow University's work in the secularization of knowledge were so profound that they reached even the theological schools. A special agreement authorized the University to train instructors for secular subjects taught at the Kiev Academy.[78] During the 1780's the Kiev Academy finally ceased teaching Scholasticized Aristotelian physics and began to adopt textbooks presenting modern physical concepts and theories.

THE NEW LEARNED SOCIETIES

During the reign of Catherine II, scientific research began to find serious support as a special mode of intellectual inquiry even among persons not associated either with the Academy or with the University. In recognition of this interest, Catherine II in 1765 suggested the founding of the Free Economic Society, a scholarly body unattached, as the name implied, to any government agency. Its membership consisted of interested persons from the top level of the service aristocracy, close to the imperial court, and selected Academicians. Although such famous Academicians as Euler and Müller were among its members, the greater part of the research conducted under the auspices of the Society was done by independent scholars. The idea of the Society was not precisely a new one—there having been such an organization in Brittany since 1756, and others of a similar sort in Switzerland, Germany, and Great Britain—but it was an innovation for Russia.

Like its Western models, the Free Economic Society was devoted to the improvement of agriculture through the spread of advanced technology, methods of sanitation, and economic knowledge. The carefully selected members of the Society conducted experiments in various branches of the national economy from agriculture, hunting, and fishing to mining and industry. They also presented papers on economic ideas developed in the West but applicable to Russia, and studied "mechanics and rural architecture." Most of these papers were published in the *Works* of the Society, which appeared at regular intervals. The original charter emphasized that all work under the auspices of the Society had to be "practical" and that no "speculative," that is, theoretical, studies should be undertaken.[79] Soon after its inception, the Society was requested by Catherine II to study the comparative advantages and disadvantages of free and enserfed agricultural work. In the course of its search for the right answer, the Society solicited 162 reports, from all parts of Europe (only seven of them in the Russian language). Catherine, to no one's surprise, paid no heed to the reports, which showed the superior economic and cultural advantages of a free peasantry. The Society, however, was quite aware that serfdom was a historical institution in need of critical examination, and it built a solid foundation for the scientific study of agricultural economics and technology.

Essentially, of course, the Society sought to improve agricultural production without changing its social context. It stimulated scholarship by sponsoring essay contests, by giving the dissidents (of whom there were fewer and fewer) an opportunity to voice their views, and by sending groups of young men to Western Europe to study the techniques of modern agronomy.[80] One of the most eminent of the original "dissenters" was A. Ia. Polenov, who, though fundamentally a moderate, produced several searching examinations of feudal institutions. It was mostly through the efforts of the Society that at the beginning of the nineteenth century Russian universities began offering courses in such subjects as rural home economics, agriculture and agricultural technology, and economic botany.

Other learned societies also enriched the intellectual life of Catherine's Russia and gave scientific thought a broader compass and a more diversified following. Some of these operated within the framework of Moscow University (the Free Council, 1777–87), others were sponsored by the Freemasons (the Learned Fraternal Society), and still others relied on a more general public (the Society of the Friends of Scholarship, founded in 1789). None of these survived as long as the Free Economic Society, which lasted more than 150 years. The most enduring and by far the most fruitful was the Imperial Russian Academy, founded by Catherine II and Princess

Dashkova in 1783. As the St. Petersburg Academy was comparable to the Paris Académie des Sciences, the new institution was modeled after the Académie Française.

According to M. I. Sukhomlinov: "The Russian Academy, dedicated to the study of the Russian language, played an essential role in the history of Russian literature. The establishment of this institution was a response to the literary needs of that time; it was the realization of an idea which had engaged our writers since the early days, and which attracted the sympathies of educated circles. . . . The membership of the Academy was made up of all the literary figures of the end of the eighteenth century: its roster included our leading scholars and writers."[81] The Russian Academy was entrusted with the noble and essential task of "purifying" and "enriching" the Russian language and of preparing a Russian grammar, a dictionary, a rulebook of versification, and a manual of rhetoric. The accomplishment of these titanic tasks was seriously complicated by Russia's lack of anything beyond the rudimentary elements of philology. The official membership of the new Academy, limited by its charter to sixty, contained no professional linguists. In selecting its members, the Academy wisely tried to assemble the country's leading representatives of all types of scientific inquiry. Among the first members were leading scientists from the Academy of Sciences, professors from Moscow University, associates of the Free Economic Society, and learned clergymen.

The tasks of the new institution were compounded by the still unresolved question of a Russian literary language. Despite its obvious inadequacy for new ideas, the rigid, anachronistic written language, overburdened with Church-Slavic lexical elements, still retained the status of "the highest form" of the Russian language. The first project of the new Academy was to begin the compilation of a *Dictionary of the Russian Academy*, which would combine the Church-Slavic and Russian languages.

The naturalist Ivan Lepekhin, of the St. Petersburg Academy of Sciences, was the new institution's first permanent secretary, an influential position which he occupied until his death. The membership included other leading naturalists—Rumovskii, Kotel'nikov, Inokhodtsev, Ozeretskovskii, Sokolov, and Protasov. In preparing the dictionary (published in 1789–94) the naturalists achieved three things: first, they amassed sufficient information to show the intrinsic incompatibility of the inflexible 1) Church-Slavic language with the new secular learning; second, they enriched the literary language by systematically incorporating the new scientific terminology; and third, they introduced the criteria of scientific pre- 3) cision into such linguistic questions as that of word structure. No war was declared on the language of the Church and "classical" literature. It lingered on, inflexible and petrified in its structure and impoverished in its vocabulary, until the initial decades of the nineteenth century, when it ceased to be a living force and became a historical relic.

The Russian Academy persistently followed Lomonosov's earlier suggestion that the Russian literary language be enlarged by the addition of important unique words of individual dialects. In this field, too, the knowledge of the naturalists was of importance. Ozeretskovskii, for example, supplied many dialectisms from North Russia, particularly words pertaining to natural phenomena and cultural traits.[82] Inokhodtsev submitted a list of local words having to do with native arts and crafts.[83]

It must be remembered that it was the writer and the scientist who really formed the modern Russian literary language in their writings, and that the work of the Russian Academy was chiefly that of culling these various contributions and giving them formal recognition. The Russian Academy's central goal was to build a Russian literary language which could be universally employed in literary and scientific communication. The Academy of Sciences was a center for scholars filled with the spirit of natural philosophy and trained in the scientific method, who searched for new knowledge in all areas of scientific inquiry. The Russian Academy solicited the services of persons representing the whole spectrum of intellectual endeavor—its membership included scientists, with or without formal training, learned ecclesiasts, unattached historians (such as Boltin), and literary figures (led by Derzhavin and Fonvizin). The Russian Academy was a truly Russian institution; it was a magnificent rallying point for a host of men with outstanding creative ability. Indeed, its marshaling of the country's talent was historically and culturally more important than the compiling of the *Dictionary* itself.

HISTORY AND IDEOLOGY

Most of the scientific development during the age of Catherine II came from institutions of one sort or another, but it was an age also of scholars working on their own, under no institutional auspices. These men came from all walks of life and from all corners of Russia. Although few of them had much formal education, their interests ran the gamut from astronomy to local history.

In the course of the scientific expeditions, the scholars from St. Petersburg invariably encountered men in farflung places who were genuine repositories of local lore. V. V. Krestinin, for example, supplied Lepekhin and Ozeretskovskii with valuable historical data on Northern Russia. Reflecting the spirit of the Enlightenment, he even tried to found a historical society in Arkhangelsk. V. G. Ruban, who attended the Kiev Theological Academy, published a mass of information relevant to local histories in the Ukraine. Many learned clergymen wrote on various aspects of the history of the Russian Church. In time, these little rivulets of local history merged, giving rise to a national history which went far beyond the antiquarian historiography of Tatishchev.

To write anything resembling a national history at this time was a formidable undertaking. Solov'ev correctly pointed out that studies in the natural sciences and mathematics were easier because of the greater number of books in these fields, in Western European languages if not in Russian. Basic books in history were virtually nonexistent, and documentary sources were scattered and often inaccessible. Tatishchev's history was scarcely more than a careful compilation of documents. Lomonosov was good at analyzing the opinions of other historians, but his manner of relating historical events was hardly more than "a dry, lifeless, and rhetorical paraphrasing of chronicles, occasionally subjected to drastic distortions."[84]

Since the time of Peter I, there had been a strong need in Russia for the study of history as a record of national progress. The Catherinean period, characterized by intensive literary activity, provided historians not only with ideological norms but also with models of literary expression. Both local and national history, the two major historiographical types of the day and the choice of the self-styled historians, were seen as a matter of assembling documentary sources in order to elucidate the depth and profound unity of Russia's past. The national historians also sought to weave the history of Russia into universal history and to blend the Russian past with that of the West. Moreover, national pride demanded that Russian scholars be the custodians of their own past. For decades, Müller dominated the field of Russian history in the St. Petersburg Academy of Sciences. When he left the Academy in 1765 for a position with the Moscow archives, his place was taken for a brief time by another German, August Schlözer. Schlözer was a man of great learning and linguistic background and he published important documentary material, meticulously annotated, but he is chiefly remembered for his bold (and highly exaggerated) assertion that the Russians had had neither religion, nor law, nor political institutions prior to the appearance of the Variags.

Until 1769 the West got its Russian history mostly through Western writers. A new period in the study of Russian history was opened in 1769—the year of the publication of the first two volumes of Prince Mikhail Shcherbatov's *History of Russia Since Ancient Times* (which eventually ran to a total of seven volumes). Shcherbatov, considerably less erudite than Lomonosov, attacked his subject with a kind of plodding determination. His place in the history of Russian historiography is best described by Solov'ev:

"Prince Shcherbatov was a wise, diligent, conscientious, and well-read man. He was acquainted with the literature of other peoples, particularly their historical writings. His study of Russian history was not thorough. It is obvious that he knew very little about his people's historical past before he began to write about it, that he lacked a clear idea about its course and peculiarities, and that he studied it solely from the viewpoint of general humanity, the only side he understood well. He viewed every event in perfect isolation—he limited himself to purely logical and moral appraisals of individual happenings . . . and he made no genuine historical evaluations. However, where Lomonosov gave only embellished presentations of materials contained in ancient chronicles, Shcherbatov pondered over these reports. Well acquainted with the great events of world history, he compared them with happenings in Russia, emphasizing and elucidating their peculiarities. He did not fully succeed in this enterprise, and sometimes he was completely wrong, because the true course of Russian history remained a secret to him. I repeat, however, that he stopped at each event, thought about it, and tried to explain it. As is well known, he rendered great service to science by being the first to draw attention to certain events and explain them, even though his explanations were not always acceptable. He was not a professional historian. However, he studied history for history-writing's sake and began to recognize—or rather sense—a science in it. This proclivity elevated his work above that of Lomonosov and subsequent writers, who were interested primarily in writing their historical studies in an elegant style."[85]

It was, however, mostly because of his uninteresting style, devoid of the poetic adornments then fashionable, that Shcherbatov's influence on his contemporaries was weaker than the scholarly qualities of his work would seem to have warranted. His excessive attention to trivial events also narrowed his reading public.[86]

The leading Russian historian of the latter part of the eighteenth century—if not of the entire century—was Ivan Boltin. Boltin, like Shcherbatov, was a self-educated aristocrat, who spent most of his life in the army *Boltin* and had no academic training; but he was steeped in philosophy, languages, and the classics, and had besides a talent for historical investigation and a facile literary style.[87] Boltin considered it the job of the historian to take inventory of the progressive developments in a society—specifically, for a Russian, to assess the growth of national consciousness, the general effects of Peter's reforms, and the place of Russia in the cultural development of Europe.

Boltin's magnum opus was a scorching attack on Nicolas LeClerc's *Natural, Moral, Civil, and Political History of Ancient and Contemporary Russia*, published in France in 1783-94. Much in the way that Lomonosov, with a true Russian's pride, had taken a dim view of Voltaire's history of the age of Peter the Great, Boltin scorned LeClerc's generalizations, which, he charged, were based on myths and exaggerations: all Russians of the ninth and tenth centuries were savages, the Slavs were incapable by temperament of founding their own states, the Russian patriarchal system made all women slaves, the Russian language was singularly lacking in words denoting abstract qualities, and so on. Boltin took it as his sacred duty to set right LeClerc's misrepresentations and falsehoods, and if anyone else stood in his way—like Shcherbatov, on whom LeClerc admittedly relied—he, too, fell under merciless attack.

In the course of countering LeClerc's many inaccuracies, Boltin was obliged to cover the entire sweep of Russian history, but he did this in a rather unsystematic way, not regarding it as the function of the historian to be merely chronological. In truth, his real purpose was to declare—somewhat prematurely—Russia's intellectual emancipation from the West. In the process of trying to achieve this end, he wrested historiography away from the Academicians and made it a moral force of the first magnitude.

Solov'ev points out that in order to understand Boltin's place in the history of Russian historiography and, more generally, in the growth of Russian culture, one must be cognizant of the extent to which the meanings of science and education had changed since the beginning of Catherine's rule.[88] In the years between Peter I and Catherine II, science was viewed mainly from a materialistic-utilitarian standpoint; its value lay in what it could do to improve the standard of living. Under Catherine II this view was expanded; science became now also a source of moral education and *ed % Cath* character building. As I. I. Betskoi, a leading proponent of this orientation, is said to have remarked, Peter I created men in Russia, but Catherine II gave them souls. It is Solov'ev's argument that the Petrine reformists, not wishing to be reminded of the age of darkness, their minds intent on new horizons, purposely ignored history in favor of science, and that as technical education and the attendant antihistoricism gradually gave way to the strictly "formal" education of the Elizabethan era, all intellectual emphasis was lost. This was the period of private tutors, often as ignorant as the pupils they taught—and of ignorant parents, whose educational methods produced the monster of Fonvizin's satire *The Minor*.

Largely under the influence of the French *philosophes,* the leading intellectuals of the reign of Catherine II came to see the value not only of Western culture but also of Russian culture, a combination of which could give historical depth to the feeling of national unity. The time had come to reconcile "the new and the foreign" in modern Russian culture with the notion of the historical uniqueness of the Russian nation. It thus became Boltin's role, as an eminent spokesman of his time, to demonstrate the importance of historiography as a means of interpreting the way in which Russian culture had emerged through a long historical development, only in part influenced by Western society.

Boltin shared Shcherbatov's aristocratic ideological point of view, blessing both serfdom and monarchical absolutism, and in the hands of the two of them historiography became a mighty weapon of official ideology. Unlike many of their contemporaries, who thought that history was a survey of selected documents made palatable by a romantic glorification of national heroes and victories in war, Boltin and Shcherbatov, with their superior knowledge and higher sense of the historian's role, went a long way toward developing a Russian historical attitude.

Other historians of the time, among them F. A. Emin and I. P. Elagin, tried to recapture Russia's history in its entirety; others, led by Ivan Golikov, limited their panegyrics to specific individuals or epochs. Most local historians, usually not of the aristocratic class, were fairly straightforward, adding geography rather than sentiment to their accounts. One interesting local historian—considerably above the norm not only in background but in eventual recognition—was P. I. Rychkov, the son of a Vologda merchant. He learned German from the customers who did business with his father, and easily obtained employment in a customs office. From there he went on, during the 1830's, to participate in the so-called Orenburg Expedition—led first by Krylov and then by Tatishchev—which was assigned to make a thorough survey of the newly acquired Kazakh areas. Rychkov's detailed reports to the government formed the basis for his excellent work on the topography and history of Orenburg (now Chkalov) as well as for his study of the ancient and medieval history of Kazan. For these he was highly praised by such eminent scholars as Müller and Lomonosov.[89]

Lacking the advantage of a formal education, Rychkov spent most of his life in a variety of government jobs remote from the world of scholarship, but by 1759 his published works had brought him such wide acclaim that he was elected the first Russian corresponding member of the St. Petersburg Academy of Sciences. He lived up to this great honor by sending the Academy valuable reports, chiefly in ornithology and geology. In 1765 he became a charter member of the Free Economic Society. During the next eight years he contributed thirty articles to the Society's *Works*, all of them dealing with the natural resources of the Orenburg region. Pallas was so impressed by his *Orenburg Topography* that he worked on a German translation of it, which he only abandoned on learning that a famous geographer had already done the job.

Rychkov belonged to a small group of able and enterprising individuals who, on their own initiative, widened their intellectual horizons and embarked on scholarly work. He was not typical of the group, for he had the good fortune to learn under the experienced and erudite (and self-educated) Tatishchev, and to receive the encouragement and counsel of Müller and Lomonosov. In becoming a corresponding member of the St. Petersburg Academy, he became a part of both scholarly worlds.

THE SELF-TAUGHT INVENTORS

Among the rather numerous self-educated exponents of science—few of whom merited the name "scholar" or even approached Rychkov in knowledge or recognition—was an important and fascinating breed of inventors in the field of industrial technology. These men had little, if any, academic training, but they kept in touch with modern scientific thought by reading the popular scientific journals published by the Academy of Sciences, by Moscow University, and by the enterprising Nikolai Novikov. They read Lomonosov's *First Principles of Metallurgy*, hundreds of copies of which were circulated in the Ural mining centers, and some managed to acquire copies of the mathematical and mechanical manuals used in the military schools.

Not just so many bright peasants with a flair for traditional common-sense science, they combined the folk science of the inquisitive Russian peasant and the spirit of modern science. Like Rychkov, they added to the flow and breadth of science by giving it a Russian tributary. What these amateurs did in the various fields of industrial technology was in itself impressive, yet their main contribution lay in bringing scientific thought and methods to places remote from St. Petersburg and Moscow and to institutions primarily interested in industrial production. Also, as Shchapov has pointed out, they were living proof that the lower estates in the second half of the eighteenth century had "a natural thirst for higher scientific education" and ample ability to contribute to all fields of intellectual endeavor.[90]

I. I. Polzunov was one of the most intelligent and sophisticated of these pioneers. The son of a Guards soldier, he attended the mining school in Ekaterinburg (now Sverdlovsk), where, in addition to an elementary knowledge of geometry, trigonometry, arithmetic, drawing, and grammar, he acquired sound reading habits and an acquaintance with the basic technological literature.[91] At the age of eighteen he was appointed a mining technician in the Altaian mine of Barnaul. In casting about for technical knowledge—of which the mines in the Altai and the Urals were in desperate want—he became acquainted with Academician Krafft's book on "simple and complex machines," Lomonosov's *Metallurgy*, and Schlatter's work on mining techniques. The Academician Erik Laxmann, on a visit to the Barnaul mine, was struck by Polzunov's remarkable technical competence and unusual inventive ability. Polzunov's greatest technical achievement—for which the Russians today honor him—was a steam engine which he constructed in the Barnaul mine in 1763–66.[92] A small-scale replica of the engine, preserved in the local mining museum with Polzunov's detailed plan, clearly shows the high level of the inventor's technical and scientific skill.[93] Unfortunately, the engine was not put into operation until several months after Polzunov's death; it worked one full day, broke down, and was never used again.

K. D. Frolov, the son of a miner, was also a graduate of the Ekaterinburg mining school. He advanced from miner's apprentice to manager of a silver mine and mastered engineering by reading the technical books he found in mine libraries. He is remembered as the designer of complex water-powered plants in the Urals and the Altai—consisting of gigantic waterwheels and intricate systems of transmission mechanisms—which handled several operations in the processing of ore.[94] For the Zmeinogorsk mine in the Altai, he designed an especially complex network of water-propelled installations, mostly underground, for which the cascading water ran a course of a mile and a half. He worked out other inventions to make mining possible in flooded areas and to handle the reflux of water from the operating sections of mines. He also designed crushing and washing machines for the extraction of gold from ores.[95]

I. P. Kulibin, another self-educated master of mechanics, came from a lower-middle-class family in Nizhni Novgorod.[96] While still in his teens he built intricately ornamented clocks. Nearly his entire collection was bought by Catherine II on one of her visits to Nizhni Novgorod and placed by her in the St. Petersburg Museum. As a special reward, Kulibin was sent to the St. Petersburg Academy to work as a mechanic. There he studied physics, mechanics, and chemistry on his own, and he constructed a telescope, a microscope, and two field glasses after models of similar instruments owned by the Academy. In 1773 he prepared a plan for a one-span wooden bridge across the Neva. Euler checked his calculations, approved them, and published his remarks in the Academy's *Novi Commentarii*. When Kulibin later submitted a huge model of his bridge to the Academy for its approval, Euler joined with the others in rejecting it as impractical, though he still thought it theoretically sound.[97] In 1777 Daniel Bernoulli wrote to Academician Nicolaus Fuss: "I am very much interested in your note concerning the self-taught mechanic Mr. Kulibin and his project for a wooden bridge across the Neva. . . . I have a high opinion of the experienced builder and carpenter, who was educated among simple peasants and is indebted for his higher knowledge only to some kind of instinct."[98]

Polzunov, Frolov, and Kulibin, and hundreds of other men like them scattered across the vast empire, were an affirmation of Lomonosov's claim that the eradication of class prejudice in marshaling the country's intellectual resources was the only way to achieve a sound and more prosperous future. The emergence of self-taught inventors in comparatively large numbers and in modern garb symbolized the readiness of Russian culture to meet Francis Bacon's thundering dictum that scientific wisdom is the surest signpost toward better days for humanity.

The honor generally accorded these men in their own time is equally significant. The appreciative attitude of the government toward them is a matter of historical record. Polzunov's work brought him not only compliments from Catherine but also occasional stipends and a rapid ascent up the ladder of mining administration.[99] Frolov was similarly rewarded for his technical contributions.[100] Kulibin was disappointed in his dream of a one-span bridge across the Neva, but he gained the praise of Euler and Bernoulli, and the government awarded him a prize of 2,000 rubles as a token of recognition. In the following generations, their life stories and their achievements were chronicled in the public press—particularly in *Fatherland Notes*—as proof of what could be done and a warning, as it were, that a vast area of the country's great intellectual resources would remain dormant so long as the lower social classes were denied direct and free access to institutions of formal schooling.

In this wide sweep of intellectual interest in the Catherinean age, from erudite Academicians to local historians and inventors, one sees the extent to which science had become a cultural function and in what manner it had been entrusted to individuals from the various sectors of Russia's tight and elaborate estate system. The natural and mathematical sciences were a virtual monopoly of the middle stratum (the sons of the clergy, Guards soldiers, successful urban merchants, and similar groups); national history attracted mostly persons of aristocratic origin; local history, codification of "folk science," and useful technical innovations were the province of the lowest ranks of the "free estates." In this unequal distribution, two facts are particularly striking as indications of the cultural legacy of the eighteenth century: first, despite its growing leisure and intensified contact with Western culture, the Russian aristocracy remained relatively indifferent to the mounting work in the natural and mathematical sciences; and, second, the intellectual potential of the Russian peasantry remained virtually untapped. In the proposal for the founding of Moscow University, it was stated that enserfed persons should be admitted neither to the university nor to its gymnasiums because "sciences are respected as *noble* pursuits and tolerate no coercion."[101]

THE NEW INTELLECTUALS AND THEIR WORLD VIEWS

Throughout the age of Catherine II, the growth of the scientific spirit really outstripped the growth of scientific inquiry. This was largely due to the support and endorsement of leading intellectuals who were not themselves scientists but who spoke of science with the utmost respect. These intellectuals—writers and philosophers, for the most part—were few in number, and they can more accurately be called prophets than spokesmen of their age. They did not adhere to specific schools of thought, nor were they models of consistent philosophy. Nevertheless, they sensed the importance of modern scientific thought, made use of it, and showed remarkable familiarity with the great issues which troubled the world of scientific scholarship during the second half of the eighteenth century.

Iakov Kozel'skii, one of these men, was neither praised nor damned by the writers of his day, even though his translations and original writings reached a considerable segment of the country's limited reading public.* From 1752 to 1757 he was enrolled in the Academic University, where he received a grounding in mathematics and physics. He met his military obligation partly by serving as an instructor in the Artillery and Engineering School. Here he also served his writing apprenticeship by preparing two textbooks for his students, one in mechanics and one in mathematics.[102] These books were unusual in being not simply copies of corresponding Western texts but original works, the result of a deliberate effort to express complex scientific ideas in a lucid fashion and to describe scientific abstractions in terms closely related to everyday life. When he had completed his military service, Kozel'skii was appointed a member of the Council for the Translation of Foreign Books (established by Catherine II in 1768), under whose sponsorship he translated a number of articles, mostly by Diderot, from the famous *Encyclopédie*.

Two years before Kozel'skii began his rather extensive translations, he published his *Philosophical Suggestions*. This work is a cross between the rigidly formalistic metaphysical ideas of Christian Wolff and the broad and effervescent humanism of Helvétius, Montesquieu, Voltaire, and Rousseau. Kozel'skii's mastery of the leading philosophical issues of the day led him to a kind of eclecticism in which he neither accepted wholly any one philosophical point of view nor offered a consistent point of view of his own. His ideas clearly show his scientific training: he was devoted to a belief in positive knowledge as a source of cultural progress.[103] He fought equally against the emptiness of Scholasticism and the sterility of idealistic metaphysics. He admired Rousseau's social philosophy, but he could not accept Rousseau's attitude toward science.[104] Whereas theology and philosophy were mutually exclusive, he argued, science and philosophy supplemented and reinforced each other. He saw all knowledge as a unity, but attainable by diverse methods—most importantly the historical (statement of facts), the philosophical (study of causes), and the mathematical (quantitative measurement).[105]

Kozel'skii is important in a study of eighteenth-century attitudes not

* As a matter of fact, he was completely forgotten by the writers of the nineteenth century. It was not until 1906 that the general public became acquainted with his work, thanks to an article carried by *Russkaia starina* (P. Stolpianskii, "Odin iz nezametnykh deiatelei Ekaterininskoi epokhi. II. Iakov Pavlovich Kozel'skii," *Russkaia starina*, CXXVIII, No. 12, 1906, 567–84).

only because of his philosophical belief in a science based on empirical fact and free from theological influence but also because he allowed his scientific enthusiasm to color some of his specific ideological views. His endorsement of the branch of the "natural law" theory which recognized the inalienable rights of the individual as well as his persistent and uncompromising attacks on war allied him with Russia's first critics of the existing social system. His radicalism, however, was considerably weakened by his inconsistencies—especially by his Voltairean disrespect for the lower social estates. He is perhaps worthy of remembrance alone for his warning to contemporaries not to accept the idea, widely held in the West, that the Russian people lacked the basic intellectual potentialities for scientific work. He asserted, with an almost twentieth-century rationalism, that science does not depend so much on inherent capabilities as it does on long and dedicated work.[106]

The most colorful and certainly the most enterprising and controversial champion of the Enlightenment during the last quarter of the eighteenth century was Nikolai Novikov. In Kliuchevskii's words: "A printer, publisher, book salesman, journalist, literary historian, school superintendent, and philanthropist, Novikov had a single aim in all his activities: the dissemination of enlightenment."[107] At the Moscow University gymnasium Novikov early came under the influence of the French *philosophes,* but he was far from being a mere sponge for the great ideas of the age. He was scornful of Russians who were enamored of Rousseau only because of his antiscientific attitude. To Russian Rousseauites he said: "He, with his intellect, and you, with your ignorance, try to prove the uselessness of science."[108] He was equally critical of contemporaries who scorned their own cultural tradition and sought to borrow everything from the West.[109]

Feeling that some of the French *philosophes* placed undue emphasis on moral education, Novikov advocated a balanced cultivation of the intellect and the moral character. The statement of the poet Sumarokov on the occasion of the opening of the Academy of Arts, that "the diffusion of science has killed natural simplicity and with it purity of heart," embodied the kind of educational philosophy to which Novikov was categorically opposed.[110] In a succession of satirical papers which were a circuitous but effective means of criticizing certain outmoded values of Russian society, he turned his mordant pen against the large group of aristocrats who were blind to the virtues of education. "Our lords," he said, "hate and hold in contempt all sciences and arts, and consider them unworthy of the attention of noble minds. They think that every little nobleman can know everything without having studied anything. They regard philosophy, mathematics, physics, and other sciences as idle occupations not deserving the attention of the aristocracy."[111]

Novikov did not agree with the contention of Catherine II and Betskoi that Russia must acquire an urban middle class before it could achieve a sound educational system. He argued that it would be much easier to start with the existing groups than to create new ones, and he envisioned the coalescence of small groups of literate members of various estates into a general reading public.[112]

To this end, he waged a resolute and uncompromising struggle against the social forces bent on preserving the traditional animosity toward learning, and did his utmost to create a reading public, or a set of reading publics, by publishing a whole series of books and journals.

Of Novikov's many periodicals, *Morning Light* (1770–80), the *Moscow Monthly Publications* (1781), and the Supplement to the *Moscow News* (1783–84) were most concerned with the development of science. *Morning Light* was the start of Novikov's long preoccupation with the evolution of ethical theories from ancient Greece to modern times. In his search for modern criteria of morality, Novikov printed in his first journal several works by Francis Bacon, including his *Wisdom of the Ancients,* and Pascal's *Pensées.* Carrying the search to the pages of the *Moscow Monthly Publications,* he wrote an article on "the main causes" of scientific and technological development, in which he declared that the growth of science required not only long periods of accumulation of knowledge but also freedom. In "the proud freedom of their thoughts," Novikov saw the main reason for England's having produced such men as Bacon and Newton. Another article presented Galileo as an uncompromising fighter for truth. Still another dealt with the influence of science on morality and "manners of thought." Occasional issues of the Supplement to the *Moscow News* carried biographical sketches of eminent scientists and philosophers, such as Buffon, Franklin, and Voltaire.[113]

Novikov informed his constantly growing circle of readers that "the cause of all human delusion is ignorance, just as knowledge is the cause of progress." He pointed to the sciences as the most powerful weapons in the hands of man, worthy of the highest respect.[114] He also used the columns of his journals to reaffirm his loyalty to the ideals of the Enlightenment as postulated by French Encyclopedists; in one article entitled "The Philosopher" he asserted that philosophers had a special social responsibility to discover truths "congruent with reason." In 1788–89 he published the *Journal of Natural History, Physics, and Chemistry,* devoted to the popularization of science and the spreading of medical and commercial knowledge.

Out of Novikov's many activities, two works—both products of the earlier part of his career—command particular attention. The first of these, a *Historical Dictionary of Russian Writers* (1772), was an attempt to present in compact form all the known facts about Russia's writers, including the great scientists, partly as a way of showing Russians and Western Europeans alike just how much Russia had done in every field of literary, artistic, and scholarly endeavor. The result was called by Belinskii "the most important document of literary criticism of its time."[115] The second work, much longer, was *Ancient Russian Bibliophilia,* a compilation of basic documentary material on Russian history. "It is useful," Novikov says in the Introduction, "to know about the morals, customs, and ceremonies of ancient foreign peoples, but it is much more useful to command knowledge about one's own ancestors."[116]

This sketch of Novikov's versatile work has been confined to those activities which had a direct bearing on the history of scientific thought in Russia. It should be noted, however, that his contributions in this general field were not unmixed blessings. Some of his translations—that of Pascal's *Pensées,* for example—were so poor that they were hardly intelligible and did gross injustice to the original works. Nor did Novikov, in his eagerness to publish, always show discrimination. Along with a great deal of really worthwhile material in the sciences and philosophy, he printed pseudoscientific and mystical writings.

During the late 1770's he was one of the leaders in the Freemasonry movement, particularly after it became identified with Rosicrucianism of the kind that made extensive use of occultism, alchemy, and mysticism. All this found expression in his journals.[117] He defined "science" as a generic term which included not only knowledge derived from Baconian induction but also "knowledge" arrived at by a manipulation of supernatural forces. These mystical quirks did not in themselves negate the remarkable extent and value of Novikov's contributions to the spread of scientific knowledge in Russia, but they led him to strange inconsistencies. He gave Russians all the lore on Paracelsus' alchemy at a time when he could have informed them of Lavoisier's systematization of modern chemical knowledge, Priestley's isolation of oxygen (1774–75), and Cavendish's *Chemical Experiments on Air* (1784).

Novikov is certainly the most controversial figure of the age of Cath-

erine II. A. N. Pypin calls him a peddler of mysticism;[118] O. Makogonenko
sees in him a true champion of modern science, whose mystical bent was
only a minor blemish on his unflagging pursuit of enlightenment.[119] Most
observers see two Novikovs: one dedicated to science and the other to mysticism. Among these is Shchapov, who, while critical of Novikov's mystic
digressions, describes him as "one of the most brilliant figures of his age
in the field of enlightenment."[120] In any case, it is difficult to deny the
tribute implicit in the following statement by Karamzin in 1802: "Twenty-
five years ago Moscow had two bookstores; now there are twenty. In Moscow, Novikov was the leader of the book trade: he rented the University
press, published and translated books, and opened bookstores in other
towns. Before him, only 600 copies of the *Moscow News* were circulated;
Novikov enriched and diversified its content by the addition of *Children's
Readings*. During the course of a decade the number of subscribers grew
to 4,000; since 1797 the *News* has published imperial decrees, and the number of subscribers has grown to 6,000."[121]

Aleksandr Radishchev, a friend of Aleksandr Vorontsov, was only
indirectly connected with the propagation of scientific knowledge, but he
was throughout his life an outspoken critic of conditions inimical to the
growth of scientific inquiry. He was one of the twelve young Russians
sent by Catherine II in 1766 to study law at Leipzig University, which was
at that time a lively center of legal study. Most of the Russians became part
of an informal circle of bright and inquisitive law students, dominated by
the studious Fedor Ushakov, who were intensely interested in the social
and philosophical thought of Mably, Beccaria, Helvétius, and Rousseau.
Although they rejected the idealistic metaphysical systems of their professors in favor of a materialistic humanism, the depth of their reading
saved them from an unquestioning acceptance of the thought of the *philosophes*. From Helvétius's treatise *De l'esprit* (1758) they "learned how
to think," yet Ushakov, relying on the ideas of the Dutch experimental
physicist and mathematician 's Gravesande, questioned the validity of some
of Helvétius's basic conclusions.[122]

To the end of his life, Radishchev continued to fight Scholasticism,
idealistic metaphysics, mysticism, and superstition; but he also launched
an offensive against the institutions of serfdom and monarchical absolutism
as the main barricades in Russia's cultural development. He chided Lomonosov for having created an unwholesome alliance between tyranny and
science in his odes in praise of Elizabeth. More strongly than any of his
predecessors or contemporaries, he urged that Russia's future prosperity

depended on freedom of thought and the abolition of serfdom. When Catherine, in the twilight of her stormy reign, was considering a general censorship to stem the stream of ideas threatening the status quo, Radishchev prepared a study of the evils of censorship, endorsing Herder's belief that "the best means of promoting good is noninterference, permission to work for a good cause, freedom of thought."[123] The essay on censorship, published as a chapter in the *Journey from St. Petersburg to Moscow* (1790), was a particular source of Catherine's anger, for it showed, and implicitly condemned, her drastic retreat from the humanistic philosophy of the Enlightenment. Under her direct influence, a criminal court sentenced Radishchev to a ten-year exile in Siberia.

Without overestimating the value of Russian scientific achievements (Lomonosov was, after all, but an artisan when compared with Benjamin Franklin[124]), Radishchev was certain that those achievements showed the way to a better future for the Russian people. Radishchev was not, of course, a scientist himself. At Leipzig he studied jurisprudence, literature, and medicine. But in contrast to the ordinary *homme des lettres* of the Russian enlightenment who skimmed lightheartedly over the whole range of French humanistic thought, Radishchev was a new sort of intellectual who navigated safely in the sea of ideas formed by epistemological empiricism, epigenesis, and socially and historically determined ethics. He had profound admiration for the great intellectual feats of Copernicus, Galileo, and Newton; however, nothing could be more untruthful than Ivanov-Razumnik's assertion that Radishchev treated man as a mathematical concept—a summation of general human qualities unmarred by the elements of individuality.[125] Radishchev viewed natural law as a historical, humanistic category rather than a transcendental-normative concept immune to social change. He was familiar with the works of Pallas, Lepekhin, Gmelin, Güldenstädt, and other participants in the scientific expeditions of the late 1760's and early 1770's. (His *Journey from St. Petersburg to Moscow* is written in the form of "daily notes" after the manner of the journals of those expeditions.) He was intrigued by the possibilities of a chemical study of soil (and the possibility of creating new kinds of soil) and was well informed about contemporary studies of atoms and matter. For a time, according to his son in a brief biography, he was greatly interested in chemistry and performed a number of experiments.[126]

Radishchev wrote in a passionate and belligerent tone, yet he developed his arguments carefully and avoided mysticism, Scholastic verbiage, didactic preaching, and cumbersome metaphysical exercises. His curiously archaic style is hard to reconcile with the advanced character of his thought. Wiener, the English translator of the *Journey from St. Petersburg to Moscow,* comments that "Radishchev's sojourn in Germany may have given him his taste for heavy, intricately constructed sentences with long-drawn-out adjectival modifiers."[127]

Together, Kozel'skii, Novikov, and Radishchev tried, if not very consistently or thoroughly, to translate the scientific achievements of their age into a new way of looking at the world. As members of the aristocracy, they were proof that Russia's ruling estate was beginning to yield at least a few intellectuals who could accept the findings of modern natural science as part of their philosophy of life and the universe. As the rulers of Russia were quick to see, the emergence of such men represented a danger to the existing social system and its values.

Methodical doubt as a precondition of scientific thought—so vigorously championed by Descartes and broadened by the Encyclopedists to apply equally to social and physical reality—had, then, found its ardent supporters among Russian scholars and writers. Skepticism and criticism became the guideposts in the thinking of a new class of intellectuals, a class so small at first that it almost vanished altogether in the last days of Catherine II and the brief reign of Paul I.[128] These intellectuals were the true heralds of a new class on the Russian social scene—the resolute proponents of systematized secular wisdom.[129]

SCIENCE AND SOCIAL CHANGE

During the second half of the eighteenth century, scientific thought spilled over the rigid confines of the Academy of Sciences to wash a vast area of Russian culture. Science itself, propelled by its own inner momentum, was strengthened by a growing specialization—a sign of the increased depth of inquiry—and by a diversification of the methods of investigation. The old science of minerals, for example, branched into mineralogy, geology, and paleontology. The old naturalist was still in his prime, but the new natural scientist—typified by the mineralogist Vasilii Severgin—had put in his appearance.

In terms of methodological views, the natural scientists were a highly diversified group. The champions of mathematical analysis included those who clung stubbornly to the Eulerian tradition and those who preferred the paths opened by D'Alembert, Monge, Lagrange, and Legendre. Some were "collectors" who took inventory of the natural resources of their native land without venturing onto the slippery ground of theory; others combined the cataloguer's skill with definite naturalistic or philosophical views.

A few were scholars of the experimental sort, particularly in chemistry, biology, and medicine. The influence of Dutch experimentalists of the school of 's Gravesande and Musschenbroek—the latter was elected in 1754 an honorary member of the St. Petersburg Academy—was strong in Russia, particularly during the 1760's and 1770's, although not among scholars of the first rank. The members of the Dutch school professed to be orthodox Newtonians, but they differed from Newton in placing their emphasis more on experimentation than on mathematical analysis. They "banned all hypotheses and recognized no principles that could not be demonstrated by experiment and confirmed by geometry."[130] Novikov in the 1780's popularized the work of the Dutch experimental physicists in his *Journal of Natural History, Physics, and Chemistry.* In 1793 P. Giliarskii published a *Manual of Physics,* written under the strong influence of Musschenbroek's ideas.[131]

Finally, the amateurs added technical experience to their limited grounding in the fundamentals of science to resolve complex practical problems. The social scientists and historians also exhibited methodological differences. While some were uncritical collectors of data, others learned and appreciated the techniques of historical criticism. Again, there were those who sought the truth, naked and unembellished, and those who put ideology ahead of the facts.

Despite its diversified development, eighteenth-century Russian science, as a specific source of wisdom and world view, was by no means a triumphant cultural force. The isolation of the peasants from the avenues of enlightenment, the absence of an intellectual class, the ideological curbs imposed by Church and State, the uncertain place of the theories of the natural sciences in the atmosphere of the Enlightenment, the growing attacks on freedom of thought (particularly during the 1790's), and the small number of schools kept the world of science from extending much beyond exceedingly small urban groups. Russian scientific thought was still largely dependent on Western ideas and suffered when their normal flow was impeded by government interference.

The social effect of science in eighteenth-century Russia, however, cannot be overemphasized. It destroyed once and for all the intellectual supremacy of the Church, which fed on outmoded Scholasticism and sacrosanct superstitions; and it became the rallying point for a frontal attack on ignorance. Science gave strength to the emergent national consciousness of the Russian people; the results of historical and geographical research and of the scientific expeditions were reflected in a broader and more widely distributed literature. As teachers, writing and translating books, the scientists also led the struggle to raise the educational level of the Russian people. Slowly and painstakingly, they made the Russian language a vehicle of scientific communication. They supplied the necessary intellectual stimulus for those moved by the Enlightenment, and they stood for the victory of reason.

Delays were due to the Church. The historical orientation in natural science, stemming from Kant's cosmogonic hypothesis, Buffon's evolutionary natural history, and Wolff's embryological transformism, had no consistent and powerful advocates in eighteenth-century Russia. Except in Pallas's developmental interpretation of the origin of mountains, Lomonosov's historical approach to the basic questions of geology was not pursued either by himself or by any of his successors. Church censorship delayed the publication in Russia of Kant's cosmogonic theory and suppressed Buffon's *Epochs of Nature,* the work in which he endeavored to throw evolutionary light on important questions ranging from astronomy to paleontology. And fear of Church disapproval had a good deal to do with Wolff's abandonment of his promising embryological studies.

In Russia, as in the West, the historical attitude brought natural science into open conflict with religion and its official guardians, for it challenged not only the biblical cosmology but also the sacred values surrounding the *ancien régime*—it created the atmosphere in which serfdom and monarchical absolutism were shifted from divine ordinances into historical categories. Weak as this historical attitude was at first, it opened the doors to humanism, and indirectly to the recognition of the individual as a social, historical, and intellectual entity. It placed the power of science behind the advocates of social change, and it wedded the new Russian journalism to the scientific view and the scientific interest. It gave rise to the intelligentsia—that rather amorphous social category which defied identification with any single estate or class, but was united in its dedication to social change.

CHAPTER FIVE

The Rise and Decline of Humanistic Rationalism

POLITICS AND HUMANISTIC PHILOSOPHY

The Pugachev rebellion marked the beginning of Catherine's retreat from liberalism and libertarian dreams. When the heat of the French Revolution reached Russia, Catherine, old and confused, was helpless to meet the challenge. Paul I, however, knew exactly what to do, for he had less philosophy and saw only the danger to Old Russia. In the four years of his rule (1796–1801), he turned his back on all the corruptive influences of the Enlightenment and undid his mother's good works. He forbade Russian students to attend Western universities, kept foreign books and music from entering the country, and refused funds to scholarly institutions. The Russian Academy virtually went out of existence, the Free Economic Society had no money for its research projects, and many vacancies in the Academy of Sciences remained unfilled.

Everywhere in Russia things were in a desperate state. "Paul came to the throne," says Nikolai Karamzin, at a time that was "propitious for autocracy, when the terrors of the French Revolution had cured Europe of the dreams of civil freedom and equality," and he "took to ruling by means of general terror, obeying no law save his own whims."[1] But his whims and his monstrous cruelties could not stifle the growth of humanitarian thought which had sprung up in the early days of Catherine's reign and had lately been stirred anew by the winds of the French Revolution. Both Russian capitals were ripe for the realization of the poet Derzhavin's prediction that "a Man will ascend the throne," a Tsar who would replace the reign of terror with a government based on broad humanitarian principles. The liberal attitude of Alexander was no secret to the alert population of St. Petersburg and Moscow, and when he ascended the throne, "in houses and on the streets people cried with joy and embraced one another as on Easter Sunday."[2]

Nearly all European societies had been forced by the French Revolution to undertake a certain reassessment of their own values. Paul I, temperamentally unsuited to consider the matter very long or very seriously, reverted to his natural conservatism, which had the sympathy of most of the aristocracy—much of which, indeed, still resented Peter's Westernizing policies. What Paul failed to realize was that the Enlightenment had left an imprint on Russian culture that could not easily be erased. Quietly but persistently, from numerous quarters and on various levels, there came a demand for general reform.

The demand came, in the first place, from a small but important group of enlightened aristocrats who held vital administrative positions in the government—notably Aleksandr Vorontsov and Petr Zavadovskii. It also came from certain literary figures like Radishchev, Derzhavin, and Karamzin. A number of scholars, including Fuss, Ozeretskovskii, and Rumovskii, while comparatively sheltered within academic walls, recognized in the French Revolution a warning to Russia that countries which failed to educate their people and keep abreast of scientific progress would fall easy prey to the military forces of their more energetic neighbors. Alexander I, by his personal inclinations and education, was close to the groups in favor of far-reaching reforms.

Alexander's liberalism was largely due to his teachers—particularly to his first teacher, Frédéric César de La Harpe, who was a humanitarian and a republican. According to Alexander himself, no person exercised a stronger influence on him than this learned man, who considered himself an idealist and theoretician, a person better acquainted with books than with people.[3] Colonel Carl Masson was entrusted with teaching the young prince the mysteries of mathematics, and two Academicians, Krafft and Pallas, introduced him to physics and botany. It was undoubtedly the influence of these men that instilled in Alexander an appreciation for the value of the natural and exact sciences. Indeed, one of Alexander's first moves on assuming the throne was to introduce the teaching of science, both theoretical and applied, in the elementary and secondary schools of Russia. The venerable Mikhail Murav'ev, who later become one of the leading figures in the formation of a modern system of educational institutions, taught the young prince Russian literature and history, imparting to him his belief in freedom and education as the proper bases for national prosperity. Murav'ev held that freedom of investigation was an indispensable condition for the virtuous life, and that it was to a "sensible freedom" of opinion that the Protestant countries owed their universal prosperity and enlightenment.[4]

By the time Alexander had become Tsar, he was the center of a reform-minded movement consisting of two distinct types of noblemen—a group of older men who were direct products of the Catherinean Enlightenment and who had long experience in public work, and an inner circle of young aristocrats close to the young monarch. His counselors included such dedicated public servants as Zavadovskii, Murav'ev, and Vorontsov; and his inner circle included the Polish Count Adam Czartoryski, Mikhail Speranskii, and Vasilii Karazin.

At one in their recognition of the urgency of reforms in the Russian body politic, these men represented an unusually wide range of educational and professional backgrounds. Czartoryski had studied constitutional law in England and had already embarked on a colorful diplomatic career. Speranskii had studied at seminaries in Vladimir and St. Petersburg, learning enough physics, mathematics, and philosophy in the latter school to be retained as a teacher in these subjects. He had also acquired an enthusiasm for the philosophical and humanistic ideas of Voltaire and Diderot. Karazin was a graduate of the St. Petersburg Mining School, where, thanks mainly to his persistent intellectual curiosity, he got a good education in the natural sciences. He had been imprisoned for attempting to leave Russia for foreign study during Paul's reign.

Murav'ev, one of the early graduates of Moscow University, showed—in his published lectures as a teacher of young Alexander in "history, letters, and philosophy"—a strong libertarian spirit and certain overtones of contemporary Scottish philosophy. Zavadovskii, a graduate of the Kiev Theological Academy, headed Catherine's Commission for the Establishment of Public Schools, and suffered imprisonment under Paul I. Vorontsov, educated in Western European military schools, abandoned an illustrious career when Catherine sent Radishchev into exile.

Besides these, there were scores of other persons whose counsel was sought by the young Tsar. They brought their own distinct educational backgrounds and professional experiences into the common pool of dedicated talent which made the initial years of Alexander's reign one of the most exciting and forward-looking periods in Russian history.

These men all agreed generally that the future of Russia as a civilized country depended on a large-scale conversion to Western European science, philosophy, education, and technology. They also subscribed to monarchism and rule by aristocracy, although the aristocracy they had in mind was one which would open its ranks to accomplished persons of non-aristocratic origin. Paradoxically, their thinking was greatly tinged with the ideas that had undermined the very foundations of the *ancien régime* in France, and they were well aware of the new cultural forces unleashed by the French Revolution. They recognized and were moved by the new values and aspirations, yet they remained monarchists.

They attempted to reconcile their libertarianism and their monarchism by citing the example of England, where a working blend of the two philosophies had been most successfully achieved. In order to prepare the general public for its extensive reforms—and also to set forth the appropriate philosophical justification for these reforms—the government sponsored translations of what were considered to be appropriate Western works. In this unusual undertaking, the works of English and Scottish scholars predominated; it was said that in questions of law, for example, *Translations* the new authorities followed Bentham, and that they looked to Adam Smith's classic work for direction in advanced economic thinking.[5] The *St. Petersburg Journal,* a new official publication dedicated to educating the general public not only through government decree but also through translations of Western works tending in effect to endorse the Tsar's new policies, carried an article in 1804 entitled "The Thoughts of Francis Bacon on Government" and in 1805 an excerpt from the work of the Scottish philosopher Adam Ferguson.[6] In 1806 it published a Russian translation of Jean Louis Delolme's *The Constitution of England.*

Having turned their eyes to England for liberal economics and jurisprudence, the enlightened Russian aristocrats not surprisingly became interested also in English philosophy and science. Admiral Nikolai Mor- *Bentham* dvinov wrote in 1806 about Jeremy Bentham: "In my opinion, he is one of the four men of genius who have made great contributions to human welfare—Bacon, Newton, Smith, and Bentham, each the founder of a new science."[7] Etienne Dumont, the Swiss disciple and editor of Bentham, wrote to a friend in 1803: "Could you have imagined that as many copies of my *Bentham* would be sold in Petersburg as in London? A hundred copies have been disposed of in a very short time, and the booksellers are asking for a new supply."[8]

The Scottish moral philosophy, as well as the epistemological thought of Bacon, Locke, and Hume, acquired an extensive following among Russian intellectuals. This philosophy supplemented—or was blended with—the ideas of the French *philosophes,* which were already familiar. Bentham, in a way, supplemented and refined the ideas of Beccaria, just as Hume reinforced the philosophical ideas of Condillac, and Ferguson the more moderate theories of Mably and Helvétius. The Russians were now engaged in translating Newton's *Principia,* and such great names in British mathematics as Brook Taylor and Colin Maclaurin became familiar in scholarly circles.

The excitement over English thought and liberal thought in general, on the part of Alexander I and his advisers (the people who, according to Turgenev, read Condillac before they attended *soirées*), was tempered by their allegiance to autocracy, which was understood implicitly or explicitly to be the cornerstone of Russian policy. The few people such as Admiral Mordvinov who became true adherents of the advanced political and economic theories of Bentham and Smith soon lost their influence with the Tsar and even formed the nucleus of an organized opposition. Reform-minded though the government of Alexander I was, it had no intention of imposing any limitations on autocracy; rather, it meant to modernize the agencies of delegated authority. The young Tsar and his counselors were determined to avoid the two most severe weaknesses of Catherine's and Paul's regimes: lack of clarity in the jurisdiction of various agencies, and the prevalence of incompetence and corruption. They also understood a major lesson of the French Revolution and its immediate aftermath: that scientific knowledge—translatable into new techniques of war and industry—was a basic source of national strength.

NEW EDUCATIONAL IDEALS

Educational reforms constituted only a part of the extensive changes envisioned by Alexander. In many ways, however, educational reforms were the most fundamental because they were directed toward national enlightenment, which, in turn, was a precondition for the successful execution of broader and more drastic social and economic changes. Because of their reading of Western books, or their participation in Catherine's humanistic endeavors, the new men in power knew that the propagation of science depended on two indispensable conditions: the accessibility of education, at every level, to all social strata, and the freedom of scientific inquiry. These two principles—even if rather moderate and not always consistently applied—profoundly affected all reforms connected with education and scientific work during the initial years of Alexander's reign.

A few weeks after the new monarch ascended the throne, he issued a decree which annulled Paul's order banning the import of Western books and music and preventing study abroad.[9] The private presses, which had been closed down by Paul, were reactivated. Alexander took a special interest in the selection of books to be translated and published under government sponsorship, even submitting some titles of his own choosing. He extended financial help to literary persons and awarded a series of special medals to eminent writers. Among the first to receive these decorations were such Academicians as Rumovskii, Ozeretskovskii, Inokhodtsev, Severgin, Gur'ev, Pallas, Krafft, Georgi, Fuss, Schubert, and Lowitz.[10] Shortly after Alexander's accession the Russian Academy was rejuvenated, and it quickly began an ambitious program of linguistic and historical investigations. Special government subsidies put the Free Economic Society back on its feet, and the facilities of the newly established Medical and Surgical Academy were greatly expanded. A committee of Academicians set about preparing a new and more liberal charter for the Academy of Sciences. In St. Petersburg, the new flurry of intellectual activity led to the foundation of the Free Society of Admirers of Science, Literature, and Arts. A member of this society described the atmosphere in which it began:

"At this time a love and a search for all kinds of knowledge were given a brilliant display. . . . This wholesome and dynamic spirit created an atmosphere conducive to the emergence of many private gatherings where young men, brought together by personal acquaintance and friendship, wrote, translated, or discussed their works, and thus improved upon their literary gifts and tastes. The societies which sprang up in St. Petersburg and Moscow sought neither fame nor special benefits; they merely enjoyed the self-generated pleasures of learning."[11]

Educational institutions, in which lay great hopes for a new and enlightened Russia, underwent several concurrent reforms, all designed to bring them under unified government supervision. National education in Russia was at this time an unusual mixture of overlapping institutions, with no fixed central authority. In 1802 a step toward achieving clear central authority was made in the establishment of a Ministry of National Education, headed by the same Zavadovskii who had presided over

Catherine's Commission for the Establishment of Schools. Among his aides were Czartoryski, Murav'ev, and Karazin. Under the jurisdiction of the new ministry, in addition to the schools, were printing and publishing enterprises, including journals, all aspects of censorship, public libraries, museums, and "all institutions dedicated to the dissemination of knowledge."[12] The backbone of the school system consisted of four types of educational institutions: parish schools, district schools, gymnasiums, and universities. These institutions formed a unified system not only because they were subordinate to the Ministry of National Education, which was responsible for their teaching programs, but also because they provided for continuity of education from lower to higher levels. The state finally had a complete network of educational institutions which could be employed to turn out such scientists, technicians, and skilled civil servants as might be called for by government programs.

Another important result of the educational reforms was a more equitable distribution of schools of all levels throughout Russia. Parish schools were opened in townships, district schools in *uezd* towns, and gymnasiums in provincial capitals. The plan also called for the inauguration of a university in each of the six newly created school districts. When Alexander ascended the throne, Moscow University was the country's only functioning school of higher education. Paul I had authorized the founding of Dorpat University in 1798, after his ban on foreign study, as a gesture to the Baltic gentry, who had traditionally sent their sons to German universities.* Dorpat was actually opened by Alexander, however, in 1802, and four new universities were founded: Vilna in 1802, Kazan and Khar'kov in 1804, and St. Petersburg fifteen years later, in 1819.

The new school system did not fully implement the accepted plan, but to a great extent it completed the ambitious enterprise launched by Peter I. Peter had opened Russia's doors to secular education of the Western variety and had created the Academy of Sciences to direct this grand undertaking, to prepare competent teaching personnel, and to serve as a fountain

---

* Dorpat University actually dated from 1632, when it was chartered by Gustavus Adolphus. When the city of Dorpat was conquered by Tsar Alexis Mikhailovich in 1656, the university was closed. Dorpat reverted to Swedish control in 1661, and in 1690 a second Swedish university was established. It lasted until 1710 when Peter I conquered the city. Peter was willing to allow the university to continue its work, but this proved impossible because all the professors fled, taking with them most of the contents of the university library. See E. V. Petukhov, *Imperatorskii Iur'evskii, byvshii Derptskii, universitet za sto let ego sushchestvovaniia (1802–1902)*, I (Iur'ev, 1902), 50–69; *Sbornik postanovlenii po Ministerstvu narodnogo prosveshcheniia*, Vol. I: *Tsarstvovanie Aleksandra I, 1802–1825*, 2d ed. (St. Petersburg, 1875), p. 6.

of new knowledge. Peter's successors tried to continue his work by building a system of lower schools which would provide adequate academic
training for young men willing to acquire higher education, and by expanding the school system to areas outside St. Petersburg. Catherine's ambitious attempt to establish primary and secondary public schools throughout the country was only a partial success, however. Many schools called
for by the general plan drawn by the Commission for the Establishment of
Public Schools were never opened, and of those that did open, many lasted
only a few years or survived with a handful of students.

Under Alexander, the existing public schools were revamped, enlarged,
and consolidated; and these new foundations, as their subsequent history
shows, endowed them with a strong capacity for survival. Before Alexander I, most attempts to create a school system were burdened with a com-
plication of purposes. Schools were supposed to serve both the cultural
needs of the apathetic masses and the very specific needs of the growing
state machinery. This was the period of experiments and frequent muta-
tions in educational plans. With the beginning of the nineteenth century,
the school system at last began to see steady, if at first almost impercep-
tible, expansion. The basic types of schools formulated at the start of
Alexander's reign were little altered thereafter; future changes were essentially limited to curricular and administrative matters. Alexander's reforms
made the European system of graded schools into an institutional continuum in Russia and an integral part of Russian culture.

In the teaching programs of the new schools, particularly the gymnasiums and universities, Alexander's educational reforms continued the
tradition of Catherine's era, which had stressed the natural sciences and
mathematics. According to the charter of 1804, the gymnasium assumed
a double function: to prepare young men for a university education, and to
give well-rounded introductory surveys of the basic natural sciences and
the humanities to persons not seeking a higher education. Among the
subjects offered in the new gymnasiums were algebra, descriptive and
plane geometry, applied mathematics, experimental physics, natural history, technology, and the Latin, German, and French languages.[13] In the
universities, there was an even greater expansion in the teaching of the
natural and the exact sciences. Whereas the Moscow University charter
of 1755 had limited the natural sciences to be taught within the Philosophical Faculty to physics, the charter of 1804 established a special department of physical and mathematical sciences which offered courses in pure
mathematics, applied mathematics, theoretical and experimental physics,

chemistry, mineralogy, agriculture, botany, and industrial and commercial technology.[14]

In stressing the natural and mathematical sciences, the new authorities followed the Russian educational tradition, but they also had in mind some of the economic and military uses of science that came into prominence during the stormy days of the French Revolution. Condorcet's famous *Rapport et projet du décret sur l'organisation générale de l'instruction publique,* which wedded the educational ideas of the *philosophes* to the demands of the liberal wings of the Republic for "new men," exercised a profound influence, directly or indirectly, on the educational philosophy of Alexander's counselors. Condorcet felt that the schools of the *ancien régime* had lost their vitality and had become unfit to educate a new generation schooled in the social and intellectual climate of the Revolution. The new education, he wrote, must be "on a level with the spirit of the eighteenth century, with that philosophy which, while enlightening the present generation, presages, prepares, and already anticipates the superior intelligence to which the necessary progress of the human race is leading future generations."[15]

Some of Condorcet's ideas were rejected by his countrymen and by the Russians as well. Few agreed, for example, with his opposition to teaching Latin language and literature on the grounds that all knowledge in Latin books "can be found, better explained, together with new facts, in books written in the vernacular."[16] The Russians gave a place to classical languages and literature in both the new gymnasiums and the universities. But these studies were placed in a secondary position, at least during the first quarter of the nineteenth century, more by the spirit of the times than by any fiat of the lawmakers. Rommel, a German scholar who served for a while as a professor at Khar'kov University, wrote in his memoirs that between 1800 and 1815, far less attention was given to Greek and Latin than to mathematics, physics, psychology, and political economy.

One of the major principles of the Alexandrine educational reforms was the explicit guarantee to all classes of equal admission to public schools of all types, including the university. A quarter of a century or so earlier, Diderot had prepared a memorandum for Catherine II outlining a plan for a Russian university in which he stated: "A university is a school whose door is open without distinction to all the children of the nation, and where teachers paid by the state introduce them to elementary knowledge of all the sciences. I say *without distinction,* because it would be as cruel as it would be absurd to condemn to ignorance the lower classes of society."[17]   Some fifteen years later, Condorcet demanded that "education should be universal," that is, "within the reach of all classes of citizens."[18]

The Preliminary Regulations of National Education, issued by the government on January 24, 1803, accepted Condorcet's plan for four types of schools; it also underscored his demand that university education be free of class restrictions. V. N. Karazin greeted Alexander I soon after he ascended the throne with an anonymous letter in which he pleaded for universal education to suit both the country's local needs and individual propensities.[19] Loyal to the spirit of his time, Karazin tied his idea of universal education to a demand that "the rights of humanity" be guaranteed to Russia's legions of serfs, since without an enlightened people, "even the most perfect laws are of no use."[20]

The 1804 charter of Moscow University, which served as a model for the charters of other universities, opened higher education to all citizens. Even serfs were not excluded by law, though they were in effect by social status. This demonstration of a desire to make university education accessible to all classes was only in part the result of an idealistic dedication to the causes of humanity, however. From past experience, the school officials knew that, for a variety of ideological and psychological reasons, the aristocracy could not be relied on to supply any great number of university students.* And it was the basic task of the new universities to train not only civil servants but also future teachers and physicians—two professions regarded by the gentry as unaristocratic.

THE SPIRIT OF THE NEW UNIVERSITIES

In a sense, the new universities were the embodiment of the noblest ideals of the educational reform. In their conception and organization they were as modern and liberal as any comparable institutions of Western Europe. Their true model was Göttingen University, a flourishing institution based on the principles of academic autonomy and instructional free-

---

* Before the beginning of the 1805–6 academic year, the administration of Moscow University issued the following proclamation: "Endowed with the gifts of the highest monarchical generosity and elevated by the royal patronage, the University takes great pleasure in inviting the young men of all estates, who desire to enrich their intellects with many kinds of knowledge, to honor it by enrolling as its students. The University solemnly promises to give special attention and patronage to its new citizens and to bestow upon them all the rights and prerogatives as granted by our emperor. After the certified completion of the three-year education, students will enter the civil service with a rank equivalent to that of army major as recognition of and reward for their university work." N. S. Tikhonravov, *Sochineniia,* III, Part 1 (Moscow, 1898), 590–91.

dom. Göttingen, Napoleon once said, belonged not to Germany alone but to all Europe.[21] It was a product of Protestant Germany which looked to "the universities and the Reformation as the two beacons of its intellectual life."[22] The Russian students found Göttingen University attractive not only because of its international reputation but also because it offered a course in Russian history—taught by August Schlözer, a former member of the St. Petersburg Academy—before such a course was included in the curriculum of any Russian university.[23]

The status of the new Russian universities can be best summed up by the following citation from an excellent study of the educational policies of Alexander I: "The [liberal] organization of the universities gave them an autonomous and honorable place in society, and it exercised a positive influence on their spirit as scholarly institutions. The rector was a true representative of the university. He defended its interests with dignity and energy, because he was fully aware of his rights and duties and was free to act in accordance with his convictions and obligations. In his lectures each professor was guaranteed freedom, but each was expected to meet the standards of modern science."[24]

As an autonomous body, the university was given many privileges incompatible with the spirit and law of autocracy. The University Council, a body consisting of the instructional staff, was considered the highest authority in all educational matters. The universities were allowed by the state to impose their own censorship and to have their independent courts of justice. Although the charter determined the courses to be taught, the University Council was granted the right to choose textbooks and reading material in general. The Council also had the power to select and appoint professors, adjuncts, honorary members, and a whole array of other official personnel.

As stipulated by the 1804 model charter, the universities were multifunctional institutions. Their fundamental and most urgent task was to fill the sparse ranks of civil servants, physicians, and teachers—a task which in time led to their being dominated by a sort of "state utilitarianism."[25] Certain responsibilities of the universities as sources of new scientific knowledge were also defined, although they were limited to specific types of research. University instructors were directed by the charter to incorporate up-to-date scientific knowledge into their lectures— implying clearly that the instructors were expected to keep abreast of the advances in their specific disciplines. The charter also required the professors to hold monthly meetings devoted exclusively to discussions of scientific papers presented by members of the faculty, thus putting the professors to the test of their colleagues as well as of their students.

One of the most important articles of the 1804 charter authorized the universities to sponsor learned societies. In 1804 the Society of Russian History and Antiquities was founded at Moscow University. Despite occasional setbacks, it became one of the most influential learned societies in Russia in the nineteenth century. Its basic task was to publish "critical— i.e., true and correct—editions of the ancient Russian chronicles, with necessary comments,"[26] which might serve as the foundation for a comprehensive history of Russia. A government decree of the same year requested the Synod to transfer to the Society all original chronicles and other documentary material. A similar order was issued to the State Archives of Foreign Affairs and the Academy of Sciences. All material was to be returned to the original repositories after it had been copied. The membership of the Society included both university professors and independent scholars, among whom were N. M. Karamzin, the historian, and A. I. Musin-Pushkin, the collector of ancient historical manuscripts.

In 1805 Moscow University sponsored the formation of the Society for the Comparative Study of The Medical and Physical Sciences. This society was dedicated to the dissemination of useful knowledge in physics and medicine, the propagation of scientific interest, and the enrichment of science through independent studies and experiments carried out by individual members. Also in 1805 the government approved the charter of a third learned body to be sponsored by Moscow University, the Society of Naturalists. The aims of this society were the study of the natural history of Russia; the systematic surveying of the country's mineral resources, flora and fauna, and agricultural and industrial products; and the search for new marketable goods. The Society published the *Journal of the Society of Naturalists* (subsequently renamed *Mémoires* and then *New Mémoires*) and a *Bulletin*, for the publication of independent studies by Russian scholars. The Society was destined to last 135 years and to make contributions of great significance.

Societies of similar nature sprang up in Moscow and elsewhere. The professors and students of Kazan University founded a literary society known eventually as the Society of Admirers of Russian Literature at Kazan University. In 1811 a Society of Mathematicians was formed at Moscow University for the purpose of giving extracurricular courses in mathematics and translating useful Western works into Russian. In 1812 a society was established at Khar'kov University dedicated primarily to aesthetics, philology, archaeology, and ancient and modern history "with the appropriate auxiliary sciences."[27]

Although some of these societies fell by the wayside, others grew in time to be highly respected scholarly organizations. All of them established a bond between university professors and scholars working outside the institutions of higher education, giving them both stimulus and opportunity for independent scholarly pursuits. The many activities of these societies, including publishing, also gave promising students a chance to work with their professors beyond the narrow limits of the classroom.

The publishing activities of these societies were extensive. The 1804 charter authorized the universities to have their own printing facilities and to publish materials chosen by the academic collegia. The university presses published a wide range of work—everything from descriptions of simple inventions in the "arts and crafts" to highly technical studies of advanced scientific problems.

At the beginning of the century, Moscow University published, in addition to the periodical literature of the school's learned societies, the *Moscow News,* the *Messenger of Europe,* the *Political Journal, News in Russian Literature,* and *Moscow News of Learning.* The last of these consisted mainly of bibliographical notices of new scholarly works published in Russia and abroad; it also reported on the scholarly activities of the professors at Moscow University.[28] Similar journals on a more modest scale were published by the Universities of Kazan and Khar'kov. All the university presses also published textbooks and Russian translations of Western scholarly works covering a wide variety of subjects ranging from aesthetics to astronomy.

In 1803-4, Moscow University enlarged its educational program by offering four courses to the general public—a venture tried several times during the eighteenth century but never very systematically or with any success. The public courses were in natural history, the history of Western European countries from the fall of the Roman Empire to the beginning of the sixteenth century, commerce and money, and experimental physics, with emphasis on galvanism and gases.

The immediate success of this enterprise was enthusiastically proclaimed by Karamzin in 1803 in the monthly journal *Messenger of Europe*: "The fortunate selection of subjects for these public lectures is shown by the number of people who gather in the University hall on the designated days. With a great deal of satisfaction, an admirer of education sees there prominent Moscow ladies, young noblemen, clergymen, merchants, students of the Zaikonospaskaia Academy, and men of all manner of learning sitting in perfect silence, their eyes turned attentively to the professor. . . . It could have been foreseen that the lectures in experimental physics would attract a greater audience than any other course. It is not my business to compare the talents of various professors; but the phenomena of electrical power, galvanism, aerostatics, and the like are in themselves interesting, and Mr. Strakhov presents them so well that the public follows his lectures with a great deal of pleasure." Karamzin predicted that Moscow University was well on its way to becoming "one of the most glorious universities in the world of learning."[29]

The new epoch in the history of the Russian higher education was marked by the willingness of private persons of noble origin to give material help to the universities. "Contributions to the establishment of universities," one writer comments, "were made by the foremost men of the country; and in their assistance to the new nurseries of learning, these men offered not only words but deeds."[30]

An official appeal to the gentry in 1804 to make donations to the universities brought very encouraging results. Pavel Demidov, who belonged to an aristocratic family of industrial magnates, gave Moscow University an endowment of 400,000 rubles.[31] In 1807 Princess Dashkova, who had been president of the Russian Academy and a director of the Academy of Sciences under Catherine II, donated to Moscow University her natural history collection numbering 15,121 items, mostly zoological, botanical, and mineralogical.[32]

The government's dedication to the cause of enlightenment and the scientific spirit was contagious: it acted as a catalyst in an intellectual fermentation which affected literate Russians far beyond the limits of the two capitals—only a small portion of the total population, it is true, but more than ever before. In his reminiscences of the early years of Kazan University, S. T. Aksakov describes how the students of that time had "great contempt for everything low and disreputable, for all selfish considerations and interests, for all earthly philosophies—and a profound respect for everything honorable and lofty, even though it might have been unreasonable."[33] Both Professor Rommel of Khar'kov University and Professor Bartels, another German who taught in Russia, noted in their diaries that Russian university students of the early Alexandrine period had a great deal of intellectual enthusiasm.

The publication of scientific works, including translations, set domestic records and demonstrated both an increase in readership and a comparatively wide range of interest. A contemporary survey listed a total of 1,955 books published between 1801 and 1806. Belles-lettres (510), theology (309), and philology (166) were the three largest single categories, but the number of works in science was impressive: 109 in geography and statistics, 97 in medicine, 88 in economics and technology, 66 in natural science, 53 in mathematics, 50 in the history of science, and 27 in military science.[34] Russia was still dependent on foreign works, however: 42 per cent of all works published in Russia during this period were translations, from a total of nine different foreign languages.

A tangible contribution to the general growth of scientific interest and to the new affirmation of the scientific world outlook was made by the advanced professional schools. Whereas the fledgling universities were starting out awkwardly and slowly, the professional schools entered the new century as well-established training centers and scientific workshops.

The Medical and Surgical Academy, which had been founded under Paul I in 1798, carried on scientific experiments in its own laboratories and offered a varied scientific curriculum, including, besides the standard medical subjects, arithmetic, algebra, geometry, physics, natural history, chemistry, anatomy, and physiology. Vasilii Petrov, one of the school's most illustrious professors and a member of the Academy of Sciences, built a galvanic battery with 4,000 pairs of disks, from which he derived experimental material for his interesting and unique *Report on Galvanic-Voltaic Experiments* (1803). In 1806 the Academy opened special clinics, and two years later it established veterinary and pharmaceutical departments.

The Communications Institute, founded in 1810, was modeled after the Ecole des Ponts et Chaussées in Paris. From the very beginning—largely because of its original faculty, most of whom came from the Ecole Polytechnique in Paris—it placed special emphasis on mathematics, the study of construction mechanics, and the theory of elasticity. The prestige of the Institute declined somewhat in 1817 with the founding of the Central Engineering School.

One of the most active professional schools of this period was the St. Petersburg Pedagogical Institute, which grew out of the teachers' seminary established in 1786. Its curriculum ranged from pure and applied mathematics to aesthetics. In 1808 this school produced its first graduates, and the twelve most promising were sent to Western European universities for postgraduate study. Seven of them later became professors at St. Petersburg University. In 1816 the name of the school was changed to the Chief Pedagogical Institute, and as such it became the central institution for the training of teachers for all school levels and for all parts of the country. The curriculum of the Institute was by this time so extensive that it was necessary to organize separate faculties of law and philosophy, physical and mathematical sciences, and history and literature.

All these schools, quite naturally, emphasized scientific education, but a most significant expression of the growing scientific orientation of the age was to be noted in the revised curriculum of the theological academies. The first move in this direction came in the late 1790's when Mikhail Speranskii, an instructor in physics and mathematics in the Neva Seminary, prepared a brief textbook on physics incorporating modern theories.[35]

In 1804 the charter of the Aleksandro-Nevskaia Theological Academy revealed the unprecedented penetration of scientific courses into the curriculum of the theological schools. The charter contained statements of the following sort: "Since physics, because of its broad scope, cannot be adequately explained by philosophy, it must be treated as a special subject made up of theoretical and experimental parts. For a better understanding of the part of physics dealing with mechanics, it is necessary to offer a course in pure mathematics. Finally, natural history should be called upon to supplement physics and medicine."[36]

Medicine was made part of the regular curriculum of several theological academies and seminaries beginning in 1802, in a course including a general introduction to medicine, anatomy, pharmaceutics, and beginning dietetics. The mathematician S. E. Gur'ev was selected to deliver the main oration on the occasion of the festive opening of the reorganized St. Petersburg Theological Academy. His speech extolled the power of mathematics and outlined its major branches. Starting in 1819 the Moscow Theological Academy offered a course in calculus. These scientific inroads into the curriculum of the theological schools should be taken as reflections of the age, however, rather than as any beginning of a trend toward secularizing the training of future priests. They were aberrations in the history of the theological curriculum in Russia; but they also indicated the extent to which respect for science had penetrated the philosophy of education.

Faith in science was displayed by all cultural centers, however distant from St. Petersburg or Moscow. It was no surprise, for example, that an Irkutsk teacher should address a local gathering, at the beginning of the century, on the history of science and the contribution of science to human well-being. The speaker's education was revealed by statements like these:

"Descartes cast off the bonds of Aristotelianism, showed how to study nature, and restored to the human mind its freedom to think, which had been lost for two thousand years. Galileo discovered the gravity of the atmosphere, explained the elasticity of air, invented the telescope and compass. . . . Bacon made a survey of human knowledge. Newton discovered the law of gravitation, showed the anatomy of the world, gave the theory of colors, and extended mathematical calculation to the infinitesimal. Leeuwenhoek, by looking at nature with the help of optical instruments, discovered things not observable to the naked eye. Harvey discovered the circulation of blood in animals; and Linnaeus, sexual organs in plants. Franklin conquered lightning. . . . Sciences and the arts have achieved a level of perfection previously unknown to man."[37]

The tenor of this speech, as of the entire Alexandrine regime in its early years, was one of unqualified optimism regarding the benefits which mankind could reap from science. It also illustrated the growth of a new rationalist point of view and a widespread demand by scientists for freedom of scientific inquiry. When the Irkutsk teacher told his audience that Protestantism's avowal of intellectual independence figured significantly in stimulating the rise of modern science, he implied that Russian Orthodoxy would do well to follow suit.

THE ACADEMY: NEW DUTIES AND PREROGATIVES

Catherine's retreat from her once wholehearted allegiance to the philosophy of the Enlightenment, followed by Paul's reign of terror, wrought heavy damage on the St. Petersburg Academy of Sciences. When the nineteenth century began, the Academy had lost all touch with the scientific bodies of the West, having been deprived by the censorship decree even of news of scientific developments abroad.

In 1803 only a few of the Academy's fourteen full members were engaged in scientific work. Several were busy in the new Ministry of Education; several others were preoccupied with teaching duties in the higher professional schools; two or three lived in semi-retirement. Wolff, Aepinus, and Georgi, the leading Academicians of the preceding century, had died, and Pallas had left Russia after some years on his estate in the Crimea. The places of these scholars remained unoccupied or were filled by men of much smaller stature. Most of the Russian scientists who had shown great promise during the last quarter of the eighteenth century—such as Ozeretskovskii, Rumovskii, and Inokhodtsev—were more interested now in administrative activities than in scientific work.

In 1801 three Russian Academicians addressed a memorandum to Alexander I which purported to explain the Academy's unmistakable deterioration. The blame lay, they said, on the imported scholars: "With regard to the Academy it may be said that its members of foreign origin are completely useless to Russia. Every foreigner who does not write in Russian does not contribute his work to Russia, but to the state in whose language he writes. . . . There is a great difference between the foreign scholar who lives and publishes his works here and the foreign scholar who lives in his country: a book written by the latter costs Russia only several kopeks, and the one written by the former—several thousand rubles."[38]

Other Academicians—particularly, of course, those of foreign background—thought that filling vacancies with scholars from abroad would be the best way to restore the crumbling Academy. All the Academicians and adjuncts elected in 1802-3 were Russians, none with outstanding accomplishment or promise. In 1804-5, however, ten of the eleven who were elected were foreigners. Clearly, the time had not yet come when the Academy could depend on Russian scholars alone in the performance of its duties.

In order to speed the Academy's recovery, Alexander I granted it a new charter in 1803. This realistic and sober document allowed for a wider participation of Academicians in the conduct of their professional and administrative affairs, and it bestowed upon the Academy certain dignities concerning which the previous charter had been noncommittal. It stipulated, for example, that the president be chosen from among persons known for their scientific knowledge and respect for science.[39] This was an attempt to avoid the misfortunes which had occurred in the past as a result of appointing persons with little understanding of scientific inquiry or, as in the case of V. G. Orlov, persons with open contempt for academic pursuits.

The first president of the Academy to be selected in the spirit of the 1803 charter, N. N. Novosil'tsev, hardly fulfilled the high expectations. Novosil'tsev was an outstanding state official with a good deal more education than most of his kind, including courses in the physical sciences and mathematics at the University of London. An anonymous contemporary noted that he was "well-educated" but too lazy to care about discussions of an intellectual sort.[40] In any event, during his term as president of the

Academy, from 1803 to 1810, Novosil'tsev spent more time on his diplomatic assignments than on Academy affairs, and it seemed clear that Alexander was not seriously concerned about the need for a thorough revitalization of Russia's leading scientific body. For the next eight years the Academy had no president whatever. But in 1818 the gifted and versatile Sergei Uvarov was appointed, and under his guidance for the next thirty years the Academy made steady progress.

By the 1803 charter the duties of the Academy had been divided into those of primary and secondary nature. The primary duties were "to expand the domain of human knowledge, to advance science by enriching it with new discoveries, to spread enlightenment, to use knowledge as much as possible for human welfare, and to work toward a practical application of theory and toward useful results in experiments and observations."[41] To these tasks the charter added an array of specific assignments, with emphasis on those pertaining to the country's natural resources and means of exploiting them. Although the existence of the Academic University and the gymnasium was not acknowledged by the new charter, the Academy was asked to train a number of Russian youths in each of the sciences with which it dealt and to admit the most promising ones to the rank of adjunct. The Academy was made responsible for the appraisal of new inventions and was expected to keep the government informed about them, particularly those whose use would be beneficial to the nation's health, industry, commerce, and sea explorations. It was also supposed to maintain direct contact with the universities and to give them advice whenever requested. Another important task of the Academy was to re-establish ties with learned societies in other countries, thus renewing the flow of scientific knowledge to Russia. The charter stipulated that the Academy publish annually a volume of scientific works of theoretical significance, as well as a volume of practical information to be known as the *Technological Journal*. From 1803 to 1822 the Academy published eleven volumes of its *Mémoires,* containing the original scholarly contributions of the Academicians.

Several liberal reforms demanded by members of the Academy were incorporated into the 1803 charter. It differed from the original charter of 1747 in the following respects: (1) it gave the scholarly staff a greater voice in administrative affairs and in the selection, or recommendation, of new members of the Academy and the governing board; (2) it relieved the scholars of many of their traditional teaching duties and made it easier for them to work with young scholars in special fields; (3) it recognized the humanities (including history, political economy, and statistics) as an area of the Academy's concern; and (4) it stressed that the Academy would need much more financial support from the state treasury if it were to keep up with the latest advances in science. In all these points, the charter reflected the liberal mood of the Russian government, but it provided no effective remedy for the ills visited on the Academy during the troubled 1790's. The depleted libraries and neglected laboratories were not quickly attended to; and the roster of scholars was unimpressive. The rising nationalist tide discouraged eminent Western scholars from coming to Russia, and the number of outstanding Russian scholars was actually smaller than it had been a generation earlier. Furthermore, despite the promises of the charter, the financial state of the Academy during the first decades of the nineteenth century was uncertain, largely as a result of the Napoleonic wars, which drained the state treasury of funds that would otherwise have gone to scholarly endeavors. Many Academic institutions could not reverse the process of deterioration, and some, including the astronomical exhibit room, disappeared altogether. The Academic Museum was turned into a warehouse, and most of the other buildings were in need of extensive repair.

With the dwindling of its financial resources, the Academy found it increasingly difficult to attract foreign scholars with established reputations. Since Pallas was in retirement for the several years preceding his death in 1811, and most Russian mathematicians and naturalists were engaged in administrative work, helping to build the new school system, the Academy had to get along with lesser scholars. Many members of the Academy were advanced to high rank long before they had shown any scholarly distinction.

In 1826, the centennial year, Academician Paul Fuss was called upon to give a brief survey of the Academy's scientific accomplishments of one hundred years. His account showed clearly, though not explicitly, that the glory of the Academy rested mainly on contributions in two fields—mathematics and natural history—and that most of these contributions had been made during its first five decades.[42]

The Academy was not, of course, completely idle in the first years of the nineteenth century. Until his death in 1813, S. E. Gur'ev did important work in mathematics, although he was primarily occupied with teaching. Most of his writing was confined to textbooks in various mathematical disciplines. His *Differential and Integral Calculus* (1801)—dedicated to Alexander I—was an enormous treatise based on the work of

Euler, Joseph Cousin, and Lagrange. Another textbook, *The Foundations of the Transcendental Geometry of Curved Surfaces* (1806), was the first really systematic presentation of differential geometry in the Russian language.[43]

Gur'ev's most original work, an *Essay on the Improvement of the Principles of Geometry* (1798), was dedicated to a critical presentation of modern efforts to adduce clear and incontrovertible proof for "the basic propositions of mathematics," and to an elucidation of the application of differential and integral calculus to mechanics and hydrodynamics. The book is mainly concerned with the contributions of Cousin, Legendre, and D'Alembert, but it shows familiarity with the contributions of such earlier mathematicians as Tacquet, Taylor, Maclaurin, and Clairaut. A. P. Iushkevich says of it:

"The significance of Gur'ev's *Essay* was primarily that it introduced the Russian reader to many new ideas. The arrangement of the book was completely new. This was the first serious Russian work dedicated to the philosophy of mathematics and to the methods of its teaching. It was the work of a man with a critical mind who subjected the mathematical methods and propositions of the leading scholars to a careful analysis, and who searched for—and sometimes found—original scientific and educational methods. Gur'ev was familiar with the new currents in mathematical thought, and occasionally pointed a critical finger at the errors and omissions committed by some of the leading scholars. In his effort to blend Russian mathematical thought with the most advanced ideas of contemporary mathematics, he showed independent judgment in regard to many questions."[44]

It is necessary to point out, however, that in his reluctance to recognize the applicability of analysis to geometry and in his demands that geometry be made the basis of mathematical education, Gur'ev was not in step with the mathematical wisdom of his time.

Gur'ev inspired a number of younger mathematicians not formally affiliated with the Academy to study contemporary mathematical thought far beyond the limits of the Eulerian tradition. The most successful of these was Petr Rakhmanov, an aristocrat who was educated to be an army officer rather than a teacher or scholar. He invited the public to his St. Petersburg mansion to hear free lectures on differential and integral calculus, and from 1810 on he published a *Military Journal* which, despite its title, was devoted less to practical military problems than to the exact sciences. Gur'ev, Rakhmanov, and a whole string of more obscure figures

represented a new kind of Russian mathematician who saw in his discipline not only a source of knowledge useful in practical ways but a
philosophy and a pure intellectual challenge as well.

From the death of Gur'ev in 1813 until the election of Mikhail Ostrogradskii and Viktor Buniakovskii to the rank of adjunct in 1828, not
one Russian mathematician graced the country's leading scientific institution. For over a decade, the great mathematical tradition in the Academy
was in the custody of Nicolaus Fuss, who, as the Academy's Permanent
Secretary, devoted all his time to administrative matters. The scientific
fortunes of the Academy would have been immensely improved if Karl
Friedrich Gauss, considered by many to have been the greatest mathematician of the nineteenth century, had chosen to accept the appointment
offered him by the St. Petersburg institution.

The names of several other Academicians were not unknown in the
West. Friedrich Schubert, who wrote a three-volume survey of astronomical theory, was widely known, and W. Wiśniewski, the youthful head of
the St. Petersburg observatory, acquired prominence as a man with remarkable vision. In 1807 he observed a comet four weeks after it was lost sight
of by Western astronomers, and in 1812, even more remarkably, he observed
a comet lost sight of eight months earlier in the West.[45]

It was time that natural history, with its crude empiricism and scant
allowance for theory and experiment, gave way to specialized natural
sciences. Vasilii Severgin, despite the descriptive character of his work,
was really Russia's first modern mineralogist. In addition to a large number
of separate treatises, he wrote a *Detailed Mineralogical Dictionary* (1807),
which in many ways enriched Russian scientific terminology. His *Foundations of Mineralogy* (1798), the first general mineralogical work in the
Russian language, classified minerals according to their chemical composition.[46] In his theoretical orientation, he followed Lavoisier, at a time
when most of his colleagues were still firmly dedicated to phlogiston
chemistry.[47] Severgin brought to Russia René Haüy's theory of the structure of crystals—and thus the beginnings of structural crystallography.
His *Detailed Mineralogical Dictionary* contains a systematic analysis—and
endorsement—of the Haüy theory that the multitudes of crystal forms can
be reduced to a small number of "primitive forms" and that crystals of the
same element, regardless of their external shapes, can be reduced to one
crystalline form. In 1809 Severgin published *A Mineralogical Geography
of the Russian Empire,* in two volumes, which brought together and systematized mineralogical data on Russia buried in the tomes of earlier

naturalists. He devoted much painstaking work to the preparation of a "manual for a better understanding of chemical studies written in foreign languages," which included a Latin-Russian, a French-Russian, and a German-Russian chemical dictionary.[48] In recognition of his scholarly contributions he was elected a corresponding member of the Göttingen Learned Society and a member of the London Agricultural Society, the Jena Mineralogical Society, the Swedish Academy of Sciences, and the Society of Natural History in Edinburgh.

Russian physics of this period was dominated by the labors of Vasilii Petrov, a graduate of the St. Petersburg teachers' seminary who became a professor in the Medical and Surgical Academy. Petrov was the first member of the Academy of Sciences to write all his studies in Russian. Basically an empiricist who did not venture into broad theoretical speculation, he conducted meticulous and systematic experiments with chemical batteries from which he assembled voluminous experimental material contradicting the phlogiston theory.[49]

Christian Pander, a graduate of Dorpat University, was elected to membership in the Academy in 1821, and in the same year he began to publish his *Comparative Osteology*, in which he developed a consistent evolutionary theory, with Lamarckian leanings, of the development of animal forms. Pander showed scant interest in elaborating and systematizing his embryological theories; he left these tasks to later scientists. Goethe endorsed his transformationist ideas; Darwin was aware of his ideas through secondary sources.[50] In the development of embryology, he was a link between Caspar Wolff and Karl von Baer, several years later. He identified the blastoderm, the disk-shaped embryo located on the surface of the yolk, as the center of activities leading to the formation of the chick. Although Wolff was actually the first to show that the blastoderm is made up of various germ layers, Pander established that these layers were the beginnings of the organs of the growing chick.

UNIVERSITIES AND SCIENCE

The 1803 charter defined the Academy as "the primary learned society of the empire,"[51] but there were of course other scholarly organizations which could now contest its supremacy in some fields, and as the century progressed these became stronger. The new challenges came from the universities, the higher professional schools, the learned societies, and independent scholars. They were many and diverse.

For some time the universities bore the burden of guarding the eighteenth-century mathematical tradition and of reinvigorating the tradition with up-to-date knowledge. In Kazan University, mathematics was taught by Johann Bartels, who had been Gauss's teacher at Göttingen. Bartels's most distinguished Russian student was N. I. Lobachevskii, the creator of the first non-Euclidean geometry. In his lectures at Kazan University, Bartels covered the mathematical contributions of Euler, Monge, Lagrange, and Gauss.[52] T. F. Osipovskii, the rector of Khar'kov University from 1813 to 1820, published a three-volume mathematics textbook which included everything from elementary arithmetic to mathematical analysis and the theory of functions. This work initiated a whole generation of Russians into the complex world of numbers. He also translated Laplace's *Celestial Mechanics* and Condillac's *Logic* into Russian. The early death of M. I. Pankevich, professor at Moscow University, as a result of the hard labor to which he was subjected by Napoleon's army in the occupation of Moscow, prevented this young scholar from completing his translation of Newton's *Principia*.

Russian mathematicians of this time were still propagators of knowledge rather than originators of problems and ideas, but as propagators they went beyond the bounds of the Eulerian tradition and led the way for a new generation of Russian mathematicians who were to make important scientific strides during the second quarter of the nineteenth century.

In every field, the scientific work of the university professors was more valuable in its diversity than in its depth and concrete contributions to the advancement of knowledge. The curriculum of the new universities as well as of the higher professional schools gave greater recognition to the differentiation of science into relatively independent disciplines than had heretofore been customary. Moreover, the theoretical foundations of each science were given a much more intensive emphasis. Astronomy was now taught as a highly involved theoretical science with mathematical foundations. The students of Moscow University, guided by Professor Leon Goldbach, took a direct part in calculating the geographical coordinates of Moscow and neighboring towns (1804–10). Dorpat University, whose observatory was by far the most modern in the empire, provided the training for F. G. W. Struve, who subsequently became one of the great astronomers of the century. (He was made director of the Dorpat Observatory at the age of twenty.) In some universities and higher specialized schools, students could study mineralogy, physiology, anatomy, mechanics, osteology, and an impressive array of other scientific fields. No single university in Russia offered all these courses, but since the universities were granted considerable freedom in interpreting the curriculum prescribed by the government, it was possible for them to offer courses representing the particular interests of their faculties. All universities, for example, were required to teach chemistry, but individual professors, depending on their training and on what foreign textbooks they were allowed to adopt, could stress general chemistry, analytical chemistry, pharmaceutical chemistry, experimental chemistry, or a combination of all.

In the universities, as in the Academy of Sciences, most of the original research in science was left to the foreign scholars, the bearers of modern Western scientific thought. None of these men were scholars of great and acknowledged accomplishment, yet many of them were capable representatives of the diverse—and often conflicting—branches of scientific endeavor. "For understandable reasons," states A. N. Pypin, "the university positions could not be filled by Russian scholars alone; it was necessary to invite foreigners, among whom were some excellent representatives of their specialties, including some who were recognized names in the European learned literature. Such were Buhle, Schlözer, Mattei, Littrow, Schad, Rommel, Fischer von Waldheim, Goldbach, Reiss, C. M. Fraehn, Graefe, Charmoy, Erdman, Lodi, Balug'ianskii, and others—classicists, historians, legal scholars, philosophers, Orientalists, and naturalists, many of whom made honorable contributions to the study of Russia and to the development of Russian science."[53]

Most of the foreign professors, as products of German universities, were active agents in transplanting the enormous enthusiasm and intellectual fermentation generated by the German academic community. These professors brought to Russia not only the newest ideas of Poisson, Lagrange, Laplace, Gauss, and the other stalwarts of their day, but also the new philosophies. The whole sweep of contemporary philosophical thought— from Locke's empiricism and the French materialists' sensualism to Bentham's utilitarianism, Kant's transcendental idealism, and Schelling's Naturphilosophie—found representatives in Russian universities, where philosophical differences frequently led to hard-fought intellectual battles.

Philosophy was not only a point of view; it was also an important part of the teaching curriculum and a reservoir of topics for scholarly writing. The Kantian philosophy had its vociferous spokesmen in almost all the universities and even in the St. Petersburg Theological Academy. Most of the Kantians were Germans, quite naturally, but among the Russians too a sect of Kantian zealots emerged.* According to Shchapov, they were most impressed with Kant's eloquent pronouncement that "philosophy is the science of the relation of all knowledge to the essential ends of human reason (*teleologia rationis humanae*) and the philosopher is not an artificer in the field of reason, but himself the lawgiver of human reason."[54] Kantian philosophy, combining agnosticism with the scientific attitude in an attempt to reconcile traditional empiricism with rationalism, was hailed as a triumph of secular wisdom over the time-honored but outworn precepts of official ideology.

The opponents of Kantian philosophy, however, were a formidable lot. Church authorities were suspicious of Kantian rationalism, and the *idéologues* of extreme conservatism were bitterly opposed to its support of the theory of natural rights. In 1807 the mathematician Osipovskii delivered an impressive oration in which he made an unsparing and highly sophisticated attack on Kant's attribution of *a priori* qualities to the concepts of time and space.[55] In his search for a new geometry, Lobachevskii came to see a philosophical similarity between Kant and Euclid in their interpretation of space as an absolute category; "in the conflict between Kant's *Critique of Pure Reason* and eighteenth-century sensualism, [Lobachevskii] was undoubtedly on the side of the latter."[56]

During this time, Schelling's *Naturphilosophie* began to win adherents in Russia, although it did not reach the peak of its influence until the 1830's.[57] Whereas Kant's philosophy was mostly epistemological, that of Schelling was ontological. Kant regarded philosophy and science as a logical continuum; Schelling's idealistic philosophy, the so-called *Naturphilosophie,* was a negation of science, denying any value to experimentation and empiricism. The influence of Schelling and Lorenz Oken was strong in Russia, as it was in Western Europe, among scholars in fields close to medicine—partly because of their desire for a theoretical and philosophical unification of the medical sciences.

It would be easy to jump to the conclusion that Schelling's influence on scientific thought in Russia was detrimental, that it hampered the development of the scientific spirit and fogged the scientific horizons with sheer speculation. On the contrary, it was a helpful influence in at least one way—in that it made itself felt at a time when the pure empiricism of Russian naturalists seemed no longer adequate or scientifically all-

---

* One of the characters in Pushkin's *Eugene Onegin* is a young Kantian "whose soul was shaped in Göttingen."

embracing and when scholars under Western influence were beginning to appreciate the importance of theory. Some scholars, such as P. F. Goria-ninov, A. I. Galich, Ia. K. Kaidanov, and M. G. Pavlov, found in Schelling-ism an easy route to theoretical inquiry and a ready-made detour around the gaps in their understanding of certain sciences; yet even the Schelling-ians had some part in displacing the old-fashioned naturalists and ushering in the new science—science as a logically and theoretically unified body of knowledge.

Although Russia in the first quarter of the nineteeth century could boast of scarcely any scientists whose work was worthy of attention in Western Europe, it had nurtured a whole generation of scholars in the various "natural philosophies" (*philosophiae naturalis*) that marked the grand transition from natural history (*historia naturalis*) to modern science. The *philosophiae naturalis* of these years were not Schelling's *Naturphilosophie* but science in the tradition of Bacon, Descartes, and Newton. Examples of this philosophy, in its contemporary form, were embodied in such works as Lamarck's *Philosophie zoologique,* Fourcroy's *Philosophie chimique,* Davy's *Elements of Chemical Philosophy,* and Geof-froy Saint-Hilaire's *Philosophie anatomique.*

In terms of their philosophical outlook, three types of naturalists domi-nated the biological research being carried on in Russian universities. The first group was headed by Ivan Dvigubskii. Especially in his earlier work, Dvigubskii was influenced by the views of Lomonosov, Buffon, and Wolff—which regarded nature as a reality that, under external influences, was continuously changing. The second group, led by D. M. Vellanskii and Ia. K. Kaidanov, was made up of the Russian followers of Schelling, who implicitly recognized the historical quality of nature but placed the primary emphasis on a unitary, vitalistic interpretation of natural phenomena. The third group, represented by Iustin Diad'kovskii, made a feeble effort to extend the mechanistic view of Newtonian physics and Goldbach's materialistic philosophy to the study of organic nature. None of these theoretical orientations showed much consistency or elaboration. Schellingism was probably the most carefully worked out, and it might have been more influential if its champions had been less barbarous in their language.[58] But in Russia, even more than in the West, it was still too soon for a codification of biological theory; and the influence of French and English humanistic thought postponed the wave of German influence until the mid-1820's.

Apart from these three theoretically inclined groups of scholars, there were also a number of old-fashioned natural historians of the narrow, empiricist sort. Led by G. J. Fischer von Waldheim, these men assembled valuable data on the natural resources of the provinces. They lacked the encyclopedic sweep of the eighteenth-century naturalists, but they had the advantage of more reliable methods of study. Timofei Smelovskii was at the same time a collector of biological data and a scholar with a keen theoretical interest; he translated Linnaeus's *Philosophia botanica* into Russian (1800), wrote a critical study of Linnaeus's plant taxonomy, and was a leading expert on the flora of the St. Petersburg province.

Kant's influence on the development of scientific thought in Russia was strong and lasting, even though during the 1820's "for each five readers of Kant there were over 5,000 readers of Schelling."[59] Kant was esteemed not only as a philosopher and cosmologist but also as a political theorist, who looked upon the existing forms of government as transitory and historical rather than absolute and immutable. He was also respected as an epistemologist, who tried to explain the foundations of science rather than to negate them. In 1808 the Faculty of Moral and Political Sciences of Moscow University chose the influence of Kant's philosophy on science and on "the life and morality of the people" as the topic for its annual essay contest. Professor Aleksandr Kunytsin of St. Petersburg University devoted an entire book, *Natural Law* (1818–20), to a systematic presentation of Kant's political and moral views.

Throughout this period the influence of the French *philosophes* in Russia remained strong, but it was largely confined to the humanities and political theory (through, for example, a widespread emphasis on the natural rights theories). The influence of the German philosophers was, for the most part, in the realm of natural science. Even the mathematical sciences, though not within the arena of ideology, were no longer completely isolated from philosophy, as attested by Osipovskii's criticisms of Kant's concept of space.

The one philosopher whom both natural and social scientists admired was Francis Bacon. His works were combed in search of appropriate quotations by those who were interested in the relationship of science to "good government" or to human welfare, as well as by those wishing to define the rigors and instrumentalities of the scientific method. In crediting Bacon and Descartes with liberating the learned men of Western Europe from many "conclusions" inherited from the ancient world, Osipovskii had in mind Bacon's dictum that "the wisdom which we have derived principally from the Greeks is but like the boyhood of knowledge and has the characteristic property of boys: it can talk, but it cannot generate, for it is fruitful of controversies but barren of works."[60] Lobachevskii, for example, claimed that it was Bacon who foretold the rise of mathematics as the basis of the new scientific method.[61] Mikhail Speranskii quoted Bacon to give weight to the philosophical background for his celebrated plan for constitutional reform. And Admiral Mordvinov's adherence to English empiricism and the Baconian philosophy of science is shown in the following aphorism found among his unpublished notes: "A method is needed for the application of superior rules [guiding human action]; otherwise they would remain fruitless. According to Bacon, the method replaces the genius and guarantees the success of all actions, large or small. Everything that man has that has not been given to him by nature has been achieved by improvements in methods."[62]

The philosophical search for theory was not the only preoccupation of Russian university scientists during these years. They were also intent on classifying the scientific concepts or principal natural phenomena investigated by the individual disciplines, and in that way defining the scope of their interests. Georg Parrot's *Foundations of Theoretical Physics* (1809–11), published by Dorpat University, and Dvigubskii's *Foundations of the Natural History of Plants* (1811) were typical of the studies dedicated to a theoretically grounded systematization and classification of knowledge. Christian Loder's *Elementa anatomiae humanii corporis* (1822) also belongs to this category. The mechanical cataloguing of empirical data—the method of the natural historian—had now given way to integrated presentations of scientific concepts. The transition was not a smooth one, for the natural history orientation was still predominant even among the most ardent champions of the new science.

As scientific centers, the universities differed from the St. Petersburg Academy in their greater emphasis on the humanities and social sciences. A number of foreign professors who had fled to Russia from Western Europe to escape the Napoleonic wars were reformists, who employed both lectern and pen in expounding their dreams of a better society. The universities were responsible for a considerable expansion of teaching and research in the classical languages and literature, philology, Oriental studies, universal history, jurisprudence, and political economy, although most of this research was limited to popular translations, condensations, or eclectic syntheses of current Western studies.

The most dynamic and challenging ideas were presented by the students of political economy and law. Through a whole array of professors, led by C. Schlözer, K. Hermann, M. A. Balug'ianskii, and K. I. Arsen'ev, modern notions of economics were spread and dramatized in Russia.[63] The Russians were introduced to mercantilism, the physiocratic movement, and Malthusianism. The dominant influence in economic thinking was Adam Smith, whose *Wealth of Nations*—or what were thought to be its ideas— had wide circulation in St. Petersburg, Moscow, and other university centers. In practice, however, the political economists of Russia held diverse opinions, ranging from a staunch belief in government-supported feudal institutions to a desire for the least possible government interference in economic matters. Few economists had any original ideas—and the same can be said of the specialists in law and so-called universal history.

It is a sad commentary on the university scholarship of this period that so little was done to promote the study of Russian history. The most noteworthy exception was the work of Johann Ewers of Dorpat University in the field of early Russian legal history. Ewers developed a theory of the Khazar origin of the Variags, and he is considered to be the founder of the school of Russian historiography that identified ancient Slavic societies as aggregates of clans, organized for defensive purposes.[64]

Especially during the first, Westernizing phase of Alexander's reign, Russian intellectuals gave little thought to the history of their own country, and the foreign professors understandably preferred fields rich in Western sources. The study of national history had never been encouraged at Moscow University, and at the start of the nineteenth century there was no university tradition in historical research. In a note to Nicholas I in 1826, Aleksandr Pushkin remarked: "The Russians still know very little about Russia. There is a need for special teaching positions in universities for Russian history, statistics, and law."[65]

NIKOLAI KARAMZIN AS A HISTORIAN: IDEOLOGY AND ART

Since Russian history was likewise ignored by the Academy of Sciences and the Russian Academy, it was left to individual scholars and private scholarly societies to develop an interest in the subject. These efforts were frequently unsystematic and sometimes trivial, but in total they combined to give Russian history a new status as a respected field of inquiry.

The Society for the Study of Russian History and Antiquities, under the auspices of Moscow University, issued a series of documents to be used as source material, and efforts of a similar nature were undertaken by the Universities of Khar'kov and Kazan.

Chiefly, however, it was among men without academic affiliations, usually aristocrats or upper gentry, that a growing interest in Russian affairs began to develop. After Napoleon's invasion of Russia, the national consciousness increased, bringing with it a certain reversal of former receptive attitudes toward Western ideals. Fortunately, in some men the desire to learn about Russia's past was more than a quick and perhaps superficial reaction, and in two men particularly it became a genuine and serious search for a fuller understanding of the national history. One of these—Nikolai Karamzin—distinguished himself as a historiographer, while the second—Nikolai Rumiantsev—initiated and sponsored the collection and publication of documentary material on a scale previously unknown in Russia.

Karamzin refused an offer to teach Russian history in the newly founded Khar'kov University in order to work exclusively and independently as a historian and as a commentator on contemporary affairs in Russia.[66] His eleven-volume *History of the Russian State* (1818–24) is generally accepted as the beginning of modern Russian historiography, being a transition from eighteenth-century history-writing to the modern studies initiated by Solov'ev. Like his eighteenth-century precursors, Karamzin considered history primarily a literary form.[67] He differed from Lomonosov, however, in that he abandoned the antiquated language of pseudoclassical literature in favor of the popular tongue, scrupulously avoiding foreign borrowings except when no adequate Russian equivalents could be found.[68] Pushkin credited him with freeing the Russian language of its "foreign yoke" and directing it back to the living source of the spoken word.[69]

Karamzin was careful about consulting published historical sources, but he bothered himself very little with obscure unpublished material and often disregarded prosaic facts in his delight in verbal embellishments—to the extent of being described by some as a proponent of historical sentimentalism. Like Tatishchev, he took Russian history to be the history of the Russian state, thus leaving himself open to attacks later on from two other groups, or schools, of Russian historiography. Disciples of the romantic school opposed too strong an emphasis on the importance of political institutions as a historical determinant, urging the study of "unpredictable" historical forces, such as the role of the masses, national character, and the unique historical missions of individual nations.[70] The second school—which consisted primarily of the generation of historians following Karamzin—advocated the study of the history of individual peoples within the framework of world history.

Despite the flaws in his monumental history, Karamzin outlasted his critics. Pushkin likened him to Columbus: he was the discoverer of Old Russia. A later historian maintained that Karamzin's greatest achievement lay in helping Russian intellectuals to discern the depths of their national past at a time when Russia was in danger of surrendering completely to Western cultural influences. Karamzin's magnum opus, he said, appeared at a moment when "Russian Europeanism reached its climax among the so-called enlightened circles," and when, as a result of these influences, "Russia's ancient history was completely unknown." It was a time, as a contemporary put it, when "the libraries of our fathers, made up of old manuscripts, gave way to worldly repositories of collected works of eighteenth-century French writers and their English prototypes, naturally in French translations"; when Napoleon's *Code* became the most popular manual in courts and schools; and when the Russian poets took their heroes straight from Racine and Molière.[71]

Karamzin's success was due largely to his elegant prose and his sophistication. As a young man, before he had settled on a career as historian, he traveled extensively in Europe, visiting such luminaries as Kant and Herder; but his reading took him even further, into the realms of Tacitus, Hume, Gibbon, and Johannes von Müller. With the help of intensive and critical reading of classics in history and the philosophy of history, Karamzin developed into a historian "not of the miseries and glories of war" but of the great cultural development of Western man—"achievements of reason, arts, customs, laws, and industry."[72] Under the obvious influence of Condorcet, Turgot, and Condillac, he saw in the growth of science and enlightenment the index of progress, the quintessence of the history of mankind. Modern science, he believed, was a force which could cross the boundaries of individual cultures and create a basis for international understanding. In a letter written as a young man in Paris, he said:

"The German scholar takes his hat off when he talks about Lalande and Lavoisier. My friend Becker can speak of Lavoisier only with the greatest exhilaration; in return, he received from Lavoisier a compliment when he heard that he was a student of the great Berlin chemist [M. H.] Klaproth. Tears of joy come to my eyes when I observe how sciences bring together people living in the north and the south, and how the men of science like and respect one another, although they are not personally acquainted."[73]

As a scholar and critical analyst of current affairs, Karamzin was not a prototype either of the Slavophils or of the Westerners, whose ideological and philosophical battle attracted much of the attention of the next generation. With the Westerners, he was opposed to indiscriminate checks on the normal flow of scientific, technological, and philosophical wisdom from the West. In his *Letters of a Russian Traveler,* for example, he writes admiringly of European enlightenment and intellectual fermentation, in scientific matters as well as in literature and the arts.[74] In the same work, however, there is biting criticism of other European developments, including the French Revolution, which Karamzin thought incompatible with Russia's interests. Like the Slavophils, Karamzin stressed the uniqueness of Russian customs, tradition, and psychology. This attitude was partly owing to the nature of his work as a Russian historian; but in addition, as a cosmopolitan with discrimination and experience, he deliberately set out to counteract the exaggerated and uncritical admiration of Western ideas that was voiced by most of his educated contemporaries.

Karamzin's detailed survey of Russian history was made possible, to a large extent, by N. P. Rumiantsev. Rumiantsev, a rich aristocrat who held high offices in the government, was largely responsible for the appointment, in 1811, of a special commission in the Moscow Archives, under the Ministry of Foreign Affairs, which was to make a collection of ancient and modern legal documents—after the model of Jean Dumont's collection of French legal acts subsequent to the reign of Charlemagne. The commission was actually headed by N. N. Bantysh-Kamenskii, but the most important work was done by the historians Konstantin Kalaidovich and Pavel Stroev, who dug out and prepared for publication a vast amount of documentary material hidden away in monasteries in all parts of Russia. Long experienced in the study of historical sources, Rumiantsev approached the ambitious task of gathering historical documents with the confidence and efficiency of an accomplished scholar. Under his direction, thirteen collections of documentary material were published from 1813 to 1824.[75] Rumiantsev and his assistants made it clear that a successful historian must perform a double function: that of collecting and evaluating written documentary material, and that of writing historical narrative in a language that would be understandable to the entire literate population.

As Karamzin grew older he became increasingly conservative in his political views. His *History of the Russian State* comes close to being an apotheosis of autocracy, the form of government which he considered responsible for all cultural advances made by his country. In his *Memoir on Ancient and Modern Russia* (1811), he stated plainly that Russia had flourished whenever autocracy was strong. He also insisted categorically that serfdom was indispensable under the cultural and social conditions of contemporary Russia.

Another independent scholar of this period, N. I. Turgenev, acquired a reputation as the most original and profound Russian economist of his time. Turgenev was educated at Moscow and Göttingen Universities and then worked for several years with Baron Heinrich von Stein, the German statesman who, with Alexander's support, was seeking to reconstitute Germany as a nation. It was undoubtedly under Stein's influence and the influence of long association with German liberalism that Turgenev wrote his *Essay on the Theory of Taxes*.[76] Generally critical of serfdom, though not consistently so, this book advocated free trade and low duties on imports. It stood openly against the overtaxing of "common folk" and against releasing the nobility from tax obligations. Turgenev warned that the comfort of the people, and not the existence of factories, was the main index of national well-being. He maintained that the success of official efforts to collect taxes depended on the form of government and the "national spirit." In his own mind, he was certain that people who live under a republican government are more willing to meet their tax obligations than people subject to despotic rule.[77] Significantly, the first edition of Turgenev's book, published in 1818, was sold out immediately, and within a year it appeared in a second printing.

As an economist, and particularly as an advocate of economic reforms, Turgenev had a larger and more appreciative audience than his colleagues in the universities and the Academy. His work was novel in one important respect: it urged that the study of political economy cannot consist merely of collected facts, no matter how abundant and diverse, but must seek to integrate the facts into theories, into a formal system of thought. Going one step further, Turgenev added to his emphasis on theory an ideological appeal: "Economic and financial theory, as well as the theory of government, has only one true basis—liberty."[78] As evidence, he pointed to the power and prosperity of England.

SCIENCE AND THE CONTRAVENING CULTURAL FORCES

History was not kind to those who favored the fundamental Westernization of Russia. Little by little, by a combination of social and cultural forces, Alexander's reforms were whittled down. Only a few scholars of great stature emerged during the early nineteenth century, and the ranks of Russian scientists remained comparatively thin.

To a student of intellectual history and, particularly, to a sociologist of science, the period of Alexander I is more interesting—and historically more significant—for its failures than for its achievements. It was a period dominated by a formidable set of cultural forces, either irrelevant to science or inimical to science, which impeded an orderly and progressive carrying out of Alexander's reforms. No single one of these social and cultural forces was powerful enough in itself to undermine the plans, but by a convergence of values and institutional commitments, mostly unrelated but favored by special historical conditions, the forces antagonistic to science managed to gain the upper hand during the first quarter of the nineteenth century. Besides the forces really antagonistic to science, there was an almost equally strong wall of opposition in the naïveté of Russian society, tradition-bound and unprepared to comprehend the lofty ideals of Alexander's youthful reformers. In an autocratic state, moreover, the whims of the emperor—and changes in his duties, ideas, and attitudes—were not without importance.

The legacy of the period of Catherine's radical retreat from her allegiance to the ideals of the Enlightenment and Paul's reign of terror was, of course, a serious handicap to Alexander's educational reforms. As before, the chief problem was lack of teachers and lack of students ready for advanced study, who might quickly become teachers themselves.

In 1800 Russia had a total of 315 schools of all types (including private boarding schools), with 720 teachers, mostly Russian.[79] Of 19,915 students enrolled in these schools, the vast majority were in lower public schools, only a handful taking courses preparatory to college education. There were no textbooks in Russian for many sciences, and few Russian students could read any Western European language. As a result of Paul's censorship decrees, the few libraries which existed were antiquated and virtually depleted. Only small circles of the privileged who found a way, mostly through the diplomatic service, to the cultural centers of the West were aware of recent developments in philosophy and science.

It was this stultifying legacy of the preceding era that had to be overcome before the new gymnasiums and universities could become vigorous and genuinely Russian institutions. Alexander's immediate reforms reopened the country to the flow of Western ideas, but the wounds inflicted by the bad years were too deep to be cured within one generation.

The shortage of instructors, particularly at the university level, proved to be a major obstacle in the way of the educational reforms and was one of the main reasons for the painfully slow increase in the number of native Russians who aspired to become scientists. Mostly because of a lack of instructors, Kazan University was not fully opened until 1814. For the same reason, Khar'kov University offered only two subjects in natural science from 1812 to 1814.[80] Instead of the four faculties originally planned for this university, only three were opened at first.[81] Similar situations prevailed in the other Russian universities.

The authorities tried to remedy this deficiency by hiring foreign professors, even though they usually could not lecture in the Russian language. As an example, at Kazan University in 1809, eight subjects were taught in Russian, five in Latin, three in French, and one in German.[82] In the exact and natural sciences, the number of lectures given in foreign languages was considerably higher. At Moscow University foreign professors were brought in to teach botany, chemistry, physics, mechanics, astronomy, the history of philosophy, and statistics.

As indicated previously, a large number of the foreign professors were competent and established persons, some of whom had been distinguished members of Western European learned societies. They brought modern scientific ideas and a full sampling of the new philosophical trends to Russia as well as an enthusiasm for scientific inquiry and the humanistic equation of science. It is doubtful that Lobachevskii would have formulated his new geometry had he not been stimulated by the foreign scholars who taught at Kazan University, notably Bartels, Bronner, Renner, and Littrow. The foreign professors re-established the avenues of Russia's scientific contact with the West.

The difficulties with which their work in Russia was surrounded, however, were gigantic and sometimes insurmountable. Deprived of adequate libraries and laboratories, many of them abandoned serious scientific pursuits altogether. When Littrow joined Kazan University in 1810 to teach astronomy, he reported to the University Council that the library did not have a single volume in his field that could be used as a textbook.[83] Some of the foreign professors were preoccupied with the writing of textbooks to fill the need. Others shifted from subject to subject without feeling any impetus to produce original work. Only a few, particularly in the social sciences and the humanities, kept up their research. As in the early years of Moscow University, the foreign professors often had difficulty learning Russian, and this of course was a drawback to teaching as well as to friendly relations with students. Most damaging of all, the universities became battlegrounds for a pernicious warfare between Russian and foreign professors. Such quarrels had occurred also in the eighteenth century, but in the new universities, after the Napoleonic wars, the antagonism to foreign professors received considerable official sanction and became more widespread. Many German instructors departed, and their places went unfilled. In 1814, for the first time, the foreign element at Khar'kov and Kazan Universities lost its numerical superiority.[84] In 1815 a government decree ruled that henceforth all university lectures must be delivered in Russian. In the same year Professor Johann Schad, a favorite of Goethe and Schiller, was expelled, not from Khar'kov University alone but from the country, on grounds of having sought to popularize Schelling's philosophy and to identify it with "natural law."[85]

Alexander I learned—as had Peter I, Elizabeth I, and Catherine II—that it was easier to open schools than to get students to attend them. The transformation of the main public schools of the Catherinean era into the new gymnasiums was an exceedingly slow process. In 1808 Russia had 54 gymnasiums and other schools of equal rank, with 409 teachers and 5,509 students.[86] Seventeen years later the number of gymnasium students had increased by only 2,000.[87] By far the heaviest enrollment was in the Baltic areas and the Moscow and St. Petersburg school districts. Owing to a lack of students, the Tambov and Kazan main public schools were not transformed into gymnasiums until 1825.

Despite their emphasis on the exact and natural sciences, the gymnasiums did not as a rule prepare young men adequately for the universities. When it became clear that an overwhelming number of students were not interested in a university education, many gymnasiums began teaching sciences along practical lines, particularly in the upper classes, which were frequently attended by government stipendists who had been selected to become teachers in district and parish schools without going on to the universities. Mathematics was rather more adequately taught than most subjects, but physics and chemistry suffered from a dismal shortage of laboratory equipment. Within a decade of the launching of Alexander's reforms, it was recognized that the gymnasiums were not giving their students the proper training for university studies, and Khar'kov University authorities proposed that college preparatory courses be offered by the universities themselves.[88]

From the outset, the gymnasiums were hampered by the skeptical attitude toward the teaching of science which was held by many government officials. In 1811 S. S. Uvarov, curator of public schools in the St. Petersburg district, expressed concern about the teaching of what he considered to be harmful subjects in secondary schools and ordered that the St. Petersburg gymnasium shift its concentration from the natural and social sciences to religion and the Russian and classical languages. In several other gymnasiums the teaching of Greek soon became obligatory, ushering in a long reign of classicism in the country's high schools and other secondary schools. In 1819 languages (particularly classical), geography, and history were adopted as standard subjects in the gymnasium curriculum. Although the natural sciences continued to be adequately represented until 1828, the pedagogical focus was gradually but definitely shifting away from these disciplines.

The plight of the gymnasium in Alexander's period is revealed in the following observation made by an eminent student of Russia's educational institutions during the first quarter of the nineteenth century: "The first inspectors were overwhelmed by the internal conditions of schools, which suffered from two main deficiencies: the moral corruption of students and the despotism of administrators. The directors of schools were mostly semi-literate retired army officers who issued orders to teachers arbitrarily, rewarding subservient favorites and dismissing those whom they did not like."[89]

Without a backlog of gymnasium-trained students, the new universities at first were hard put to fill their classrooms. In 1808–9 even Moscow University had only 135 students, and the new Universities of Dorpat, Khar'kov, and Kazan had enrollments of 193, 82, and 40, respectively. Most of the students were lured to higher studies by liberal government scholarships and promises of various privileges.[90] Gradually, however, and at first almost imperceptibly, the universities began to grow. In 1823–24 the enrollment at Moscow University had increased to 820, at Dorpat University to 365, at Khar'kov University to 332, at Kazan University to 118; and at the new St. Petersburg University (founded in 1819) there were 51 students.

At the start, the universities were filled mostly by graduates of the theological schools, who knew much Greek and Latin but little science and no modern European language. The first 40 students at Khar'kov University were sent, by order of the Synod, from the Kursk and Khar'kov seminaries. No stringent criteria were used for the selection of students, nor did the universities in general encourage work of high quality. The classrooms of foreign professors were poorly attended, and personal contact between professors and students was practically nonexistent. Laboratory needs were almost ignored: chemical laboratories existed in all universities, but their equipment did not meet even minimum standards. The almost total absence of university laboratories for the physical sciences left the Academy of Sciences with a virtual monopoly in this field. Moscow University had more extensive laboratory facilities than the new universities, but it suffered heavy losses from a fire started during the French occupation of Moscow in 1812.

The tribulations of the universities were further aggravated by the shelving of some of the more liberal provisions of the 1804 charter. The legal rights of university councils were often violated by extralegal actions of individual superintendents. The absence of a parliamentary tradition in running university affairs and constant fear of the ascendance of foreign professors to positions of power exerted a negative influence on university autonomy. Professors were often deprived of their legal right to select textbooks, and, from the very beginning of Alexander's school reform, the whim of a school district superintendent could make important changes in the curriculum and the educational philosophy. The universities did not enjoy enough independence to protect themselves from powerful outside forces of antiscientific orientation.

After the initial enthusiasm expressed by such sincere spokesmen of enlightenment as Murav'ev and Karazin, the attitude of the government toward the universities soon hardened into one of sheer utilitarianism. The universities were looked upon, in the first place, as training grounds for future government officials, physicians, and teachers, and, in the second place, as the administrative centers of each of the six school districts into which the country was divided. N. P. Zagoskin, the author of a history of Kazan University, stated the position clearly:

"The training of government officials 'for various positions' emerged as a factor of primary significance in the establishment of Russian universities; in the eyes of the government, the university professors were not independent representatives of free sciences but officials ('official of philosophy,' 'official of literature,' and 'official of natural law' were normal expressions in the good old days for the representatives of various subjects), who were expected to teach their courses along the lines of strictly prescribed programs and textbooks."[91]

EDUCATION, SCIENCE, AND SOCIAL STRATIFICATION

The implementation of Alexander's educational reforms of 1802–5 was seemingly accompanied by enough zeal among the various representatives of the gentry to assure the success of the ambitious undertaking. Sukhomlinov, for example, recounted in some detail the substantial contributions made by Ukrainian gentry toward the founding of Khar'kov University. But as the new gymnasiums and universities began opening their doors to the young men of Russia, various problems of social and class origin began to appear.

The aristocracy continued to oppose liberal and scientific education, particularly since it was entrusted to public schools and universities which were open to all free estates. Speranskii had the aristocracy in mind when he asserted at the beginning of the century that education was not a luxury but a moral obligation to new generations. The aristocracy were reluctant to send their children to gymnasiums past the age of fourteen, since that would mean a delay in embarking upon their careers. Even as late as 1819, the superintendent of the Moscow school district complained that many gymnasiums had virtually no students enrolled in their upper classes.[92] The gymnasiums were attended mostly by children of poor government employees, merchants, and other middle urban classes, who, as a rule, seldom carried their secondary education to completion. Most of them were obliged by circumstances to seek early employment either in government service or in private trade, and few had any real desire for further schooling. The government was thus forced to rely on scholarships as a way of attracting young men to university study. It is interesting to note that class exclusiveness was stronger at this time than at any time during the eighteenth century, and it was no small factor in the generally low attendance of the aristocracy in the higher schools.

According to V. V. Grigor'ev, the chronicler of St. Petersburg University, one of the main reasons for the disappointingly low attendance at the University's first lectures in November 1819—only twenty students—was that the gentry, the only estate which could afford to take advantage of the school, "were hesitant to send their children to schools in which they would sit together with children of nonaristocratic origin . . . because the university was opened to all free classes."[93]

The social exclusiveness of the aristocracy now became part of an ideology, an ideology with an intellectual base constructed in part within the domain of scholarship. This was the period, for example, when efforts were made to justify the feudal social system by making it an integral part of the general order of nature, as interpreted from a metaphysical and theological standpoint. This was also the era of the proliferation of plans for separate estate schools with differential curricula. An influential journal of the time endorsed the following view: "Not all segments of the people should receive the same kind of education. Sciences, the so-called liberal arts, and all other branches of knowledge which meet the educational needs of men engaged in the affairs of the state are totally inappropriate for the masses and are even dangerous for their well-being. God help us if the entire nation were to be made up of learned men, dialecticians, and contemplative minds!"[94]

Prompted by sober arguments set forth by Speranskii,[95] the government issued the famous decree of August 6, 1809, which restricted a whole bloc of government positions to university graduates and introduced civil service examinations for certain posts, to be administered by local universities.[96] The government undertook this drastic measure in order to speed the solution of the country's most acute problem: the severe shortage of teachers, physicians, and various expert personnel for industry, the army, and the government apparatus. It was a clear notice to the members of the hereditary and service aristocracy that the ranks from collegiate assessor to state counselor, heretofore attained almost automatically by the highest nobility, were to be reserved in the future for worthy officials "trained and tempered at universities."[97]

A sizable group of enlightened aristocracy were by this time fully aware of the need for education and ready to meet the challenge of Speranskii's reforms. But they continued to regard university education as time wasted in embarking on a government career. Added to this, of course, was their reluctance to break the lines of class exclusiveness and isolation, to which even the most enlightened seemed wedded.

Their dilemma was awkward, but not without what appeared to them a practical solution. The immediate result of the Speranskii reform was a mushrooming of boarding schools open only to young aristocrats. At this time the foreign population in Russia, especially in St. Petersburg, was more numerous than ever before. Most of the new immigrants were intellectuals who had fled Western Europe in the aftermath of the revolutionary turmoil of the 1790's. They formed a reservoir of teachers reasonably accomplished in both scientific subjects and the humanities. Not surprisingly, the best of these easily found employment either in the universities or in government work or translating. The mediocrities became the faculties of the new aristocratic boarding schools.

The typical urban aristocrat of this period usually recognized the charms and virtues of education, but he was likely to be content with light and superficial knowledge. Foreign observers came to regard intellectual frivolity as the trademark of St. Petersburg aristocracy. Madame de Staël, who had intimate acquaintance with St. Petersburg's high society, both private and official, remarked: "The character of the Russians is too passionate to allow for a concern even with the least abstract ideas; only facts give them amusement. They have had, so far, neither the time nor the taste to transform fact into theory."[98] In such an atmosphere, the foreign teachers, often of dubious backgrounds, easily ingratiated themselves into aristocratic homes or elegant boarding schools.

Since the time of Catherine II, the government had cast a cool eye on private teachers and boarding schools. Speranskii objected to them on the grounds that they did not meet the necessary standards and were not coordinated with the needs of the state.[99] When Aleksei Razumovskii became the Minister of Education in 1810, he followed the advice of the French Royalist philosopher Joseph de Maistre, then Sardinian Minister in St. Petersburg, and encouraged the founding of Jesuit boarding schools; almost overnight a dozen such schools were founded.[100] Many Jesuits had come to Russia after the suppression of their Society in several Western countries following the papal Brief of Suppression issued in 1773. The opening of Jesuit schools in Russia coincided with a renewed conservative trend, which was especially pronounced in the public criticism of Alexander's educational reforms. There was a particular outcry against the imitation of the educational system of Protestant Germany, as well as a vehement attack on the teaching of the natural and social sciences.[101] In such an atmosphere, the Jesuit schools for a time had considerable popularity.

The Jesuits went too far, however, when they began converting their students to the Catholic faith, and in 1820 they were officially expelled.[102] But it is true that their schools had not been adequate, and that their restricted curricula had scarcely trained men to pass the examinations for government service. Even before the Jesuit expulsion, young aristocrats had found it necessary to look for some other sort of exclusive school.

The first answer to the problem was the founding of the Tsarskosel'skii Lyceum in 1811. This school was designed to educate young aristocrats who had been carefully chosen for future high government office. The educational level lay somewhere between the gymnasiums and the universities.

Until 1822 the Lyceum was under the Ministry of National Education; then it was transferred to the Department of Military Schools. A similar school, but with somewhat lower standards, was the Richelieu Lyceum in Odessa, founded in 1817.

A second and more effective answer to the educational challenges with which the young noblemen were faced was provided by the aristocratic boarding schools set up under the jurisdiction of the established universities. In actual fact, the first of these was established by the St. Petersburg Pedagogical Institute. When the Institute was transformed into St. Petersburg University in 1819, the aristocratic boarding school was retained as one of its component parts. A year earlier a similar boarding school was organized by Moscow University. These boarding schools were actually schools within schools; they gave young aristocrats a university education without disturbing their isolation from other social groups. According to an eminent student of the history of Russian education: "The founding of aristocratic boarding schools and lyceums was not subject to any general legal regulations. Each of these institutions had its individual characteristics. But the general course of their emergence and development had one dominant tendency: they were results of a reaction to the educational reform of 1803–4 and to basing education on the *all-estate principle*; they were also an expression of the desire to ensure for noble youths short and smooth roads to government service, which by tradition the nobility considered the privilege of their estate."[103]

After 1818 university enrollment grew steadily—though only in part because of the aristocratic boarding schools. Within another decade, however, the government had changed its course, and instead of encouraging students from the lower estates with scholarships was, on the contrary, making it increasingly difficult for them to attend the universities. The gentry made up more and more of the university enrollment, and as this occurred the curricular emphasis shifted from the natural sciences to law and the humanities. From the late 1820's on, for several decades, every student in the field of natural science was matched by at least two students who were studying law.[104] By Shchapov's count, twenty-five Moscow University professors taught various social sciences and the humanities during the period 1814–26, while only fifteen were engaged in teaching the natural and exact sciences.[105] In 1828 the Committee for the Establishment of Schools concluded that the education of Russian youths during the first quarter of the nineteenth century suffered from "the luxury of half-knowledge" and the students' propensity for selecting easy subjects.[106]

SCIENCE AND IDEOLOGICAL REVERSALS

Alexander's liberal reforms met a fate familiar to students of Russia: before reaching their full flowering, they were smashed by antithetical forces. Since these forces were much more belligerent than those of the short-lived age of reason with which the nineteenth century began, it can truly be said that one of the most promising periods in the history of higher education in Russia was followed by one of the darkest.

The transition, however, was not sudden. Radical though the reforms may have been in conception, a good many of them never got beyond the paper on which they were written, and a good many others were, in actual practice, ignored by unsympathetic school administrators. Even Alexander's apparent effort to eradicate Paul's system of censorship failed to secure complete freedom of expression for scholars.

One typical example of the kind of censorship that continued to haunt the liberal writers—even though their ideas were shared by most of the Tsar's counselors—was the fate of Pnin's *Essay on Education in Russia.* Written in the intellectual atmosphere created by the Preliminary Rules of National Education, which set forth the basic principles of Alexander's educational reforms, this book was immediately sold out following its publication in 1804. But when in the same year Pnin tried to publish a second, revised, edition in which he took a definite stand against serfdom, the censors refused permission and also ordered all copies of the first edition to be withdrawn from all libraries. Despite their flirting with the humanistic thought of the time, Alexander and his chief counselors were uncompromising in their ideological commitment to serfdom.

When Joseph de Maistre arrived in St. Petersburg in 1803, he was already well known as an uncompromising critic of the philosophy and republican political theories of the French Revolution. As a Legitimist and a devout Catholic, he had no use for the secularism and rationalism characteristic of the philosophy of the Enlightenment and its postrevolutionary intellectual heirs. In St. Petersburg, de Maistre gradually charmed his way into Court circles, and in 1810 he was gratified by the appointment of his personal friend and admirer Razumovskii to the post of Minister of National Education. It was owing to de Maistre's influence that the Jesuit schools attained their temporary position of favor. When Razumovskii submitted the plan for the organization of the Tsarskosel'skii Lyceum to de Maistre for his appraisal and suggestions, de Maistre replied by recommending in no uncertain terms that all the courses in the natural and social sciences be discarded. He was particularly displeased with scientific theories of the physical origin of the earth and with current notions about natural rights. De Maistre's suggestions were largely ignored, and the Lyceum offered a well-rounded program in the natural and social sciences; but de Maistre nevertheless became the herald of new forces, nurtured on Christian dogmatism and antisecularism, which soon began to threaten the very existence of the universities.

De Maistre spoke for a great many ultraconservative Russians who looked upon science and humanistic thought as mental aberrations and shameless flirtations with immorality. He claimed that the Russian schools —particularly the universities—were appallingly weak, and that this was so because they were modeled after the German Protestant schools, which freely challenged many basic truths contained in the Bible. Rigidly Catholic, he believed Protestant theology and philosophy to be riddled with materialism, which, if it prevailed, would destroy the values of Western civilization. He wrote an essay attacking Bacon as a "mock doctor," a "bizarre and ridiculous charlatan," and, worst of all, the progenitor of modern materialism.[107] Humanism and rationalism he considered especially dangerous because they tended toward an increasing independence of religious thought. He preferred an alchemist to a chemist, for the alchemist at least did not deny his religion. Science, de Maistre claimed, needed surveillance by the leaders of the State and the Church rather than encouragement and protection.

It was not so much de Maistre's great intellectual power and skillful persuasion that gained him influence, however, as it was the growing tendency toward conservatism in general among the ruling elite, including Alexander himself. While not accepting de Maistre's exaltation of Catholicism, many members of the Russian elite did accept his antirationalism and antihumanism, attitudes more or less in accord with their own fears of secular learning and equalitarianism.

The awakening of nationalist pride as a result of Napoleon's invasion of Russia also added to the new conservatism; indeed, after 1812 criticism of Alexander's liberal reforms became open and fairly common. Karamzin, who less than a decade earlier had been enthusiastic about the prospects of the new universities,[108] now became a relentless critic. In reference to Russian universities, he declared:

"The professors have been invited before there were students to hear them. Though many of these scholars are prominent, few are really useful; for the students, being but poorly acquainted with Latin, are unable to understand these foreign instructors and are so few in number that the latter lose all desire to appear in class. The trouble is that we have built our universities on the German model, forgetting that conditions in Russia are different. At Leipzig or Göttingen a professor need only appear on the platform for the lecture hall to fill with an audience. In Russia there are no lovers of higher learning. The gentry perform service, while the merchants care only to obtain a thorough knowledge of mathematics or of foreign languages for purposes of trade. . . . The constructing and purchasing of buildings for universities, the founding of libraries, cabinets, and scholarly societies, and the calling of famous astronomers and philologists from abroad—all this is throwing dust in the eyes. What subjects are not being taught today even at such places as Khar'kov and Kazan! And this at a time when it takes the utmost effort to find a teacher of Russian in Moscow, when it is virtually impossible to find in the whole country a hundred men who know the rules of orthography thoroughly, when we lack a decent grammar, when imperial decrees make improper use of words. . . .

"Having done much to promote in Russia the cause of learning, and noting with displeasure the gentry's lack of interest in university studies, the government resolved to make academic pursuits mandatory. . . . [Now] the official presiding in the civil court must know Homer and Theocritus; the Senate Secretary—the properties of oxygen and all the gases; the Deputy Governor—Pythagorean geometry; the superintendent of a lunatic asylum —Roman law. Neither forty years of state service nor important accomplishments exempt one from the obligation of having to learn things which are entirely alien and useless for Russians."[109]

Speranskii, undoubtedly the most enlightened Russian statesman of the day, was dismissed from his important government position and sent to Siberia shortly before Napoleon entered Russia—partly because of his unpopular ordinance of 1809 that university degrees and examinations be required for high government positions.[110]

The universities, in the meantime, had become the scene of a bitter struggle between the Russian professors and the foreign professors, and it was no wonder that the latter were, in many cases, uneasy about their future. Scholarship lagged, and the learned societies at the universities lapsed into inactivity. The Moscow University Society of Mathematicians, established in 1811, disappeared altogether.

In contrast, branches of the Russian Bible Society multiplied throughout the country. Patterned after the Bible societies of Great Britain, this society at first concentrated on translating the Bible into the non-Slavic languages of the Russian empire, but subsequently turned its attention to translating it into the Russian language. A Russian New Testament was published in 1819, and by 1824 the Society had distributed 450,000 copies of books containing various Christian writings rendered into forty-one different languages and dialects.[111] For a time the Bible Society did not stray beyond its goal of carrying the gospel to all parts of the Empire, Christian or non-Christian; but, relying on Alexander's patronage, it gradually began to wage a concerted attack on what it termed un-Christian books, becoming in fact a self-appointed inquisitorial court.[112] Thus altered, the Society served as a rallying point for believers in mysticism and obscurantism, biblical mystics who, Pypin writes, "were not satisfied with the traditional church, which supplied very little food for their aroused religious feeling and excited imagination; they . . . strove toward higher religious states, miracles, visions, and communication with the Holy Spirit."[113]

De Maistre's influence, the smoldering nationalist fires at the universities and elsewhere, the successes of the Bible Society, the aftermath of the war of 1812, Alexander's personal associations with the leaders of Western conservatism and his rapid intellectual conversion to mysticism—all these were not isolated forces but manifestations of a broad ideological retreat from the avowed liberalism of the first decade of the nineteenth century. The reactionary movements in the West which flourished in the atmosphere of the Holy Alliance found a sympathetic and eager following among the Russian groups opposed to the reforms of the preceding decade. Following the 1812 war, with all its economic and moral havoc, Russian society found itself uncertain of its direction and its values, on the edge of a major crisis.

S. S. Uvarov, who served as the superintendent of the St. Petersburg school district, described the intellectual confusion of this critical period in a letter to Baron Karl vom Stein, who was an adviser to the Tsar in 1812–13: "Some persons want education which is not dangerous—that is, fire which does not burn; the others (who happen to be more numerous) lump together Napoleon and Montesquieu, the French army and French books."[114] Even theologians underwent a hectic churning of their views: some returned to the basic teachings of Orthodoxy; others fell under the influence of the Jesuits; and still others were attracted to a new wave of mysticism.[115]

The new mysticism acquired a powerful impetus when Alexander I became one of its converts. Razumovskii, the Minister of National Education, was vice-president of the Russian Bible Society, but he was too much under the influence of de Maistre's neo-Catholic philosophy to be a staunch exponent of the new mysticism, and in 1816 he was replaced by

Aleksandr Golitsyn, the president of the Bible Society. During the next ten years or so, the proponents of mysticism were in complete control of Russian education, and under them the universities withered into intellectual wastelands. Golitsyn considered it one of the imperative tasks of the Bible Society to fight the "would-be educated enemy." He had a strong supporter in St. Petersburg's Metropolitan Serafim, also a member of the Bible Society, who thought the Enlightenment was the devil's work and believed that education led to independent action, political disobedience, and revolts.[116]

Under Golitsyn, changes in the educational program came rapidly, thanks to the *Burschenschaften* in Germany. This movement, which had been founded at Jena University in 1815 and had thence spread to other German universities, stood for national unity and the strengthening of moral rules. It was basically a liberal force directed against the status quo. On October 18, 1817, in Wartburg, 468 young men of the *Burschenschaften* held a festival to celebrate the three hundredth anniversary of Luther's revolt and the fifth anniversary of the Battle of Leipzig, which forced Napoleon out of most of Germany. The festival ended with a ceremonial burning of books written by the leading German conservatives of the day. The unrest fomented by the *Burschenschaften* led to the assassination of the ultraconservative poet Kotzebue in Mannheim in 1819.*

Metternich, who had long been very suspicious of student movements, and Frederick William III of Prussia jointly drew up a number of ordinances which were in turn approved by the 1819 Carlsbad Congress, representing all German states interested in suppressing the liberal agitation in German universities. There were three important decisions made at the Congress: (*a*) to enforce a vigilant censorship and press control; (*b*) to strengthen the supervision over all universities and other schools by appointing special directors to ferret out all subversive students and instructors; and (*c*) to establish a central committee in Mainz to investigate all revolutionary tendencies and designs as well as all secret societies.

The action of this Congress had a profound impact on Russian educational policies. In a book by Aleksandr Sturdza entitled *Mémoire sur l'état actuel de l'Allemagne,* which received wide circulation in govern-

---

* At the time of his assassination Kotzebue was employed by the Russian Ministry of Foreign Affairs, apparently to report on the ideological conflicts in Germany. His sarcastic remarks concerning the liberal patriotic movement among young Germans brought him many bitter enemies. His son, Otto, was educated in a Russian military school and, at the time of the assassination of his father, was the commander of a Russian naval expedition being sent around the world.

ment circles, the revolutionary nature of German student liberalism was described, and the Russian government was urged to guard against similar tendencies at home. The universities, Sturdza warned, if left to their liberal charters and their emphasis on teachings incompatible with religion and the established political authority, were a titanic threat to the spirit of Russia. Sturdza described Germany as a country rife with confusion, lawlessness, and uncurbed emotions, and German universities as anarchistic states within states, contaminated by ideas of autonomy. German students were portrayed as open violators of law and morality, and professors as unscrupulous seekers of "high honorariums and popularity." The most grievous sin, Sturdza claimed, was that professors had transformed theology into an adversary of religion. They had tried, moreover, to make medicine into a magician's tool for penetrating the sanctuary of the soul, and jurisprudence into an argument for the law of force.[117]

The ultraconservatism of the last decade of Alexander's reign can hardly be laid to Sturdza's warning and the Carlsbad Decrees, but it did acquire additional inspiration from the German example, as well as a plan of action to be imitated. The policies of Russia's opponents of liberalism had begun to take concrete form in 1817 when Alexander established the Ministry of Religious Affairs and National Education. The imperial decree stated: "In our desire to make Christian piety a permanent basis of education, we have found it necessary to unite the work of the Ministry of National Education and that of all religions into one administration, to be known as the Ministry of Religious Affairs and National Education."[118]

Golitsyn's profound distrust of science became apparent as soon as he assumed the post of Minister of National Education. Nicolaus Fuss, who in his youth had helped the blind Euler to prepare his numerous manuscripts for publication, wrote regretfully in 1817: "My heart bleeds when I compare the present-day position of our schools of higher education with those expectations which we nourished thirteen years ago under the influence of the new currents of life which flowed from the heights of the throne to all spheres of Russian education."[119] Since Golitsyn and his closest advisers believed that the autonomy of universities and foreign (particularly German) influences were the main sources of the contamination of Russia's intellectual life, Russian youths were forbidden to attend the Universities of Heidelberg, Jena, Giessen, and Würzburg.[120] The next step was to prevent Russian universities from employing any Russian citizen who had studied in a German university.

Golitsyn's aim was to destroy the system of higher education prescribed by the 1804 charter and to eradicate the philosophy of education which had emerged under the influence of the Enlightenment. Science was somehow to be blended with Christian morality, as this was defined by the proponents of mysticism who dominated the thinking of the Ministry of Religious Affairs and National Education.

The turbulent years after 1817 are known as the Magnitskii era, for it was Mikhail Magnitskii who was chiefly responsible for formulating and carrying out the attack on science and the established universities. Magnitskii was a man of some education. He had written poetry in his youth and had served on the staff of the Russian embassy in Paris. He was appointed governor of Simbirsk in 1817, and the following year he established the Simbirsk branch of the Bible Society, of which he was an influential member. He urged a concentrated campaign to cleanse libraries and bookstores of "atheistic literature," calling on Society members to submit the titles of offensive books.[121] He became an outspoken enemy of Kazan University, which he considered a deplorable den of atheism and immorality.

In 1819 Magnitskii was sent to investigate alleged misappropriations of funds by officials of Kazan University. After a high-handed inquiry, he made the fantastic recommendation that the University should be either closed or, better yet, publicly destroyed. The authorities were wise enough to disregard these two suggestions, but they did appoint Magnitskii superintendent of the Kazan school district, thus giving him authority to do just about as he liked with the University. The Central Administration of Schools in St. Petersburg authorized him to dismiss all professors whose teaching he considered to be incompatible with Christianity and to fill the vacant positions with Russians or, in exceptional cases, with foreigners who had passed a thorough character investigation.[122]

Magnitskii came to Kazan equipped with his own philosophy of science. He divided science into two categories: the exact or real sciences (theology, law, the natural sciences, and mathematics) and the dreamy sciences (philosophy, ethics, and political science), which he said were arbitrary and changed their content every second decade. He believed that education was gravely endangered whenever the "dreamy" sciences corrupted the "real" sciences by subjecting them to the influence of their fallacious assumptions. It was the eleventh hour, he claimed, for saving the "real" sciences from contamination by the so-called pseudosciences. As illustrations, he mentioned the corruption of geology by the theory of the physical impossibility of the occurrence of the Flood, and the corruption of law by the theory of the origin of political authority through social contract.[123] He was particularly disturbed by the theory of natural rights, which he considered an invention of modern atheistic (Protestant) North Germany. This theory, according to Magnitskii, had always been dangerous, but it had become especially so since Kant's "pure reason" began to question the validity of divine truth.[124] Eventually he demanded that philosophy be completely eliminated from the university curriculum.

Magnitskii also insisted that Russian science should be unique in nature. "Russia," he said, "has its own character in religion, morals, and form of government. Consequently, its education must be brought into harmony with its distinct qualities; the opposite would inevitably produce an injurious shock—first moral, then civil, and finally political."[125] His ideal was to build new sciences and arts, imbued with the spirit of Christ, which would replace the false science that had allegedly developed under the influence of heathenism and atheism.

In 1819 the government ordered that theology be made a required subject in all universities. A special decree called for the immediate removal of undesirable professors and for the establishment of a position of director, in all universities, to be filled by a government watchdog over "administrative, moral, and police affairs."[126] In 1820 Magnitskii sent instructions to the rector of Kazan University telling him how various subjects were to be taught from a religious point of view. Philosophers were to teach their students that human wisdom is but a meager reflection of divine omniscience. Political scientists were to show that monarchical government was "the oldest government and was established by God." Professors of theoretical and experimental physics were to demonstrate "throughout the course divine omniscience and the limited power of our senses and tools for the understanding of the wonders which surround us eternally." Professors of natural history were to prove that the great kingdom of nature was just a faint shadow of the higher order of the other world. Professors of astronomy were to point out "how the omniscience of the Creator is written in fiery letters in the heavenly bodies, and how the beautiful laws of the celestial universe were revealed to mankind in the most distant past."[127] Professors of world history were to concern themselves primarily with the history and religious superiority of Christianity.

Magnitskii's instructions to Kazan immediately became a guide to be followed by other universities. In 1821 similar instructions were issued to St. Petersburg University, and various reflections of the same principle were applied in all other universities. The effect on the universities was doubly unfortunate: they not only lost many professors (either through outright dismissal or, particularly in the case of foreigners, through voluntary departure from Russia) but also became centers of mystical thought.

The spirit of the new crusade can be clearly realized from the stated reasons for the dismissal of individual professors from St. Petersburg University. Professor Aleksandr Kunitsyn was dismissed because his book *Natural Law* contained favorable comments on Rousseau's discourses on the rights of man; Professor Ernst Raupach did not use the holy scriptures as a source of material for his lectures in world history; Professor Karl Hermann was accused of having declared that the Bible's representation of the creation was unscientific; and Professor Aleksandr Galich was found guilty of having said that highly educated intellects were capable of understanding the essence of matter.[128]

Charges of the same sort led to mass dismissals or resignations at Kazan and Khar'kov Universities. At Khar'kov University, the charges were particularly bizarre. The reactionary superintendent of the Khar'kov school district, after attending a physics lecture, suggested to the professor, Vasilii Komlishinskii, that he should have told the students that each lightning streak had a triangle in its tip which stood for the Holy Trinity.[129] The rector of Khar'kov University, T. F. Osipovskii, who was one of the most eminent mathematicians in Russia during the first two decades of the nineteenth century, was summarily dismissed because during an examination given to a graduating student he allegedly remarked that it was more appropriate to say that God "exists" than that God "lives."[130] Even at Dorpat University, which escaped the main wave of reactionary mysticism, four professors of the Theological Faculty were dismissed because of their rationalist leanings.[131]

The results of the mystical revolution were calamitous. During Magnitskii's tenure as superintendent of the Kazan school district, the University's press did not publish one major scientific work. Many textbooks which had heretofore been sanctioned by the government were now forbidden, causing professors in some cases to turn reluctantly to textbooks of the previous generation. It was not uncommon to find professors using eighteenth-century textbooks which were completely alien to the modern scientific spirit.

The rigorous censorship had deplorable ramifications. Golitsyn's first act as Minister of National Education in 1816 had been to establish an Academic Committee, the main function of which was to determine whether manuscripts were ideologically sound and worthy of publication. Special instructions for the Committee, prepared by Sturdza, stipulated that any scientific book intended for university use should be granted a publication permit only if it showed "the close unity of knowledge and religion."[132] All interpretations of the origin and transformation of the earth were to be avoided in books on natural science. Physics and chemistry books were to deal only with practical knowledge and to contain no speculation. Textbooks in physiology, pathology, and comparative anatomy were to avoid all theories that minimized the spirituality and inner freedom of man and his search for a place in the world hereafter.[133]

The most essential function of the Academic Committee was to suppress any manuscripts or books not written in the spirit of the newly defined Christian unity of "religion, knowledge, and authority." Supporters of the new mysticism rejected Lomonosov's firm belief in the intrinsic and fundamental compatibility of religion and science.[134] In their criticism of Professor Lubkin of Kazan University for the ideas presented in his *Metaphysics,* the members of the Committee showed especial annoyance with the author's effort, as they saw it, "to reconcile two totally opposite principles": religion based on knowledge given by divine revelation, and science based on man's rational endowment. A similar criticism had been leveled earlier against Johann Schad of Khar'kov University. In his attack on Professor Solntsev's political theory, Magnitskii declared: "Natural law presents the rights and duties of the rulers and the ruled; it derives these from rational principles; however, human reason cannot be the leading power—it must reverently accept and fearfully obey the supreme [i.e., divine] lawgiver." In a word, the Magnitskii group directed its heaviest ideological and police pressures against the rationalistic and humanistic approaches to the study of social phenomena. Acting from the most extreme antirationalist premises, they endeavored to suppress all theories that recognized the historical nature of the sacred institutions and ethical code of Russian autocracy. They denied the importance of man's rational search for positive knowledge and the intrinsic right of the individual and human collectivity to seek improvements in living conditions. They attacked the natural sciences for offering theoretical and methodological models which the humanists could emulate, and also for supporting conclusions which challenged the truth of the gospel.

By 1824 censorship had become so severe that professors were compelled to submit their lecture notes to the Ministry of Religious Affairs and National Education for approval;[135] and it ranged far beyond the universities. Controls were exerted not merely on textbooks but on the works of such eminent conservative writers of the time as the historian Karamzin and the poet Zhukovskii; nor were exceptions made for Western writers like Sir Walter Scott, Schiller, and Goethe, whose works were considerably pruned for Russian readers. The first poems of the young Pushkin, pervaded with the spirit of free thought, did not escape the censor's eye. In 1821 a versatile censor rewrote part of a poem by Pushkin to rid it of offending ideas.[136] Thenceforth the censor exercised full editorial freedom on the works of Pushkin and others, checking spelling and correcting grammar. Under this sort of rigorous control, the quality of university periodicals rapidly deteriorated. The *Kazan Messenger* (1821–33), a typical publication of the time, lauded Magnitskii's intellectual "achievements" and printed almost as many articles on mysticism as it did scientific articles.

It was the pronounced mystical aspect of the new conservatism that won it its most formidable enemy—the hierarchy of the Russian Orthodox Church. Golitsyn's excessive religious fanaticism involved some essential disagreements with Orthodox belief, and in 1824 the Church obtained his dismissal. His replacement, Aleksandr Shishkov, was more suitably conformist, but in educational philosophy he scarcely differed from his predecessor. His views are neatly summarized in the following statement which he left for posterity:

"Science, while sharpening the mind, is not a national asset unless it is allied with religion and morality. . . . Moreover, science, like salt, is useful only when used and taught within proper limits and when the status of persons and their needs for knowledge are taken into account. An over-emphasis on science is as contrary to true education as the absence of any emphasis on science. To teach every person to be literate . . . would bring more harm than good. To instruct a peasant's son in rhetoric would be equivalent to training him to become an inferior, useless, and even harmful citizen."[137]

By 1826 Magnitskii and Dmitrii Runich (another devout member of the Bible Society) had been removed from their positions as superintendents of the Kazan and St. Petersburg school districts, but it was another twenty-five years before the universities in those cities had fully recovered from the effects of their reactionary measures. Shevyrev put it this way: "The opposition to Western materialism dedicated the temple of national education to God's throne, the Cross, and the prayer; this legacy was the most burdensome problem of our education during the thirty years preceding the middle 1850's."[138]

How low university teaching standards had sunk during the 1820's is sharply revealed by Nikolai Pirogov, a famous scholar and surgeon of the next generation. Pirogov studied at Moscow University—which, like Dorpat University, escaped the worst of the blight. But even at Moscow University, where there were several competent professors, "a considerably larger group" presented "a living and laughable contrast to their successful colleagues." Many students, Pirogov said, attended the lectures of certain professors "just for laughs." V. M. Kotel'nitskii and A. L. Lovetskii, for example, read their lectures out of outdated textbooks, and so clumsily that it was a comic spectacle.[139] "Laughable situations were not just a Moscow University phenomenon, for in European universities one also met queer and curious professors; but in Moscow the situations created by these men were not simply funny but outrageously stupid, indicating as they did how far we lagged behind modern scientific developments. Actually, the backwardness of that period was beyond imagination. The professors read lecture material written in the 1750's, and this at a time when most students had access to textbooks written in the nineteenth century."[140] The chemistry and physics professors were obliged to teach without any laboratory equipment.

The situation in the Academy of Sciences was equally dismal. During the Magnitskii era, only five new scholars were added to the Academic rostrum; of these, only Pander proved by subsequent scholarly work that he deserved the title of Academician. Whole years passed without any Academic scientific publications whatever. Whereas in its first twenty years the Academy published fourteen volumes of the *Commentarii*, containing scientific articles written mostly by its own members, during the first nineteen years of the nineteenth century it issued only eleven volumes of the *Mémoires*.[141] From 1822 to 1830 the Academy did not publish a single work based on the materials gathered by the various expeditions of naturalists. The Academy was so intellectually impoverished that it could offer no help to the universities in filling vacant teaching positions or in replacing incompetent instructors in science.

THE CONTINUITY OF SCIENTIFIC EFFORT

Despite the ultraconservatism of the government and the ruthlessness with which it turned on the strongholds of enlightenment, somehow the forces of liberalism managed to stay alive. One important reason for their survival was the fact that thousands of Russian soldiers who fought in the Napoleonic wars returned from Western Europe with a certain awareness of political currents opposed to autocracy.[142] It is clear from the auto-biographical writings of the participants in the Decembrist uprising that they acquired their conceptions of civil rights and obligations from reading the classic Western European political and social theorists. The Decembrists had little to do with science, but their limitless thirst for knowledge and their belief in humanistic values made them the guardians of the grand intellectual tradition of Montesquieu, Voltaire, Rousseau, Bentham, Condillac, and Helvétius.[143] If the Decembrists had one thought in common, besides their wholehearted condemnation of serfdom, it was their unswerving conviction that Russia's progress was dependent on freedom of thought, and that freedom of thought could not exist without a constitutional government. The Decembrists were the most radical of the social forces that were responsible for the ultimate failure of Magnitskii and his followers to stifle learning.

There were other encouraging developments. The devoted work of S. S. Uvarov, who became the president of the Academy of Sciences in 1818, saved the Academy from full disintegration. His efforts to improve the intellectual caliber of the staff were not immediately successful, but he did manage to increase the number of specialized scientific bodies operating within the Academy. The Asiatic Museum, founded in 1818, served the growing ranks of Orientalists. In 1824 the Academy acquired its first botanical museum, and in 1826 special physical and astronomical collections were put into use.

During the 1820's the quality of university instruction was woefully inadequate; yet this was the decade during which the universities became firmly established in Russia, as evidenced by the rise in enrollment even without the traditional lure of government stipends. The appeal of the universities to all social classes became so widespread that the government began to concern itself seriously with instituting hindrances to higher education, especially for the nonaristocratic classes. Whereas at the beginning of the century the government had been occupied with attracting students to the gymnasiums and universities, the 1820's saw the government commencing to work out designs aimed at making schools accessible only to small segments of the population.

During the 1820's the marked success of Dvigubskii's *New Journal of Natural History, Physics, Chemistry, and Economic Knowledge* (1820–30) showed that Russia had a comparatively large and appreciative reading public interested in surveys of up-to-date scientific knowledge. It was through the pages of this journal that a wider public was introduced to such great contemporary ideas as Dalton's atomism, Lamarck's biological transformism, and Biot's polarization of light.[144] Oersted's theories in the field of electricity, Faraday's experiments in electromagnetic induction, and Seebeck's discoveries in thermoelectricity were also presented to Russian readers in this periodical. The *Journal* published a series of articles on the history of individual natural sciences as well as translations (from the Latin) of several of Lomonosov's scientific papers.[145]

At the very end of Alexander's reign, mathematical thought received a new and powerful impetus. In 1825, Viktor Buniakovskii received a doctorate at the Faculté des Sciences in Paris in the fields of analytical mechanics and mathematical physics. He subsequently played an important part in rebuilding the Russian mathematical tradition, which had been seriously weakened during the first decades of the nineteenth century. In that same year an even more important event also took place: the publication of a treatise by the French mathematician Cauchy, *A Note on Definite Integrals Between Imaginary Limits,* in which he acknowledged that Mikhail Ostrogradskii, "a young Russian, *donné de beaucoup de sagacité, et très versé dans l'analyse infinitésimale,*" had given independent demonstrations of some of his intricate formulas.[146] This was a great moment in the history of Russian mathematical thought.

Before the word of Ostrogradskii's achievement had been spread in his own country, another mathematical milestone was reached—one that was to prove of even greater importance than Ostrogradskii's. In 1826, Nikolai Lobachevskii, a Russian-trained professor at Kazan University, read to his colleagues a paper which contained the first hints of his attempt to construct a new geometrical system independent of the Euclidean axioms.

The major work of Buniakovskii, Ostrogradskii, and Lobachevskii remained to be done, but their early successes stand as proof that, for all its severities, the reactionary period did not crush the vitality and power of science and the men of science. The Magnitskii era was not kind to Lobachevskii and Ostrogradskii. Lobachevskii was compelled to share the teaching of mathematics at Kazan University with mystics who tried to transform this science into a system of divine symbols. One of them even attempted to construct a whole mathematical system based on what he regarded as the fundamental principles of morality; the function of mathematics, according to him, was not to encourage free thought but to confirm

the existence of divine truths.[147] The *Messenger of Europe* added to the
reactionary climate by publishing, in 1821, a Russian translation of excerpts
from Chateaubriand's *Génie du christianisme*, which pointed out the
limitations of mathematics as a method of inquiry, particularly in the realm
of social and moral life. In 1823 Lobachevskii's manuscript of a geometry
textbook was rejected by the government press mostly because Academician
Fuss objected to his acceptance of the meter—an innovation of the French
Revolution—as a measurement unit for length and the degree as a measurement unit for the curvature of the circle.[148]

Ostrogradskii was not allowed to graduate from Khar'kov University
because he refused to take a required course in theology.[149] Ironically, it
proved to be his good fortune that the universities in his own country were
closed to him. Determined to study, he went to Paris, where he had the
great experience of working in an intellectual atmosphere alive with the
spirit of such giants as Legendre, Fourier, Poisson, Laplace, Cauchy, and
Ampère, and where men talked of the ideas set forth in Fourier's *Analytical
Theory of Heat* (1822), in the fifth and last volume of Laplace's *Celestial
Mechanics*, in Ampère's *Theory of Electromagnetic Phenomena*, and in
Cauchy's *Course in Analysis* and *The Infinitesimal Calculus*.

During the first quarter of the nineteenth century there were no important scientific expeditions to Siberia, but there was for the first time a
good deal of sea exploration. These expeditions usually had a practical
purpose—such as the study of the best ocean routes between Russia's European ports and various ports in Eastern Siberia and Alaska—but as their
secondary assignments they were expected to gather information of scientific value. A series of round-the-world seafaring expeditions was inaugurated by Adam Krusenstern in 1803–6; his published materials, full
of detailed information, were a model for later sea explorers. Krusenstern, who is considered the founder of Russian oceanography, collected
interesting astronomical and hydrological information; he surveyed many
islands and a portion of the northwestern shore of the Pacific; he studied
and recorded the temperature of ocean water at various depths to 1,200 feet
below sea level. He collected good zoological and botanical materials as
well as valuable ethnographic information. For his contributions to various
scientific fields he was elected an honorary member of the St. Petersburg
Academy of Sciences.[150]

Iurii Lisianskii, Vasilii Golovnin, Otto Kotzebue, Faddei Bellingshausen,
Ferdinand Wrangel, and Fedor Lütke were other leading Russian explorers who, in the course of sea voyages to many parts of the world,

added valuable information to the common pool of scientific knowledge. Accompanying Kotzebue's Pacific expedition (1823–26) were a physicist, an astronomer, and a mineralogist; the ship's physician was assigned the task of collecting botanical and zoological information. Physical observations were conducted by Heinrich F. E. Lenz, who soon after his return to St. Petersburg became a member of the Academy and one of the world's leading experts on electromagnetism. Lenz was especially interested in sea salinity. He established the existence of a maximum of salinity in tropical waters and the uniformity of the composition of salt regardless of the salinity of ocean water, and he advanced the hypothesis that the salt content of the Atlantic Ocean is somewhat higher than that of other waters. He also studied changes in salinity and temperature at various depths of sea water.[151]

THE EPOCH'S CRUCIBLES

The age of Alexander I, rich in historically significant events and dominated by reversals and paradoxes, eludes easy characterization. In its intellectual history, it was not the scientific *output* that was the true measure of cultural progress; rather, this age is to be remembered mainly for its contributions to the development of new conditions affecting scientific work and the future of science in Russia.

During these twenty-five years Russia finally established an integrated and organizationally sound school system, ending the period of educational experimentation. After a century of wavering, it was at last in a position to build upon an established tradition in education; to take the structure for granted and concentrate on the content.

Even with the government's inconsistency, education became clearly an important element in the dynamics of social stratification; with education, persons from the lower social strata could break down the wall protecting the estate exclusiveness of the gentry. This development was the result of a combination of factors. In the first place, the new universities followed, at least to a degree, the model of the new German Protestant universities, which admitted students regardless of social origin. In the second place, the government was compelled to rely on educated nonaristocratic groups in several vital fields which had no appeal for the gentry. The gentry would study law and go on to high administrative positions, but they scorned most other professions.

Circumstances thus compelled the government to employ more and more educated nonaristocrats—many, indeed, even before it was actually legal for it to do so. The first official step toward recognizing the right of nonaristocratic university graduates to fill government positions was made by a decree of November 10, 1811. This important document reiterated the government's determination to keep the country's universities open to all estates and ruled that nonaristocratic persons "who planned to dedicate themselves to scholarly pursuits or to military and civil service" would not be freed of their lower-class obligations until they had completed their university courses.[152] The really important meaning of this decree was not that the lower-class students retained their original estate identification until they received university diplomas, but that all sorts of government positions were publicly opened to them. This was an important date both in the evolution of Russian universities as "all-estate" institutions and in the gradual weakening of the once-rigid lines of class stratification.

In 1819, owing to the serious shortage of physicians, the government decreed that qualified young men from the lower estates be admitted as medical students with government stipends.[153] Gradually, the universities were becoming a broad corridor through which, as Kliuchevskii put it, "the social forces spilled over from lower to higher positions." In 1826 Prince Carl Lieven, the Minister of National Education, made clear his opposition to the establishment of estate schools: "In countries where the groups are rigidly separated from one another, where the transition from one group to another, particularly from the middle group to the gentry, is exceedingly difficult, . . . it is very easy to introduce such a system. But in Russia, where there is no middle estate . . . , where the artisan is equal to the peasant . . . , where a well-to-do peasant can at any time be considered a merchant . . . , where the gentry form such a widely ranged estate that at the one end they reach the very base of the throne and at the other they are almost lost in the peasantry, and where annually many persons of peasant or urban middle-class origin, by the acquisition of a military or civil-service position, enter the ranks of the gentry—the [estate] school system is hardly feasible."[154]

Russia's "age of ideology" began during the second half of Alexander's reign. The government's eyes turned from the expansion of educational and scientific facilities to a synchronization of intellectual currents and scientific knowledge with ideological maxims. The Magnitskii oppression made ideological issues important, but it was in the waning of this ultra-reactionary period that the stage was set for the debut of the official ideology of the reign of Nicholas I. The crystallization of this ideology, based on the sanctity of autocracy, nationality, and Orthodoxy, was accompanied by what Shchapov called the growth of archaeologism in the development of Russia's social thought. The new ideology (officially enunciated in the early 1830's) had a profound effect on social scientists and historians, in that it discouraged them from studying contemporary problems and forced them instead to take up archaeology, historical philology, ethico-juridical studies, idealistic philosophy, and aesthetics.[155] By the 1840's, with scholars in full retreat from the burning questions of the day, these fields had acquired real prominence.

The development of the basic principles of official ideology was accompanied by a gradual growth of ideological opposition: Alexander's age produced the first important secret societies through which "dangerous" Western ideas and ideologically impure thoughts filtered into Russia. These societies were soon replaced by the literary circles that nurtured so many of Russia's great writers and revolutionaries.

PART III

AUTOCRATIC IDEOLOGY AND SCIENCE

CHAPTER SIX

Official Nationalism and Countervailing Thought

CENSORSHIP AND SCHOLARSHIP

In the wake of the Decembrist uprising, Nicholas I vowed to dedicate his life to an uncompromising opposition to the forces opposing the power and social standing of the autocracy. Russian scientific thought in the period between 1826 and the end of the Crimean War was profoundly affected by the growing oppression, by means of which the state contrived to hold together the somewhat disparate elements of reaction. This was the era of official nationalism, of nationalism by decree. The mainstream of nationalism fed on many tributaries, each endowed with great historical significance. Officially, there was a rededication to the principles of autocracy and a vigorous affirmation of the importance of Russia as a unique historical and cultural phenomenon. Along with this there was a renewed and intensified suspicion of the West, which, more than ever before, was seen as incurably afflicted with decadent materialism. Not only were Russians to be saved from thoughts and ideals incompatible with the soul of Russia, but the Western periphery was to be made thoroughly Russian as well.

Official nationalism and political oppression went hand in hand. Immediately after the Decembrist uprising, Nicholas I ordered all professors to sign sworn statements that they did not belong to any secret societies. Soon the students were asked to sign similar statements.[1] Censorship became firmly consolidated and emerged as one of the key elements in the arena of intellectual endeavor. In 1826 the government issued a new and more rigorous censorship decree, replacing the decree of 1804, and appointed a Supreme Censorship Committee consisting of the Ministers of National Education, Internal Affairs, and Foreign Affairs. Article 6 of the new statute specifically provided that censorship activities were to be concentrated on (*a*) science and education; (*b*) morality and internal security; and (*c*) the orientation of public opinion.[2]

So broad were the areas covered that, as a contemporary observer noted, the statute could suppress not only individual books but whole branches of science: it included as censurable, along with all writings found to be inimical to the interests of the state and religion, books and writings in "philosophy, political science, geology, and generally every study in which the author arrives at the ideas of divinity from the observation of nature."[3] The censors were cautioned to be especially alert for statements incompatible with the established spiritual, moral, and civil order in manuscripts dealing with topics in the natural sciences. Medical works were not allowed to endorse ideas that could be interpreted as denying "the spirituality of the soul, and its internal freedom, as well as the divine determination of future life."[4] Furthermore, no book was to be approved if it "openly violated the rules and purity of the Russian language," i.e., if it contained grammatical errors. Ambiguous statements which could be interpreted in a manner incompatible with official ideology were to be deleted; this particular article was so vaguely worded that it in fact gave the censors extraordinary powers; one of them acknowledged that "even the Lord's Prayer could be interpreted in Jacobin terms." The statute forbade the publication of any book that endorsed natural rights and social contract theories —that is, theories which viewed the autocratic government as a passing historical phenomenon rather than an institution ordained by God.

A revised censorship statute was passed in 1828, and this remained in force throughout Nicholas's reign, until 1855, undergoing occasional amendments. It was essentially the same as the 1826 statute but was infinitely more detailed, indeed was designed to rid the earlier statute of vague and ambiguous phrasings. It was also broader, laying a foundation for the institution of so-called multiple censorship, by which censorship powers were distributed among a wide range of agencies. Nothing pertaining to royal personalities could now be printed without prior approval of the court minister. Ecclesiastical authorities, as before, censored religious materials. Imported foreign publications were censored by the agents of a special post-office section. The Central Administration of Schools censored all textbooks. During the 1830's "only poetry and *belles-lettres* were subject to censorship committees—everything else was watched over by special offices."[5] This multiple censorship, fully implemented during the 1830's and 1840's, was designed to strengthen official control over published material by entrusting the surveillance activities in specialized fields to professional personnel. By introducing a certain amount of duplication in official assignments, it provided an additional safeguard in the censorship system.

Universal censorship had disastrous effects on scientific work. In 1845 Count Stroganov, the superintendent of the Moscow school district, complained to Minister of National Education S. S. Uvarov that "our writers are drastically limited by censorship in the publication of their works," with the result that "well-meaning articles dedicated to general enlightenment either remain unpublished or appear after they have lost their timely significance."[6] The learned societies lost their traditional privilege of publishing monographs without prior approval from censorship authorities. Many social and political questions were officially suppressed as topics for literary treatment. The magnitude of the effects of the new censorship on Russia's intellectual life in general and on scientific thought in particular was indicated by Shchapov in *The Social and Educational Conditions of Russian Intellectual Growth*:

"In the period of full censorship, a special category of 'unpublishable books' was created in the general field of Russian science and literature, particularly in the natural sciences, sociology, political economy, and natural law. In the natural sciences, for example, 'unpublishable' were the treatments of the physical formation of the earth, geological eras, the origin of species, the antiquity of man, Neanderthal and other human fossils, the place of man in the organic world and his natural-historical and organic relations to apes, the importance of force and matter in nature, the physico-chemical and mechanistic explanations of nervous energy (and particularly of human mentality), reflexes of the brain, the psychopathic nature of mysticism, and many other topics. In the area of the social sciences censorship regulations were applied to all discussions of the natural and physico-physiological bases of social life, and, in general, of the natural-scientific laws of community life and the formation of state authorities by men's physical force and will. Censorable also were discussions concerning despotism, serfdom, inequalities of class and wealth, the right of lower social classes to university education, utilitarianism, the fallacies of official ideology, the national benefits of natural-science education, the spread of radical views in various countries, freedom of thought, problems of the press, the workers question, autonomous organizations, and numerous other problems. The Russian public was not allowed to read many Western scientific and literary works. The ban included Voltaire's books and Kant's positive philosophy, but extended also to volumes on Russia written by Johann Kohl, Custine, and others."[7]

The mounting censorship during the 1830's was responsible for "the suppression of the popular journals *Moscow Telegraph* and *Telescope*, the discontinuation of literary polemics in journals, the government decision, in 1836, not to accept applications for new periodicals, the abolition of the right to serve simultaneously on the editorial boards of two journals, reduced publication quotas for books, a smaller book trade, and the decreased circulation of inexpensive journals, which it was feared might spur the lower classes to start undesirable movements."[8]

As reports of the 1848 revolutionary uprisings in Western Europe began to reach Russia, the censorship machinery became tighter and more relentless. Whereas in 1847 Russia imported 836,262 copies of foreign books, the total figure in 1848 shrank to 522,085 copies.[9] A new agency known as the Committee of April 2nd became the supreme censorship body. It had independent administrative status, and its duty was to prevent the spread of revolutionary ideas in Russia by preparing lists of ideological issues to be suppressed by the censors. From 1848 to 1854 all attacks on government agencies were prohibited, as were all literary works that might contribute "to the weakening of the idea of subordination" or stir up class antagonism. Censors were also ordered to suppress studies of "unrest and national uprisings," "existing law," and universities. All references to foreign books on the banned list were prohibited. Scientific inquiry was directly affected by the ruling that no favorable reports of unverified and untested scientific discoveries were to be allowed to pass the censor's desk. This ruling was, of course, designed to suppress such "unverifiable" theories as the geological interpretation of the formation of the earth, physiological speculations on the human nervous system, and biological transformism.

THE ARISTOCRATIZATION OF SCIENCE

Censorship was the most obvious and easily applied means of preserving the autocratic regime of Russia from corrosive influences, but it was equally important for the government to prevent the estate system from deteriorating because of inherent weaknesses or forces already set in motion. For that reason, a series of legislative measures was enacted, some for the strengthening of the upper estates, others for the repression of the lower ones. A number of honorific but nonhereditary positions such as "honorary citizen" and "official" were set aside for outstanding civil servants of common origin, but the mass of persons from the lower estates was increasingly discouraged, in a variety of ways, from attending schools that would prepare them for university work and perhaps lead to their elevation to a higher estate. These measures were indirectly related to the growth of scientific ranks and scientific thought, and should be looked into in more detail. As added safeguards, estate limitations were placed on admission to universities.

In 1827 A. S. Shishkov, the Minister of National Education, ordered that "the subjects and methods of teaching in all schools be oriented toward the most likely future occupations of students." He also recommended that students be discouraged from choosing careers traditionally inaccessible to their estates. A special order stipulated that universities, other schools of higher education, gymnasiums, and other secondary schools be accessible "only to persons belonging to free estates."[10]

In 1828 a gymnasium statute was passed, by which a system of district schools operating on the elementary level was to be established, nominally open to all groups but particularly intended for the children of tradesmen, artisans, and so on. The gymnasiums, as college preparatory schools, were to concentrate on educating the children of the gentry and government officials. Parish schools were to be opened for the peasantry, to give them as much education as seemed fit.

Under Alexander I, Russian schools had been based on the principle of educational continuity, with each level preparing for the next. Now this principle was abandoned. The parish and district schools were not necessarily preparatory for admittance to gymnasiums as intermediate steps leading to university education. Thus, by law, most of the population of Russia was deprived of the right to acquire scientific training, and the gentry—though traditionally unwilling—became the legal custodians of scientific thought.

Not surprisingly, in view of its complexity, the 1828 gymnasium statute was not fully enforced; here and there, members of the middle and lower estates continued to enroll in the gymnasiums. In 1843, 10,066 children of the gentry and government officials, 218 children of priestly parentage, and 2,500 young men from other nonaristocratic groups were enrolled in fifty-one gymnasiums. Ten years later the situation was essentially the same.[11]

Determined, at any rate, to preserve the aristocratic privilege of university education, the government introduced special measures to prevent the admission of persons of middle and lower social status. From 1837 on, the university entrance examinations were administered in such a way as to make higher education a virtual monopoly of young gentry and the children of high government officials. A secret memorandum sent to the superintendents of school districts from Minister of National Education S. S. Uvarov in 1840 advised that no student was to be admitted to a university unless he had proved that his social status entitled him to hold positions commensurate with a higher education. The superintendent's job, Uvarov cautioned, was not to expand the ranks of educated persons but to preserve the *ancien régime*. "Owing to a general growth in the thirst for education," the memorandum said, "the time has come to employ the necessary measures to prevent the new aspirations from disturbing the order of civil estates."[12] Soon Uvarov reported proudly to Nicholas I that university classrooms were finally filled with young men of aristocratic background.[13] Ikonnikov called this "the aristocratization of science."[14]

In the event, it proved something of a problem to keep university doors tightly shut to the middle and lower classes. The demand for university education was so great that new safeguards had to be introduced from time to time. After 1845 university tuition was gradually raised. In 1846 the universities were explicitly prohibited from admitting any person who could not produce a certificate of high social origin.[15] In 1847 it was made legally impossible for nonaristocratic students even to enroll as "private listeners"—a means which heretofore had admitted a few, at least, to university lectures. In 1848, in the wake of the revolutionary rumblings in the West, the universities, excluding the medical schools, were ordered to reduce their enrollments to three hundred students each.[16] This policy made higher education impossible not only for the lower and middle classes but also for most of the gentry. In the meantime, changes in curricula were introduced in the gymnasiums: Latin and Greek, for example, were required only of students planning to enter the universities.[17]

The aristocratization of universities was never fully achieved; however, the representation of lower social strata remained very low. In the academic year 1836–37, the enrollment at St. Petersburg University was made up of 193 young gentry and children of high government officials and 48 youths of more modest origin; in 1860–61, in the same university, there were 1,228 students in the first group and 203 in the second.[18] The social class distribution of the students of Kiev University from 1834 (the year of its founding) to 1839 was as follows:[19]

	Gentry and High Government Officials	Clergy	Middle and Lower Urban Classes
1834	57	3	2
1835	99	7	7
1836	179	8	13
1837	235	7	16
1838	235	7	18
1839	94	15	13

CURRICULUM CHANGES

Since the time of Peter I the curricula of schools in Russia had been determined by the highest political authorities. Hence Nicholas I had only to use a traditional prerogative of the state to strengthen his elitist policies and to suppress dangerous political and scientific ideas in the schools. In the curricula of these years one can find a good indication of the government's attitude.

The 1828 gymnasium statute, the first expression of the new educational policy, clearly showed a switch from humanistic and scientific goals to didactic formalism and classicism. The true architect of the new orientation, Uvarov, shortly became the Minister of National Education, and during his tenure of nearly two decades he carried his principles of educational conservatism to full realization.

Under the 1804 statute, based on the principle that secondary education should be available to all persons, a curriculum broad enough to satisfy the educational needs of all estates was worked out. The natural sciences received special emphasis because they were expected to steer the lower and middle urban classes in the direction of advanced technology.[20] The 1828 gymnasium statute, with its new limitation of secondary education to the children of gentry and high government officials, reordered the curriculum on the principles of didacticism. All the natural sciences except physics were removed from the gymnasium curriculum, and even physics was barely touched upon. Latin and Greek were made the most important subjects: they were "the best method known for elevating and strengthening the mental capacities of young people." French, which Uvarov maintained led students to undesirable literature, was greatly reduced in importance. Mathematics received continued emphasis, but it was now valued primarily as an intellectual exercise that helped students to develop "logical thinking."[21]

Some reasons for the changed curriculum were purely ideological. Neither the classical languages nor mathematics had much to do with burning philosophical and social issues, and they could be used to sharpen the minds of young people without filling them with ideologically dangerous thoughts. Classical studies, particularly, would keep "distracted students from vain and useless books."[22] Furthermore, the classics and mathematics were difficult subjects, and might easily be important in keeping down the gymnasium enrollment. The transformed gymnasium became the model institution of secondary education; in 1831 the government decreed that the graduates of private boarding schools who wished to attend universities would be required to pass an entrance examination in the courses which received special emphasis in the gymnasium curriculum.[23]

The educational philosophy set forth in the 1828 statute remained virtually the same until 1849. The one change of major importance during this period was the dropping of analytical and descriptive geometry from the gymnasium curriculum. With both natural science and humanistic subjects woefully neglected, the gymnasiums during those years were hardly adequate either as schools of general education or as preparatory schools for the universities. And they suffered increasingly from official efforts to transform the whole school system along the lines of Uvarov's promise—enunciated in 1833, on the occasion of his appointment as Minister of National Education—to imbue Russian education with "the united spirit of Orthodoxy, autocracy, and nationality." Uvarov's official ideology placed a heavy burden on gymnasium teachers, who were forced to rely on omission, selectivity, and distortion of facts in order to conform. They were supposed to prevent the spread of French republican ideas and of modern scientific thought, mainly from Germany. In history, they were ordered to pursue the Schellingian notion of the uniqueness of individual cultures and to avoid all allusions to the ideas of certain proponents of critical and skeptical thought in Russian historiography.

Unlike the gymnasiums of the preceding quarter-century and earlier, which had more or less followed the Western pattern, gymnasiums under Nicholas gave students a new and intensive appreciation of their own national history, political as well as literary. The weaknesses of the gymnasiums were their undue emphasis on pure formalism, with a great deal of mechanical memorizing of officially approved material, and much superficial folderol—"festive programs, pretentious examinations, and loud commencement celebrations." The students hardly received training for university scientific study, such as it was, and, in fact, it was not intended that they study science. The university entrance examinations, as modified in 1833, required only proficiency in theology, Russian letters, Latin, and French or German.

The echoes of the 1848 revolution extended to the gymnasium. Clearly, the forces hostile to the *ancien régime* were vigorous; the aristocracy itself, with increasing education and new economic challenges to their security, began to produce a revolutionary nucleus. Classical studies, too, were now regarded as a source of dangerous republican thought—in Herodotus, for example, and in Thucydides, Livy, and Tacitus.[24] This discovery was accompanied by the realization that in forcing the gymnasiums to ignore natural sciences, the government had thwarted Russia's total emancipation from the West.

The immediate reaction was to curtail the teaching of classical languages and to supervise with great care the selection of classical writings that gymnasium students were allowed to read. At first, the additional classroom time thus gained was used for more Russian subjects. Russian law was added to the gymnasium curriculum in 1849, to guide future citizens in their civic duties and to give preliminary training to boys who might become government administrators. Plans were made for the preparation of a textbook in world history—assuming that the proper writer could be found—which would show the place of Russia in the history of mankind and would explain "the monarchical principle as the quintessence of Russian history." "The monarchical principle," commented the historian T. N. Granovskii (who was essentially a Westerner), "is at the basis of all great developments in Russian history; it is the root system of our political life and of our political importance in Europe."[25]

The government was even ready to accept the resignation of Uvarov as Minister of National Education as part of its abandonment of the classical approach, but it was far less willing to strengthen the natural science curriculum. Granovskii commented bitterly: "God save us if we suspect any science of ill intentions. There are and there can be no harmful sciences. Each science holds a part of divine truth, revealed to our intellect in its various spiritual sides. The natural—and for that matter the classical—sciences did not produce the French Revolution or the current moral ailments of Western Europe."[26] In the words of M. P. Pogodin, part of the Russian reaction to the 1848 revolution was that "classical education was seriously undermined" while the teaching of the natural sciences did not make any gains.[27]

Early in the 1850's, under strong German and French influence, the Ministry of National Education gradually began to weaken in its resistance to natural science as a school subject. Clearly, the strength of individual countries had come to be dependent on technical competence no less than on manpower and resources, and the stubborn opposition would have to fall. In 1851 the new Minister of National Education, Shirinskii-Shikhmatov, impressed by the contributions of science to the rapid growth of French and German military might, recommended that in thirty-one gymnasiums the teaching of Greek be replaced by the natural sciences. Indeed, he said, the government had never been against the teaching of the natural sciences, and it had permitted them to be taught without interruption (though at no great length) in the military and boarding schools. The new measure, the Minister pointed out, "would not only ensure a more adequate education of students who intend to enter government service immediately after graduation, but would also significantly increase the study of the natural sciences in the physico-mathematical and medical faculties."[28] In 1852 the Minister's recommendations were carried out and Greek was replaced in all gymnasiums by a number of scientific subjects, from an introductory "natural science" to zoology, botany, mineralogy, human anatomy, and human physiology. The change was so abrupt that both textbooks and instructors were lacking, and thus the gymnasiums lost their classical orientation without really gaining a scientific one. But the foundations, at least, had been laid for an intensified growth of scientific thought and for the bountiful dividends of the 1860's.

The philosophy of official nationalism left a heavy imprint on the university's curriculum as well as on the gymnasium's. In 1835 a revised university charter was passed, avowedly for the purpose of expanding and strengthening the curriculum. In fact, however, it was designed to neutralize the undesirable effects of potentially dangerous subjects. The university was now divided into philosophical, juridical, and medical faculties; the philosophical faculties were, in turn, subdivided into departments of history and philology, and of physics and mathematics.[29] The grouping of subjects in the first two faculties expressed Uvarov's aspiration to give higher education a national character by ridding the social sciences and the humanities of all potentially subversive ideas. The rigid control of scientific thought was accompanied by an expansion of the curriculum dealing with "national" subjects; Russian history was introduced as a special university subject, as were special courses in Slavic languages and literatures. The teaching of philosophy, political economy, and statistics was transferred from the faculty of law to the philosophical faculty, thus saving the students of law—the future high government officials—from dangerous exposure to theoretical and ideological issues. Students of law—more than fifty per cent of the total university enrollment during the 1830's and after—were now expected to know only the workings of the contemporary Russian legal system. Generally the curricular changes were intended "to reduce the teaching of the theoretical foundations of individual subjects and to emphasize information of an applied and dogmatic nature."[30] The students of all three faculties took special courses in theology, church history, and contemporary Russian law. One somewhat biased interpreter of the 1835 university charter stated that this document did "not consider the university a scientific society with two equally important goals, teaching and scholarly pursuits; the meetings of [university] councils are no longer the meetings of scientific societies for reports and discussions; the university has ceased to select the themes for prize-winning studies by individual professors." The same author added nostalgically that "the university is now only a school," and that it had ceased to be a center of scientific inquiry.[31]

Since a university education was not only a privilege of the gentry but also a condition of promotion in the civil service, the government was alive to the necessity of safeguarding its future employees against ideologically dangerous knowledge. The students, for their part, had their eyes fixed more on the ladder of government positions opened to academically trained persons than on the virtues and challenges of education itself. The educational process was thus inhibited not only by government censorship but also by the self-serving indifference of students. In addition, there were glaring inadequacies in teaching, particularly in subjects requiring laboratory work. The sad picture of Russian higher education during the late 1830's and early 1840's was vividly described by the novelist N. Shchedrin:

"The deceivers stuffed us with bits of knowledge . . . and the subservient custodian of the higher school impressed upon us the idea that the purpose of knowledge was to fulfill government plans.

"Information imparted to us was fragmentary, disconnected, and almost meaningless. It was not assimilated. Because it was learned mechanically, its fate depended completely on whether a student had a good or a poor memory. No one could build a fund of knowledge for future use.

"I repeat: that was not education, but a part of the system of privilege, which divided society by a sharp line: above the line were we, the idle ruling group; below the line stood one word—the muzhik. We were here to be impressed with the idea that we were not at the same social level with the muzhiks and to learn that the Seine River flows through Paris and that Caligula once brought his horse to the senate. . . .

"With this stock of knowledge, the school graduated thousands of students annually. Equipped with the required diploma, these aristocratic youths moved from lower to higher government offices. The meager knowledge they acquired served only in rare cases as a basis for further self-education; in a majority it only stimulated a yearning for a faster and fuller utilization of the acquired privilege."[32]

Shchedrin's picture makes no allusion to a certain amount of intellectual give and take that went on in the universities outside the classrooms, to which some other writers have attested. Konstantin Aksakov, who attended Moscow University during the same period, noted: "In our time the professors' lectures were often dismal, but the students' life and intellectual activity, inextricably woven together, were not suppressed by formalism and produced good results."[33]

THE NATIONALIZATION OF EDUCATION

Uvarov's unceasing work of saturating the schools with the values and precepts of official nationalism was only one aspect of the nationalist fervor of Nicholas's regime. In the western areas, particularly around the Baltic and in Byelorussia, the doctrine of official nationalism assumed the form of Russification. During the first quarter of the nineteenth century the schools in these areas enjoyed a great deal of local autonomy, but after the Polish revolt of 1830–31 the Russian government put them under firm control, and what they taught soon came to be decided by the national interests of Russia as these were officially defined. Many Catholic and Uniate schools were abolished. All gymnasiums were placed under Russian supervision, following the terms of the 1828 charter. The Russian language was taught everywhere, and the teaching staffs were adjusted so as to give native Russians numerical superiority in each school. A special decree ruled that knowledge of the Russian language be a factor determining the civil service category of gymnasium graduates. The establishment of special boarding schools for children of noble origin was authorized to ensure a tightly supervised education in the spirit of official ideology and to neutralize "negative" influences.[34]

The policies of official nationalism affected higher education in the western territories also. Vilna University, a Jesuit institution which had been re-established in 1803 and had become a center of Polish revolutionary activities, was abolished in 1832 as a punitive measure. Its medical faculty was converted into a special medical and surgical academy, and its theological faculty into a seminary.

For the Polish aristocracy, Uvarov founded, in 1833, the University of St. Vladimir in Kiev. This institution was intended to symbolize "the close relation of intellectual strength to military power"; it was also expected to stimulate the emergence of "a separate Polish nationality, blended with the spirit of Russia."[35] The philosophical faculty of the new university (for some time its only faculty) was an ill-mixed lot of Russians, Ger-

OFFICIAL NATIONALISM AND COUNTERVAILING THOUGHT 259

mans, and Poles. Few of them possessed higher academic degrees, much less an interest in scholarship, and for five years there was general intellectual apathy and scarcely any interest in science.[36] In 1838 student disorders led to a temporary closing of the university, and subsequently most of its Polish professors were dismissed.

Dorpat University, an old and honorable institution of higher learning which had given the St. Petersburg Academy of Sciences a number of its most eminent scholars, was also seriously affected by Uvarov's nationalist policies. The teaching of Russian was expanded, and much coercion was employed to increase the use of the Russian language in the lecture halls and in academic affairs. The Minister of National Education acquired unlimited authority in selecting and appointing instructors, although in practice the university managed to retain its autonomy in choosing its staff until the 1850's.

In Russia, as well, Uvarov's policies had a profound effect quite apart from the curricular changes he brought about. The "nationalization" of the universities had several converging ramifications, all of which were clearly defined in the 1835 university charter and subsequent directives. As government control over higher education increased, the university's autonomy was curbed. Whereas the university council had formerly controlled legal and business activities and the university police, now the district superintendent was given almost complete charge.[37] The superintendent was now permanently stationed in the university city of his school district, specifically empowered with university administration. According to the statute: "He is concerned with the competence, diligence, and good behavior of professors, adjuncts, teachers, and university office personnel; he warns those whose work is inadequate and takes steps for the removal of untrustworthy persons."[38] New "rules of internal order" were issued to control student behavior. The 1835 university statute was essentially a denial of university republicanism as defined by the 1804 charter; it was a document dedicated to making the schools of higher education an organic part of the Russian social and political system.

Probably the most shortsighted of the nationalist policies had begun even before Uvarov's appointment as Minister of National Education: the replacement of foreign professors with Russians. Under Magnitskii, Runich, and the other radical mystics, official dismissals, voluntary retirements, and resignations of foreign scholars seriously depleted the ranks of university instructors. And everywhere but Dorpat University, where most of the lecturing was in German, the quality of instruction fell so low that only an occasional graduate was adequately prepared to work toward a higher degree. During the final turbulent days of Magnitskii the shortage of professors was so acute that many positions could not be filled. Since one reason for this development was the decree of 1818, which ruled that only persons with higher degrees were acceptable candidates for teaching positions on the university level, the authorities now faced the critical question whether to lower the educational standards for professors and thus enlarge the numbers of qualified personnel, or to solve the problem by an intensified postgraduate training of students with ascertained intellectual gifts and scholarly promise. The government adopted the latter plan and amplified it so as to allow for postgraduate training of native Russian students exclusively.

In September 1827 the Committee for the Establishment of Schools began to work out the details of a plan for the training of future professors. The Committee accepted the principles and basic procedures outlined by Academician Georg Parrot, a former professor at Dorpat University. Parrot recommended an immediate selection of the most promising young men from Moscow, Khar'kov, and Kazan Universities (St. Petersburg University was, in his opinion, so weakened as to be beyond salvation), who would receive advanced education first at Dorpat University for a period of three years and then abroad for an additional two years.[39] He further recommended that most of the old professors be retired as soon as the first group of these students completed their training and were ready for teaching. Parrot recommended that the first group to be trained number thirty-two for each of the three major universities, but the plan as submitted to the Tsar reduced the number to twenty students in all. Nicholas I approved the whole scheme, but he added the explicit order that all the young men selected be native Russians.

Thus, more than a century after the founding of the St. Petersburg Academy of Sciences, which Peter I had ambitiously thought would foster the appearance of native universities and scholars, Russia was still critically dependent on Western institutions for the training of her academic personnel. In discussing the Parrot plan, the members of the Committee split along national lines: the native Russians, headed by Speranskii and Stroganov, wanted the whole plan rejected; the "German" group, led by Lieven, Lambert, Krusenstern, and Storch, sought its immediate enforcement. Storch asserted—and the other members could hardly have disagreed with him—that Dorpat University was undoubtedly the best university in the Russian empire, that it boasted excellent professors and had graduated many eminent scholars. Because Uvarov was on the "German" side, the plan won approval and was passed on to Nicholas I, who was known to favor it.[40] Thus the Professors' Institute was put into immediate operation by a special government order.

In the fall of 1828 twenty-two young men arrived in Dorpat. The prospect of long years of higher education had proved so unappealing to the students themselves that among those finally selected there were several who had no university education at all and were therefore enrolled as freshmen. As had happened so often in the past, the carrying out of the plan was beset with difficulties. The 1830 revolution in France interrupted Franco-Russian relations, making it impossible for Russian students to attend French universities; this was followed by the 1830–31 Polish uprising, as a result of which the government decided not to allow Russians to attend any Western universities. This order was in effect until 1833, which meant that the future professors stayed five instead of three years in Dorpat.[41] The official views expressed in the decree of February 18, 1831, are interesting. It noted with disapproval that "occasionally young people return home with false ideas about Russia," that they forget "her true needs, laws, morals, order, and sometimes even the language," and that "they become aliens in their own country."[42] The decree stipulated that young men ten to eighteen years of age receive all their education in Russia and that persons educated contrary to these rules forfeit their right to enter government service. When the ban on foreign study was rescinded in 1833, the students were split up and sent to Berlin and Vienna.

The program of training for future professors and scholars in Dorpat and abroad, limited though it was, helped to solve one of the major crises in the history of Russia's higher education. The first young scholars returned from Western Europe in 1834. A year earlier the government had authorized the second (and last) recruitment of promising students for the Professors' Institute at Dorpat University. Nine students were actually selected, but only six appeared in Dorpat. The Professors' Institute thus gave Russian universities some twenty professors, some of whom became distinguished scholars (Pirogov and Granovskii, in particular).

Although the Professors' Institute ceased to exist after the second group of candidates had completed their training, the government continued up to the time of the 1848 revolution to send students, individually or in groups, to universities in Western Europe. Uvarov justified this action by insisting that it was a sacred duty of Russian scholars to blend universal learning with the Russian spirit. It was because of his influence that the government began to offer a variety of inducements to those who would successfully pursue higher studies abroad. A decree of 1846, for example, ruled that years spent in foreign universities would be counted as years in government service and reckoned in the determination of retirement benefits.[43]

Undeniably, part of Uvarov's official nationalism—despite his liberal allowance for foreign education—was the belief that higher education was a monopoly of the gentry and high government officials, and that the curriculum should convey nationalist dogma rather than instill any spirit of challenge. To the guardians of the new educational philosophy, morality, not knowledge, was the ultimate goal of higher education. And the highest mark of morality was devotion to the state. Aleksandr Benkendorf, the chief of the secret police, wrote to Pushkin that "morality," "industrious service" to the state, and "zeal" were the pillars of true education. On the occasion of his appointment as the superintendent of the Moscow school district, General A. A. Pisarev received an official request that most careful attention be paid "to the moral orientation of instruction" and to a careful elimination from lectures of all ideas which might "weaken the teachings of our religion." He was advised to prevent the school libraries from holding any books "opposed to religion, the government, and morality."[44] These were some of the reasons why Uvarov insisted on a thorough screening of all persons considered for teaching positions.

Uvarov paid particular attention to the selection of professors on the basis of demonstrated nationalism and conservatism. In 1843 he stated that any impartial observer could see that the universities had become the schools for the education of higher estates alone, and that during the last ten years the government had no reason to question the "Russian feelings" and "purity of thought" of young university instructors. Paul Miliukov, however, observed that Uvarov's assessment of the "Russian feelings" of new professors was not so accurate as he imagined—that it applied only to one wing of professors, typified by Pogodin and Shevyrev.

Miliukov's observation is an indication that one must look far beyond the narrow limits of official nationalism and allied conservative forces for an understanding of the conditions that influenced the growth of science during the second quarter of the nineteenth century. Despite Uvarov's pronouncements and administrative efforts, during his entire tenure as

Minister of National Education the universities maintained a spirit of intellectual inquiry, philosophical debate, and profound ideological curiosity. The official nationalism applied to the universities was, in perspective, little more than a hopeless effort to direct the growing intellectual fermentation and national consciousness into government-approved channels.

THE EMERGENCE OF CRITICAL THOUGHT

Nicholas I had enough police power to determine the curriculum and the social composition of the universities, to censor books, and to abolish undesirable journals, but the cultural affirmation of Russia's national consciousness was largely beyond the scope of his power. This affirmation coincided with what may be called the beginning of the classical period in the intellectual and aesthetic expression of Russian life and Russian culture. Pushkin's *Eugene Onegin,* Glinka's music, the whole gallery of Gogol's characters, and Lermontov's poetry were products of great artistic quality, but they were also genuinely Russian. Pushkin has been justifiably compared with Peter the Great in his titanic influence on Russian society. In search of freedom for poetical expression, he strove also for the right to speak his mind about Russia's society and culture. According to Pypin: "Russian life was for him a subject of constant investigation; he studied its past and present, its language and customs."[45] Dostoevskii stated that Pushkin was the first "to give us artistic types of Russian moral beauty, which had sprung directly out of the Russian soul, which had its home in the truth of the people, in our very soul."[46] The significance of Gogol's early work was that, more than any other Russian writer before him, he wrote for and about all classes, and tried to interpret social questions with a sense of social justice and humanity.

There were others who displayed the same concern for humanity. Nikolai Polevoi, for all his faults, was the first to write a history of the Russian *people,* as contrasted to a history of the Russian *state* like Karamzin's. He dedicated his history to Niebuhr, the great German historian who had urged a critical attitude toward "historical traditions." Mikhail Kachenovskii showed the value of a skeptical attitude toward the ancient Russian chronicles and the intellectual sterility of the dogmatism of official historiography. P. Ia. Chaadaev introduced the philosophy of history in Russia, contending that Russian history can be understood only if placed in the context of "universal history." Russia's cultural poverty, he claimed, which had made her a "cultural thief," was the result of centuries of isolation from the rest of the world and the main currents of universal thought.[47] In varying degree, and with varying success, these scholars called upon Russia to make a cultural self-assessment, and in so doing they became a powerful countervailing force against Uvarov's nationalist dogmatism.

If there was a single general characteristic of Russian intellectual life during the 1830's and 1840's, it was the diversification of ideological, aesthetic, and sociological ideas and standards. The literature of this period, as A. M. Skabichevskii rightly remarks, suddenly ceased to form a unitary pyramid dominated by a handful of Olympians. The pyramid gave way to a "federation of literary camps," each with its champions, its philosophy, and its journals.[48]

The literary and historical activity of this period, and the fermentation of scientific and philosophical thought, were quite independent of official nationalism. For despite official propaganda to the contrary, the structure of feudal institutions was cracking. A class of industrial workers, although small and disorganized, was a social force which could no longer be ignored. The increasing pauperization of a considerable segment of the gentry, which led to the creation of a *déclassé* aristocracy, was an equally important sociological phenomenon. Hereditary aristocracy ceased to be the social locus of power; the new ruling class consisted of aristocrats who combined the ascribed noble status with achieved personal wealth. There was, furthermore, a new social class of university graduates who, in order to preserve their independence and freedom of thought, shunned government service. Thus the official nationalism of Nicholas I was in fact unrealistic, oblivious to trends that were moving inevitably toward a national awakening—first of the intellectuals, then of lower estates. In the strictly defined limits of government decrees and university statutes, the Russian way was based on a definition of autocracy and serfdom as immutable parts of Russian history. To the intellectuals Russian culture was a historical phenomenon which should be examined systematically and critically. The two opposing forces, alike in their profound interest in Russian history as a key to a fuller comprehension of the present, were bound to clash.

Some idea of the official attitude toward Russian history and the efforts to enforce this attitude is shown dramatically in the following autobiographical note of S. M. Solov'ev: "In August 1850, Shirinskii [-Shikhmatov, who succeeded Uvarov as Minister of National Education] showed up in Moscow; his first job was, of course, to inspect the university and to visit classrooms during lecture hours. He came to one of my lectures. It happened to be the first lecture of the new academic year, and I talked about the sources of Russian history. I discussed the chronicles, appraised their authenticity, and took issue with the proponents of the skeptical school; I concluded that Russian history has come to us in the form of collected documents and that it is difficult to establish the original text ascribed to Nestor. What happened? The next day Shirinskii requested that I come to see him, and in an imperious tone he reprimanded me for my skepticism. . . . 'The government does not want that kind of attitude!' cried the furious Tatar, paying no attention to my explanations."[49] Solov'ev goes on to mention a number of ancient chronicles which the historian was officially expected to treat as established historical fact.

Boris Chicherin, a graduate of Moscow University who became an eminent professor of constitutional law at that university in the 1860's, related his personal troubles with official nationalism in one of his autobiographical essays. In 1853, when he submitted his Magister's thesis—dealing with regional administrative institutions in seventeenth-century Russia—to the faculty of law, the examining committee rejected it despite its evident merit. It was based on a conscientious examination of sources and showed no political-ideological bias. However, the views expressed on the ancient administration of Russia were very unfavorable, Chicherin was told by the Dean; "now the times are such that censorship authorities will not even pass a reference to Grand Prince Vladimir's words 'In Russ it is a joy to drink.'" One professor told him that the thesis was a libel and an insult to ancient Russia, and that he would never approve it.[50]

Ironically, although no Russian government had worked more diligently to control the interpretation of Russian history, none had ever been faced with such a vast number of interpretations differing from official dogma—Uvarov's official nationalism was, in fact, a desperate reaction to the spread of critical evaluation. Nicholas I's era had been distinguished both by official efforts to achieve the maximum intellectual regimentation and by a spontaneous cultural fermentation which produced new thoughts and dynamic ideological crosscurrents. The new intellectual effervescence came from all directions and expressed many thoughts, some of them contradictory. Much of it lay in the realm of *belles-lettres*; some was purely political. Many ideas cut across the entire spectrum of intellectual and aesthetic endeavor and left a profound imprint on their age. Slavophilism and Westernism, the pre-eminent intellectual movements of the age, embraced a colorful diversity of ideas and social programs. Both had definite ideas on science, but their chief interest was in history and the humanities.

It is not our purpose to discuss Slavophilism and Westernism in their complex intellectual and ideological settings, but only to indicate their relationship to the scientific thought of their time. Both schools germinated in the literary circles of university students, informal groups of young men who in their search for wisdom went far beyond the university lectures and official textbooks. Both had a deep philosophical background: their members were educated in an atmosphere alive with the philosophies of Schelling and Hegel, which influenced their ideas about the meaning of history, the nature of knowledge, and the dynamics of political behavior. Both developed under the influence of Western philosophical thought, but both had unique Russian features.

Although the Slavophils were influenced in some measure by Hegel, their philosophy of history was dominated by the Schellingian idea that each culture is a unique historical phenomenon, dependent on its own motive forces and capable of making a specific contribution to universal culture. The Westerners, on the other hand, were close to the Hegelian philosophy of history, which treated the development of individual cultures as interdependent parts of universal history. The Slavophils actually combined the Schellingian concept of the historical uniqueness of each society with Herder's hypothetical idea of the democratic constitution of ancient Slavic society. They amplified the democratic myth by portraying the Russian national character in terms of imaginary qualities of the so-called organic collectivity (*sobornost*), the alleged quintessence of early Christian beliefs.

Despite the naïveté of some of their ideas about the true holiness of non-Westernized Russia, the Slavophils made significant contributions in the field of intellectual endeavor. They stimulated the study of ancient Russian society in all its aspects, including ethnography. Petr Kireevskii, one of the most fiery of the Slavophils, distinguished himself as a collector of folk ballads. Ivan Beliaev, a believer in the Slavophil philosophy of history, wrote monographs on such topics as the service aristocracy, the clergy, the peasants, cities, agriculture and land ownership, the monetary system, finances, the army, historical geography, and various ethnographical matters—frequently unsound in interpretation but always richly documented.[51] Contributions of a similar sort by other Slavophils could be counted in dozens.

For all its rashness, Slavophil propaganda had its good points. Until the middle of the century, the learning of Western languages was—as Nikolai Pirogov, the distinguished surgeon and anatomist, put it—an end in itself, rather than a means to an end.[52] The Slavophils would have preferred to do away with the study of foreign languages altogether, but they deserve credit for their influence on increasing the use of the Russian language in intellectual communication.

What did the Slavophils think of the natural and exact sciences? How could their spiritualistic, mystical, and thoroughly idealistic blend of history and theology be made to fit the study of experimental science in the nineteenth century? The Slavophils were, of course, accused of being fundamentally antiscientific. The Westerners charged them with "scientific emptiness."[53] An answer may be found in an article written in 1847 by Aleksei Khomiakov, a leading Slavophil, on the nature of science. Science was not the same everywhere, he argued; contrary to popular belief, it does not consist of "truths," but of methods whereby truths are established. These methods can be different at different times and in different places. The scientific method is essentially an analysis of facts, not as these really are but as they are directly perceived by the mind. "The direct knowledge of facts"—the substratum of science—"is always accompanied by a hidden synthesis that is fully dependent on the nationality of the observer." In every country, Khomiakov said, science assumes a specific, national character: "Obviously, there can be no identification of science in England—a nation that has never known how to distinguish the law from the accident—and in Germany, which has reduced itself to a pure analytical machine that has lost all consciousness of facts."[54] Khomiakov was eager not so much to show what he considered the uniqueness of Russian science as to prove the futility of scholarly efforts to import "Western science" into Russia.

By 1856 the Slavophils, under pressure from many directions, decided that it was time to express their ideas on "sciences and arts" in more detail, and therefore devoted a special column in their journal *Russkaia Beseda* to this issue. The first such column consisted of an article by Iurii Samarin analyzing the role of national character in science and the development of science.[55] Samarin admitted the universal character of scientific laws and the limiting influence of nationality on the development of science: "Scientific thought is essentially impartial and colorless, and therefore the scholar who cannot or will not rid himself of ideas, concepts, and feelings unwittingly instilled in him by the surrounding environment cannot be a worthy custodian of science." Without elaborating on how this attitude specifically affected the natural sciences, he immediately turned to history and the social sciences in an effort to illustrate his belief that all historical and social analysis or description must have a point of departure, inevitably tinged with a national or religious sentiment. Political economy, he argued, might be called a science; we must nevertheless explain why the Physiocrats were a French phenomenon and mercantilism an English one. He also argued that to understand the past of a country one must first of all capture its spirit and only secondarily apply the methods of the trained historian. "Can it be denied," he asked, "that the spirit of our history, the nature of our poetry, and the entire course and orientation of our national life are almost fully understandable to a Russian because he is a Russian, and, depending on the degree to which he is a Russian, more fully than to a Frenchman, even though the latter may have full command of the Russian language and access to a vast amount of material such as has never been available to a single Russian scholar?"

The Slavophils, it should be added, helped to create an atmosphere conducive to a methodical study of culture and history because of their avowed opposition to some of the basic principles of official nationalism. They viewed autocracy not as an absolute category but as a historical aberration, an artificial and deliberate corruption of the ancient Slavic communal life in which there was no political organization whatever. Along with their profound cultural conservatism, they stood for a revival of the primitive *obshchina*, and were thus foes of serfdom, the cornerstone of Uvarov's official nationalism. The opponents of Slavophilism argued in reply that this philosophical romanticism was, in the final analysis, more injurious than beneficial to scientific thought. They claimed that because the Slavophils made religion the basic condition and manifestation of thought, they necessarily made science a reflection of the religious outlook. According to Boris Chicherin, it was in part Slavophil conservatism that kept the Russians in the 1840's and 1850's from asserting themselves in scientific ways, and showing "a creative power in science."[56]

The Westerners were far less unified in their ideas than the Slavophils. They were a more diversified group in terms of social origin; their ranks were dominated by members of the liberal intelligentsia from the middle strata of the aristocracy, but they also included clergy, government officials, and even merchants and a few peasants. Their philosophy was essentially idealistic, like that of the Slavophils, with a strong early-Hegelian slant and certain religious undercurrents, but it was more subtle and much more sophisticated than Slavophil philosophy. To the Westerners science was a basic secular force which would determine the future prosperity of Russia. The Slavophils agreed with the advocates of official nationalism that the West had entered an age of decadence, dominated by a materialistic world view; the Westerners asserted that since Russian culture so obviously lagged behind that of the West, Russia must still continue for a time to be the pupil of the West, in science as in other fields.

During the late 1840's and early 1850's the Westerners lost more and more of their early conservatism and came to disagree strongly with one another. As one adherent commented: "Among the so-called Westerners there were no generally accepted ideas. This group included persons with the most different convictions: genuine adherents of the Orthodox faith and those who rejected all religions, followers of metaphysics and champions of experiment, worshipers of the state and advocates of pure individualism. They were united only by their respect for science and enlightenment. Both of these could be borrowed from the West, and for this reason they considered the growing rapprochement with the West a great and fortunate development in Russian history. The Westerners fully realized that when young people came in contact with a higher civilization they would accept at first the predominantly external cultural elements, sometimes very shallowly and frivolously. In a basic understanding and adoption of the fruits of enlightenment, rather than in a return to the dead past, they saw the best guaranty for the prosperity of their people."[57]

Few Westerners, for all their support of science and the scientific method, were actually scientists. Their scholarly work was mainly historical, though strongly scientific in method. They believed in a critical examination of documentary source material, not from an antiquarian point of view but as part of an analysis of the whole cultural process. They tended in their enthusiasm to romanticize the culture of the West, overlooking some of the unpleasant facts of Western social and economic life, and to minimize the vitality and resourcefulness of Russian culture.

"Never," wrote Belinskii in 1847, "has the study of Russian history taken on such a serious character as it has in recent times."[58] We can add that during the 1840's and 1850's the study of history far outdistanced all other scholarly efforts in Russia. When some contemporaries boasted of the "scientific flowering" of this period, they actually had in mind the wide range and diversity of historical studies. Chicherin noted that in 1844 when he entered Moscow University "it was going through the most flourishing phase of its history," but he made no mention of the natural and exact sciences as part of this productive phase.[59] S. M. Solov'ev attributed the blossoming of Moscow University to the appointment of Count Stroganov as superintendent of the Moscow school district and to his willingness to end the monopoly of such proponents of official nationalism as Pogodin, Shevyrev, and Davydov in the teaching of political, legal, and literary history.[60] Thanks to this new emphasis on historical interpretation, and to the proliferation of informal discussion circles, Moscow University and some of the other universities became what Pirogov called "the best barometers of social pressure."

It may be recalled that the 1835 university statute provided for a significant expansion of the humanistic curriculum, and that the official educational policy favored a historical approach in all humanistic subjects. History was for some an avenue of scholarly escape from awkward contemporary problems. For others, however, the study of history was an integral part of the classical period in Russian culture, closely related to the growth of literature, music, painting, and architecture. Thus Shchapov's assertion that this period was dominated by what he called archaeologism—a convenient scholarly retreat from burning and touchy contemporary problems—seems at best only partly true.

HISTORIOGRAPHY: CHIEF REPRESENTATIVES

A division of the historians of this period in terms of their allegiance to the three basic ideological-philosophical orientations—official nationalism, Slavophilism, and Westernism—would fairly represent the period's dominant trends in the broad field of historiography. It would, however, tend to obscure the full scope of the work of individual scholars. Some historians, like Pogodin and Shevyrev, saw some merit in both nationalism and Slavophilism, even though they were essentially adherents of the official line.[61] Among the Westerners, individual philosophies and theoretical orientations were often of much more significance than the general Western allegiance. There were some Slavophils, such as Khomiakov, to whom history was no more than an extension of ideology; to most Westerners, typified by Solov'ev and Chicherin, history and the historical method were broad fields, largely independent of an author's ideological commitments. The one characteristic common to all historiographers of this age was a profound belief in the use of abstract sociological or philosophical principles as a means of determining the nature—sometimes prophetic—of historical events.

In 1835 Pogodin, the historian who adhered most consistently to the philosophy of official nationalism, was asked by Moscow University to teach "historical Orthodoxy," partly as a way of defending Russia's history against the criticisms of the "skeptics," who openly challenged the reliability of certain ancient documents. With government approval, and equipped with Uvarov's triple pillars of official ideology (Orthodoxy, autocracy, and nationality), he mercilessly bombarded his colleague Kachenovskii, one of the leading skeptics, known for his questioning of the authenticity of "Russian Justice," "The Tale of Igor's Campaign," and other documents. Pogodin, a dedicated collector of ancient documentary material, was a persuasive lecturer despite his lack of philosophical dexterity, and wholeheartedly supported the idea of official nationalism. He blended Schlözer's theory of the Variag origin of the Russian state with nineteenth-century nationalism, and, unlike his Slavophil friends, saw in Peter the Great the true builder of Russia's power.

Pogodin's writing, according to K. Bestuzhev-Riumin, was essentially a reflection of his nationalist enthusiasm.[62] He taught his students a profound respect for historical inquiry. Yet he felt that the Russian historian's first duty was to social tranquillity.[63] Never did he admit that the study of Russian history could benefit in any way from Western historical studies, although he did relent—after visiting Prague in 1835 and meeting such Slavist stalwarts as Shafařik, Hanka, and Palacky—so far as to allow the study of other Slavic nations in conjunction with the history of Russia. The scholarship of this historian was marred by a number of clearly fantastic notions, including the claim that Russian history could not be explained in terms of any general laws because its course was much influenced by supernatural and miraculous forces.

Official nationalism had several other eminent historians on its side. S. P. Shevyrev, who taught the history of literature at Moscow University, believed that Nicholas's determination to make education a vigilant struggle against materialism—a dedication to "the divine throne, the cross, and the prayer"—was indeed the great blessing of his generation.[64] He is remembered chiefly, however, for his competent and well-balanced history of Moscow University, written at the time of the centennial observances in 1855, and for his pioneering efforts to subject ancient Russian literature to a systematic study. The social life of Old Russia provided him with models of high morality dominated by the principle of unqualified subjugation of the individual to society. His writings betray a man desperately trying to escape from a society in which the elements of individuality—in the form of skepticism and individual interpretation of cultural values— had appeared throughout the entire range of intellectual endeavor.

N. G. Ustrialov, another consistent supporter of Uvarov's official nationalism, wrote as his major work a *History of the Reign of Peter the Great,* which is an interesting example of the nationalist idealization of Peter. Particularly during the 1840's, Peter I was the great hero of the guardians of official ideology, although at the same time the Slavophils— with whom the nationalists had in other ways so much in common—saw in him the source of all the evils of enforced Westernization.

Almost every Slavophil was a historian of one kind or another. The most impressive Slavophil historians, however, were not the ideological codifiers and activists but the professional historians who were imbued with the broad Slavophil attitude, as embodied in Khomiakov and the Kireevskii and Aksakov brothers. I. D. Beliaev, according to Miliukov, was the first professional historian to use an extensive familiarity with legal documentary material to prove the validity of the Slavophil theory.[65] The stubborn survival of the *obshchina*—the Slavophils' pet institution—is the theme of his *Russian Peasantry.* This, incidentally, was the first Russian historical work of any length to deal with the social and economic vicissitudes of the peasants as an estate. In numerous other studies Beliaev took up a wide range of social and judicial problems, unfortunately treating them in a very mechanical and uncritical fashion.

The Slavophils were for the most part inclined to agree with Khomiakov's claim that history cannot be a subject of scientific inquiry because "the essence of the life of mankind" was "beyond the range of inquiry of the investigator," and because "logical formulas are inadequate for the understanding of life."[66] The Westerners, on the other hand, assumed that historiography could and should become a science and that the historian must study the workings of universal processes within the context of individual societies—in other words, that the inner logic of history is scientifically demonstrable.

History had its official apologists and Slavophil romantics, but it also had students of a more realistic and critical determination. Some of these belonged to the loose category of Westerners, and some were quite free even of that vague affiliation. Nikolai Polevoi was one of the latter sort. The son of a merchant, largely self-educated, he became a writer of historical sketches, poems, plays, literary criticism, and stories which appeared in a whole series of journals. He also wrote several novels, a volume of essays, and a six-volume *History of the Russian People* (1829–33). He was firm in his insistence that history must be judicious, scientific, and fully independent of the personal inclinations of the author. He argued that history should not be "a precisely written chronicle of times past," but "a practical rendering of the philosophical ideas of the world and mankind, an analysis of philosophical synthesis."[67] In his eagerness to make history a science, he extolled the scholar who "treats nations and peoples—the planets of the moral world—as concrete expressions of mathematical formulae." Relying on an aphorism of Bacon's, he insisted that no inquiry can produce fruitful results unless it is placed in a theoretical framework. He argued that even literary criticism could and must conform to the immutable laws of scientific precision.[68]

The *History* shows the clear influence of Guizot's monarchical liberalism and is a sweeping answer to Karamzin's monarchical conservatism and historical sentimentalism. Polevoi believed that Karamzin was too narrow in his concept of history and lacked historical perspective, so that his multivolume study was hardly more than a gallery of historical portraits. Furthermore, Karamzin had failed to describe and discuss the weaknesses in Russian society in his overriding concern with political institutions.

In answer, Polevoi tried, not wholly successfully, to write a history of events of social and political significance in which events in Russian history within a given period were related to events in the history of the world. Inevitably, as he approached the modern period, he found the state looming larger and more complex, so that he was forced into some of the same emphases for which he had chided Karamzin. Despite this weakness, however, and an unfortunate journalistic style, his *History* was an alarming denial of official ideology. Uvarov, busily at work codifying his philosophy of nationalism, criticized the book; others called Polevoi a rebel, and insults of all descriptions were hurled at him. As the first nonaristocrat to write a general survey of Russian history, he was a particular target for vicious attacks by the supporters of official historiography. Crushed and demoralized, in 1846 he published a survey of Russian history prior to Peter I in which he clung tenaciously to Uvarovian nationalism.[69] Polevoi was neither a careful student of historical documents nor a capable exponent of his own historical method, but he was important in demonstrating the need for unofficial interpretations of the national past. He showed eloquently the interaction of Russian history with "world history" without underestimating Russia's historical individuality; and he made a sincere effort to prove that the history of a society is much more complex than the history of a state.

Like Polevoi, the Westerners considered Russian history a part of world history, which they saw as an unfolding of certain universal principles of cultural and social development. Without any dominant ideological motive, they sought no radical changes in the structure of the Russian polity except the abolition of serfdom (they had no quarrel with autocracy). Certain of them were proponents of a "scientific" approach to history—namely Granovskii and Solov'ev.

Granovskii taught "universal history" at Moscow University from 1839 to 1855. Steeped in Western medieval history, he acquired prominence and a wide appeal that reached far beyond the university halls as a historical sociologist, or a philosopher of history; he first introduced in Russia the view of world history as a progressive march toward the highest and noblest ideals of humanity.[70] He brought to his students not only a broad, philosophically sophisticated, and intellectually challenging interpretation of Western history but also the most modern Western views on the meaning of history and the nature of the historical method.

Granovskii was one of the fortunate few who attended the Professors' Institute at Dorpat University and went on to graduate study in the West in the late 1830's. At Berlin University he studied history under Leopold von Ranke and Roman law under Friedrich von Savigny. Ranke taught him respect for the cold, unadorned historical fact and showed him how to lecture lucidly on historical subjects.[71] Savigny taught him to appreciate the ties between the history of a people—political, social, and juridical—and "national spirit." And from both Ranke and Savigny he acquired a belief in the historical individuality of nations. A secondary influence came from the geographer Karl Ritter, who expounded the influence of natural environment on the development and activities of man.[72] Hegel had died in 1831, but Hegelianism was at the peak of its influence. Granovskii accepted the Hegelian idea that history is a creation of the reason, which has its own laws and ideals, and that the universal laws of reason are matched by the universal laws of history.

In the early 1850's, after more than a decade of writing and lecturing, Granovskii began to question the value of the Hegelian scheme of the universal historical process and to look toward the natural sciences for models for the historical method. In 1852 he delivered a lecture entitled "The Present-Day Status and Importance of World History" in which he paid special attention to the weaknesses of contemporary historiography. The historian, he claimed, should be concerned less with an aesthetic presentation of his narrative than with a critical and scientific evaluation of content; he must try to build "the unity of science" upon "the diversity of historical events." The influence of Niebuhr was noticeable in his plea for a more rigid and critical study of historical sources. Granovskii argued that history could become "an experimental science" only if the historian undertook a balanced and integrated study of two grand variables: "the free creativeness of the human spirit" and "the natural conditions," independent of human mind. "History," he insisted, "must of necessity leave the circle of philology and jurisprudence and become a science."[73]

During the sixteen years he taught at Moscow University, Granovskii wrote and lectured on various aspects of Western European history, always placing them in their broad historical and sociological context. He had a particular interest in what he considered to be the transitional historical phases, and he urged that historians pay more attention to ethnographic studies.

Granovskii's fame was really due to his public lectures, which were attended "by Moscow's highest society." In 1843–46 he gave a series of lectures devoted to a comparative study of the histories of England and France; and in 1851 he lectured on four personages who played a great role in shaping the course of world history—Tamerlane, Alexander the Great, Louis IX, and Bacon. These persons were selected not because of their similarities but because of their differences. In reference to Bacon, Granovskii told his audience: "Among the contemporaries of Bacon there were persons whose biographies would be more interesting and of stronger dramatic effect; I selected him in order to indicate the importance of science." Bacon's achievement, he pointed out, lay not in "particular discoveries and studies, but in his total view of science and in the influence that he exercised on the future enlightenment of Europe. His thoughts

have become a part of the intellectual atmosphere of the last two centuries."[74]

Contemporary observers who recorded in their diaries the blossoming
of Moscow University during the 1840's were unanimous in their praise of
Granovskii's lectures as events of great cultural significance. They introduced the general public to new views, approaches, and interpretations of
history—a history not deadened by antiquarianism. Coming in a period of
official nationalism, with a general national awakening and great emphasis
on national history, these lectures did much to counter the growing
antagonism toward foreign cultures. One perceptive Russian woman noted
in her diary that Granovskii's public lectures, refreshingly devoid of classroom formalism, had opened a new epoch in Moscow's cultural history
by bringing the traditional animosity between the University and the community to an end.[75] They acquainted the general public with a new kind
of history—a history of great ideas and moral principles. Chicherin, subsequently a Moscow University professor, remembered Granovskii's statement that the true sense of history lies in an understanding of the diverse
facets of the human mind.[76] Solov'ev remembered him for his "highly
delicate religious convictions" and his moderate views on current problems.[77] Another contemporary stated that "in Granovskii's lectures history
became for the first time a scientific study of society."[78] Years later, Kliuchevskii wrote an appreciation on the occasion of the fiftieth anniversary
of Granovskii's death:

"In Granovskii's lectures history attained a purely scientific character
and became a true teacher. Granovskii taught his audiences to value
scientific knowledge as a social power. His lectures helped make Moscow
University a center of great hopes and ideas for the educated segments of
Russian society. Granovskii forged the internal spiritual unity of Moscow
University and the community, which has remained strong until the
present time and has become an old tradition for both. 'Our university, our
Granovskii'—has become a habitual saying in Moscow since that time."[79]

Solov'ev observed in his autobiographical notes that he had two things
in common with Granovskii: moderate political views and a serious
interest in Christianity.[80] Both rejected the Slavophil interpretation of
Russian history after Peter I as an era of decadence, and endorsed the view
that the historian's job was not only to record events but also to unveil the
processes—the regularities—of historical change.

Born in the family of a Moscow clergyman, Solov'ev read Karamzin's
and Ewers's historical works while he attended the local commercial high

school. When he went on to Moscow University, however, he found Granovskii's views more stimulating than Pogodin's. He continued to cling to Slavophilism in its religious aspects, but a two-year sojourn in Paris, Berlin, Heidelberg, and Prague ultimately helped him to arrive at a firm conviction that Russian history must be studied in the light of universal historical processes and in close conjunction with the histories of other Slavic nations. Guizot was his favorite nineteenth-century historian; of the eighteenth-century works, he admired most Vico's *Scienza nuova*. From the former he learned to appreciate the broad context of history, and from the latter the role of legal norms as dynamic agents in social change.

Solov'ev began his teaching career at Moscow University in 1845, the year in which he defended his Magister's thesis there, a treatise on the grand princes of Novgorod. During the next three decades his life was closely bound up with this institution. In 1851 he published the first volume of his *History of Russia from the Earliest Times*; and until 1879 every year saw the publication of an additional volume of this monumental work, considered by many to be the masterpiece of Russian historiography. A versatile background and profound historical sense made him an outstanding teacher of his generation. The following statement, made by Kliuchevskii, who was one of his students, shows the happy combination of Solov'ev's formidable scholarship and pedagogical genius:

"Solov'ev offered to his students an admirably integrated . . . view of the course of Russian history. The young people, new in scholarly endeavor, were particularly pleased when they were given a comprehensive view of a historical subject. In Solov'ev's lectures this broad conception and its intellectual impact were closely tied with a single method, which can be easily abused, but which when skillfully employed exercises a powerful educational influence on students. Solov'ev explained a mosaic of facts by illuminating them with general historical ideas. He did not offer a single historical fact without throwing the light of these ideas on it. The student felt immediately that the stream of life thus presented flowed in accordance with historical logic; his mind was not confused by unexpected and accidental events. Solov'ev explained the course of history by the dominant thoughts of each period. Thanks to his lectures, we learned to appreciate the methodological significance of the study of local history. . . . He firmly reiterated . . . the consistency of historical development, its general laws, and what he labeled by the unusual term *historicity*."[81]

Solov'ev was a tireless collector and a careful student of historical source material. He broadened the traditional concept of history to allow room for a study of the development of ideas, and he strongly objected to splitting the past into rigidly defined periods. In the introduction to the *History of Russia* he states that his scientific credo is "not to divide nor to splinter Russian history into special parts or periods, but to bring these together, to search primarily for forces which give unity to historical phenomena."[82] This orientation exercised a strong influence on the subsequent development of Russian historiography; from this time on historians tended to substitute dynamic and continuous *stages* of development for the previous static and discontinuous *periods*.

Although Solov'ev did not subscribe to the Slavophils' notion of Russia's national exclusiveness, he emphasized that Russia was historically unique, mainly because of its topographical features. Whereas the history of Western European nations had been determined by the geographical remoteness of areas enclosed by mountains, the history of Russia had been determined by its openness—vast, flat areas devoid of natural boundaries, which had made the country easily accessible to migratory peoples from Asia. Russian history, he maintained, was dominated by two motive forces: the gradual spread of Russians over the cultivable lands, and the protection of the steppe from the marauding nomads. These primary forces, Solov'ev argued, generated the need for a powerful centralized state which could organize and control all components of society.

Solov'ev succeeded where Polevoi had been only partly successful: he introduced a concept of history that was broader and more inclusive than Karamzin's.[83] In the spirit of the eighteenth century, Karamzin saw history as a gradual consolidation of the state structure and as a series of heroic episodes. Solov'ev, by contrast, saw history as a study of social development, a series of distinct social systems, beginning with the clans and clan alliances, which gradually disappeared with the rise of governmental institutions. Thus the history of the Russian state was, as Polevoi had also seen, the quintessence of the history of Russian society. Solov'ev did not make Karamzin's mistake of identifying the Russian state with the glorious features of autocracy and career aristocracy. Writing in the spirit of his time, Karamzin glorified the past in order to give moral support to contemporary autocracy; Solov'ev considered the study of the past useless unless it aided in a realistic understanding of the present. Far more than Karamzin, Solov'ev lived in a period of changing ideological currents and social aspirations—a time in which a critical and more versatile study of national history was urgently needed. He gave Russian history a unique richness of historical analysis—unmatched even by later historians. No other author, for example, in a single general history of the Russian nation, has covered the development of scientific thought in more detail and with more understanding and sympathy.

Solov'ev subscribed to the theory of the organic process of historical development; he made an extensive use of the comparative method, mostly in historical analogies with Western Europe; he took note of the historical significance of the ethnic composition of Russia; he identified history as a science of national awareness and recognized its academic, pragmatic, and moral aspects; and he adduced formidable evidence to show that the Westernizing reforms of Peter I were not the caprice of one individual but part of a cumulative process whose beginnings could be traced to the time of Ivan the Terrible.[84]

Solov'ev's work became a model for other scholars of his time and of the succeeding generation. He showed the depth of Russian history and the versatility of the historian's tasks. Even more important, he established rigorous standards of accuracy. The succeeding generation of historians did not make him a saint, but in criticizing his weaknesses they worked toward an improvement in their own work. Miliukov felt that Solov'ev's main weakness was his nationalist orientation in the analysis of foreign policies and his Western bias in the interpretation of Russia's internal developments. Also, pressing himself to publish a huge volume of his *History of Russia* every year, he did not allow himself sufficient time to digest his material and to view it from the vantage point of his own theories. The *History* was therefore loose and bottomless, a vast collection of raw material. Miliukov also suggested that Solov'ev's preoccupation with the idea of Westernization had prevented him from analyzing in full all the diverse aspects of Russian development.[85]

Solov'ev, Granovskii, and other historians of Nicholas's era should not be judged only in terms of their contributions to Russian historiography. Equally important was the part they played in the creation of an intellectual atmosphere that invited serious concern with scientific thought. These scholars brought to an end the monopoly of official historiography in the study and interpretation of the national past. The struggle between the skeptics and the proponents of official nationalism, the followers of Schlözer and his foes, the Westerners and the Slavophils, was primarily a struggle of conflicting opinions—a struggle without which true science is impossible. Thanks to these scholars, Russian history acquired greater logical and methodological precision, greater depth and reliability. Even more important was their contribution to the emergence of new intellectual attitudes that favored the growth of the natural and exact sciences. They were motivated by skepticism in judging values, ideas, and institutions, by individuality in interpreting the events of the present and the past, and by social realism or utilitarianism in judging the value of knowledge. These criteria were vital parts of a rising puritan ethic which contributed to the creation of a moral and intellectual climate conducive to the growth of scientific inquiry.

Slavophilism and Westernism were distinct blends of ideological and philosophical principles; they were also a distinct intellectual framework within which unofficial studies of Russia's culture and history were cast. So far as scientific inquiry was concerned, neither Slavophilism nor Westernism extended its influence beyond a certain spirit of systematized investigation within the humanistic field. To examine the relationship of philosophical thought to natural science during this period we must therefore go beyond the relatively narrow confines of the two major ideological currents and look at the main trends in the general development of philosophy in Russia.

During this period the teaching of philosophy at universities was done mainly by clerics, whose outlook was basically antiscientific. Some of them merely ignored science, but others bitterly opposed it. Owing to their dogmatism and their predominantly theological brand of philosophy, they were of little real influence on their contemporaries; nor did they add much to the tradition of Russian theological thought.

In an effort to remedy this situation, professors of the social and natural sciences broadened their lectures into philosophical analyses of their specific subjects. In the literary circles, also, there were lively discussions of philosophical ideas. The secret societies of the Alexandrine period had, of course, shown markedly philosophical influences. It was said of the Decembrist Pavel Pestel that he was "a rationalist to the marrow of his bones, a true disciple of the French philosophers of the eighteenth century, a champion of the theory of social contract, a follower of Montesquieu, Rousseau, Voltaire, and Helvétius, and an admirer of Say's economic theories and Benjamin Constant's political ideas."[86] The Decembrists were generally a product of humanism, liberalism, and positivism, opposed to the official brand of mysticism or to any sort of idealistic metaphysics. To them, human history was dominated by progress, and progress was measured in terms of enlightenment and the accumulation of positive knowledge, which were the true paths to human welfare and social justice.

In the years immediately preceding the Decembrist uprising, the influence of French philosophical thought had gone into a rapid decline. Many Russian intellectuals had turned away from French sensualism and "materialism" to German idealistic philosophy, which they felt was more universal in its application. The salons of St. Petersburg and Moscow were flooded with manuscript translations of the works of Kant, Fichte, and Schelling. The *Naturphilosophie* of Schelling and Oken thus entered a period of full bloom and became a paramount intellectual force. A Society of the Lovers of Wisdom was founded to promote the ideas of Schelling, and professors such as D. M. Vellanskii and M. G. Pavlov used their lectures to propound the Schellingian theories.

Vladimir Odoevskii, one of the more subtle and sophisticated Lovers of Wisdom, saw fit to pen an essay opposing the influence of English philosophy and science, feeble though this was in Russia, and in so doing indirectly affirmed the basic postulates of Schellingism. He objected to English philosophy's "crude" empirical foundations: "Even if the English philosopher allows for the existence of the soul, religion, morality, and poetry, he recognizes them only in so far as they can be touched, seen, or heard." Odoevskii had to concede that Bacon was owed respect for "having directed our attention to the importance of the scientific method," but he found him guilty of the crime of separating science from theology. Odoevskii attacked the "incompleteness" of English philosophy as well as its "chaotic" nature—try, for example (he told his readers), to disentangle the snarl of Bentham's thoughts!

Russian intellectuals were well acquainted with the philosophy of Spinoza, Kant, Fichte, and Jacobi, but it was Schelling who most satisfied their needs, because his philosophical system was complete, comprehensive, idealistic, dynamic, and challenging. The brand of Schellingism that the Russians settled on was at once a rebellion against the burden of the past and a withdrawal from the troublesome present.

Like the Decembrist societies, the Society of the Lovers of Wisdom was made up of aristocratic members; but the Lovers were no revolutionaries. Their concern was not with changing Russia's social fabric but with saving its cultural values, threatened as they were by reaction. They looked for the salvation of Russia through a purification, rather than a rejection, of her social myths. Their interests were ontological, not prosaic, and at first they were wholeheartedly antirationalist. They agreed with the spokesmen of Magnitskii's mysticism and Church dogma in recognizing the supreme importance of theological thought, but whereas the mystics and official theologians subordinated science and philosophy to theology, the Schellingians subordinated science and theology to philosophy. They became entranced with the philosophy of art—never before heard of in Russia—and spent much time searching out subtle philosophical implications in Goethe and in Beethoven.

Odoevskii called Schelling a Columbus who had found the way to the innermost recesses of the soul. In his *System of Transcendental Idealism,* Odoevskii said, Schelling showed that the only true study of nature is the one in which the objective arises from the subjective, which recognizes that the laws of nature are only the laws of intelligence.

In Schelling's philosophical growth there were two distinct phases: an early preoccupation with the *Naturphilosophie* as a unitary idealistic view of nature, and a later attempt to build a system of philosophy upon mysticism, divine providence, irrationalism, and theosophy. The Russian Schellingians gathered in the Society of the Lovers of Wisdom were not so much influenced by the latter phase of Schelling's philosophy as by the *Naturphilosophie,* particularly as it was applied to physiology, physics, and medicine. (The Slavophils, it should be noted, found the later Schellingism, which was antirationalist and mystical, more suitable to their tastes.) The *Naturphilosophie,* the essence of which was phenomenalism, opposed the mechanistic interpretation of nature or any view of the universe as a static, self-propelled, external phenomenon made intelligible by the methods of mathematics. On the contrary, nature was seen as a unitary force, a dynamic phenomenon, and an objective extension of the human intelligence. The *Naturphilosophie* did not deny science; it merely emphasized the study of the "inner" forces of nature as against mathematical and experimental description of "external" phenomena. It sought the essence of nature in unifying "living" forces, deploring the dissection of nature into isolated mechanisms. Odoevskii criticized physics for considering only the "dead side" of gravity—the fall—and for overlooking the "living side" which takes part in the formation of bodies. He thought that chemistry did not explain the inner ties between various kinds of matter. Astronomy, likewise, suffered from a tendency to compare nature with "dead clocks" and to limit itself to a minute description of "the wheels, the gears, and the springs" of these clocks without trying to find the key that wound them up.[87]

The *Naturphilosophie* was thus in some ways a negative force, and in Russia it became a means whereby professors of natural science could sail freely into metaphysical waters and thus hide their inadequacies in the work of their specific scientific disciplines. Yet the positive effects of the *Naturphilosophie* on the development of scientific thought were overwhelming. With the exception of Vellanskii, the Russian followers of Schelling and Oken modified the *Naturphilosophie* to include science as a cultural value, and some of the leading Schellingians were scientists.

From the account of Odoevskii, who was a student at Moscow University in the 1820's, it seems evident that the Schellingian professors, despite their vituperous attacks on experimentation, left no doubt of their conviction that scientific knowledge alone could provide the ultimate answers to many questions of prime importance. Odoevskii comments in his journal that the Russian Lovers of Wisdom were especially attracted to anatomy as "a science of man"—and particularly to the anatomy of the human brain. Although they "never dissected a single organism," their theoretical interest in anatomy led them to physiology, then in its infancy, and physiology in turn, says Odoevskii, stimulated students to ask questions which could be answered only by physics and chemistry. "Many statements of Schelling (particularly in his *Weltseele*) remained unclear without a knowledge of natural science."[88]

Even the physicist M. G. Pavlov, while conceding the value of science as a source of objective knowledge, questioned, from the Schellingian point of view, the adequacy of its methodology and substance. He postulated that nature can be studied in two ways: analytical-empirical and synthetical-theoretical. The first is based on experiment, proceeding from individual phenomena to general principles, the second on speculation, moving from general principles to individual phenomena. For this reason, experimental natural science cannot reach the level of "unified truth"; it can only produce an atomistic theory, based on materialistic foundations. Pavlov was willing to concede that experimental natural science had enriched our knowledge, but he claimed that it did not and could not penetrate into the innermost depths of nature. Experimental science could make discoveries in electricity, galvanism, magnetism, and other natural forces, but it could not explain what they were: "An experiment can lead to discoveries, but not to the understanding of them."[89]

Despite their metaphysical obstinacy and lack of scientific erudition, the Russian Schellingians in the universities impressed upon their students the fruitful idea that empirical and experimental data are merely the "raw material" of science and that theory is the essence of science. As Pavlov said, "Positive information is the beginning of knowing; theory is its culminating achievement. Therefore, information without theory is inadequate, and theory without information is impossible. Each science must strive toward a full understanding of its subject; therefore, each science must include the totality of factual and theoretical information."[90]

Pavlov viewed the coalescence of empirical facts and theoretical postulates as a coalescence of science and philosophy: "The speculative information of philosophy is possible only because of the existence of the experimental information that makes up science. Clearly, then, science could exist without philosophy . . . but philosophy is impossible without science." He believed philosophy to be the highest form of inquiry, but he recognized that science and philosophy were essentially supplementary sources of knowledge. According to him: "The subjects of our knowledge —that is, all things that we can comprehend—are the subjects of both science and philosophy, but in quite different ways. In science they are described and portrayed, in philosophy they are constructed; sciences study various subjects as they are, philosophy studies also their origins. . . . Therefore, philosophy is not a science of sciences, but a science of the possibility of the subjects of our knowledge, or, to put it differently, of the possibility of scientific subjects. Therefore, the experimental information that comprises science must precede philosophy."[91] As Pavlov speculated on the relationship of science to philosophy, he drifted away from Schellingian metaphysics into the new regions of a philosophy of science, which was subsequently to attract the attention of Herzen and Chernyshevskii.

Herzen attended Pavlov's lectures at Moscow University in the early 1830's and was favorably impressed with his teacher's enthusiasm and lecturing skill. He praised Pavlov for giving his students an understanding of the fundamental problems of philosophy. Most of them, Herzen notes, had no background whatever in philosophical thought, for only the seminarists were exposed to philosophy, and they got it in a "completely distorted" form. Herzen felt, however, that Pavlov gave his students hardly more than a general idea of science, building "houses without roofs, foundations without houses, and magnificent entrance halls to humble dwellings."[92]

Miliukov commented on the nonprofessional Schellingians, "These people were well-situated and were not compelled to make a living either from literary work or from teaching." "Unlike the professors, they did not look on intellectual activity as heavy work but as a noble diversion."[93] With a romantic obliviousness to the vagaries of everyday life, they sought a sublime and universal philosophy of national life elevated above the prosaic demands of daily living: they sought to discover the spiritual forces that govern both nature and society. In doing this they covered the entire range of intellectual effort, from experimental science on the one hand to Boehme's unqualified mysticism on the other.

Most of them appreciated the value of science, whether or not they knew anything about it, but they were not concerned with the harnessing of natural forces for the benefit of man. To them, nature was an allegorical representation of the limitless potentialities of man's ego and intellect. In this they showed the traditional attitude of the Russian aristocracy toward science, as best expressed in Odoevskii's statement that "the goal of science is science itself—it has no other external goal."[94] Since the time of Catherine II, Russia had always had an earnest group of "admirers of science" from the aristocratic ranks—people like Prince Dmitrii Golitsyn, A. A. Musin-Pushkin, Aleksei Razumovskii, D. P. Baturlin, Princess Dashkova, and Pavel Demidov, who built their own museums, botanical gardens, and laboratories and sponsored learned societies.

The Schellingians of the 1820's and 1830's differed notably from their aristocratic predecessors in not being collectors of books, museum items, and scientific objects. They were interested only in ideas and speculation. In their search for the keys to an understanding of the unity of nature, scorning the inadequacies of mechanistic and atomistic studies, they were in a sense the forerunners of vitalistic, organismic, and Gestalt theories in natural science, and it is on this account that Chernyshevskii, some two decades later, could say that Schelling's philosophy "exercised a powerful influence on the development of science, particularly of the natural sciences." It was Chernyshevskii's belief also that some of Schelling's earliest ideas were subsequently recognized by "all natural scientists."[95] To Schelling, he claimed, belonged the idea of the basic unity of "electricity, magnetic power, light, heat, and mechanical power," as well as the idea of "the unity of the chemical laws of organic and inorganic nature, verified by Liebig and his students."[96] Liebig, the chemist, in fact had no philosophical commitments, but it is true that certain great scholars such as Oersted in physics and von Baer in biology went through a phase of ardent adherence to the *Naturphilosophie*.

While irrationalist metaphysics was dominant in Russian philosophical thought during the 1830's, it did not go unchallenged. The influential journal *The Son of the Fatherland* seems to have been committed to a popularization of English empiricist philosophy, usually viewed in terms of its compatibility and close association with modern natural science. Unexpectedly, the same journal published in 1839 a Russian translation of a lengthy article on Kant by Victor Cousin on the occasion of the publication of Kant's *Werke* in Leipzig. The significant feature of this article was the emphasis on Kant as a relentless critic of both the grand idealistic philosophical tradition of the seventeenth century and "the petty sensualistic thought" of the eighteenth century. The author viewed the *Critique of Pure Reason* as the greatest intellectual monument of the eighteenth century, and gave prominence to Kant as a philosopher and logician of science—a giant who revolutionized modern man's views of the ontological and epistemological problems of all sciences.[97]

HEGELIANISM

During the 1830's the Hegelian philosophy made its entry into Russia. Its first stronghold was the Stankevich *kruzhok,* a group of young aristocrats detached from social and political reality and dedicated to the search for abstract ideas of a universal nature. They were immediately attracted to Hegel's idealistic metaphysics, and explored his works at length for evidence that knowledge should be unencumbered by elements of pragmatism. All leaned on Hegelian idealism to support their own deep religious convictions. Gradually, however, Hegelian philosophical ideas began to have a more serious influence, as the Russian Hegelians recognized in philosophy a unique logical approach to the study of knowledge as a unified system. Hegel's dialectic was accepted as the basic principle of natural and cultural change. The Russians were receptive to Hegel's view that the state is the ethical idea turned into reality; they also accepted the notion that history is dominated by three principles: rationality (everything happens according to reason), regularity (historical change is subject to general laws just as much as natural change), and progress (judged in terms of expanding freedom).

The influence of Hegel's philosophy on Russian scientific thought was mostly indirect. The historian Granovskii was one of his earliest followers, having studied Hegel more or less at the source. In his belief in history not as a mere record of events but as a study of the regularities of the historical process, with a predictable outcome, in which the struggle between the old and the new is the essence of change, Granovskii was basically Hegelian. Like Hegel also, he made the state a sociological category, though he made it a historical category as well.

Hegel reversed the trend set by Schelling's "philosophy of revelation" and irrationalism, bringing philosophy and science into an organic relationship. Despite its metaphysical foundations, his philosophy was a defense of rationalism which set logic above revelation, intuition, and mysticism. The Russian Hegelians thus helped to counteract the antirationalist orientation of the clergy-professors who taught philosophy in the universities. In their writings, they gradually made the public accustomed to the idea that there is no such thing as the absolute truth. The Hegelian influence did not do much to advance natural science, but it helped to make such natural-science criteria as objectivity, organic and functional interdependence of concrete variables, and predictability acceptable standards of the historical method. The Russian Hegelians saw in Hegel's philosophy a critical method of inquiry rather than a closed system of ontological wisdom. Granovskii, Solov'ev, Kavelin, and a number of lesser historians relied on Hegel's ideas for a philosophical justification of their identification of Russian history with the history of the Russian state—for to Hegel the state was the highest realization of a universal spirit.

It should not be assumed that Russian Hegelians were a consistent group, much less an organized one like the Society of the Lovers of Wisdom. Hegel's influence was fragmentary, and it usually represented a transitional phase in the intellectual history of Russian thinkers. Belinskii was at first influenced, but he rapidly abandoned Hegelian idealism as well as its ideological conservatism. Mikhail Bakunin, who relied on Hegelianism in his fervent defense of religion, soon became a champion of anarchism and a foe of idealistic philosophy. Konstantin Aksakov and Iurii Samarin became the stalwarts of Slavophilism and reverted to Schelling's philosophy of "wholeness," national individuality, and irrationalism. Granovskii, the most deeply influenced by Hegel's philosophy of history, became a Westerner with liberal leanings. Hegelianism did, however, offer a basis for the philosophy of such advocates of liberal thought as Herzen and Chernyshevskii, and even Belinskii—men who, though not themselves scientists, were consistent and outspoken supporters of scientific thought.

These men rejected Hegel's metaphysics but they accepted his dialectic, which not only stood for constant change in nature and society but subjected history to interpretations irreducible to mechanical laws. They also rejected Hegel's idealism, but they accepted his rationalism. Thanks to them, the generation of the 1840's brought philosophy down to earth from the lofty metaphysical perches to which it had been elevated by the generation of the 1830's. To them, the importance of Hegel's philosophy was that it marked "the transition from an abstract science to a science of life." Chernyshevskii saw in Hegelian philosophy a precursor of the new intellectual orientation which raised itself above "the Scholastic form of metaphysical transcendentalism" and accorded with the theories of natural science.[98] Thus, if the Hegelian influence on the Russian thought of the 1840's cannot be gauged in terms of shaping the views of individual men of knowledge, it clearly helped to create a new intellectual atmosphere in which revelation was replaced by reason, nationalist dogmatism by social criticism, and romanticism by realism. Herzen observed that thinking in terms of sheer logic, formal principles of abstraction, and universal laws was alien to the Russian mentality and that Russian Hegelians were bound sooner or later to shift their interests from abstract forms to concrete content.

When Belinskii ceased to interpret Hegelian "rational activity" as "internal life" and equated it with "concrete activity," he signaled the end of Russian philosophical romanticism and a transition from idealism to realism.[99] This transition was also heralded by Belinskii's bold attack on the tendency of the Slavophils to view "every modern thought as a sign of invasion by the cunning and decadent West." Belinskii recognized the great intellectual and literary talents of Odoevskii, but he censored him severely for his claim—in *Russian Nights*—that the pre-eminence of experiment and "petty analysis" in the natural sciences was a sign of moral degeneracy.[100]

Despite its intrinsic conservatism, Hegelianism appeared in Russia "as a 'realism' in reaction to an exceedingly abstract idealism." As Martin Malia states, "From this recognition of reality to criticism of it was only a step, and Herzen, by a bolder use of Hegel than his predecessors, was the first of his generation to take it."[101]

HERZEN'S VIEWS ON SCIENCE

Herzen recognized his debt to Hegel, whose philosophy he considered "the algebra of revolution, which gives man a great new freedom and does not leave a stone unturned in the world of Christianity and the world of worn-out tradition."[102] After a passing identification with Westernism, he took the side of the "left" Hegelians, who sought drastic social and political changes in Russia and repeatedly asserted the basic compatibility of philosophical and scientific thought.

Herzen is important to us because of his modern views on the logical, epistemological, and sociological aspects of science as a whole, seen in a general, not simply Russian, perspective. He was primarily interested in the utility of natural science, but he was also intrigued with Granovskii's belief that historiography, developed on the model of the exact sciences, could and should become a science. At a time when the guardians of official nationalism were looking nervously at science as a source of dangerous ideas, Herzen stated:

"The circulation of accurate and meaningful natural-science ideas is of vital concern to our age. These are abundant in science but scarce in society. They should become an integral part of public consciousness, and should be rendered accessible to all. . . . They should be presented in a language as plain as the one in which nature unfolds . . . her essence in majestic and harmonious simplicity. It seems to me that without education in natural science it is impossible to develop a strong intellect. . . . By placing natural science at the beginning of the course of education we would cleanse the child's mind of all prejudices; we would raise him on healthful food until the time when, strong and ready, he discovers the world of man and history which opens the door for direct participation in the issues of the day."[103]

Herzen had great awareness of important scientific trends. He was cognizant of the widening experimental base of physiology and of the growing dependence of physiology on chemistry. He sensed the struggle of contemporary chemists to raise chemistry to the theoretical level already achieved by physics. He anticipated the growing academic respectability of historical geology and biological transformism. He claimed forthrightly that he and his generation were on the threshold of a new epoch in which the need for scientific discovery would be felt by all.[104]

Herzen acknowledged, however, that science had powerful foes, some deliberate, some unintentional. The avowed enemies were the dilettantes— the people who felt "a need to philosophize, but to philosophize easily, pleasantly, and within certain limits."[105] He counted as dilettantes also those who regarded science as a good but considered scientific pursuits effortless and who actually had neither the temperament nor the determination to dedicate themselves to the search for truth. Such people were unintentional enemies. "The caste of scientists" were also unintentional enemies. These were "the scientists by virtue of calling, diploma, and sense of personal dignity," who, by being an exclusive group, introduced a conflict between science and society.[106] Owing to the excessive specialization of some scholars, and to their immoderate reliance on technical terminology, scientists found it difficult to communicate with nonprofessionals, and even with one another. The third enemy of science was what Herzen termed "Buddhism in science"—the tendency of scholars to build ivory towers far removed from the practical problems of everyday life. "The fault of the Buddhists is that they feel no need for a contact with life, for the actual realization of an idea."[107]

Herzen spoke for many Russian scholars when he said that "science has entered the age of maturity and liberty." He was quite successful in his bold efforts to describe the unique characteristics of science as a special kind of inquiry. Science, he warned, does not possess as much "majestic propylaea" as religion, for its way lies across the arid steppes and leads to austerely cold abstractions. Science demands no pledges and no taken-for-granted principles. It does require "a complete man, with unqualified dedication, for which he is rewarded by the heavy cross of sober knowledge."

In his *Letters on the Study of Nature*, written in 1845–46, Herzen traces the growth of scientific thought from its origin in the philosophies of Anaxagoras, Democritus, and Pythagoras to the consolidation of the foundations upon which modern science was built. In bold strokes, and with considerable insight, he discusses the relationship of science to the philosophies of Plato, Aristotle, the Epicureans, the Skeptics, Scholasticism, the Renaissance, and the Reformation. He pays most attention to the philosophical origins of modern science. The modern scientific attitude, he believes, can be traced to a blending of the contrasting approaches of Bacon and Descartes, the former relying on induction and experiment, the latter on logical deduction and mathematical calculation. The two were alike in their unqualified opposition to Scholasticism, yet one was the founder of modern empiricism and the other of rationalism. Herzen emphasizes that modern science, unlike the modern arts, was not in truth a break with medieval thought; the growth of science has been uninterrupted. In modern empiricism one can occasionally detect the elements of medieval realism—as, for example, in the work of eighteenth-century French materialists. In modern rationalism, on the other hand, the elements of medieval idealism are obvious, as in the scientific orientations growing out of Schelling's *Naturphilosophie*. While acknowledging the fact that modern science is the result of a happy alliance between moderate empiricism and moderate rationalism, Herzen recognizes the objective nature of the external world and the unity of being and thought.

Herzen wrote his *Letters on the Study of Nature* and his other short observations on science or events of scientific significance at a time when most Russian scholars identified "science" with historical and philological studies, Schellingism, or pure experimentalism. Herzen rejected all these orientations. To him, philosophy and science were inseparable, and the natural and exact disciplines were the most genuine sciences and models for humanistic inquiry. "Philosophy," he claimed, "is the unity of individual sciences, which flow into it and feed it."[108] On the other hand, philosophy that did not rely on the contributions of individual sciences became "a phantom, metaphysics, idealism."

In the history of Russian philosophy Herzen was the champion of a new orientation—a philosophy which was continually stimulated by advances in science and which in turn reinforced science by clarifying its epistemological, logical, and methodological foundations. Even more than any of his predecessors, he scanned Western philosophical thought in pursuit of what he considered to be a sound philosophy of science. He may be considered a philosophical eclectic, of Hegelian derivation, but he was not an imitator. Showing intimate acquaintance with the leading scientific ideas of his time, he stressed the unity of nature and the physical and chemical properties of physiological processes, though he firmly insisted that organic processes cannot be reduced to the laws of physics, chemistry, and mechanics. He believed in a "historical" rather than a static approach to the study of nature: the basic weakness of the descriptive orientation in comparative anatomy arose, according to Herzen, from the fact that it did not view nature as an active interrelationship of the organic and inorganic worlds. Similarly, the study of animal morphology was inadequate because it was static and ahistorical.[109]

Herzen believed in the over-all unity of scientific knowledge, in which individual sciences were but limbs of a single tree. And the body of science, he thought, was universal, crossing the boundaries of individual countries and cultures. The universality of science did not exclude the existence of different attitudes and tendencies within individual nations or cultures, and certainly science could "never be harvested where its seeds have not been sown," for it "must germinate and mature not only in every nation but in every individual as well." On the relationship of the Russian national character to science Herzen had the following to say:

"One of the essential qualities of the Russian character is the extraordinary ease with which it accepts and adopts the fruits of other people's labor. This is managed not only with expediency but also with dexterity. Although this is one of the most human traits of our character, it has a serious drawback: we are rarely capable of sustained and thorough effort. We have become accustomed to making others draw the hot coals out of the fire, and we take it for granted that every truth and discovery should be a result of Europe's hard toil. Europe goes through the strains of burdensome pregnancy, painful childbirth, and exhaustive nursing—and we take the child. We overlook, however, that the infant is an adopted child, that there are no organic ties between it and us."[110]

Arguing for the existence of a close relationship between science and philosophy, for the fact that each culture develops its own philosophical attitudes, Herzen postulates that every people displays its own unique scientific attitudes and proclivities. The French, for example, who combine observation with materialism, are best in the natural sciences and mathematics. The Germans, who are more inclined toward Scholastic dialectics and logical formalism, preoccupy themselves with philosophy, with pure rather than applied science, and with modern theology. The differences in underlying philosophies have led to important differences in the status of the scholars in the two countries. The French scholars emphasize their specialties but do not form a caste; even though they tend to overspecialize, they are usually concerned with practical applications of scientific discoveries and with the popularization of science. The German scholars, on the other hand, do not overspecialize but they do form a caste—"a state by itself, which has nothing to do with Germany."[111]

Herzen felt that Cartesian rationalism could have appeared only in France, just as Lockean empiricism was a pure product of England and Schellingian metaphysical idealism of Germany. It is a pity that he did not write more specifically about the characteristics of Russian views on the interrelationship between science and philosophy. He opposed German idealism, French materialism, and the empiricism of Hume; yet his thinking was influenced mostly by Hegelian critical idealism. Actually, in a blend of Cartesian rationalism and Lockean empiricism he saw the best guaranty of scientific development. In his views on the social status and the social role of the scholar, he was closer to French than to German ideas —the existence of a caste of scientists in Germany was particularly repulsive to him, and he included "the caste of scientists" in his list of the foes of science. He had no kind words for Lomonosov's aloofness, although he was full of praise for Lomonosov's scientific achievements and versatility. He was also impressed with the French emphasis on the popularization of science, in which he saw a cornerstone for the building of a better future. A knowledge of natural science must be disseminated widely and intensively because "no other branch of knowledge trains the mind to advance so firmly, to submit to the truth so readily, to work so conscientiously, and, what is most important, to accept conscientiously the *consequences that follow.*"[112]

Herzen hailed the public lectures of Granovskii and Rouillier during the 1840's as a splendid means of uniting science and society. But in most instances he was more a prophet than an acute observer of current sentiments. He could sense large trends, and his historical significance was primarily in the extent to which he felt—and was able to show—that the dying autocratic system would find in modern science not a friend but a formidable enemy. With due cause, the authorities could be alarmed at Herzen's enthusiastic support of science, for he went so far as to bestow scientific qualities on Saint-Simon's socialist plans for a future community, a community totally incompatible with Russia's social system, which was anchored to the institution of serfdom.

Despite his eloquent dedication to modern natural science, Herzen did not believe in the omnipotence of science or the infallibility of its method. "We see," he wrote, "in all the domains of natural science signs of perplexity: something is lacking, something for which no abundance of facts and theories is a substitute; the truths which it reveals contain a basic inadequacy. Every domain . . . leads inevitably to a painful realization that there is something elusive and irrational in nature . . . and this brings to man an awareness of nature's irresistible strangeness."[113] Science was the highest achievement of intellect and the most bountiful source of the future prosperity of mankind, yet its intellectual compass and methodological precision covered only one aspect of man's unceasing effort to solve the mysteries of nature and society.

As part of his view of philosophy and science as interdependent, Herzen contended that the advance of science leads to a corresponding advance in philosophy, and that philosophy contributes to the progress of science by clarifying its basic premises and bringing its contributions into unified systems of thought; furthermore, neither one can advance unless it supports the other. This view of the symbiotic relationship of science and philosophy was not shared by most of Herzen's Russian contemporaries. The dwindling numbers of Schellingians continued to regard philosophy as the only true science, beside which pure science was but a pale shadow. In an extension of this notion, the Slavophils Khomiakov and Samarin postulated that the inferiority of science stemmed from its preoccupation with the external world. Unlike the Schellingians, however, they limited philosophy to the study of the Russian mind, and they considered religion the basic philosophy: to them Eastern Orthodoxy was the true repository of the cardinal values which gave Russian culture its historical individuality and uniqueness.

While Herzen equated philosophy and science as sources and embodiments of secular wisdom, and while the Schellingians and Slavophils reduced science to a weak sister of philosophy, Osip Senkovskii, an eminent linguist and ethnographer, spoke for still another faction, the uncompromising adversaries of modern philosophy. He was a firm believer in the supremacy of real knowledge and experimental science and a supporter of Uvarov's views on public education, which had little use for secular philosophical thought. Exceedingly conservative and withdrawn from the mainstream of intellectual life, he was ignorant of contemporary trends in both philosophy and science—and, for that matter, of the new developments in Russian literature. He considered philosophy a treacherous way leading either to the corrupting ideas of the French socialists or to the misty realms of the German idealists. He thought that science had gradually moved into the areas which were previously occupied by philosophy, and that philosophy had nothing more to contribute.[114]

Senkovskii—here again one of Herzen's foes of science—reduced science to "observation" and "experiment." He depended on Galileo and Descartes to prove the superiority of science over philosophy, and he knew virtually nothing about the great men and problems of contemporary science. He attacked philosophy because of its susceptibility to ideological bias; he liked the substrata of science—observation and experiment—because of their ideological aloofness. But he stayed a safe distance from the core of modern scientific thought, its theory. Thus he condemned philosophy without advancing the cause of science. His ideas were no serious challenge to Herzen's eloquent defense of the unity of philosophy and science—which Fedor Dostoevskii was convinced represented "the best philosophy, not only in Russia, but in Europe as well."[115]

CHAPTER SEVEN

The Widening Horizons of Natural Science

THE GIANTS OF THE ACADEMY

Also, see author. comm. pp. 353-4; 360.

During his term as Minister of National Education from 1833 to 1849, S. S. Uvarov did his utmost to harmonize the philosophy of public education with the ideology of official nationalism. He tried to eliminate ideologically dangerous subjects from the school curriculum, to staff schools at all levels with native Russian instructors, and to Russianize the educational institutions of the empire's western provinces.

Uvarov was not only Minister of National Education during these years. He was also president of the St. Petersburg Academy of Sciences from 1818 to 1849, and in this capacity he displayed an open distrust of scientific theory. He had, however, a healthy respect for applied science, and believed that the Academy was of importance as a repository of useful facts which could be called on by government agencies for help in solving urgent practical problems. He was also eager to use the Academy as a showcase of Russia's contributions to modern scientific thought.

In 1836 a new charter was issued to replace the one in effect under Alexander I. Uvarov's notions of the purpose of the Academy are everywhere evident in the new charter, which throughout implies that the Academy is more or less an agency of the government. One article reads: "The Academy must keep the government posted on all discoveries made by its members or foreign scholars that will abet the safeguarding of public health or lead to improvements in industry, the arts, manufacturing, trade, and shipping."[1] In order to leave ample time for such work, the Academy was freed of its traditional responsibility of preparing a selected number of students for higher degrees. Academy members were, however, allowed to take part-time teaching positions at universities and other schools of advanced learning so long as this did not interfere with their research assignments—this in recognition of the acute shortage of teachers. In 1848 even those members of the Academy who did not have higher degrees were granted permission to teach in universities.[2]

Uvarov was the first president of the Academy with some background in scholarship. As a young man in diplomatic service, he became personally acquainted with Goethe and Humboldt. He prepared a "Project for an Asian Academy," advocating the founding of a learned society devoted to a systematic study of the history, ethnography, and geography of Asian countries.[3] For this enterprising project, the Göttingen Learned Society elected him an honorary member.[4] An interesting correspondence between Uvarov and Joseph de Maistre, whose comments on the proposed project were invited by Uvarov, shows the two to be in agreement in their dislike of the philosophy of the French Enlightenment, but at odds on the Protestant humanism of Germany, to which de Maistre was also opposed.

When he was made president of the Academy in 1818, Uvarov undertook at once to halt the patent deterioration of this institution. Nationalist though he was, he realized that there were too few outstanding Russian scholars to restore the excellence of the Academy, and he therefore sought help first from the German professors at Dorpat University and then from the universities of Western Europe.

Owing to his thoroughness and a measure of good luck, Uvarov was able to enlist the services of a whole array of truly great scientists who, with a small number of Russian Academicians, ultimately brought the St. Petersburg Academy to new heights of scholarship and won for it a distinguished name among the scientists of Western Europe. The work of these foreign scholars played a large part in the swelling intellectual currents of nineteenth-century Russia. Unlike their eighteenth-century predecessors, the new Academicians assumed a position in the social elite. They were eminently respected men, and their counsel was sought by those who held the reins of government.

The foreign Academicians raised the standards of scientific inquiry beyond all expectation. They also greatly improved the quality of education in the natural sciences at the university level and took part in the formation of learned societies operating outside the Academy. Some of them even altered their scientific interests so as to relate them more specifically to Russia's practical needs.

The most widely acclaimed of these scholars was Karl Ernst von Baer. An Estonian German by birth, he received his higher education in the Universities of Dorpat, Vienna, and Würzburg. He was on the faculty of Königsberg University when he was elected a corresponding member of the St. Petersburg Academy of Sciences in 1826. Two years later he was elected to fill the vacant Academy position in zoology. In 1829 he was made a regular member, but it was not until 1834 that he settled in St. Petersburg permanently and became fully a part of Russian scientific life.

Six years earlier, von Baer's two basic works—*Epistola de ovi mammalium et hominis genesi* and *Über Entwickelungsgeschichte der Thiere* (Part I)—had reported his discovery of the mammalian ovum, presented his "law of corresponding stages," and introduced what was later named comparative embryology. Von Baer's reputation was largely based on these embryological contributions, which of course preceded his complete absorption into the St. Petersburg Academy of Sciences. It was during his long association with this institution, however, that the great scholars of Western Europe began to acknowledge the full value of his contributions by using them in support of their own theories, postulating new scientific laws and opening new avenues of scientific inquiry. It was also during this period that he was honored by foreign learned societies by being added to their membership rolls.

Von Baer's opinions were widely sought and respected, and he earned a certain amount of notoriety by his severe criticisms of some of the great scientific ideas of the time. He disagreed, for example, with some particulars of Schwann's cell theory, and subsequently with Darwinian evolutionism, although his own scientific achievements were important links in the development of both.[5] Despite the mortal blow dealt to the theory of preformism by his contributions, von Baer himself was unwilling to recognize the implicit evolutionism of his embryological conclusions. Like Cuvier, he was not an evolutionist, yet he contributed greatly to the victory of the evolutionist cause. He never outgrew an inclination toward teleological and vitalistic views, absorbed from the *Naturphilosophie,* with which he was briefly identified in the beginning of his scholarly activity and which gave a lasting metaphysical slant to his transformist ideas.

Von Baer's direct contributions to the development of scientific thought in Russia were of many distinct orders. His scientific point of view reinforced trends toward modernization of the scholarly pursuits of Russian natural scientists. When he finally settled in St. Petersburg, his intellectual association with Schelling's and Oken's *Naturphilosophie* had passed, and his historical, experimental, and theoretical orientation had fully crystallized, despite the lingering traces of idealistic metaphysics. Von Baer replaced the mechanistic description of the old-fashioned "natural historian" by a study of organic life in flux, and the idealistic speculations of the proponents of the *Naturphilosophie* by a theory neither alien nor antagonistic to laboratory work. To von Baer, science was not a disconnected mass of facts but a logically coherent summation of ideas interconnected by established causal relationships. He regarded a critical attitude and a reliance on proofs as the imperative ground rules of sound scientific work. According to von Baer, "Science is unending in its sources, limitless in its compass, infinite in its tasks, and unsurpassable in its goals."[6] His arrival in St. Petersburg coincided with the beginning of the rapid decline of Russian Schellingism, although he was not the only cause of this decline.

Von Baer was, in addition, one of the pioneers of the modern approach to the scientific study of Russia's natural resources—the approach which substituted the detailed studies of specialists for the earlier broad approaches of natural historians. In this field he followed the tradition established by Alexander von Humboldt, who, on the direct invitation of Nicholas I, had conducted an expedition in 1829 to the Altai, the Urals, and the Caspian Sea, the most important findings of which had been subsequently published in a monumental work. Soon after his arrival in St. Petersburg von Baer undertook a trip to Novaia Zemlia, and in 1840 he was instrumental in starting a new journal, in the German language, devoted to the study of Russia's natural environment. In addition to these scholarly activities, he found time in the years 1841–52 to lecture in the Medical and Surgical Academy. This institution provided an important stimulus for the remarkable development of physiology in Russia during the second half of the nineteenth century. He was also one of the founders of the Russian Geographical Society and was the first president of the Russian Entomological Society.

In Königsberg, von Baer had concentrated on highly specialized embryological studies; in St. Petersburg, on the other hand, he engaged in diversified scientific pursuits. It has been said that in Germany von Baer studied the animal microcosm and in Russia the human macrocosm—man in the totality of his physical environment. His continued interest in the developmental phases in the history of animal forms gave the two periods a general and consistent theme. In his Russian work von Baer's most noted contributions were in the fields of ichthyology, physical anthropology, geography, and ethnography. His ichthyological work consisted of a general study of the development of fishes, a monographic coverage of the fish world of the Caspian Sea, and detailed suggestions for the improvement of fishing methods.

During the early 1820's, some years before his association with the St. Petersburg Academy, von Baer began to develop an interest in physical anthropology. In 1824 he published *Lectures in Anthropology,* devoted to human anatomy and physiology; a second volume, never written, was to have been a study of the origin, development, and physical characteristics of individual tribes. Von Baer's intensive work in embryology, which brought him instant fame, temporarily interrupted his work in anthropology, but in 1845 he issued a craniological study. In this and subsequent papers he worked out an original and complex set of methodological devices for the measurement and description of the human cranium. In 1851 his essay on "Man in His Natural-Historical Relations" was published as a long chapter (255 pages) in *Russian Fauna,* a work edited by Iu. I. Simashko. This essay was the first study in physical anthropology to appear in the Russian language.[7]

Some of von Baer's particular interests were the origin of racial characteristics, racial classification, the relationship of physical environment to racial features, and the uncorrelated differences between racial and cultural characteristics of human groups.[8] He was simultaneously the founder of physical anthropology in Russia and the creator of a rich tradition of coordinated study of race, language, geography, archaeology, and ethnography.

As a geographer, von Baer was chiefly concerned with the preparation of minutely detailed descriptions of limited areas, but he also formulated a number of laws in physical geography, as, for example, the von Baer law on the asymmetry of the banks of meridional rivers. In addition, he was a historian of geography. One of his most valuable works in this field, a detailed study of the contributions of Peter I to various branches of geography and to the stimulation of geographical research in Russia, demonstrates the thoroughness and scholarly zeal with which von Baer immersed himself in a complicated and challenging phase of Russia's intellectual history.

Hermann Heinrich Hess, born in Geneva but brought to Russia at the age of two, became a member of the St. Petersburg Academy in 1834, the year in which von Baer made Russia his permanent home. In 1825 he received the degree of doctor of medicine from Dorpat University and was immediately sent to Stockholm to specialize in analytical chemistry under the guidance of Berzelius. In the history of modern science, Hess is known as the founder of thermochemistry and as the discoverer of four minerals, one of them named uvarovite in honor of the president of the Academy. As a teacher Hess was in great demand, and he significantly improved the standards of chemistry teaching in the newly founded Technological Institute, as well as in the Main Pedagogical Institute, the Mining Institute, and the Artillery School. He wrote *The Foundations of Pure Chemistry,* the first modern chemistry textbook published in Russia.

Friedrich Georg Wilhelm von Struve, founder of a scholarly dynasty of astronomers matched only (if at all) by the Bernoulli dynasty in mathematics in the preceding century, became a member of the St. Petersburg Academy in 1832. Born in Altona, Germany, he studied physics and astronomy at Dorpat University, where he was appointed a professor in 1813 and where, by his efforts, the University Observatory became the leading institution of its kind in the Russian empire. The Observatory's acquisition of a five-foot refractor by Troughton enabled him to take the position angles of double stars with remarkable precision. The acquisition, in 1825, of the Fraunhofer achromatic lenses permitted him to undertake a review of the entire heavens down to 15 degrees south of the celestial equator. His well-known work *Mensurae micrometricae* provided information on the positions, distances, and relative brightnesses of over three thousand double and multiple stars.

In 1830 the Russian government decided to build an astronomical observatory in Pulkovo, near St. Petersburg, and in 1834 von Struve was appointed its director; the remainder of his unusually rich scientific life was connected with this institution, officially opened in 1839. The modern and versatile equipment of the Pulkovo Observatory and the fruitful scientific work of its expert staff led the American astronomer Benjamin A. Gould to name it "the astronomical capital of the world."[9] An English historian of astronomy noted, in reference to von Struve and the Pulkovo Observatory: "Boundless resources were placed at his disposal, and the institution created by him was acknowledged to surpass all others of its kind in splendor, efficiency, and completeness. Its chief instrumental glory was a refractor of fifteen inches aperture by Merz and Mahler (Fraunhofer's successors), which left the famous Dorpat telescope far behind, and remained long without a rival."[10] Simon Newcomb, the American astronomer, stated: "The two great observatories of Greenwich and Pulkovo, through their rich resources, the excellence of their instruments, and the permanence of their policy, have taken the leading place in supplying material for the fundamental data of astronomy."[11]

The scientific work of the Pulkovo Observatory covered a wide field from highly theoretical stellar astronomy to geodetic measurements. Von Struve's *Études d'astronomie stellaire* (1847) anticipated modern methods of star statistics. The observatory's staff determined the coordinates of many geographical points in various parts of Russia—an undertaking called for not only by military needs but also by the construction and planning of new roads and railways, the development and colonization of newly acquired territories, the expansion of administrative units, and the growing complexity of the economy.[12]

Von Struve was the prime mover behind the measurement of an arc of the meridian from the north coast of Norway to Ismail on the Danube, an undertaking which involved the cooperation not only of a number of Russian astronomers and geodesists but also of Swedish and Norwegian experts. The measurement of the Russo-Scandinavian arc, as it has come to be known in the annals of astronomy, was one of the greatest scientific undertakings of nineteenth-century Russia. Its success stimulated the growth of a whole series of disciplines dependent on astronomy.

Throughout the century, the Pulkovo Observatory, with its splendid facilities, was the leading institution for the practical training of young Russian astronomers; it also supplied experts for various natural-science expeditions sponsored by the Academy or individual government agencies.[13] Many visiting foreign scholars were given the opportunity to work at Pulkovo on their particular problems within the general realm of astronomy. Giovanni Schiaparelli, famous for his discoveries of "canals" on Mars, and the astronomers Schweitzer from Switzerland and Lindhagen of the Swedish Academy of Sciences were among these visitors.

Academician Heinrich F. E. Lenz, who is known to the world of science for propounding Lenz's law on the direction of induced current, was even more intimately associated with Russian science and education than von Baer, Hess, and von Struve. After an early interest in theology, he turned to physics, studying under Georg Parrot at Dorpat University. After his second year at Dorpat, he was recommended by Parrot to serve as a physicist on the world voyage of the sloop *Enterprise,* commanded by O. E. Kotzebue. This adventure took him around Cape Horn to the Pacific Ocean. The scientific assignments of the *Enterprise* staff were secondary in importance to the main objective, which was to discover the shortest trade routes along the shores of China, Kamchatka, and Alaska and to make recommendations on how to eliminate smuggling. For his part, Lenz gained valuable practical experience in collecting oceanographic material and in handling (and even designing) equipment to explore the ocean depths. The voyage, however, did not distract him from his primary interest in physical theory. It was exactly for his promise in the theoretical field that he was elected an adjunct of the St. Petersburg Academy in 1828 and an Academician in 1834.

His scientific successes in the field of electricity were a triumphant manifestation of his scholarly attributes: he combined intuitive insights with an unusual ability to design his own experimental methods and to subject experimental data to mathematical analysis. He devised a formula expressing the dependence of electrical resistance on temperature. He was the first scholar to apply the mathematical method of least squares to an analysis of physical data, a method which had been recommended somewhat earlier by Gauss for the analysis of astronomical data. He preferred to study small problems of theoretical significance, rather than speculate on the larger questions with which many other scientists were preoccupied. His work on these smaller problems showed Lenz to be a master of the experiment. According to Savel'ev, his experiments were always "exceptionally precise, clear, thorough, and convincing."[14]

In the Academy, Lenz soon became a model of the new scientist. His example made the traditional collector of empirical data, who presented findings in a narrative form, quite a thing of the past. His research ventures in cooperation with such accomplished scholars as Moritz Jacobi, Adolph Kupffer, and Aleksandr Savel'ev demonstrated the fruitfulness of joint research at a high level.[15] It was his individual work in electricity and magnetism, however, that earned him his high reputation as one of the pioneers of modern physics. Helmholtz and Sir William Grove depended on his findings in their formulation of the law of the conservation of energy, and both Neumann and Maxwell were aware of his work in electrodynamics.

Lenz's work extended far beyond his laboratory in the Academy of Sciences. In Russia the reverberations of his high standing in international scientific circles were greatly accentuated by his excellent command of the Russian language. In this respect he ran counter to the popular image of typical German Academicians in St. Petersburg; his versatility in Russian made him an important and exceedingly effective link between the Academy and other scientific and educational institutions.

In 1836, two years after his election to full membership in the Academy,

Lenz was appointed professor at St. Petersburg University, thus beginning the ultimately very fruitful relationship between the University and the Academy. For the next twenty-nine years he was associated with the University—for twenty years as dean of the Faculty of Physical and Mathematical Sciences, and thereafter as rector. His lectures were systematic, well documented, and delivered with the mastery of a gifted teacher who knows and loves his subject. He gave courses in the theory of electricity and magnetism, physical geography, and general physics, and improved the teaching of these subjects by the publication of two textbooks. According to one of his outstanding students during the early 1840's, Lenz had the reputation of being the most profound and the most learned professor in St. Petersburg. The public lectures that he delivered on various intricate aspects of the theory of electricity and magnetism were well attended and widely discussed.

It was in large measure Lenz's influence that gave the Russian Geographical Society a scientifically respectable start. When, soon after its founding in 1845, the Society was beset by the old battle between the Germans and the Russians, Lenz was a conciliatory and constructive element. When the Society decided to sponsor an expedition to the North Urals in 1846 to establish the precise boundary between Europe and Asia, Lenz and Kupffer were asked to prepare the instructions for the physical geographers who were to accompany the expedition. In 1847 the Committee on Physical Geography of the Geographical Society began the mass collection of climatic data on all regions of Russia. This committee, of which Lenz was a member, worked for a year on the instructions for procedures to be used in gathering the data. The instructions were sent to all the provinces, and the data thus assembled made possible a systematic study of Russia's climate.

Lenz had a genuine interest in the development of Russia's native scientists and scientific bodies. His encouragement of P. L. Chebyshev and D. I. Mendeleev is a matter of historical record. As dean of the Faculty of Physical and Mathematical Sciences, he greatly improved teaching standards; this division had an almost exclusively Russian faculty, including Korkin in mathematics, and Beketov and Famitsyn in botany. Owing to the diversity of his scholarly activities in the Academy, the Russian Geographical Society, and St. Petersburg University, Lenz acquired many disciples over a broad field—scholars of great accomplishment as well as promising students, for whose welfare he was continually concerned.

OTHER ACADEMICIANS

Von Baer, Hess, von Struve, and Lenz were the giants of the Academy, whose scientific contributions became widely known in the world of scholarship outside Russia. The prestige they brought to this scientific institution easily matched the prestige lent to the Academy in the eighteenth century by Euler's enormous erudition. But more than in the previous century, the prestige of a few was supported by a solid foundation of scholars who, though not world-renowned, were nonetheless scholars of the first rank. One of these was Moritz Jacobi, the founder of galvano-plastics, who was far ahead of his generation in the understanding of the practical application of electricity; in 1838 he constructed an electric motor-boat and sailed it on the Neva. There were also the physicist A. T. Kupffer, the zoologists Johann Brandt and Alexander Middendorff, and numerous classicists, Orientalists, linguists, and historians.

One of the new challenges of this time—or an old challenge once again taken up—was the study of Siberia. Curiously, it came, in part, from outside Russia, mainly through the publication of two important works by Germans. The first of these works was Karl Ritter's *Die Erdkunde,* never actually finished although it ran to twenty volumes (the last of which appeared in the year of his death, 1859). Nineteen of the twenty volumes were devoted to Asia. The central thesis of Ritter's work is that the geography of individual continents or countries must be studied as an integrated structure of interrelated and interdependent physical features. He regarded geography as a kind of physiology and comparative anatomy of the earth—a study of the morphological and functional parts of topography, united into larger physical and historical systems. The Academy was immediately attracted to Ritter's work because of its concern with Russian Asia as well as its unusual approach, and one of the first undertakings of the Russian Geographical Society was the translation of *Die Erdkunde* into Russian.

The second great work which stimulated the Academy's renewed interest in Siberia was Alexander von Humboldt's *Asie Centrale* (1843). This work, dealing with configurations of mountain chains and "comparative climatology," illustrated a new style of analysis of geographical data, and one very close to the interests of the St. Petersburg Academicians. Humboldt's book also showed the wide range of specialized knowledge required by modern students of geography. It was a synthesis of detailed information based on competent astronomical observations, collections of minutely classified organic and inorganic specimens, the geological analysis of soil, climatological charts, surveys of gold and platinum deposits, and various theories concerning the formation of mountain ranges.

Humboldt came to Russia in 1829, immediately after his famous lecture series at the University of Berlin which was eventually enlarged into his most celebrated work, *Kosmos* (1845–62). These lectures "proclaimed a new age" marked by "a protest against the excesses of speculation." They praised "the empirical sciences, descriptions of the world, and the study of history" for their great contributions to undermining the foundations of the old order.[16] The new science was opposed equally to the unthoughtful empiricism of early natural historians and to airy philosophical speculations without empirical foundations; and it was full of implications that tended to erode the ideological structure of the old social system and to promote the questioning of many previously unchallenged values.

The zoologist Alexander Middendorff, an Estonian, was the leader of the Academy's Siberian explorations. In 1837, upon receiving his doctorate at Dorpat University, Middendorff was appointed professor at Kiev University. In 1840 he was a member of Karl von Baer's expedition to Lapland, where he collected ornithological and other zoological material and made detailed geological observations. The impressive amount of scientific material derived from this expedition was convincing proof that a similar study, coordinating the efforts of natural scientists, might profitably be undertaken in the vast stretches of northern and eastern Siberia.

In 1843, the year of Humboldt's *Asie Centrale,* an Academic expedition led by Middendorff began its work in Siberia. It is generally agreed that this was the largest and most fruitful expeditionary scientific endeavor sponsored by the Academy in the nineteenth century.[17] It took no less than three decades for a dozen scholars to scrutinize and coordinate the material collected by Middendorff's expedition: Lenz interpreted the magnetic observations; Helmersen, the geological materials; Göppert, the paleobotanical materials; and Alexander Keyserling, the mollusk fossils. The result of this collective work was the four-volume *Travels in the Far North and in Eastern Siberia,* published between 1848 and 1875, a truly monumental work. This study was known as the first scientific encyclopedia of Siberia, and in the quality of its scholarship it had no competitor before the end of the nineteenth century. Paradoxically, Middendorff's expedition and others of the 1840's and 1850's contained fewer native Russian scholars than those of the Catherinean age—one of many reasons why the label "German Academy" was commonly used by Russians in scientific circles.

Middendorff's books were the beginning of a modern scientific literature on Siberia and Central Asia that grew to huge proportions during the second half of the nineteenth century. Part of the explanation for this revived and expanded interest was the territorial expansion of the Empire during the same period. In the 1850's the Amur area was annexed by Russia; the Usuriisk and Littoral areas were annexed in the subsequent years, followed by vast stretches of Central Asia. The newly acquired territories became the subject of intensive scientific inquiry sponsored either by the government or by private organizations. The scientific investigation of Asian territories by the members of the Academy now assumed even broader scope. Since the issuing of the 1836 charter the Academy had embraced the study of Oriental languages as well as ethnography and linguistics, and Academicians in these fields did excellent work with the Siberian expeditions. The works of Leopold Schrenck in the ethnography of the Amur Basin tribes, for example, and Otto Böhtlingk's study of the Iakut language have become classics in their respective disciplines.

Middendorff and his colleagues not only expanded the range of scientific interests in the Academy; they also introduced more modern research techniques and theories. In processing the materials gathered by the expeditionary teams, the scholars were now guided by the methods, theoretical criteria, and insights of such new disciplines as comparative craniology, microscopic anatomy, comparative zoology, zoological geography, paleontology, applied zoology, and animal physiology.[18]

Johann Brandt, who joined the Academy in 1831 as an accomplished scholar, typified the new Academician-naturalist; instead of traveling in search of new material, he concentrated on a critical assessment and coordination of data collected by earlier expeditions. As a result, he produced numerous monographic studies of living or fossilized species of Siberian vertebrates, including the mammoth, the rhinoceros, and the lamantin, which earned him an honorary membership in Western Europe's most renowned naturalistic societies. His works contain precise comparative-osteological analyses which produced valuable taxonomic results.

Although Uvarov had tried in a number of ways to increase the number of Russian professors in the universities, the membership of the Academy was overwhelmingly foreign until well into the second half of the nineteenth century. In 1840 there were twenty-eight full Academicians, of whom only one was Russian and three Ukrainian. A few, notably the mathematicians Paul Fuss and Edward Collins (both of whom were members of the distinguished Fuss and Euler families), were Russians by birth but not by ancestry.[19] In a deliberate move to strengthen the Russian representation in the country's highest scientific body, Nicholas I—against Uvarov's wishes—signed an order in 1841 that the Imperial Russian Academy, predominantly Russian, be combined with the St. Petersburg Academy of Sciences as a special department. The newly expanded Academy of Sciences consisted of three departments: the Department of Physics and Mathematics, the Department of Russian Language and Literature, and the Department of History and Philology. This organization remained virtually unchanged until 1927.

All but one of the sixteen members of the Imperial Russian Academy were Russian or Ukrainian. Many of them—V. A. Zhukovskii, I. A. Krylov, and P. A. Viazemskii, among others—were literary figures whose interests had little to do with those of the Academy of Sciences. Most of those who became active Academicians were undistinguished, usually without much training, and steeped in antiquarianism. Two of the new members were high-ranking churchmen with little affinity for scholarship. Pogodin and Shevyrev, two ardent proponents of Uvarov's official nationalism, became members of the Academy of Sciences without having been members of the Imperial Russian Academy.

The Department of Russian Language and Literature—the Second Department, as it was usually referred to—was subjected to a more direct control by the Minister of National Education than the other two departments. The functions of the Second Department were threefold: (a) to study Russian grammar and to work on a Russian dictionary; (b) to undertake the necessary preliminary studies for the preparation of a comparative Slavic dictionary; and (c) to study Slavic philology in general and the history of Russian letters. It was not until the next generation that this department was fully integrated into the Academy of Sciences and that the impact of its publications began to be strongly felt. *Materials for a Dictionary of the Old Russian Language* was one of the first important productions of this department.

During the 1840's, interest in science increased at a comparatively rapid pace. Some of this interest was genuine, but some was merely part of a new vogue—the dilettantism that evoked Herzen's wrath. Most of this interest, whether earnest or trifling, was without effective direction and purpose. Undoubtedly, a larger Russian representation in the Academy would have strengthened the ties between this learned body and the enlightened public, and might have helped to direct the enthusiasm for science into more solid channels.

Foreign scholars could not so easily establish intimate relations with the larger community, and some, of course, had no desire to make the effort, preferring to retain their foreign ways and foreign friends. The Pulkovo Observatory, for example, was staffed by foreigners for a whole generation. An intensified chauvinism within the Russian middle class undoubtedly contributed to the comparative isolation of many Academicians. At all events, few were willing to surround themselves with Russian disciples, to give public lectures, or even to contribute articles in the Russian language to the Academy's *Scientific Notes of the First and Third Departments*—which, significantly, was published for only three years (1840–42) during the twenty-eight-year period 1823–51.[20]

It has been asserted that the Academy discriminated against Russian scholars and that in this policy it was supported by Uvarov, who was aware of the incompatibility of many principles, laws, and working hypotheses of modern science with the ideology and the social order of feudal Russia; it is said that he wanted to create an isolated sanctuary for scientific theory without forfeiting the advantages of applied science. Although it is impossible to prove that Uvarov's ideological fears were directly responsible for the small number of Russians in the Academy, it is certain that the Academy would not have attained the lofty heights of scientific achievement nor the prominence in the world of scholarship that it did during the second quarter of the nineteenth century if it had depended for its membership primarily on native Russian scholars. With some notable exceptions, Russia was not yet ready to produce scholars of the stature of a Struve, a von Baer, a Lenz, or a Hess. The Academy of this period did not represent the status of "Russian science"; it represented the high status of science in Russia.

MATHEMATICS: THE CLIMAX OF SCIENTIFIC ACHIEVEMENT

In mathematics—"the queen of sciences"—Russia needed no foreign scholars, in the Academy or outside. In the second quarter of the nineteenth century the Academy elected three mathematicians into its ranks— all Russian or Ukrainian. The Russian mathematician of this period was of a new kind. The eighteenth-century mathematicians were men of talent and assiduity, but they were too busy bringing modern scientific knowledge to Russia to engage in original research. The mathematicians of the nineteenth century, however, earned their positions in the Academy after first gaining recognition in the West as scholars of originality and energy. This was especially true of Mikhail Ostrogradskii and Pafnutii Chebyshev, who joined the Academy at the beginning and the end, respectively, of the reign of Nicholas I.

Another mathematician, Viktor Buniakovskii, though less illustrious than Ostrogradskii, Chebyshev, and the great Nikolai Lobachevskii, was granted a doctorate of mathematics in 1825 by the Faculté des Sciences in Paris for his great promise—which he never fully realized, despite his creditable work in the theory of numbers and the theory of probability. His *Lexicon of Pure and Applied Mathematics* (never actually completed) did much to enrich and standardize mathematical terminology in Russia. In 1846 he published his most important work, *The Foundations of the Mathematical Theory of Probability,* a lengthy study tracing the development of this branch of mathematics since Pascal and Fermat. The book was so well written that Gauss used it as a way of learning the Russian language. Buniakovskii is remembered primarily for his efforts to find a practical application for the theory of probability, particularly to the fixing of insurance rates and the recruiting of soldiers.[21]

Buniakovskii was not only a recognized scholar, some of whose works were translated into foreign languages, but also a great teacher. He is, indeed, a classic example of the type of great scholar-educator still rare in Russia in the mid-nineteenth century. His lectures at St. Petersburg University and in several professional schools were noted for their lucidity and for their colloquial but graceful style. One of his students commented: "Buniakovskii was the most brilliant lecturer in the whole country. He had a charming manner, yet was very strict—as was fitting a man of knowledge. He lectured with astonishing clarity and precision."[22]

Ostrogradskii, Chebyshev, and Lobachevskii towered over their Russian peers by the originality and impact of their achievements in varied fields of mathematics. They spanned three generations, and yet for more than a decade their creative work was concurrent. They gave a herculean impetus and a vital continuity to the evolution of mathematical thought in Russia.

Coming out of different traditions, they also made their contributions in different fields. Ostrogradskii was loyal to the end to the French mathematical tradition from Legendre to Fourier, Cauchy, and Poisson, which emphasized the refinement of the tools of analysis and their application to the study of various physical sciences. Chebyshev combined the Eulerian concentration on the theory of numbers with the French interest in the application of mathematical analysis; but he, like Buniakovskii, also recognized the potential value of the theory of probability for the study of various theoretical and practical problems at a time when Western mathematicians were ready to abandon it as unreliable and unscientific. It was because of him and the formidable mathematical school of which he was the official progenitor that probability theory—in our time one of the mathematical cornerstones of theoretical physics—was subject to continuous study and elaboration in Russia and attracted the attention of the country's leading scholars. Lobachevskii, the creator of the first non-Euclidean geometry, developed under the strong influence of the newly formed German mathematical tradition, which had produced Gauss and which demanded that scholars exercise unprecedented rigor in logic and the formulation of thought and a skeptical attitude toward the validity of time-honored postulates.

The French tradition, to which Ostrogradskii completely and Chebyshev in part belonged, was committed to an elaboration and refinement of the eighteenth-century heritage; the German orientation, which attracted Lobachevskii, challenged it and sought new openings in the labyrinth of mathematical thought. This differentiation had, of course, only rough outlines and was by no means absolute.

Another difference between the three great mathematicians lay in the circumstances of their recognition by the world. Ostrogradskii became a recognized scholar at the age of twenty-four when Cauchy acknowledged some of his original work in *A Note on Definite Integrals*. Chebyshev was thirty-nine before he began reaping honors; at that age he was named a corresponding member of the Académie des Sciences in Paris. Lobachevskii, whose ideas were truly revolutionary, received but little recognition during his lifetime. Revolutionary ideas do not generally win immediate applause—indeed, the greatest mathematician of the century, Gauss, preferred to leave his own papers on non-Euclidean geometry unpublished rather than expose them to the vituperation of his tradition-bound contemporaries.

Lobachevskii, as a matter of fact, though considerably older than Ostrogradskii, was still an obscure professor at Kazan University when the young Ostrogradskii won fame in Paris. Ostrogradskii, a Ukrainian, was born in 1801 in a village near Khar'kov. He received his secondary education in a boarding school for poor gentry and attended Khar'kov University before going on to Paris. He was fortunate in studying mathematics in France during one of its most flourishing periods: celestial and analytical mechanics, mathematical physics, and several neighboring areas were popular lines of inquiry, and they quickly attracted the attention of the young Russian. So brilliant was his work that the Académie des Sciences accepted and subsequently published his paper on wave-motions of liquids in cylindrical containers. Ostrogradskii's fame preceded him to St. Petersburg, and his career seemed certain of success—despite a secret police order, of which he was probably unaware, that he be kept under surveillance. He was elected an adjunct of the St. Petersburg Academy in 1828, a corresponding member in 1830, and a full member in 1831.

Possessed of seemingly boundless energy, Ostrogradskii did not limit his work to the Academy alone. In 1829 he gave a series of public lectures in celestial mechanics to a limited enrollment of thirty students; they were of such high quality as to receive the praise of Arago and Poisson, and subsequently to be published (in 1831) in St. Petersburg, although in the French language. Many of his projects in the Academy were practical ones: he was a member of special commissions for the introduction of the Gregorian calendar into Russia, for the determination of geographical coordinates, and for studying methods of piping adequate water supplies to St. Petersburg. In 1828 he joined the faculty of the Naval Cadet School as a teacher of mathematics and descriptive geometry, and in 1830 he lectured on analytical mechanics at the Communications Institute. Later he also taught at the Artillery School, the Main Pedagogical Institute (which had been re-established in 1828), and the Engineering School.

As a lecturer Ostrogradskii was a great success, even though it took him many years to become fluent in Russian (Ukrainian was his native tongue). He was particularly effective in the schools in which students were prepared to cope with higher mathematics. His lectures at the Naval Cadet School, for example, gradually became so advanced that they covered Abel's work on algebraic functions and Sturm's studies in the methods of isolating the roots of real equations. In the lower classes of the Engineering School, where the students had little curiosity or appreciation of mathematics, Ostrogradskii fell back on more lively topics, such as the military campaigns of Julius Caesar, Hannibal, and Napoleon.[23] But he wrote a two-volume textbook on algebraic and transcendental analysis for the benefit of his students at the Naval Cadet School. His teaching in the Communications Institute was also of a high level. V. A. Panaev, one of the Institute's eminent graduates, made the following observations about Ostrogradskii:

"Ostrogradskii lectured in our school on analytical mechanics, a science which was very dear to him, and which was indebted to him for the solution of one of its basic problems in general motion, on which all the great geometers of the last century and the present century had worked without success. . . .

"He loved this science also because it treats, along with the totality of the fundamental laws of physics, the basic principles of the creation of the world. Without a full understanding of this science, every philosophy is only idle talk. . . .

"All serious young men waited for Ostrogradskii's lectures with feverish impatience, as if they provided heavenly manna. To listen to his lectures was true joy, just as if superb poetry were being read to us. He was not only a great mathematician, but, if the expression is correct, a philosopher-geometer, capable of reading the minds of his listeners. The clarity and succinctness of his presentations were astonishing; he troubled his audience with no calculations, but kept their attention constantly affixed to the essence of the problem under discussion. He seriously endeavored to make it possible for the students to follow and understand him. . . .

"In the year in which I took his course, he lectured with rare enthusiasm, probably because in our class, made up of one hundred persons, there were at least fifteen students who not only understood him fully but also appreciated the treasure which he was sharing with us. Subsequently, when the Institute was reorganized to admit boys from eleven to twelve years of age, and when the students' aptitude for mathematics was no longer taken into consideration—and, also, when mathematical education was limited and Ostrogradskii's method of appraising students' achievements was ignored —he naturally lost his enthusiasm for the Institute. Then he compressed his lectures and began to treat his students as children."[24]

It is unfortunate that Ostrogradskii was never given the opportunity to teach in one of the country's universities, where he could have given a much fuller expression to his challenging ideas. Throughout most of his life his scientific work was of necessity on a plane widely separated from his teaching. It was also unfortunate that he wrote all his original scientific papers in French. According to N. D. Brashman, a contemporary who taught mathematics at Moscow University, "If Ostrogradskii had written in the Russian language, our mathematical literature would have occupied an honored place in Europe; but all his works addressed to the world of scholarship are written in French. It is to be hoped that our famous geometer will leave for us a Russian monument worthy of his rare gifts."

In the same article, Brashman prophesied that in the future people abroad would read not only Russian poets but also Russian geometers.[25]

Some other scholars considered Ostrogradskii's extensive teaching a drain on his energy; according to V. V. Bobynin, later in the century, it was responsible "for the comparatively small number of his published scientific works."[26] Bobynin, however, was evidently not aware of a whole series of papers which Ostrogradskii read before his colleagues in the Academy, some of which are still unpublished.[27]

Ostrogradskii's broad concern was that of expanding the mathematical basis and the methodology of various branches of physics. He studied the motion of elastic bodies, waves on the surfaces of fluids, the distribution of heat, and the theory of percussion, but always with the idea of working out a new mathematical approach or refining an old one. As a scholar, he handled specific problems but sought to cast his answers in terms of general theory.

In 1831 the Academy published a paper by Ostrogradskii—submitted three years earlier—on the theory of heat, which for the first time stated the formula relating the volume-integral to the surface-integral. The same formula was more fully developed by Ostrogradskii in a paper read in the Academy in 1834 and published in 1838. Maxwell, in his major work on electricity and magnetism of 1881, mentioned Ostrogradskii's original contribution to this theorem.[28] Ostrogradskii's paper was subsequently translated into English and reprinted in Isaac Todhunter's *History of the Progress of the Calculus of Variations* (1861), along with papers by such great mathematicians as Lagrange, Gauss, Poisson, Legendre, and Cauchy.[29] Even before that, however, Ostrogradskii had been elected a member of several learned societies in the Western countries, including the American Academy of Arts and Sciences.

Ostrogradskii's reputation in the West was an enormous boost to the morale of Russian scientists as well as an inducement and encouragement to young Russians contemplating scientific careers. Quite as important, however, was its effect on the relationship between traditional and modern mathematics in Russia. Ostrogradskii was the man of the day, admired not only by fellow mathematicians and scientists in general but also by legions of students, who, as civil servants, spread his fame to the most remote sections of the country. In the Academy, during the third, fourth, and fifth decades of the century, he enjoyed unquestioned authority in such important matters as the selection of mathematical papers for annual prizes, the nomination of adjuncts and Academicians in mathematics and related fields, and the acceptance of mathematical papers for publication.

Ostrogradskii made one serious error in judgment by ruling in 1832 that the Academy should reject for publication Lobachevskii's *Elements of Geometry*, which had been printed in installments in the *Kazan Messenger* in 1829–30. Ostrogradskii felt that the book was not sufficiently precise and that its "new method" consisted of two definite integrals, one of which was already known and "was easily deducible from the elementary principles of the calculus of integration" and the second of which was false.[30] Just how much Ostrogradskii should be blamed—if at all—for the slowness with which Lobachevskii's theories were accepted is a question that cannot now be answered with any certainty. Ostrogradskii continued to direct harsh criticism at Lobachevskii's scholarly work until his death, but his attitude was shared by many other scholars. Indeed, he was typical of many critics in all ages: he lived in his time, while Lobachevskii was a generation ahead of it.

LOBACHEVSKII

In background, training, and scholarly interests, Nikolai Lobachevskii was very much unlike Ostrogradskii. Ostrogradskii came from the gentry; Lobachevskii was born into the family of a poor government employee. Ostrogradskii studied under eminent scholars in Paris; Lobachevskii never went farther than Kazan University. Ostrogradskii worked in the leading intellectual center of Russia, to which all the important scientific ideas from the West first came; Lobachevskii worked in remote Kazan, on the periphery of the West, in what was for years the easternmost university in Europe. And, of course, Ostrogradskii was eminently respected and rewarded, whereas Lobachevskii died without having one word of public approval from any of the leading mathematicians of his time.

"Despite the fact," said A. V. Vasil'ev, "that Lobachevskii presented his theory in several ways, he received no recognition during his life from the scholars of Kazan, nor, for that matter, from anyone in Russia."[31] In the West, Gauss alone recognized—in a letter to Schumacher written on November 28, 1846, but not published during his or Lobachevskii's life—the gigantic contributions of the Kazan University professor, presented "with masterly skill in the true geometrical spirit."[32] Ostrogradskii was a great and imposing ambassador of Russian scholarship; Lobachevskii was an obscure scholar, not even noticed by his own countrymen, much less their spokesman. But, in the words of a modern Russian scholar, whereas Ostrogradskii had a great mathematical talent, Lobachevskii was a genius. Ostrogradskii was made great by society—by the intellectual impact he made on men of his time and by the perceptive scientific ideas he presented in his works. Lobachevskii has been made great by history—by the great new ideas that came out of the intellectual stream which he originated but did not live to see become a recognized part of modern scientific thought.

Lobachevskii was hailed as a true giant by succeeding generations of mathematicians. Beltrami, Klein, and Poincaré confirmed the remarkable logical consistency of his non-Euclidean geometry; Einstein added the concept of relativity of time to Lobachevskii's and Riemann's relativity of space; and J. J. Sylvester, looking into the philosophical implications of his work, called Lobachevskii the Copernicus of geometry. According to William Kingdon Clifford: "What Vesalius was to Galen, what Copernicus was to Ptolemy, that was Lobachevskii to Euclid. There is, indeed, a somewhat intructive parallel between the last two cases. Copernicus and Lobachevskii . . . [each] brought about a revolution in scientific ideas so great that it can only be compared with that wrought by the other."[33] According to D. I. Mendeleev, Russia's famed chemist: "Geometrical knowledge has formed the foundation of all the exact sciences, and the originality of Lobachevskii's geometry has marked the dawn of independent scientific development in Russia."

Lobachevskii built a new geometry on the basis of a parallel postulate contradicting Euclid's. The fifth postulate of Euclidean geometry states that through a given point there is only one parallel to a given line; Lobachevskii constructed his geometry on the proposition that through a given point there is more than one parallel to a given line. His work demonstrated that there are geometries which are different from Euclid's but just as valid. For his day this was a claim of colossal proportions. At that time, as Helmholtz had stated, geometry had more logical unity and a larger assemblage of time-sanctified and incontrovertible facts than any other science.[34] The ten axioms of Euclid's geometry were considered so self-evident that no "responsible" scholar dared question them. The colossal scientific discoveries of the Newtonian era added new strength to Euclid's system. Some of Euclid's postulates—particularly the parallel postulate— had troubled scholars throughout the ages because of the difficulty of finding satisfactory proofs of them. But because scholars worked entirely within the framework of Euclidian geometry, trying to bolster its inner logical unity and consistency, the possibility of a non-Euclidean geometry was overlooked.

The Hungarian mathematician Bolyai, working independently of Lobachevskii, arrived at basically the same ideas, and he, too, was ignored. Both Lobachevskii and Bolyai challenged the most firmly established and what was regarded as the most complete science—the authority for which stemmed mostly from the obviousness of its basic axioms. It was, therefore, not so much the stubbornness or unimaginativeness of his contemporaries as it was the sanctity of classical geometry that was Lobachevskii's real foe. So great, indeed, was the sanctity of classical geometry that although Lobachevskii was admired and respected by his students, none of them followed the mathematical course that he charted.

It was easy enough for the traditionalists to reject Lobachevskii's geometry because there was no proof, either practical or theoretical, of its applicability; it seemed no more than a sort of intellectual exercise. Non-Euclidean geometry could seem of value only when succeeding generations, according to Morris Kline, "were ultimately compelled to appreciate the fact that *systems of thought based on statements about physical space are different from that physical space.*" (As we shall see later, however, Lobachevskii did not subscribe to this epistemological orientation.) Kline also comments perceptively that non-Euclidean geometry "rudely thrust mathematics off the pedestal of truth" but, in return, "set it free to roam," and thus bore out Georg Cantor's statement that "the essence of mathematics is its freedom."[35]

Non-Euclidean geometry, of which the Lobachevskiian system is one variety, achieved this liberating feat not because it invalidated Euclid's postulates, but because it showed that other geometries could exist which are equally valid. As a result of scientific ideas developed in the wake of Lobachevskii's postulates, geometry has become a "set of conventions." Today, "no conceivable experiment can supply evidence to show that one such geometry is less able than another to serve as a vehicle for formulating a theory of spatial measurement."[36] Newtonian mechanics, concerned with the motion of bodies in absolute space, achieved its great feats by relying on Euclidean geometry as the theory of space measurement. Einstein's theory of general relativity, on the other hand, dispensed with absolute space and Euclidean geometry.

From the vantage of the present, it is easy to point to the great reorientation in mathematics—as a science, a philosophy, and an instrument—which Lobachevskii spearheaded. It is much more difficult to explain in significant detail why he became a rebel against Euclid. The sophistication and mathematical depth of his arguments show that he was a scholar endowed with a great intellect, a rebellious spirit, a stubborn determination to stand in defense of his ideas, and, above everything else, high educational accomplishment. His intellectual biography, however, has not yet been fully told, and many events of importance for understanding his life are no doubt forever lost. Unrecognized by his generation, he did not present an attractive and challenging subject for biographers, nor was he even much mentioned in personal reminiscences.

It has only recently been established that Lobachevskii was born in 1792 rather than in 1793, as thought by earlier writers. In 1802 he entered the Kazan gymnasium, and five years later he enrolled in Kazan University (then only a few years old), planning to prepare for a medical career. During the first two years of Lobachevskii's study, the University had the good fortune to acquire as professors four distinguished Germans: Johann Bartels in pure mathematics, Kaspar Renner in applied mathematics, F. X. Bronner in physics, and Joseph Littrow in astronomy. These ambitious and enlightened men brought advanced thought as well as modern educational concepts to Kazan, and their work converted the University from an isolated intellectual outpost on the threshold of Siberia to a thriving cultural center alert to modern scientific developments. Under their tutelage, Lobachevskii plunged headlong into the study of mathematics.

Of the four, it was Bartels who had the most profound and lasting influence on the keen student of mathematics. Bartels was a highly skilled mathematician, known more for his teaching ability than for his theoretical work. He introduced his students to Euler's differential and integral calculus, Lagrange's analytical mechanics, Monge's studies in the application of analysis to geometry, and Gauss's *Disquisitiones arithmeticae*.[37] As a young man, he had taught the twelve-year-old Gauss, who even at that young age "was already looking askance at the foundations of Euclidean geometry" and by sixteen "had caught his first glimpse of a geometry other than Euclid's."[38] Although Gauss's papers on non-Euclidean geometry were not published until after his death in 1855, it is highly probable that Bartels was familiar with this special interest of his former pupil and that he passed some of it on to Lobachevskii. It seems certain, however, that even though Lobachevskii may have heard something of Gauss's non-Euclidean geometry from Bartels, he did not receive any inkling as to how the problem could be treated mathematically, for he did not take up the problem of a new geometry until the mid-1820's; during his school years and for a decade or so thereafter, he followed the current mathematical fashion in attempting to find incontrovertible proofs for the parallel postulate. Undoubtedly, Bartels had told Lobachevskii about Gauss's personal determination to strengthen the rigor of mathematical analysis by establishing a more skeptical attitude toward "proofs" and the uses of individual postulates.

Ostrogradskii was identified with the work of French mathematicians who aspired to add the finishing bricks to the edifice of Newtonian celestial mechanics. Lobachevskii was identified with the initial Gaussian orientation in one important respect: he, too, was convinced that mathematics should straighten out its own house—refine, enforce, and verify its own concepts and axioms—before it placed itself at the disposal of so-called applied sciences.[39] Ostrogradskii challenged no established authorities, but Lobachevskii was afraid of no one, from ancient Euclid to modern Legendre.

As a student, Lobachevskii was a rebel and subject to many reprimands by school authorities. He was accused on different occasions of being "obstinate," "impertinent," "overly self-centered," and inclined toward atheism.[40] Two events which occurred in 1811 shed light on the personality and potentialities of the young scholar. On August 23 of that year the University Council had a request from the superintendent of the Kazan school district "to express to Nikolai Lobachevskii, the *leader* in unruly behavior, our regrets that his irresponsible actions overshadow his superior abilities." At about the same time, Bartels, Littrow, Hermann, and Bronner recommended that Lobachevskii be granted a Magister's degree in recognition of his "extraordinary successes and gifts in the mathematical and physical sciences."[41] One guesses that these two events, rather than being antithetical, show a good deal about Lobachevskii's character—he was a man with great genius and no respect for tradition-bound authority, either of men or of ideas.

Lobachevskii began his teaching career in 1812, the year following his graduation from Kazan University. His first classes were in geometry for government employees, who, in accordance with the law of 1809, were required to have college degrees in order to advance in the civil service. Just what kind of geometry Lobachevskii gave his students is unknown, but he continued to specialize in geometry after becoming a regular lecturer at the University in 1814, when he also lectured in physics and astronomy. He taught geometry, both plane and spherical, from his own notes.

In 1823 Lobachevskii sent the manuscript of a textbook in geometry—which contained three "proofs" of Euclid's parallel postulate—to Academician Nicolaus Fuss for criticism. A. V. Vasil'ev suggests that the textbook was not published because of Fuss's recommendation against it and also because of Lobachevskii's own dissatisfaction with it. Despite the "proofs" of the parallel postulate which he advanced, Lobachevskii admitted in the manuscript that there were actually no conclusive proofs.[42] It might well have been that Lobachevskii, in trying to complete the manuscript satisfactorily, abandoned the search for proofs of the absolute validity of the fifth postulate and began looking instead for logical evidence to demonstrate that its applicability was not necessarily universal and that it was therefore not a "postulate" but a "convention." A remark he made in 1825 is significant: "In synthesis [i.e., in the geometrical method] will always be hidden rich sources of ideas for mathematicians, but these can be discovered and utilized only by men of genius."[43]

In 1826 Lobachevskii read to his colleagues at Kazan University a paper concerned with what he called an "imaginary geometry." The essence of this unpublished paper (of which, unfortunately, not one copy survives) was incorporated into the *Elements of Geometry*, which appeared in installments in the *Kazan Messenger* (published by the University) in 1829–30. This work marked a definite point in Lobachevskii's thought— a turn from the attempt to perfect the structure of Euclidean geometry to an ambitious effort to build an entirely new geometry.

Apparently in hopes of giving his revolutionary ideas wider circulation, Lobachevskii submitted the *Elements of Geometry* to the St. Petersburg Academy for possible republication in one of its journals. Not only did the Academy reject it, under Ostrogradskii's persuasion, but the journal *Son of the Fatherland* soon afterward published an unsigned and highly critical review of the work, which went out of its way to make it, as well as its author, an object of public ridicule. The emphasis in the review on what it said was Lobachevskii's use of an integral that "was already known" makes it very probable that Ostrogradskii was the man behind this attack —if not as its writer, then as its source of information.[44]

One detail in Ostrogradskii's criticism as submitted to the Academy seems to have impressed Lobachevskii: Ostrogradskii said, and many people would have agreed with him, that Lobachevskii was so careless about the manner in which he presented his ideas that they were "unintelligible."[45] At any rate, Lobachevskii revised the work into his *New Elements of Geometry*, and it is this second work which is usually considered the most comprehensive presentation of the first non-Euclidean geometry. It appeared in the *Scientific Journal of Kazan University* in the years 1835–38. Lobachevskii made no further attempt to communicate with the Academy of Sciences, but he did try very hard to reach the scholarly world outside Russia, by publishing in both French and German. With the sole exception of Gauss, however, he found no responsive readers.[46]

Lobachevskii was elected rector of Kazan University in 1827, at the age of thirty-four. The honor may possibly have been in recognition of his genius and the revolutionary geometrical theories expounded in his 1826 paper, but it is more likely that it came as a reward for his dedicated work as a member of the library and construction committees and for his staunch resistance to government pressure during the Magnitskii era. In 1833, when the superintendent of the Kazan district recommended to the Minister of National Education that Lobachevskii continue to serve as rector, he supported his recommendation by praising Lobachevskii's intimate knowledge of the school's construction program rather than enumerating his scholarly attainments.[47]

Lobachevskii's intellectual interests went far beyond mathematics, and at an early age he was aware of the important epistemological questions brought out by Kant, particularly in the *Critique of Pure Reason*. Kant regarded the category of space as subjective and absolute at the same time: *subjective* because it was "an intuition *a priori*," injected into, rather than derived from, experience; and *absolute* because it had invariable and universal applicability. Though this definition of space as an absolute category of thought implied philosophical acceptance of Euclidian geometry, Kant was generally considered the champion of a "critical philosophy" which called for a thorough reassessment of the very foundations upon which Western knowledge and values were built. Through Professor Bronner, who first brought Kant's ideas to Kazan University, and A. S. Lubkin, who joined the philosophical faculty at the University in 1812, Lobachevskii became acquainted with Kantian ideas. Lubkin was the first to make a systematic presentation in Russian of Kant's philosophy, although he personally took exception to some of Kant's concepts.[48]

Kazan University at the time of Magnitskii's vicious crusade was known as the stronghold of Russian Kantianism. Magnitskii regarded this philosophy as a source of what he identified as pseudo-science, a science totally alien to the Russian spirit; he was more or less indifferent to Kantian epistemology, but he was disturbed by Kant's humanism and his defense of human dignity. Lobachevskii, who was at that time dean of the Faculty of Physics and Mathematics, survived the troubles, but two of the University's promising professors—I. E. Sreznevskii in philosophy and G. I. Solntsev—lost their teaching jobs because of their Kantian beliefs.

The attack on Kant came not only from those who saw in his system a codification of the new humanistic outlook and a challenge to the sacred values of the autocracy, but also from a sophisticated group of professional philosophers who could not accept transcendental idealism as an epistemological orientation. Lubkin stated in 1805 that he could not subscribe to the concepts of time and space as *a priori* categories. M. T. Kachenovskii, the editor of the *Messenger of Europe*, carried in his journal a series of anti-Kantian articles, mostly translated from Polish. By 1819–20 a lively journalistic debate on the merits of Kant's philosophy had developed. A Polish astronomer-encyclopedist, Jan Sniadecki, attacked Kant's idealistic interpretation of the origin of ideas; this article, in the *Messenger of Europe*, was rebuffed by a pro-Kantian article in the *Kazan Bulletin*, which in turn led to another anti-Kantian essay in the *Messenger of Europe* (1820) written by Kachenovskii.

Kantianism suffered its most serious setback in Russia under the powerful and uncompromising criticism of Timofei Osipovskii, a professor of mathematics at Khar'kov University. Osipovskii attacked Kant's definition of space as a subjective category antecedent to external experience; to him, space was objective, that is, inherent in matter itself. Although he criticized the Kantian space as a subjective category, he accepted the Kantian—and Euclidean—definition of space as an absolute category. Lobachevskii made the next step, the one without which his non-Euclidean geometry could not have emerged: he rejected the Kantian idea of space both as a subjective and as an absolute category. His epistemological orientation, which was the foundation of his non-Euclidean geometry, was the result of a serious and sophisticated preoccupation with the philosophy of science, a discipline which at that time was under the strong influence of Kantianism.

It should be stressed that Lobachevskii, in formulating his non-Euclidean geometry, was compelled to treat epistemological problems in order to give his new geometry a philosophical as well as a scientific foundation. In both *Elements of Geometry* and *New Elements of Geometry,* he accepted the view of the eighteenth-century sensualists that all ideas derive from experience and that the function of science is to reduce the multitudes of unique experiences to the least possible number of concepts.[49] Space is one of these concepts. But where, outside the mind, is space? Osipovskii believed that it was "in nature itself";[50] to Lobachevskii, it was an *a posteriori* concept—a concept, that is, abstracted by human reason from external experience.

Lobachevskii also maintained that motion was the source of all sensations, and that ultimately such geometrical concepts as space were nonexistent without motion; thus, space was a category not only of geometry but also of mechanics. Geometry was therefore dependent on the forms of the motion of matter. This epistemological argument enabled Lobachevskii to assert that there were no inner contradictions in the claim that "certain forces in nature follow one geometry, and others their own unique geometries."[51]

Lobachevskii would not have agreed, however, with Poincaré, who claimed that non-Euclidean geometries are logical exercises or intellectual plays, which, while having no basis in the external world, have freed human intellect from the tyranny of nature. To the Russian mathematician, geometry and all its categories must have a basis in the external world. The same thing applied to all fields of mathematics. "All mathematical principles," he said, "that are formed by our mind independently of the external world will remain useless to mathematics."[52] In Lobachevskii's thinking, there was no room either for apriorism or for relativism, although relativism was nourished by his influence.

The philosophical and logical questions that troubled Lobachevskii filled the intellectual air of his time. His failure to attend or visit a Western university gave him a broader perspective by making it easier for him to avoid identification with a single philosophical point of view and to roam freely in the world of clashing philosophical currents. It was his genius that enabled him to rise above these influences and to produce an idea of remarkable originality.

Lobachevskii showed certain strong influences of the French sensualists and the English empiricists, despite his general independence of thought. He was particularly influenced by Condillac (whose *Logic* was translated into Russian by Osipovskii) and by Locke. "Undoubtedly, the basic facts," Lobachevskii wrote, "are always the ideas received from nature by means of our senses."[53] Sensations, of course, must be subsumed under "as few" basic categories as possible. He saw in mathematical calculation the best and most successful method for arriving at "broad concepts."[54] He also emphasized that the basic ideas of mathematics are received directly from nature by our senses.[55] Thus, mathematics, which helps us to formulate concepts from empirical data, is itself based on concepts ultimately derived from sensations. This combination of full empiricism and the mathematical method was, according to Lobachevskii, the main reason for the triumph of modern science.

It was for this reason that Lobachevskii considered Bacon and Descartes to be the founders of modern scientific thought. He considered Bacon the first philosopher to have held clearly and persistently that the observation of nature is the source of all scientific knowledge. Like Bacon, Lobachevskii was a firm believer in experiment; even geometrical postulates, he insisted, must be subject to experimental verification.[56] He praised Descartes for having pointed out and demonstrated the inestimable value of mathematics as a scientific tool. Lobachevskii regarded the progressive mathematization of science as the best index of its advancement, and it was Bacon and Descartes who had determined the downfall of Scholasticism.[57]

Lobachevskii's praise of Bacon and Descartes as the twin inaugurators of modern science was not exactly new, however. Osipovskii, in 1795 in an oration delivered to Moscow's Main Public School, had spoken of Bacon and Descartes as having alerted philosophers against "the teachings of Peripatetics" who scorned observation and experiment.[58] Again in 1813, at the annual lecture sponsored by Khar'kov University, Osipovskii asserted that Bacon and Descartes freed modern science from the unjustified apriorism of ancient Greek philosophy.[59]

Lobachevskii's excursions into philosophy came to a halt during his struggle to convince the scholarly world of the merits of non-Euclidean geometry. Time and preoccupation with the logical and scientific intricacies of his new geometry may have been the cause, but it is just as probable that he lost faith in philosophy as it was taught in the universities of Nicholas's era, when it was the province of antirationalist clergymen steeped in the mysticism of Boehme, the religious philosophy of Jacobi, and a diluted blend of Fichtean and Schellingian idealism and English empiricism. Whatever the reasons, by 1842 Lobachevskii had reached the conclusion that "philosophy in its present state is not heeded by mathematics because the mathematician thinks that philosophy as a science is useless to him."[60]

Lobachevskii regarded mathematics as modern man's most powerful intellectual tool, and he anticipated the future expansion of its use in various sciences. In this connection, an incident recalled by V. F. Kagan is illuminating. At the urging of the Kazan Economic Society, the University decided to offer courses in agriculture. Before the final decision was arrived at, there was a heated discussion about which of the existing faculties the new subject would fall under. Gorlov, an economist, argued that the Faculty of Law was the logical one, but Lobachevskii insisted with great vehemence that it should be part of the Faculty of Physics and Mathematics, which included all the biological sciences. The study of agriculture, he asserted, must be part of the study of zoology, botany, physics, and physical geography, and the study of all these sciences required a broad grounding in mathematics. It was Gorlov who scored the initial victory, but Lobachevskii's views ultimately prevailed.

Because of his extensive philosophical background and his definite philosophical point of view, Lobachevskii possessed not only a unique scientific orientation but also a clear conception of the role of science in education. In 1827, one year after the end of Magnitskii's rule as superintendent of the Kazan district, Lobachevskii, as the new rector of the University, delivered a famous speech on the aims of education. This speech throws additional light on the enormous breadth of Lobachevskii's intellectual capacities and also gives an inkling of what the typical educational philosophy was in these early years of Nicholas I's reign, when he was first attempting to weld higher education to the policies of official nationalism. Lobachevskii, in the best tradition of the eighteenth-century Enlightenment, praised education as the source of "honor and glory" for modern society.[61] This was an important sociological datum: it was a direct and unequivocal onslaught on the lingering elements of aristocratic ideology which gave pre-eminence to "purity of blood" over the acquisition of wisdom, to the inheritance of status over the educational achievement of the individual. In 1827 the gymnasium curriculum was rapidly being limited as the government cut out subjects that might threaten official ideology; the university curriculum had already been reduced under the pressure of the mystics in the Ministry of Religious Affairs and National Education.

Lobachevskii asked himself rhetorically what kind of knowledge should be imparted to students in order to ensure society of the benefits of modern wisdom. He answered, "It is my opinion that nothing should be eliminated, that everything must be perfected." He cited Mably's dictum that no passions should be curbed, "for the stronger they are, the more useful they are to society." In other words, no aspect of knowledge should be suppressed, and no talent should be stifled. Education, he insisted, must be balanced; it must impart knowledge and develop the intellectual capacities of young people, but it must not overlook their emotional needs. In Lobachevskii's view, ignorance was a two-headed monster, for it swallowed up both the intellect and man's noblest emotions. The real target of his attack was ignorance.

In a clear allusion to the Russian gentry, Lobachevskii criticized those who favored education through private tutoring over education in public universities, which were, in fact, the only places in Russia where competent teachers were concentrated and where the teaching was synchronized with the requirements of society. On another occasion, he talked about the importance of incorporating the aristocratic boarding schools into the system of public education.[62] It is to be conjectured that his statements in praise of the methods and attainments of the physical and mathematical sciences as the highest intellectual achievements of modern man—"the triumph of the human mind"—were more than simply an expression of his opinion. They may well have been an appeal to students, who were enrolled at that time in overwhelming numbers in the Faculty of Law as the surest way to good civil service positions, to turn to the natural sciences as their major field of study.

Though neglected for his revolutionary ideas in non-Euclidean geometry, Lobachevskii was a highly respected member of Kazan University, first as dean of the Faculty of Physics and Mathematics, when he stood firmly against Magnitskii's attacks on academic freedom, and then as an outstanding rector, under whom the principles of free scientific inquiry were upheld—both in word and in deed. He was responsible, after much tireless effort, for the launching of the *Scientific Journal of Kazan University* and for the establishment of such scholarly institutions as the Society of the Admirers of Science and the Kazan Economic Society. One of the early historians of this university said of him: "Not a single development in our university, nor any important event in its history from the beginning until now, can be referred to without mention of Lobachevskii's name. His noble life was closely and inseparably linked to the history of Kazan University; it was a living chronicle of the university, its hopes and aspirations, its growth and maturation."[63]

There is ample evidence to show that Lobachevskii was highly esteemed by his colleagues as a scholar also, despite the skepticism with which his geometrical theories were regarded at Kazan and, more especially, elsewhere. Through Gauss's influence, he was elected a corresponding member of the Göttingen Learned Society.[64] In 1835, in a review of three of his studies—

none dealing with non-Euclidean geometry—the Moscow *Literary Chronicle* stated that "Lobachevskii is known as one of our best professors of mathematics."[65] It is quite probable that Brashman, a professor of mathematics at Moscow University, was instrumental in the publication of an article by Lobachevskii in Moscow University's *Messenger* (1835)—the first time that one of his studies was printed outside Kazan. Brashman, a great admirer of Ostrogradskii, disapproved, however, of Lobachevskii's studies in geometry and criticized them in his reviews.

Actually, the first clear recognition in print of the revolutionary significance of Lobachevskii's non-Euclidean geometry came from P. I. Kotel'nikov, a professor of mechanics at Kazan University. In a paper read and published in 1842, Kotel'nikov tried to rebuff "some of the prejudices against mathematics" that were increasingly exhibited by Kazan's professors. His essay was precipitated by an article of N. Kalinovskii, published the previous year, which, referring to mathematics, asserted that there was no other science "in which under the cloak of great wisdom and scholarship so much poverty is hidden."[66] Kotel'nikov in his learned and eloquent defense of mathematics mentioned Lobachevskii as a scholar who "repudiated the centuries-old futile efforts to prove one of the main theorems in geometry with complete mathematical precision" and undertook to construct an entire geometry on new foundations.[67] He was undoubtedly thinking of Lobachevskii's daring contributions when he predicted that the time was coming when Russia would "repay with interest" its intellectual debt to the West.[68]

Aside from Kotel'nikov, however, all the writers of the time who expressed a favorable opinion about Lobachevskii's scientific contributions referred not to his work in geometry but to his work in algebra, astronomy, and mechanics. E. Knorr, a colleague at Kazan and subsequently a professor at Kiev University, went so far as to endorse Lobachevskii's postulate that the sum of the angles of a triangle is not necessarily equal to two right angles, but he denied the possibility of a non-Euclidean geometry.[69]

Ironically, at the very time when Lobachevskii, approaching old age, was doing his utmost to acquaint the scholarly world with his grand departure from Euclidean geometry, a young Russian mathematician named Pafnutii Chebyshev won fame for his attempt to answer a question that had puzzled the greatest minds in arithmetic since the time of Euclid: the distribution of prime numbers within the sequence of all natural numbers. No one since Euclid had made such a fruitful approach.[70] Chebyshev's first two works—*Theory of Comparisons* (1849) and *Prime Numbers* (1850)—were instantly recognized in Western Europe as important mathematical contributions. His reputation was subsequently enhanced by his monograph on the approximative representation of functions, published by the St. Petersburg Academy in 1857, which illuminated many intricate structural qualities of functions. He became a regular member of the St. Petersburg Academy in 1858, and the Académie des Sciences in Paris elected him a corresponding member in 1860.

Although Chebyshev did most of his scholarly work after 1860, it was during the 1850's that he produced some of his most formidable scientific achievements and laid the foundations for what came to be known as the St. Petersburg school of mathematics, a group of scholars trained and influenced by him, whose studies, though diversified, exhibited a great deal of over-all unity. Without underestimating his role in the founding of this school, it can be said that his job was made much easier by the strong mathematical tradition in the Academy dating back to Euler and Daniel Bernoulli, as well as by the accelerated growth of mathematics in St. Petersburg University and elsewhere in the 1830's and 1840's.

Chebyshev, like Brashman, was influenced at first by Ostrogradskii's studies in mathematical physics. This influence was passing in nature, however, for the young mathematician's attention was soon attracted to the work of Buniakovskii and N. E. Zernov in the theory of probability. Shortly after completing his studies at Moscow University, Chebyshev was invited by the Academy of Sciences to help in preparing Euler's works for publication; it was in the course of this work that he became interested in the theory of numbers.[71] He considered Euler's mathematical genius second only to Newton's. In many mathematical "discoveries" of his age he saw only elaborations or refinements of subtle ideas scattered through Euler's voluminous works.

When Chebyshev became an instructor in mathematics at St. Petersburg University in 1847, he entered a department that already enjoyed high prestige because of the scholarly achievements of two of its most illustrious professors—Viktor Buniakovskii and O. I. Somov. In 1850, Somov published *The Foundations of the Theory of Elliptic Functions*, which was highly praised by Academicians Buniakovskii and Ostrogradskii as "the first full and systematic study in Russian of one of the most important and most difficult branches of integral calculus." By the end of the 1860's four Russian mathematicians—Ostrogradskii, Buniakovskii, D. M. Perevoshchikov, and Chebyshev—were members of the St. Petersburg Academy of Sciences; mathematics was the first science in the Academy of Sciences to outgrow its dependence on imported scholars.

By his social origin, Chebyshev typified a new kind of scholar: the scholar who came from a noble family faced with economic dislocation and the threat of pauperization. Impoverished aristocrats, compelled by their economic plight to seek employment in the so-called liberal professions, were the first Russian social class to seize upon science as a vocation of prestige and social value. Despite their dwindling fortunes, Chebyshev and other members of his class were able to get excellent private tutoring, which offered them a much better preparation for university study than they would have received from the gymnasiums.

When Chebyshev enrolled at Moscow University in 1837 it had just expanded its mathematical curriculum to include analytical geometry, higher algebra, differential and integral calculus, integration of differential equations, and the calculus of variations. In 1840–41, he received a silver medal for his paper dealing with numerical solutions of algebraic equations of higher ranks; this work marked the beginning of a long and steady pre-occupation with scientific work which lasted up until his death in 1894. His last paper was published a year after his death.

Although Chebyshev received all his education in Russia, after he joined the St. Petersburg University faculty he made a great many extremely valuable trips to Western Europe which enabled him to maintain personal contact with numerous leading mathematicians, including Cauchy, Liouville, Bienaymé, Hermite, Serret, Sylvester, Cayley, and Lejeune-Dirichlet.[72] His mathematical work was highly respected by these scholars, some of whom, including Sylvester, worked on certain of his formulas in an effort to give them more precision and wider application. Chebyshev was one of the first of a new type of scientist-traveler, who visited the Western scholars and scientific centers not as a mere seeker of new knowledge but as an active participant in an exchange of ideas. When he died, two of his students, A. A. Markov and N. Ia. Sonin, stated: "The name of P. L. Chebyshev is known abroad no less than in Russia, in Paris no less than in St. Petersburg."[73]

Chebyshev and his disciples conferred new dignity and importance on probability theory, which had been losing some of its prestige. It has been said that the theory of probability received a special impetus in Russia from the growth of insurance agencies and also from government requests associated with military recruiting and the elaborate tax system. Chebyshev's pronounced interest in the theory of mechanisms was also a scholarly response to the growing industrialization of Russia and the expanding polytechnic curriculum.

THE UNIVERSITIES AS FOUNTAINS OF KNOWLEDGE

The development of scientific thought in Russian universities was un-even, partly because of special local conditions. St. Petersburg University logically became an important center of the natural and exact sciences because of its proximity to the Academy of Sciences. It was able to draw heavily upon the Academy's talent, which included such renowned scholars as Hess, Lenz, Buniakovskii, Chebyshev, and Somov. Kiev University, on the other hand, because of its late start (1834), produced no important man of science during the first three decades of its existence. Moscow Univer-sity, through the combined influence of the policies of official nationalism and "unofficial" intellectual stirrings, developed into a leading center of research in subjects pertaining to history in general and Russian history in particular. Khar'kov University was exceedingly slow in recuperating from the wounds inflicted upon it by the mystical crusaders of the 1820's. Kazan University—small, yet relatively well-balanced—had Lobachevskii, its poorly recognized titan, and also began to develop a specialized interest in chemistry owing to the acquisition of an excellent chemical laboratory and to the talents of two ambitious scholars, Carl Claus and N. N. Zinin. Dorpat University, always strong in the natural sciences, found it increas-ingly difficult to hire established German scholars after the late 1840's, and its scientific fortunes declined accordingly.[74]

This was the period in which all Russian universities—consonant with the policies of official nationalism—concentrated on the development of faculties of native scholars. The undertaking proved to be a long and tedious process. Only a handful of scholars resulted from the short-lived Professors' Institute at Dorpat; the revolutions of 1830 and 1848 disrupted foreign study; and tightened qualifications for faculty rank made hiring a problem. The revised university charter of 1835 stipulated that no person without a doctorate should be promoted to the rank of professor, and that assistants must have Magister's degrees. To make matters even more complicated, requirements for the doctor's degree were made exceedingly stringent. From 1832 to 1842 the six Russian universities issued only 28 doctoral degrees (not including those conferred in medicine) and 55

Magister's degrees. During the fifteen-year period from 1844 to 1859, the country produced 71 doctors and 254 magisters.[75]

Despite Uvarov's policies, which frowned on the hiring of foreign scholars, all universities were to some extent forced to seek professors in Western Europe. In fact, many of the foreign scholars were survivors of the reign of Alexander I who had somehow got through the Magnitskii era and at last become fully Russianized. Prior to the 1860's the typical professor of natural sciences at the Russian universities was a foreigner who had adjusted to Russian mores and values. In the humanities and mathematics, on the other hand, the faculties were overwhelmingly native Russian.

Indeed, only a few of the Russian natural scientists were of outstanding scholarly ability. According to Sechenov, during the thirty years preceding 1860 Russian natural scientists not only were few but also were isolated from the community at large. Sechenov claimed that the prevailing educational philosophy put little emphasis on the role of universities as research institutions. "[In those days] professors were actually not required to do scientific work—which, according to present-day standards, is synonymous with true scholarship. Scientific work was entrusted to a few specially selected persons, who were isolated in the tranquillity of their studies and seldom made an appearance in the lecture halls."[76] Because the genuine scholars were cut off from the students, they had no personal following of young scientists. Poorly equipped laboratories were another reason for the slow development of university research in the natural sciences. Sechenov stated that prior to the 1860's he did not know of a single specialized investigation in microscopic anatomy, physiology, or experimental pathology carried out by "professors with Russian names."

But Sechenov's harsh judgment of research in the natural sciences in Russian universities from 1830 to 1860 deserves some modification. In all universities during this period, the exponents of natural science fought fiercely and successfully for freedom from metaphysical restrictions and for the laying of a solid experimental base. Still, this was also an age of nationalist ferment and of great emphasis on the humanities: the historian and the social scientist were in the limelight, and the natural scientist was pushed into the shadows, with little opportunity even to communicate with his colleagues. When the famous surgeon Nikolai Pirogov declared that the universities were "the best barometers of social pressure," he was not thinking of the scientific pursuits of professors but of the close ties between historians and social scientists and the increasing concern of these groups with the social, political, and intellectual currents which were exciting the broadening body of educated Russians. The same can be said of Herzen's praise for Moscow University, which, he said, purified the minds of young men by helping them to overcome worn-out prejudices and reach a higher plane of thinking. A. N. Afanas'ev was impressed by the absence of formalism and constraints at Moscow University, as well as by its rich and diversified curriculum; but in his autobiographical papers he makes no reference to the University's offerings in the natural sciences.[77] Accompanying the intensive growth of the humanities was the inconspicuous and neglected work of those natural scientists who managed to survive the onslaughts of Schellingism—particularly strong in Moscow University and the Medical and Surgical Academy. These scholars were now ready to absorb the current scientific achievements, hypotheses, or theories which challenged, and undermined, both the traditional mechanistic view in the physical sciences and the anti-transformism of the biological sciences.

Thus, in the universities a new kind of natural scientist evolved: no longer an encyclopedist, wandering from one field to another, but a specialist with a concentrated interest in a limited number of closely related fields. At Moscow University, for example, significant contributions were made by M. F. Spasskii in what are now called geophysics and climatology, A. M. Filomafitskii in experimental physiology, A. A. Iovskii in analytical chemistry and its application to medicine, and K. F. Rouillier in theoretical zoology and ecology.

The encyclopedists were still very much in evidence, of course, and some of them became worthy popularizers of modern science. S. S. Kutorga of St. Petersburg University, who lectured on such broad and varied subjects as zootomy, zoology, paleontology, and anatomy, was widely acclaimed as a public lecturer and writer of popular scientific articles and monographs. K. F. Rouillier's public lectures on the psychology of animals were heralded by Herzen as an important step in the modernization of Russia's educational ideas.

University research was spurred by the inauguration of the *Scientific Journal of Kazan University* (1834) and the *Scientific Journal of Moscow University* (1838). These publications greatly facilitated scholarly contact between men working in the same and related fields. It need scarcely be added that in number, quality, and stability of scientific journals, Russia at this time was far behind Western Europe.

Since the time of Lomonosov, progress in chemistry had proceeded at an uneven pace. Lomonosov's firm opposition to the phlogiston theory was part of the great intellectual tradition which foreshadowed the modern chemistry of Lavoisier, Cavendish, and Dalton. But interest in theoretical chemistry was poorly sustained by Lomonosov's successors in the Academy —Johann Georgi, Nikita Sokolov, and Tobias Lowitz—who confined their attention mainly to the chemical analysis of various raw materials. The development of chemistry in Russia was stimulated by the vast collection of empirical data pertaining to the country's natural resources and by the steady rise of pharmaceutics.

Thus, during the first three and a half decades of the nineteenth century the progress of chemistry in Russia left much to be desired. Kazan University, for example, did not have a professor of chemistry until 1832. In Moscow University the teaching of chemistry was entrusted to F. F. Reiss, who was trained in medical chemistry but who had no use for theory. His successor, R. G. Heimann, stressed what he called technical chemistry, which relied solely on laboratory work and had no affinity with theoretical ideas. He found it more profitable to serve as a chemical expert on various government committees and to transfer most of his teaching assignments to laboratory assistants.

The 1835 university charter authorized all universities to create modern chemical laboratories and special libraries. Soon chemistry began to attract not only promising students but also established experts in other natural sciences. The new laboratories became the centers of involved theoretical discussions. During the late 1830's and 1840's the graduates of Russian universities were adequately prepared to undertake advanced chemical training in the laboratories of such leading Western chemists as Liebig, Wöhler, Rose, and Dumas.

The combination of adequate undergraduate training at home and superior graduate work abroad made chemistry the field in which university science of the 1840's and 1850's produced its most fruitful results. Curiously, its development was strongest at Kazan University, which had virtually no tradition in this field.

As we have seen, two men were responsible for developing chemistry at Kazan—Carl Claus and N. N. Zinin. Claus (a follower of Berzelius), who was trained in pharmaceutics and "phytochemistry," carried on extensive research in inorganic chemistry. In the course of his impressive investigations into the nature of platinum, he discovered ruthenium, the forty-fourth element in Mendeleev's periodic system. Several of Claus's chemical studies were published in the St. Petersburg Academy's *Bulletin* and thus were brought to the attention of chemists abroad, thanks to which, in the later years of his life, he was elected to the Berlin Academy of Sciences as a corresponding member. Before his departure from Kazan in 1852, Claus won many promising Russian students to the field of chemistry, but his frequent preoccupation with other scientific matters, such as a regional study of the South Russian steppe, somewhat reduced his effectiveness in chemical research.

N. N. Zinin, who received his training in Liebig's laboratory at Giessen University, was a professor of technology at Kazan University from 1841 to 1848. His brief stay was long enough to permit him to create the remarkable "Kazan school of chemistry" and to earn the following eulogy from one of his eminent disciples: "Thanks to Zinin, chemistry in Russia began to live an independent life. . . . His studies compelled the scholars of Western Europe to give an honored place to Russian chemistry."[78] Zinin's fundamental scientific achievements were made during his comparatively short connection with Kazan. It was the evident importance of this work which brought him an invitation to join the faculty of the St. Petersburg Medical and Surgical Academy, which in the late 1840's raided the country's universities for their best talent in various natural sciences. In 1856 Zinin was elected associate member of the St. Petersburg Academy of Sciences.

In the second year of his tenure at Kazan, 1842, Zinin reduced aniline from nitrobenzene, thus making possible the industrial production of this chemical substance. He also conducted a highly successful experiment in preparing aromatic amines by using alcoholic ammonium sulphide as the reducing agent. Nearly forty years later, in a speech before the German Chemical Society, A. W. Hofmann said of this work: "If Zinin had not achieved anything but the transformation of nitrobenzene into aniline, his name would have been inscribed forever in large letters in the annals of chemistry."

Zinin's success as a scholar and the founder of an eminent school of Russian chemists was made possible by several factors. As a student he acquired a solid grounding in both mathematics and the experimental method, but he went on to approach chemistry from a theoretical point of view; his Magister's thesis was devoted to a study of theories of chemical affinity and "the superiority" of Berzelius's theory of permanent "chemical proportion" over Berthollet's "chemical statics." As a teacher he demanded an adequate preparation in mathematics. In the laboratory he favored an atmosphere of informality, encouraging the students to initiate their own experiments in addition to those that were assigned. Most significant, how-ever, was the opportunity given to the students to observe him conducting his own experiments. Thus, in systematic laboratory work the students acquired a basic knowledge of organic chemistry, which Zinin's theoreti-cal background and alertness invested with considerable scientific depth. While Zinin was officially a professor of technology, he was widely known at the University as a professor of "pure chemistry." His following ex-tended far beyond the classroom and the small circle of chemists; persons interested in physiology, comparative anatomy, zoology, and other natural sciences were inspired and influenced by his work. Zinin was a model lecturer, with a propensity toward dramatization and a philosophical bent. A. M. Butlerov, his most eminent disciple, noted that he had the ability to make the best use of simple and lively language and "to show graphically every side of the subject under discussion."[79]

Despite Zinin's impressive successes as a scientist, a lecturer, and the founder of a school of chemistry, it was for years the fashion to identify Aleksandr Voskresenskii as "the grandfather of Russian chemistry." Vosk-resenskii, Zinin's contemporary, was primarily a teacher rather than a research chemist. He did all his teaching in St. Petersburg, being simul-taneously on the faculties of St. Petersburg University, the Main Peda-gogical Institute (where Mendeleev was one of his students), the Commu-nications Institute, and an assortment of military schools. His background was impressive: he studied chemistry under Mitscherlich, Rose, and Mag-nus in Berlin, and under Liebig in Giessen; according to Mendeleev, Liebig once said that Voskresenskii was his most promising graduate student. He published several studies on such topics as the composition of quinine acid, naphthalene, and various alkaloids. His real contribution was as a teacher, for which he was justifiably praised, particularly for his diligent effort to keep his students informed of the mass of new chemical ideas. Berzelius and Liebig furnished him with a starting point, but he gradually expanded on their ideas by absorbing the provocative suggestions of men like Jean-Baptiste Dumas, Auguste Laurent, and Charles Gerhardt, the representatives of the French "school" in chemistry.

Modern chemistry, based largely on the study of chemical reactions in terms of specific and regular combinations of atoms, found not only an echo in Russia but also important contributors. The chemists of the 1840's were concerned with the properties of atoms which enter into chemical compounds and with the dynamics of chemical reactions. The atomic orientation created the necessary foundations for organic chemistry: by the 1840's no chemist would argue against the scientific fruitfulness of the chemical analysis of organic matter. The atomic orientation also challenged the chemists to synthesize new forms of matter. Zinin's discovery of aniline resulted from adherence to the atomic theory as applied to the study of organic substance. Voskresenskii also subscribed to the atomic theory, but he was inclined more toward chemical theory than toward laboratory work. Hess, as previously mentioned, was one of the founders of thermochemistry.

In biology Russian scholars kept pace with the fast-growing body of fact and theory, subsequently coordinated and codified by Darwin into the grand idea of evolution. Karl von Baer furnished the theory of biological evolution with an embryological foundation. The universities had a whole array of professors who can be justly numbered among Darwin's forerunners; the best-known and most productive among these were I. E. Diad'-kovskii, G. E. Shchurovskii, and K. F. Rouillier. Most scholars, however, were not completely free of Schellingian idealism and Oken's vitalistic biology.

The most eminent and influential member of Russia's pre-Darwinian evolutionists was Rouillier, a professor of zoology at Moscow University. A graduate of the Moscow Medical and Surgical Academy, Rouillier combined a broad background in a number of disciplines with a serious theoretical interest in current zoological and geological-paleontological investigations. Anuchin called him "a zoologist-philosopher in the spirit of Geoffroy Saint-Hilaire."[80] In his essay "Doubts About Zoology as a Science," published in 1841, Rouillier questioned the infallibility of the common belief in the immutability of species without explicitly subscribing to any evolutionary ideas. He did feel, however, that zoologists should not confine their study to museum specimens but should observe animals in their natural habitat. Subsequent research convinced Rouillier that "the earth did not always have the surface that we see today," and that geological changes have been accompanied by changes in flora and fauna. Although his evolutionary ideas were not systematized and elaborated, they were pronounced enough to bring him into conflict with the guardians of official ideology some eight years before the publication of Darwin's *The Origin of Species*.

Specialized biological sciences such as comparative anatomy and embryology did not have important followings within the Russian universities. It should be remembered, however, that even in the West at this time the various branches of biology were far below the scientific standards achieved by physics and chemistry. It was not until 1825 that an achromatic microscope objective was achieved, thus making possible the construction of high-power microscopes. The cell theory of plants and animals, announced by Schwann and Schleiden in 1838–39, came as a result of two developments: the widening of the experimental foundations of biology, and the realization among biologists that the future of their discipline required the abandonment of the vitalism of the *Naturphilosophie* and the acceptance of the chemical analysis of living matter as the most promising way to a fuller understanding of the organic world. Until close to the middle of the century biologists, not only in Russia but in Western Europe as well, limited their studies mostly to an analysis of conspicuous biological phenomena; they increasingly cooperated with geologists, with the result that such disciplines as paleontology and comparative anatomy won adherents.

During the 1860's physiology emerged as a widely studied science of impressive achievements, despite its having been virtually nonexistent in Russia during the first half of the century. Before 1840 it was not even a part of the university curriculum. Of the natural sciences in Russia, the slowest to develop were the biochemistry of plants and animals and physiology. In France, Germany, and England in the 1830's there had already been a large number of worthwhile studies in experimental physiology, carried out by François Magendie, Sir Charles Bell, Johannes Müller, Johannes Purkinje, and others. But Russia was still under the full sway of Schellingian metaphysical idealism and vitalism, and the Russian followers of Schelling—whether interested in physiology as an academic subject or not—were impressed less by the solid results of the experimentalists than by Carl Gustav Carus's Schellingian physiological studies, which combined "positive learning" with a "poetical element."[81]

In the Medical and Surgical Academy, the leading medical school in Russia, physiology was taught by the anatomist Petr Zagorskii, who adhered to nonexperimental comparative anatomy.[82] He was succeeded by the pathologist D. M. Vellanskii, who, as a fervent and consistent adherent of the *Naturphilosophie*, was opposed to the whole idea of experimentation. He was a skillful lecturer, however, who attracted large numbers of students to his classes, and he has been credited with paving the way for the establishment of physiology as an independent and attractive field of scientific inquiry.

Vellanskii represented the usual type of Russian theoretical biologist of the 1820's and 1830's. Referring to this epoch as one dominated by metaphysics, V. F. Odoevskii, who was a student at the time and who developed a great affection for Vellanskii and his philosophy, noted in his memoirs: "We believed in the possibility of an absolute theory with the help of which it would be possible to comprehend nature in its totality." Odoevskii made it clear, however, that the "physiology" of Schelling and Oken was actually not a closed system of thought, for "it raised so many questions whose answers could be given accurately only by physics and chemistry."[83] In its self-destruction this idealistic "physiology" provided ample proof to interested students that the future belonged to experimental science.

In 1836 there occurred two events of importance in the history of Russian physiology. In that year Vellanskii published the first Russian textbook in physiology, a collection of diatribes against scientific experiments, particularly vivisection, and against the mechanistic orientation of the biological sciences. The publication of this book marked the high point of Russian Schellingism; the next year or two saw the beginning of its rapid decline. One of the reasons for this decline was the full collapse of *Naturphilosophie* in Western Europe. But a more important reason was the publication, in the same year, of the first volume of a textbook in physiology by A. M. Filomafitskii, a book whose orientation was diametrically opposite to Vellanskii's philosophy and which established Filomafitskii as Russia's first consistent champion of experimental physiology. Filomafitskii attended the Professors' Institute and studied at the University of Berlin under Johannes Müller, a remarkable scholar who combined meticulous experiments on sensory and motor nerves with an idealistic and vitalistic philosophy not far removed from the theories of Schelling and Oken. In his book Filomafitskii presented numerous experimental findings of his own along with analyses of the latest theoretical positions in physiology. He is remembered mostly for his experiments in the transfusion of blood and the use of ether as an anesthetic.

Experimental physiology did not achieve complete triumph during the 1840's, but the end of *Naturphilosophie* had clearly come. Aleksandr Zagorskii, who replaced Vellanskii in 1847, looked upon experiment not only as an essential research technique in physiology but also as an invaluable aid to teaching. He gave his students at the Medical and Surgical Academy information about the many new advances in physiology made by Bernard, Helmholtz, and other eminent Western physiologists.

Emil du Bois-Reymond's systematic, thorough, and devastating criticism of vitalism and metaphysical oversimplification, as well as his categorical claim that physiology is inseparable from organic chemistry and physics, found a quick response among Russian physiologists. In 1858 A. A. Soko-lovskii of Kazan University published a paper on du Bois-Reymond's theory of the biophysical effects of various artificially induced influences on the nervous system. At Kiev University, E. E. Miram's work led to the estab-lishment of a modern physiological laboratory and to original research concerning deformities and intestinal parasites. In 1847 A. I. Khodnev of Khar'kov University published the first volume of his *Course of Physio-logical Chemistry,* based on the studies of Liebig, J. B. Boussingault, and G. J. Mulder. In the Preface the author noted that "physiological chem-istry" was relatively unknown as a special discipline, not only in Russia but also in Western Europe. Khodnev hoped that his textbook would stimu-late the thinking of students in the natural sciences and that it would also reach the general reading public.[84]

Russian physiologists produced no major works in their field until the 1860's. Russia, not surprisingly, was somewhat slower than Western Eu-rope in overcoming the paralyzing effects of the *Naturphilosophie*; and it took even longer to throw off the tradition of comparative anatomy and to see the advantages of the contributions of organic chemistry and experi-mental physics to the understanding of physiological problems. Physiology was slow to achieve academic respectability; laboratories were few and teachers were frequently ill-prepared. It was in many ways the inade-quacies which made this an important age of scientific apprenticeship for young Russian scholars, for the barrenness of experimental facilities in their own country sent them in droves to Western Europe, where they studied in the splendidly equipped laboratories of such pioneers of modern physiology as Müller, Bernard, Helmholtz, Purkinje, du Bois-Reymond, and Ludwig.

The slow progress of physiology in Russia before the 1860's can be best explained by comparing it with the progress of mathematics. Mathematics was, of course, an old and established science, with a long and brilliant tradition in Russia, whereas physiology was a comparatively new discipline even in Europe, with virtually no tradition in Russia. Moreover, mathe-matics required no expensive laboratories, whereas modern physiology was impossible without them. Mathematics was generally believed to be ideo-logically neutral, and no mathematician *qua* mathematician was likely to be subjected to the indignities of censorship. Physiology, on the other hand, was subjected to ideological scrutiny by censorship authorities on two counts: first, it interpreted the functions of human bodies in terms of

chemico-physical processes and seemed to leave little room for divine interference; and second, it offered a basis for "materialistic" psychology, which
tended to strip human cognition, will, and emotions of their lofty, divine
attributes. It was primarily for ideological reasons that physiology was
either kept out of the school curriculum during the reign of Nicholas I or
taught by priests, who avoided all favorable reference to physiological ideas
or principles.

Another very important difference between mathematics and physiology as scientific pursuits deserves special attention. The mathematician,
who expressed his ideas in logically complex formulas, did not have a responsive audience except in the classroom and among his fellow scientists.
His remoteness from the public at large and his apparent ideological
neutralism meant that he was largely ignored by the leaders of the social,
political, and philosophical movements of the time. It was quite a different
matter in physiology, a branch of knowledge viewed by some as the leading modern science and by others as a very disturbing influence on the
sacred values of the autocratic system.

The reading public early became acquainted with physiology. The
Decembrists read Richerand's *The New Principles of Physiology* and P.
Jacotot's three-volume *Course in Experimental Physics and Chemistry*.[85]
"The task of physiology," wrote Aleksandr Herzen, "is to trace the life
from the cell to the activity of the brain. It ends where consciousness
begins; it stops at the threshold of history. The social man steps away from
physiology; sociology, on the contrary, takes hold of him before he emerges
from the condition of simple animal."[86]

Vissarion Belinskii—the man whose every word, according to Ivan
Aksakov, his Slavophil foe, reached even the most isolated provincial
teacher, and whose name became a symbol for the growing legion of
men dedicated to a struggle against the "abomination, oppression, and
baseness which threatened to annihilate man by depriving him of all humanity"—considered physiology a key science and an indispensable link
between psychology and anatomy.[87] He said: "Psychology which does not
depend on physiology is just as unsound as physiology which ignores
anatomy. Contemporary science goes even further: with the help of chemical analysis it tries to penetrate into the mysterious laboratory of nature
and there, by observing the embryo, to trace the *physical* process of *moral*
development."[88] Later Nikolai Dobroliubov made physiology a central
point in his analysis of the irreconcilable struggle between metaphysical

"idealism" and scientific "materialism." In his criticism, he found himself defending physiology from two kinds of enemies: university professors with metaphysical inclinations, and clergymen with an antiscientific bias.

In 1857 Archimandrite Gavril Voskresenskii, a professor of logic and psychology at Kazan University, published a book entitled *The Foundations of Experimental Psychology,* in which he contended that human thought transcends the capacity of the brain and that, therefore, it must have a supernatural origin. His intent was to combat the scientific trend toward a more thorough and experimental study of the physiological basis of man's mental activities. In attacking the transparent arguments of the belligerent theologian, Dobroliubov stood firmly on the side of modern physiology; yet he admitted that the learned clergyman's work contained a surprisingly rich assortment of modern physiological knowledge.[89]

Dobroliubov used his strongest ammunition against V. F. Bervi, a professor of physiology and general pathology at Kazan University, who published a paper in 1858 entitled "A Comparison of the Views of Physiologists and Psychologists on the Beginning and the End of Life." The study was tantamount to a declaration of ideological war on "materialism," "sensualism," and the experimental method. Physiology was Bervi's immediate target, but he expanded his arguments into a general condemnation of modern natural science. In response, Dobroliubov did much more than point to the weighty ideological issues associated with physiology in particular and natural science in general.[90] He clearly stated the necessity for general public concern with the welfare of science; he made society, at least in so far as it was represented by the growing reading public, conscious of its right and duty to hold scholars responsible for the scientific merit of the ideas which they disseminated as teachers and writers.

In his writings during the 1850's Dobroliubov ushered in a new period in the development of science in Russia, a period in which a natural scientist's wholehearted acceptance of the official ideology rendered him liable to relentless attacks by ideological antagonists and, at the same time, made his scientific ideas the subject of merciless scrutiny. Bervi, as dissected by Dobroliubov, was the kind of scholar who made use of his fervent nationalism to hide the mediocrity of his scientific knowledge. It was not his scholarly competence but his crusade against the ideological dangers of modern physiology that prompted the Minister of National Education to attend his lecture in 1851 on "excitability" as an organic phenomenon.

In his criticism of Bervi, Dobroliubov showed that an ideological commitment forced the Kazan professor into a highly unscholarly position: first, in condemning modern physiology, he showed no familiarity with such contemporary leaders in the field as Emil du Bois-Reymond, Karl Vogt, and Jacob Moleschott; and, second, he implicitly acknowledged the incompatibility of the ideology of the autocracy with modern science by expressing a basically pessimistic attitude toward the future development of a science-dominated culture.

Dobroliubov's blistering attack on Bervi's essay was occasioned by Bervi's dismissal from his teaching position as the result of a petition signed by seventy-one Kazan University students (20 per cent of the total enrollment) who objected to his arrogant attitude toward modern natural science.[91] Dubroliubov wrote his review of Bervi's paper in order to support the student petitioners and perhaps prevent recriminatory action by the authorities. It was also a good way of alerting the educated public to the deep struggle between official ideology and natural science. The article was successful in both ends: no disciplinary action was taken against the students, and articles on the natural sciences began to appear in popular journals with increasing frequency.

The dismissal of Bervi marked the end of an era for natural science in Russia. Bervi was the last Russian physiologist to hold a metaphysical point of view. Dobroliubov's excursion into the field of physiology was part of the general intellectual advance that subsequently produced such great physiologists as I. M. Sechenov and Ivan Pavlov.

Anatomy in Russia had a longer history than physiology, and it was less hampered by the negative influences of the *Naturphilosophie*. Beginning in the 1820's, interest in comparative anatomy grew perceptibly and in the succeeding decade popular scientific journals printed many articles pertinent to the discipline. Russian scholars showed special interest in the theoretical work of Etienne Geoffroy Saint-Hilaire and his stand against Cuvier.[92] The first Russian anatomist of acknowledged reputation was I. V. Buial'skii, an accomplished surgeon, who published *Anatomical-Surgical Tables* in 1828; this was a substantial contribution to topographical anatomy, and it was noted in scientific circles in Western Europe and America. Buial'skii's *Brief General Anatomy of the Human Body,* published in 1844, aroused considerable talk because of its marked evolutionary slant.

One Russian anatomist of this period was of gigantic stature, a man whose achievements reached far beyond Russia's boundaries—Nikolai

Pirogov. Pirogov, born in Moscow in 1810, was graduated from Moscow University's Medical School at the age of eighteen. Of his education in this school, he wrote: "I received a physician's diploma and had mastery over life and death without ever having seen a single typhus patient and without ever having had a lancet in my hands! My entire medical practice in the clinic was limited to writing the history of an illness, having seen my patient only once in the hospital. For the sake of simplification, I appended to this history a mass of excerpts from the books I had read—so much so that it was transformed from a history into a story."[93]

Pirogov went on to Dorpat University, however, for five more years of study, and then to Berlin, where he became an anatomist of the first rank. In his published journals, he makes some interesting observations on the difference in atmosphere between the universities of Berlin and Moscow. In contrast to the Russian scientists, among whom Schellingism still flourished, Berlin's scientists in the early 1830's had rejected idealistic philosophies; and medicine, for decades the particular target of Schellingism, had at last made a "triumphant entrance into the realm of exact science."[94]

Pirogov's success in Berlin was so outstanding that Johann Christian Moier, his professor at Dorpat University, selected the young anatomist to be his successor. (The Theological Faculty, citing Alexander I's assurance that only Protestant professors would be allowed to teach at Dorpat, waged an unsuccessful battle against his appointment.[95]) Pirogov immediately proved himself a notable contributor to the field of anatomy and a great and daring surgeon. Two of his best works appeared in 1837-39—a *Surgical Anatomy of Arterial Trunks and Fasciae,* in German and Latin, and a monograph on injuries to the Achilles' tendon. In 1841, after six years of fruitful work, Pirogov left Dorpat for the Medical and Surgical Academy in St. Petersburg, where he remained until 1854.

In St. Petersburg Pirogov produced original studies on such subjects as the organization of clinical service in hospitals, pathological anatomy, and surgical anatomy. His major works during this period were a study of the pathological anatomy of cholera based on his own experimental findings, a textbook in applied anatomy, and *Clinical Surgery,* a collection of monographs on a variety of medical topics related to his surgical and anatomical work. *Clinical Surgery* included a description of his unique contribution to foot surgery and to the surgical use of gypsum bandages. Pirogov was always abreast of the latest techniques and discoveries in medicine. In 1847, for example, during the Caucasian War, he used ether as an anesthetic in the treatment of wounded soldiers only a few months after the efficiency of this technique had been publicly demonstrated by the American dentist William T. G. Morton.

The four volumes of Pirogov's major work, *Anatomia topographica* (1851–54), ensured their author of a high reputation abroad as well as at home. This lengthy work described the topographical relations of individual organs and tissues in various planes. Pirogov is also considered to be one of the founders of modern military medicine, a field to which he dedicated his *Principles of General Military Field Surgery* (1864), originally published in German.

Pirogov resigned from the Medical and Surgical Academy in 1856 because of his impatience with academic quarrels and administrative duties, and from then until his death in 1881 he devoted himself mainly to practical medicine and education.[96] In 1856 he published his famous article "The Problems of Life," in which he pleaded for a new educational program that would recognize the value of specialization and yet would not ignore the more fundamental need for general education. In 1856 he was appointed superintendent of the Odessa school district, and two years later he became the head of the Kiev school district.

Pirogov's dynamic efforts, directed in some cases against antiquated ideas, in other cases against corrupt ethical precepts, proved less immediately influential than they deserved to be. According to a writer of the succeeding generation, the indifferent attitude of the military authorities toward Pirogov was the main reason why "the colossal proportions of his genius and personal sacrifice received no recognition from the government and the people."[97] The next generation, however, learned to appreciate both the scientific and psychological contributions of this great man, and honored him by naming one of the country's leading medical associations after him.

Because of its obvious conflict with Church writings, the study of geology did not advance until the second half of the nineteenth century. According to Odoevskii, geology was not taught in Russian schools, and "no Russian books on the formation of the earth's crust could be published, while geological works in foreign languages were a source of headaches for perplexed censors." The official watchdogs were thrown into the unenviable position of being expected to analyze complex geological theories and match them with the biblical account of creation.[98] They successfully kept Charles Lyell's *Principles of Geology* (1830–33)—which declared that only geological forces, still at work, could explain the earth's history—from reaching Russia until the 1860's.

Odoevskii lamented that geology, which his country needed more than any other natural science, received the least help and encouragement be-cause of its "un-Christian" theory. The government was aware of the im-portance of geological surveys, but it was forced by the dismal shortage of trained geologists to entrust much survey work to amateurs. Thus, as Helmersen observed, the comparatively large government funds allocated to geological research were largely wasted, for they brought in nothing more useful than mountains of erroneous information gathered by sur-veyors unskilled in theory.[99]

The turning point in the history of Russian geology is associated with the name of Sir Roderick Murchison, a famous Scottish geologist and paleontologist, who is often called the founder of modern Russian geology. In 1840 Murchison, whose extensive geological researches in England, Wales, and various parts of Western Europe had led to the establishment of the Silurian and Devonian systems, decided to extend his studies to Russia. He was pleasantly surprised when the Russian government accepted his project with great enthusiasm, particularly because of his interest in pre-paring a geological map of Russia.

Murchison spent two years in European Russia, accompanied by Ed-ouard de Verneuil, a noted French paleontologist, and Alexander von Keyserling, a Baltic German and an established geologist who had come to St. Petersburg in 1840 to take part in Middendorff's expeditions. The re-sult of their great effort was a work of remarkable excellence, *The Geology of European Russia and the Ural Mountains* (1845). The book was not a definitive study of Russia, but Murchison's observations—thanks to his erudition, experience, and highly perceptive mind—were basically correct, if often incomplete, and they were assembled and coordinated with mas-terly precision. Murchison also made use of certain findings of his prede-cessors, after subjecting them to careful evaluation. His rich store of knowledge of Western European geology and his remarkable ability to systematize regional information enabled him to present the first geological picture of all of Russia and to produce the first comprehensive geological map of the country. The work of succeeding generations of Russian geol-ogists was primarily to refine and amplify Murchison's conclusions and to follow new lines of inquiry suggested by modern geological theory.

The magnitude of Murchison's contributions to the scientific study of Russia's geology is best expressed by Helmersen: "Murchison's *Geology of Russia* . . . revolutionized the geological study of Russia in the same way that *The Silurian System,* his earlier work, opened new vistas for the study of the paleozoic formations of the earth."[100] He added that Murchison was to geologists and paleontologists what Pallas had been to zoologists and botanists: a beacon throwing light on new scientific problems, concepts, and methods. The St. Petersburg Academy honored Murchison by electing him as its first nonresident member.

No Russian geologist in the 1840's approached Murchison's caliber, but a number of university professors made solid contributions, both as scholars and as popularizers of scientific ideas. The most productive among these scholars was Karl Eduard Eichwald, who worked mostly in paleontology, although his versatile interests, expeditionary research, and teaching duties took him also into zoology, botany, geology, mineralogy, physical anthropology, ethnography, archaeology, and medicine. Born in Mitava, Latvia, in 1795, Eichwald received his higher education at Berlin University. After teaching at Vilna and Kazan Universities, he became professor of zoology and mineralogy at the Medical and Surgical School in St. Petersburg (1837–51); he served at the same time as professor of paleontology at the Mining Institute and as professor of mineralogy at the Engineering Academy. He was the first Russian scholar to offer a systematic course in paleontology. In his two-volume book *The Primeval World of Russia* (1840-47)—later refined and expanded into *Paleontology of Russia* (1854-61)—he made a monumental effort to coordinate and synchronize the available Russian paleontological material. He made a similar but more modest effort in geology (1846).

In 1839 D. I. Sokolov, then a professor at St. Petersburg University and the Mining Institute, published a three-volume semipopular textbook in geognosy, which provided an introduction to some of the broad ideas concerning the nature of geological processes. The work was of great value for its abundance of Russian geological information, although Sokolov clearly had no notion of the great treasure of scientific ideas set forth in Lyell's recently published *Principles of Geology*. Sokolov's *Manual of Geognosy* (1842) shows full acquaintance with Lyell's theories, but it is largely practical rather than theoretical in its concerns.[101]

The first Russian scholar to be directly inspired by Murchison's work and to follow his footsteps successfully was S. S. Kutorga. He was the author of *Contributions to the Paleontology of Russia* (1842–46) as well as of a geological survey of southern Finland (1851), a geological map of the St. Petersburg province, and numerous studies in other natural sciences. He was a pioneer in geological fieldwork and a master in the popularization of the new scientific point of view; he conducted a series of highly popular geological trips to various localities in the St. Petersburg province.

G. E. Shchurovskii, like Kutorga, came to geology via zoology and paleontology, but his first geological studies preceded Murchison's work in Russia by several years and were inspired by his reading in the field of contemporary geology in the West. He undertook extensive fieldwork in the Urals in 1838 and in the Altai region in 1841, collecting sufficient material for two monographs published during the 1840's. A geological survey of the Moscow basin which appeared in the 1860's contains material collected by earlier scholars supplemented by his own observations. He was the first Russian scholar to write articles on geological subjects for publication in such popular journals as the *Atenei* and the *Russian Messenger*. His researches in the Moscow province were extensive, detailed, and remarkably accurate. His classification of the mountain deposits of Central Russia into four layers was accepted by all the leading Russian geologists of the second half of the nineteeth century.

Something of the scope of Shchurovskii's scientific interests is given in the following statement of D. N. Anuchin: "He was primarily a self-made man. Having received only a meager education at Moscow University, he found it necessary to create a new course, new scientific methods, and new collections by relying on his own resourcefulness. Shchurovskii established geology at Moscow University and at the same time did more than anyone else to foster the dissemination of geological knowledge among the general public. By means of scientific lectures and articles of a popular nature and public excursions to Moscow's environs, he took science far beyond the domain of the university and helped to engender scientific interest throughout Russian society."[102]

It is difficult to summarize scientific developments in Russia during the 1840's. This was the decade in which Lobachevskii tried without success to reach the Western world with his non-Euclidean geometry, while Ostrogradskii, the acknowledged master, and the younger Chebyshev received acclaim for their mathematical contributions. In this decade modern chemistry took deep root in Russian culture; the old geognosy began to retreat before geology; Schellingism was roundly defeated in physiology and medicine, and experimentation achieved major victories in the field of anatomy.

Scientists, particularly Russian-born scientists, were still rare, partly because they were expected to meet high educational standards and partly because the rewards for scholarship were still negligible. An important explanation of the shortage of scientists is contained in the following pertinent observation made by Pirogov:

"The educated part of our society consists of two segments. The upper segment, with all the means for sound education at their disposal, are prevented by birth, position, and prejudice from dedicating themselves to scientific work. They have no use either for the native scientific literature or for Russian translations of the classic works of other peoples. The second —lower—segment is made up almost completely of the proletariat, the people who do not know Western European languages, who are without sufficient means, and whose children get an inadequate education in lower schools and then enter the schools of higher education only to be plagued by the absence of adequate Russian textbooks."[103] In other words, although Russia had two social classes from which scientists could have been recruited, the class equipped to study science was not so inclined, and the other class, however greatly inclined to study science it might have been, was not equipped.

In addition, science was overbureaucratized. Whether teaching in a university or in a professional school, whether employed by a government bureau or by a learned society, the scientist was subordinated to a more or less unsympathetic government official who was paid to guard science from the corruptive influences of alien ideologies. With the issuing of the new university charter in 1835, academic authority rapidly shifted from autonomous University Councils to the political office of superintendent, usually held by persons with scant understanding of the goals and the ethos of scholarship. In 1849 even the position of university rector ceased to be elective, and the rector was no longer expected to be a learned man.

In 1859 a thoughtful writer sought to explain why Russia had produced only one great scholar in the broad field of medicine during the first half of the nineteenth century, namely, Pirogov. His answer was simple. In the first place, although Russian medical instructors, foreign-trained, were, as a rule, modern in their thinking and knowledge, they were unaware of the specific social and cultural background of medical problems in Russia. In the second place, doctors, hospitals, and medical schools were controlled by the government, and a rigid system of government administration impeded the flow and absorption of new scientific ideas. The author mentioned in particular that provincial physicians were at the mercy of minor bureaucrats who sought to suppress medical innovations emanating from the central medical authorities.[104]

From roughly 1830 on, for the next thirty years, nonaristocratic students accounted for only twenty per cent or so of the total enrollment of all universities, with the exception of medical schools. Until the 1850's the gentry continued overwhelmingly to prefer the study of law. But science was definitely on the upswing. The Russian professor had ceased to be a rarity. The antiquarian professor of the 1820's, whose scientific ideas were those of the eighteenth century, was supplanted in the 1840's by the modern professor who, though chiefly dedicated to the spread of knowledge, was likely to be alert to the most modern scientific developments in Western Europe.

Those who stood for rationalism and positive knowledge now found solid support in an enlightened section of the general public, led by such antitraditionalists as Herzen, who fully endorsed the Baconian belief in natural science as the key to the future progress of mankind. After nearly two decades of official nationalism, the antirationalists and antimaterialists were stronger than ever, but for the first time they were on the defensive. Between the protagonists and antagonists of science was a growing group of dilettantes—including some highly placed officials—who respected the great promise of science and were ready to give it moral support. Such people as these attended Granovskii's public lectures on Bacon and read Herzen's *Letters on the Study of Nature.** The circulation of public library books rose sharply. In 1854, for instance, 20,645 persons made use of the facilities of the St. Petersburg Public Library and borrowed 34,475 library books.[105] The Library's total holdings then numbered over 500,000 books and manuscripts. (Official reports list 49 public libraries in Russia in 1857, but many of these probably existed only on paper.)

The existence of a reading public interested in science led several popular journals to carry occasional articles on highly sophisticated scientific themes. During the last three months of 1847, for example, the journal *Contemporary* carried an article on the life and work of the German astronomer Bessel (based on the papers presented by Sir John Herschel before the Royal Astronomical Society in London), a Russian translation of Herschel's paper on double stars and nebulous spots, as well as articles on the electric telegraph, the physiology of the human brain, Liebig's chemical analysis of the fluids in tissue, and the basic ideas of Humboldt's *Kosmos*.

The journal *The Reading Library* was a true pioneer in the popularization of modern scientific thought. Published in St. Petersburg from

---

* On his return from the Urals, Humboldt was honored at a jubilee meeting of the Society of Naturalists of Moscow University, whose members were senators, governors, and other persons with no special interest in the sciences. Herzen, *Byloe i dumy* (London, 1861), I (1812–38), 158.

1834 to 1863, it often carried discussions of a scientific nature. For example, the January-February 1836 issue carried a lengthy discussion of "the present-day theory of electromagnetism," a detailed description of "the most recent travels" of Sir John Ross, a survey of modern theories of sound, a lengthy article on Thomas Young, a short review of the astronomical studies conducted by the Paris Académie des Sciences, and a report on the annual meeting of the German Natural Science Society. Most of these were translations from Western European journals. The journal also published occasional reports on the activities of the St. Petersburg Academy of Sciences as well as the Paris Académie. Many of the articles were surveys of the work of such early scholars as Erasmus, Kepler, Galileo, and Newton, and modern scientists like Ampère, Arago, Biot, Davy, Félix Savary, Oersted, Herschel, Jussieu, and Agassiz. The work of the London Statistical Society did not escape the attention of this journal, nor did that of the Paris Phrenological Society. From the very beginning *The Reading Library* had lengthy sections on industrial and agricultural technology, and its editors seem to have had a particular fondness for the scientific expeditions conducted by such renowned travelers as Humboldt, Lütke, and Ross. The pages of this publication also introduced Russian readers to the historiographical ideas of Niebuhr and Guizot. It greeted the publication of Lyell's *Principles of Geology* with a short review long before the theoretical ideas propounded by the great geologist penetrated to the Academicians and university professors.

Scientific articles also found their way into the *Son of the Fatherland, Beacon, Fatherland Notes,* and the *Literary Gazette.* The *Journal of the Ministry of National Education,* published for teachers on all school levels, contained long articles of a scientific nature, ranging from astronomy to practical chemistry, as well as reviews of scientific articles published in other journals. One section was especially devoted to current scientific discoveries.

THE LEARNED SOCIETIES

Some of the dilettantes who began by reading the popular journals and attending public lectures became important amateurs in scientific research and the backbone of the learned societies which abounded during the 1840's and 1850's. The greatest virtue of these societies was that they brought professional scholars and amateurs, both dedicated to the search for scientific knowledge, into close and effective association.

In 1855, on the occasion of the first anniversary of the founding of the *Messenger of the Natural Sciences,* an organ of the Moscow Society of Naturalists, another journal of the day made the following statement: "Concentrated primarily in the narrow sphere of specialists and learned societies, science was not at first accessible to society. Independent studies by Russian scholars were published more often in foreign languages than in Russian, obviously because these works were more useful to science in general than to Russian society. Thanks to the teaching of natural science in the higher and secondary educational institutions and to private initiative, the distance separating science from society was in the course of time narrowed so much that at present it is possible to publish a natural-history journal intended for the general public."[106]

The process of bringing science closer to society would have been much slower without the learned societies, both old and new. Not only did these societies provide an opportunity for enthusiastic amateurs to work in the company of skilled scientists in several disciplines, but they also created an intellectual climate conducive to freer discussion than was sometimes possible in institutions closely connected with the government. Furthermore, they worked energetically to enlist private financial backing for extensive research projects.

Most of the amateurs were aristocrats, and many of them were men genuinely dedicated to science; some made valuable gifts from their own collections to the societies. In 1832-33, one Shelaputin, a typical amateur, donated some 1,350 books on natural science to the Moscow Society of Naturalists.[107] Before 1840 a number of these amateurs, not surprisingly, were members more or less in name only, particularly in the older societies like the Moscow Society of Naturalists. The shallow scientific interests of these people were an object of Herzen's biting criticism. They were gradually crowded out of the learned societies in the 1840's, however, as new and more serious aristocratic amateurs joined, along with greater numbers of professional scholars. The new amateurs were not a mere chorus of enthusiasts applauding the professional performers in the world of science; they, too, produced work of high quality. For some, work in learned societies was an apprenticeship that eventually led to dedicated careers.

In tune with the national exuberance of the time, with wide evidence of a real Russian cultural spirit in literature, drama, music, and philosophy, many of the learned societies of this period were concerned with the study of Russia in various aspects—early history, language, culture, society, law, and geography. Two societies in particular, the Russian Geographical Society and the Russian Archaeological Society, rendered important service in meeting the pressing demand for a more thorough and systematic understanding of the country's cultural history and the diversity of its habitat, population, and customs.

The Russian Geographical Society was founded in 1845 by a group of scientists including von Baer, Struve, and Helmersen. According to some reports, Murchison, during his geological fieldwork in Russia, urged the authorities to establish a society which in its aims and organization would follow the model of the Royal Geographical Society in London. Among the original members of the society were also such prominent explorers as Lütke, Wrangel, and Krusenstern; M. P. Vronchenko, V. I. Dal', A. I. Levshin, M. N. Murav'ev, and Odoevskii were some of the other charter members. The founding members convened for the first time in the famous Conference Hall of the St. Petersburg Academy of Sciences— a symbol, as it were, of their dedication to true scholarship as well as proof of the Academy's willingness to treat the Society as a serious enterprise and to enter into a close working relationship with it.

The charter of 1849, which remained unchanged until 1931, divided the Society into four departments: mathematical geography, physical geography, ethnography, and statistics. The scope of the Society's scientific interest can best be seen by the functions assigned to the individual departments. The Department of Mathematical Geography dealt with geodetics, cartography, and ways of determining geographical coordinates; the Department of Physical Geography with geology, climatology, hydrology, botanical and zoological geography, and topography; the Department of Statistics with gathering quantitative data relevant to economic and sociological phenomena; and the Department of Ethnography with the collection of anthropological data, and "the study of the dialects, morals, and customs of various peoples and in particular the study of the various aspects of the life of the Russian people."[108]

During its first years, the Society was occupied as much with an intellectual clarification and delimitation of the branches of science in which it was interested as it was with organizing its first expeditions and publishing its *Journal*. At the Society's first meeting, N. I. Nadezhdin read a paper entitled "The Ethnographic Study of the Russian People" in which he analyzed what the scientific study of culture should be. With considerable foresight, he outlined the field of ethnography by describing briefly what he considered its major branches: ethnographic linguistics (or linguistic ethnography), physical ethnography (a part of zoology), and psycho-ethnography.[109]

From the beginning, the work of the Society was highly diversified and intensive. In its first two years, 1846–47, it initiated major studies in ethnography and geography. In the summer of 1846, Academician Johann Sjögren was sent to Lithuania and Kurland to study the remnants of two tribes, the Livs and the Krevings, in the hope of discovering new clues to a fuller understanding of the ethnic origin of various Baltic nationalities and the historical transformations of their languages. Two detailed studies of these tribes were subsequently published. Also in 1846, Academician Peter Köppen began his work on an ethnographic map of Russia, which was published in 1851, and Ia. V. Khanykov prepared a map of the area between the lower Volga and the Ural River.

In 1847 the Society sent an expedition to survey the boundary between Europe and Asia along the entire length of the northern Urals. The material collected by this expedition made it possible for the Society to publish in 1852 a map of the northern Ural area based on 186 geographical coordinates, and in 1851 and 1855 two geographical reports on this area.

The year 1847 was also the beginning of the Society's comprehensive study of Russian ethnography, a collective project requiring the work of men in all provinces. Seven thousand copies of a report by Nadezhdin on the aims of the program and methods of collecting data were sent out. Data to be collected were divided into such categories as physical features, linguistic characteristics, family life, intellectual and moral characteristics, and customs. By 1852 the Society had received some two thousand reports from widely dispersed field workers, mostly clergymen and teachers, containing information in such quantity that it still has not been fully processed. This material was most useful to Vladimir Dal' in the preparation of his *Interpretive Dictionary of the Russian Language* (1864–68) and his monumental collection *The Proverbs of the Russian People* (1862).

This was only the beginning. During the 1850's the work of the Society expanded to gigantic proportions. It acquired special fame through geographical explorations in the newly annexed territories in Central Asia and the Amur basin. In 1851 branches of the Society were opened in Tiflis and Irkutsk, both of which soon began to issue their own reports, dealing exclusively with regional findings. In St. Petersburg, the original *Journal,* to which had been added in 1847 a second publication called *Geographical News,* was further supplemented: in 1851 by the *Messenger of the Geo-*

graphical Society and by a special journal devoted to economic, sociological, and demographic topics, in 1853 by the *Ethnographic Symposium*, and in 1860 by the *Meteorological Symposium* (in German).

The systematic study of Russian history by learned bodies operating independently of the Academy of Sciences and the universities antedated the study of Russian geography and ethnography by similar bodies. The Moscow Society for the Study of Russian History and Antiquity, for example, was founded in 1803. A decade later, N. P. Rumiantsev began to sponsor a group of highly skilled historians in the preparation of the well-known *Collection of State Documents and Agreements* and several other compilations of pertinent historical material.

Both the Moscow Society and the Rumiantsev group had been primarily intent on bringing about the publication of material already collected. The searching out of still other historical documents buried in provincial archives and monasteries was a job yet to be done. In 1828 the Academy of Sciences prepared a detailed plan for mounting an "archaeographical" expedition for the systematic collection of historical source materials in northern and central Russia. Painstaking work from 1829 to 1834 through some two hundred chaotic libraries and archives in fourteen provinces produced three thousand documents. In order to inspect and catalogue the collected material, the government established the "Archaeographical" Commission, which received its official charter in 1837. The work of this institution—particularly its *Full Collection of Russian Chronicles*—surpassed all expectations; it enabled the professional historians to give more depth to their studies and to correct many erroneous interpretations made chiefly by foreign writers of the eighteenth century. Without the labors of this Commission Sergei Solov'ev could not have undertaken his monumental *History of Russia,* and there would have been little chance for the formation of such new disciplines as the history of Old Russian literature and the history of Russian jurisprudence.

The Commission was also authorized to collect historical documents up to the year 1700. Two main types of historical material were sought out: works which made up so-called Old Russian literature, such as chronicles, chronographs, genealogies, and other writings containing historical data; and official government papers, including certificates, charters, instructions, and court records. Soon it also began to publish foreign documents pertaining to Russian history and to collect and study old coins.

Although the "Archaeographical" Commission was fundamentally a government institution, it owed its support to the enthusiasm of individuals —to certain high-ranking government officials, to eminent clergymen, and to members of the Academy of Sciences. Its ambitious programs were stimulated alike by the intellectual aggressiveness of the champions of official nationalism and by encouragement from independent thinkers. Since the mass of new documentary material, often containing contradictory information, demanded historical analysis of considerable sophistication, Russian historians were eager to learn more about the methodological precepts advanced by such great contemporary Western scholars as Guizot, Niebuhr, Ranke, and Savigny; Solov'ev, for one, found it necessary to go to Western universities in search of models for modern historical inquiry.

The "Archaeographical" Commission was devoted to the collection and publication of early written historical documents, not to an investigation of archaeological artifacts. Since the beginning of the nineteenth century, however, archaeological fieldwork had been receiving increasing attention in Russia, first from Russian amateurs, who were eager and persistent but usually short on experience and scientific skill, or by solitary foreign adventurer-scholars, most of whom were interested in excavating ancient settlements by the Black Sea in search of evidence concerning the cultural boundaries of ancient Greece, as well as for valuable artifacts.* The work of both groups was of great interest to Russians, who, with growing national consciousness, were curious about the beginnings of their culture. Geography and archaeology were often combined as supplementary disciplines, one exploring the last remaining mysteries of Russia's vast territorial possessions, the other probing into the mists of prehistory.

Early in the century, G. I. Spasskii, a mining engineer, conducted on his own a series of archaeological excavations in Siberia which yielded rich finds. These, and his two journals, the *Siberian Messenger* (1818–25) and the *Asiatic Messenger* (1825–28), both devoted to archaeological reports on early Siberian cultures, won him election to the Academy of Sciences as a corresponding member.

Another early archaeological amateur was Ivan Stempkovskii, the son of an impoverished nobleman, who, though an army officer, became so fascinated with the subject of archaeology that he spent four years studying at the Académie des Inscriptions et Belles-Lettres in Paris. He

---

* The most successful and popular of these scholars was J. Blaramberg, born in Flanders, whose findings enriched the Odessa and Kerch museums and whose long list of publications included an interpretive essay on the artifacts excavated in an ancient site near Kerch and a study entitled *On the Location of Three Scythian Fortresses Mentioned by Strabo* (1831).

became a close friend and colleague of Désiré Raoul-Rochette, the permanent secretary of this institution, and ultimately was elected a corresponding member. Stempkovskii read widely and took extensive notes about excavation techniques, which he applied with great skill when he returned to Russia. He carried on extensive digs in the Black Sea area, and found enough material, including the famous Kul'-Oba vase, to establish two archaeological museums—one in Odessa (1825) and another in Kerch (1826). Among his numerous writings, the most important were four methodological and substantive papers published in the Marquis de Castelano's symposium dealing with the ancient and modern history of the Novorossiisk Territory (1820).

One of the foreign archaeologists whose work proved particularly valuable to Russia was P. I. Köppen, the son of a German physician, who arrived in the Crimea in 1829 determined to study local artifacts and statistics. It was his work in "statistics" that attracted the attention of the St. Petersburg Academy of Sciences, which elected him an adjunct and eventually a full member. Köppen also published two important general works on Russian archaeology and did much to establish archaeology as an independent science in Russia.

The government's growing interest in the preservation of national antiquities was a further important stimulus to the emergence of archaeology as a separate and respectable academic discipline. Until 1820 the Russian government made no serious efforts to regulate excavations and to safeguard excavated material. In 1820, however, it granted permission specifically to N. P. Rumiantsev, the founder of the Rumiantsev Museum, to conduct excavations in certain *kurgans,* and it began for the first time to finance excavations of its own.[110] Archaeological articles began to appear in the *Journal of the Ministry of the Interior.* These and other Russian studies of prehistory quickly attracted the notice of Western scholars, and archaeology soon was an important bond of intellectual exchange between Russia and Western Europe.

Since the archaeological excavations in the Black Sea were particularly extensive, it was natural that the first Russian learned society dedicated to the study of prehistory should be founded in Odessa (1839). It was not a purely archaeological society, in that it was also dedicated to the task of collecting statistical and geographical data pertaining to conditions in the Novorossiisk Territory.

The first society dedicated exclusively to prehistory was founded in St. Petersburg in 1846; known first as the Archaeological-Numismatic Society, it was soon renamed the Imperial Russian Archaeological Society. The aim of the Society, as stated by its twenty-two founders, was to enrich science by sponsoring the collection of useful archaeological and numismatic materials, and this it proceeded to do in a variety of ways. Starting in 1847 it issued a scholarly publication, *Mémoires,* with articles in German or French, and two years later, when the Russian members assumed the dominant role, it began to publish an archaeological journal in Russian.[111]

The founding members of the Society were foreigners; as Russian membership increased, changes in program appeared. The main interest shifted from Western archaeological work to an intense interest in Russian and Oriental (particularly Moslem) prehistory. Russian became the official language of the Society, and the key position of secretary went to P. S. Savel'ev. Annual prizes were awarded for outstanding studies. These prizes proved to be a great stimulus to archaeological and historical research, much of it of high quality, as evidenced by such works as Ivan Zabelin's *Metallurgical Work in Old Russia,* and D. A. Rovinskii's *History of Russian Schools of Iconography.*

Zabelin made an impressive plea for a synthesis of historical and archaeological approaches to the study of the Russian past. While history, according to him, was valuable as a critical examination of important political *events* that influenced the growth of the Russian state, the strength of archaeology lay in the study of cultural *processes* that revealed "the soul of the people" and the "national personality." The future showed Zabelin more successful as a historian than as an archaeologist.

The Archaeological Society was at first but little interested in sponsoring new excavations, being more concerned with its numerous publications —the *Mémoires,* the Russian *Journal,* bulletins for its section on Russian and Slavic Archaeology and its section on Oriental Archaeology, and assorted journals and monographs. Until 1873 the Society did very little archaeological excavation, and what little was done was due mostly to the financial sponsorship of individual members.[112] During the 1850's, I. P. Sakharov, an influential member of the Society, prepared a special "Instruction for the Collection of Russian Antiquities," 20,000 copies of which were distributed among the corresponding members of the Society in the provinces. The "Instruction" was concerned mostly with the collection of inscriptions on religious objects and ancient artifacts.

It should be emphasized that although the Geographical Society and the Archaeological Society were born in the period of Russia's rich and diversified cultural self-assertion and rising national consciousness, both so-cieties were founded by foreign scholars. It was perhaps inevitable that in both there should have developed unpleasant quarrels between the Russian and German members—despite the fact that most of the so-called foreigners were firmly identified with Russian society. Indeed, many of them were Russian in all but name. Those who founded the Geographical Society were either navigator-explorers associated with the Admiralty or members of the Academy of Sciences. Many of the explorers were famous men, men whose around-the-world or Arctic voyages had won wide acclaim in the West as well as honored positions in Russian society. A few were foreign-born, but the leaders of this group—Lütke, Krusenstern, and Wrangel—were actually members of aristocratic Russian families whose origins, and names, could be traced to various Western European countries. It was said of Admiral Lütke, for example, that he knew only as much of the German language as he had been able to learn in a Russian gymnasium. The opposition to men of this sort was therefore based solely on national pride of an extreme kind, which wanted more and more Russian names in the world of scholarship.

A number of Academicians were natives of the Russian-occupied Baltic countries, or else they had been on the faculty of Dorpat University; in either case, they were accustomed to Russian life long before they joined the Academy in St. Petersburg. Struve, von Baer, Middendorff, and Helmersen, the leading Academicians in the Geographical Society, were typical of those great nineteenth-century scholars who, after accepting their Academic appointments in St. Petersburg, became forever a part of Russian science. Since membership in the amateurish Geographical Society could hardly have been expected to improve the professional or financial status of these scholars, it seems fair to say that they joined this society for the sheer love of science, hoping to further the cause of scientific investigation in a very specific, Russian, context.

Even at its highest level, the world of Russian scholarship was still dominated by foreigners. In 1852 none of the fifteen regular and associate members of the St. Petersburg Academy of Sciences working in the important fields of astronomy, physics, chemistry, botany, zoology, geology, physiology, and anatomy was a Russian by ethnic origin.[113] In the same year, in the Department of History and Philology, only two of the ten Academicians were native Russians. Many people thought of the Academy as a German institution, and it is small wonder that they were eager to join scholarly societies directed by Russians. The more extremist Russian groups were equally critical of what they considered the exaggerated and unwarranted concern of the Geographical and Archaeological Societies with Western geography and archaeology. The nationalist upsurge at first threatened the very survival of these learned bodies, but in the ensuing battles a compromise was reached, the great foreign scholars gracefully giving way to the obviously more powerful Russians and still continuing to work for the good of the societies. Within a decade or so, nationalism ceased to be an important factor in selecting the officers of the two societies. It should be added, however, that the conflict between the two factions was inspired by Russian nationalist sentimentalism and extremism only to a degree. Among the members of the Geographical Society, a strong faction resented the conservatism of the so-called foreign scholars and the defenders of Russia's social and political status quo. In the Geographical Society, a group of Russian liberals led by N. A. Miliutin insisted that whereas geographers must indeed study the ethnic characteristics and habitats of the Russian people, they must also pave the way for social reforms, and particularly for the emancipation of the serfs.

There were other scholarly associations, some founded before this period, but their work lacked vitality and was of limited compass. The Moscow Society of Naturalists, founded in 1805, followed an unsteady course and sponsored very little fieldwork by competent scholars; yet its annual report for 1852 showed that it had 736 honorary and regular members (including 356 who lived abroad) and that twenty-eight original scientific papers had appeared in the four issues of its *Bulletin* for that year. In this Society the predominance of foreign members, who resisted the admittance of young Russian naturalists, was a serious handicap. In 1831 Mikhail Orlov pleaded that the charter of the society be amended to make membership more widely available, but Uvarov paid no heed whatever to this demand, and the Society entered a prolonged period of dullness. Anuchin stated that the Society simply failed "to meet the needs of the day." It convened once a month to hear one or two papers to which only a handful listened while "the remainder drank tea and engaged in friendly chatter." For several decades, the Society was dominated by Fischer von Waldheim, who lectured at Moscow University in the German language. Until the 1850's, all its publications appeared in French or German, and the minutes of its meetings were kept in French. Anuchin was essentially correct when he said that this Society contributed more to Western Europe's reservoir of knowledge than to Russia's.[114] It was primarily because of the widespread dissatisfaction with the work of this Society in the 1850's and beginning 1860's that the Moscow Society of the Admirers of Natural Science, Anthropology, and Ethnography was founded in 1863.

After the 1830's the old and respected Free Economic Society turned mostly to practical studies in agriculture and agricultural economics; it also collected valuable information on agricultural techniques and problems in other countries for use in analyzing farming conditions in Russia. In 1851 it established a special fund for the publication of popular economic and technical manuals.[115]

The Mineralogical Society, dating from 1817, was for years a listless organization, in part because its membership included many St. Petersburg dilettantes but also because neither geology nor paleontology inspired a wide interest in Russia during the first half of the century. Determined to publish exclusively in the Russian language, it contrived to issue only two volumes of its *Works* (in 1832 and 1842) during the first twenty-five years of its existence. After it switched to German in 1842, its output increased enormously.

During the first half of the nineteenth century, medical societies were founded in Moscow, Vilna, Warsaw, St. Petersburg, Kiev, and Odessa, but they were limited in their activities and did little or no publishing.[116]

All of these learned societies, including the two most important ones, operated far below their potentialities and paid virtually no attention to scientific theory: they functioned in the realm of empirical science, being dedicated primarily to gathering raw scientific data. True, this contribution, modest in terms of scientific sophistication, added up to a great storehouse of valuable knowledge. By the end of the first half of the nineteenth century, the physical and human potentials of Russia had been sufficiently well investigated for scholars to make geological, soil, hydrographic, and ethnographic maps of European Russia and to prepare comprehensive surveys of climatic conditions, flora, and economic geography.

The real contribution of these learned societies, however, was to facilitate the flow of private donations into scientific research, and in general to help science achieve an honored place in Russian culture. Lacking in broad objectivity as they were, these societies made little attempt to keep up with modern scientific developments in Western Europe. They also tended to place undue emphasis on "sponsored science," and in that way to promote an uneven development of the various branches of science. They made participation in scientific research possible for people who were not professional scholars, but in thus creating a new class of patrons of science, they overlooked the challenge of popularizing modern advances in scientific theory and the philosophy of science. The most glaring weakness of many of these societies was that they published most of their material in foreign languages. This prompted the famous plant physiologist K. A. Timiriazev to state cynically that their main job was to keep the Western countries informed about Russia's economic, human, and physical resources.[117]

THE SYSTEM OF SCIENTIFIC INSTITUTIONS

The Academy of Sciences, the universities and other schools of higher education, and the semi-independent learned societies were not the only fountains of scientific knowledge in Russia, but their work was the most important in terms of both volume and quality of output. These three types of institutions had much in common, yet they made very different contributions to the growth of scholarship in Russia.

The Academy of Sciences made Russia an active contributor to modern scientific thought. Struve, von Baer, Hess, Ostrogradskii, and Lenz helped to widen the horizons of their respective sciences or to found new scientific disciplines. The leading Academicians met the highest standards of scholarly work and formed a true scientific elite. In this capacity, they influenced contemporary Russian culture more through their published writings than by their work as teachers and members of independent learned societies.

The universities performed a historically more important role: they laid the indispensable foundations for the training of Russian scholars and for a triumphant emancipation of Russian science during the 1860's. These schools were not yet able to produce as many really competent scholars in the natural sciences as Russia needed, but they prepared a large number of students to undertake postgraduate work under the most distinguished scientists in the West. Thanks to the work of these institutions, Russia began to depend on its own scientific manpower during the 1860's, and the imported scholar became a rarity. The university was helped by a whole network of higher professional schools, led by such notable institutions as the Medical and Surgical Academy, the Artillery Academy, the Engineering Academy, the Main Pedagogical School, the Mining Institute, the Communications Institute, and the Technological Institute. The training in natural science was particularly effective in these schools. Since they placed an emphasis on applied science, they received ample funds from the government to build and equip laboratories, which, in turn, made it possible for them to obtain the services of Academicians and eminent university professors, not only in applied science but also in mathematics.

The independent learned societies, which, as we have seen, added little to pure scholarship or to the actual training of future scientists (though they inspired a good many), provided a meeting ground for the Academy and society at large. They were, in a sense, a grass-roots movement clamoring for—and supporting—the idea of Russia's national independence in the world of science. They laid the groundwork for scientific congresses during and after the 1860's which made possible personal and scholarly exchanges between the scattered forces of Russia's scientific manpower. They established relations with the analogous scientific societies abroad and maintained regular exchanges of scientific publications with them, thus adding a good deal to Russia's prestige abroad—Darwin was pleased to be elected an honorary member of the Moscow Society of Naturalists. Behind the founding of the Geographical Society, the most successful and popular of the learned societies, were two powerful motives: first, the awareness of the acute need for an expansion of the ranks of persons engaged in the scientific study of Russia's physical and human resources; and, second, the urgent need for a central coordinating body to which the rapidly growing quantity of geographical material could be entrusted.[118] Both of these assignments were parts of the pressing national demand for fuller self-understanding.

In addition to these three broad types of institutions dedicated to scientific work, the Russian government itself directly acted as the organizer and financial sponsor of research projects. The Admiralty and the Russo-American Company supported round-the-world voyages which gathered valuable information in physical, economic, and human geography. Many government bureaus sponsored special committees concerned with practical problems of scientific import. N. N. Zinin, for example, was a member of the Manufacturing Council of the Finance Ministry and of the Military Medical Scientific Committee. Carl Julius Fritzsche, an organic chemist of international repute and a full member of the St. Petersburg Academy of Sciences, belonged to a special government committee for the study of the Caucasus mineral waters, was an official chemist of the Medical Department of the Ministry of the Interior and acted as a consulting member of the Medical Council of the same Ministry.[119]

In 1842 the Mining Department, a part of the Finance Ministry, secured the services of the famous embryologist Christian Pander to help in its study of the paleontological specimens that were being collected in abundance in many parts of Russia. One result was Pander's monograph on fish fossils of the Silurian system in the Baltic area.[120]

During the 1830's the Finance Ministry, through its Mining Department, supported a study of the distribution of mineral resources in European Russia and in the Ural and Altai areas.[121] In the 1840's it supported Murchison's expedition, which resulted in the publication of the first systematic study of the geology of Russia and the Ural Mountains.[122] The hiring of men of such repute by various government agencies was not unusual, but a large part of government research suffered from a narrow concern with practicality.

The disadvantages of government ventures into activities requiring scholarly competence were summed up by Academician Helmersen in an investigation of why geology had developed slowly in Russia. According to Helmersen, the failure of government-sponsored geological studies had three converging origins: first, the research was strictly of a local sort, with no broad organizational or scholarly plan, and no coordination; second, the work was done mainly by incompetent men who succeeded only in amassing mountains of erroneous information; and, third, the narrow practical aims of government geological research left many areas unexplored because it was assumed that they contained no useful minerals. Helmersen also added that the same locality was often investigated several times by different persons working for different ministries, who were unaware of any previous investigations. In sum, the government had done little to help geology. Geology had become established in Russia as an independent and vital science principally because of investigations carried out for purely scientific purposes and conducted by university professors and private persons.[123]

The direct contributions of government-sponsored research should not be taken lightly, however, nor should its practical ends be undervalued. To be sure, there was some research of a pedestrian nature, but the government undertook many serious scientific enterprises, and in all of these it sought the help of competent scholars, frequently the best available. Its expeditions not only achieved their immediate practical ends but stimulated the curiosity of an important part of the intellectual elite. Its meteorological stations supplied the raw data without which no scholarly study of Russia's climatic variations could have been undertaken. Its round-the-world voyages performed many practical functions—for example, the discovery of the best sea routes between Russia and its American possessions and other countries. And most ships on government missions carried professional scientists engaged in the study of marine physics, marine biology, or astronomy.

CHAPTER EIGHT

The End of the Formative Age.

"THE WATERSHED OF TWO HISTORICAL CURRENTS"

No great scientific achievements blessed the Russia of the 1840's, but during this decade scientific thought flowered in many and diverse endeavors. Science became clearly separated from metaphysics. It rose to prominence as a topic of ideological debate. It found new and formidable supporters, but it faced equally formidable foes.

The Academy and several of the independent learned societies could now afford to give handsome annual prizes for superior papers on challenging scientific themes. The government placed larger sums than ever before at the disposal of scholarship; but it also imposed more rigid controls over creative intellectual endeavors. The censorship, however, was not very successful: the new ideas were too rich and too expansive to be policed successfully. Science grew faster than the institutional mechanisms of autocratic control over the flow of ideas.

The 1840's laid the groundwork for the scientific triumphs of the 1860's, the years of Russia's scientific emancipation from the West and the emergence of scholars of outstanding importance—Dmitrii Mendeleev and Aleksandr Butlerov in chemistry, Ivan Sechenov in physiology, Vladimir Kovalevskii in evolutionary paleontology, and Aleksandr Kovalevskii in evolutionary embryology. But what happened during the 1850's?

Russia in the 1850's fell into two different epochs, with February 18, 1855—the day of the death of Nicholas I—serving, in the words of Kliment Timiriazev, as "the watershed of two historical currents."[1] The first five years of the 1850's were turbulent years of recuperation from the setbacks perpetrated by the fearful imperial government in its strenuous efforts to forestall the spread of ideas and ideals incompatible with the autocratic system. The second five, dominated by the profound consciousness of impending radical social changes, ushered in the modern age of Russian science.

The swiftness, thoroughness, and mercilessness with which the government moved into action immediately after the word of the 1848 upheavals reached Russia signified its unflinching opposition to the spread of subversive ideas. The government, now fully realizing that the gentry, its traditional backbone, had produced a strong core of men dedicated to sweeping social and political reforms, sought to restrict the universities even further, making them not simply the exclusive domain of the noble estates but the domain of the highest aristocracy. It also began to encourage young aristocrats to select military rather than civilian occupations and to enroll in military schools rather than in universities. University education, it assured the young gentry, was not a requirement for the attainment of higher military ranks.

The government was obviously determined to close the doors of universities to persons to whom higher education would have brought higher social status, including the impoverished gentry, who were the most likely source of trouble. Measures were sought to make universities inaccessible to persons "who own no real estate, but who dream too much of their abilities and knowledge and who very often become restless and dissatisfied with the existing conditions, particularly if their highly aroused ambitions have not been satisfied."[2] Tuition fees were raised, and entrance requirements were changed to make a diploma from a public gymnasium mandatory for university enrollment.

Censorship regulations also were tightened. The government admitted that the censorship of foreign books had not so far been effective, and that minds were being contaminated by imported books being circulated surreptitiously. Books condemned by the censors, it appeared, were particularly valuable black-market commodities.

A special committee known as the Committee of April Second, made up of the most reactionary of Nicholas's counselors, instituted a two-pronged censorship: manuscript censorship and postpublication censorship. University professors who had been acting as manuscript censors were replaced with well-paid government employees who knew nothing about scholarship. Postpublication censorship was put under the control of special boards, appointed by the Committee, that were authorized to impose stiff penalties, not only on the authors and publishers of censorable materials but also on the manuscript censors who passed the offending materials. This of course led to many excisions from manuscripts by manuscript censors who feared trouble.

The victims of the strict censorship practices were legion. *Readings,* the journal of the respectable Society of Russian History and Antiquities, was forced to discontinue publication temporarily for printing a Russian translation of Fletcher's account of Old Russia which contained unfavorable comments about Ivan IV and certain parts of the Orthodox ritual. Sergei Stroganov, the chairman of the Society, wrote to Uvarov: "I thought that Fletcher's work, written in 1588, contained not even a single line that could apply to the Russia of our time. . . . Karamzin expressed himself on several occasions in favor of the publication of this document. . . . I took it for granted that in our age, when all Europe looks with envy at our spiritual and state power, neither the Church nor the government leaders would be disturbed by a few harsh statements in a work written three hundred years ago and published in a scholarly symposium."[3]

In 1850, an enterprising landlord published an article in the journal of the Free Economic Society, with a circulation of 6,500 copies, describing how he had improved one of his farms by selective purchases of livestock in various districts and by transferring a number of Ukrainian peasants from other holdings. The author received 100 reprints of his article and chose to send many of them to highly placed officials in St. Petersburg. One of the recipients was Faddei Bulgarin, a mediocre writer and a widely detested informer of the Third Section, who was angered with what he affected to regard as the author's deliberate equating of livestock and peasants. Incited by Bulgarin, the censors saw in this kind of writing a revolutionary design to start unrest among enserfed peasants. In order to forestall similar happenings in the future, the Committee of April Second resolved that (1) the writer be prohibited from managing his farm and be placed under police surveillance; (2) the censor who allowed the publication of the manuscript be dismissed and forbidden to hold any government position; (3) the editor of the journal be relieved of his duties and barred from future editing and writing; and (4) the Free Economic Society be reprimanded for its laxity in the selection of editors and contributors. Paradoxically, the journal was acquitted because Nicholas, in reviewing the case, found the accusations unwarranted.

Nicholas wanted no intellectual traffic whatever with the West. In 1848 the flow of young Russians to Western European universities in search of postgraduate education came to an abrupt end. In 1848–49, police surveillance over the movements of foreigners in Russia was expanded and measures were undertaken to curtail their contact with the West. A special decree issued in 1852 forbade the inviting of foreign scholars to Russia.

As the forces of darkness descended on the university halls, men of learning either allowed themselves to be intimidated or became vulnerable to all kinds of recriminations. S. M. Solov'ev, caught in the wave of repression, noted in his diary: "The 1848–1855 period was similar to the first phase of the Roman Empire—the time when the mad Caesars relied on the pretorians and the mobs to squelch everything noble and spiritual in Rome."[4] "It was easy for Belinskii," said Granovskii, "for he died at the right time"—that is, in 1848, on the eve of the devastating inquisition. "Our position is deteriorating from day to day," Granovskii wrote in 1848. "Every movement in the West is reflected here by another oppressive measure. Denunciations number in the thousands. Despotism makes thunderous announcements to the effect that it cannot get along with enlightenment."[5]

In the meantime, rumors circulated that the government was ready to take drastic steps to bring universities under its full control. In January 1849, A. V. Nikitenko noted in his diary: "Unbelievable rumors about the closing of the [St. Petersburg] University are circulating in the city. It is alleged that [Ia. I.] Rostovtsev has submitted to the Tsar a memorandum suggesting a complete revamping of educational and scientific activities in Russia. The memorandum is also reported to contain a recommendation to replace St. Petersburg and Moscow Universities by two higher military schools that would provide scientific education only for persons belonging to the highest estate."[6]

Whether or not Nicholas thought seriously of closing the universities is difficult to determine, but it is certain that he ordered the enrollment in each university to be reduced to 300 students (excluding the medical faculties) in addition to state stipendists. Since the number of state stipendists, all carefully selected, was high, this could mean that they were in the majority in every university. The total university enrollment in Russia was considerably reduced—from 4,016 in 1848 to 3,256 in 1849 and finally to 3,018 in 1850.

Even before the revolutions broke out in 1848, Nicholas was apprehensive of the ideological restlessness in Russian universities, where philosophical and literary circles discussed alarming ideas. The revolution in Western Europe was therefore a convenient pretext—if a frightening one—for a frontal attack on the universities aimed at subordinating them to full and thorough autocratic control. Guided by his close advisers A. S. Menshikov and M. A. Korff, Nicholas decided to make a swift attack on "the subversive work of liberalism," as reflected mainly "in the teaching of sciences and the orientation of journals,"[7] and to build up the military schools at the expense of the universities.

Nicholas's severity toward the universities had an almost personal nature; he himself assumed control over university regulation. In 1848 he assumed the prerogative of selecting rectors. The right of university councils to elect deans was substantially limited; an elected dean must now be confirmed, and could be unilaterally replaced, by the Minister of National Education. Having in mind even more sweeping changes, Nicholas appointed D. N. Bludov to head a special committee charged with working out a thorough reorganization of the whole school system. The committee met only a few times, however, and no substantial changes resulted. Of the total of eleven meetings ten were held in 1850 and 1851. The committee favored a school system differentiated along estate lines and the elimination of courses incompatible with religion and autocracy. On all other questions the committee's members were widely split, and by 1852 Nicholas forgot about its existence.

The Tsar and his closest advisers were keenly interested in the relationship of science to Christian morality and of education to the differing needs of the various estates. They hoped somehow to make scientific knowledge less dangerous to traditional values by "synchronizing" it with Christian morality, but this would mean that every fact, theory, and hypothesis incompatible with religion must be suppressed. It was an enormous and vague hope, impossible to achieve, the dream of a man mortally afraid of modern scientific thought.

In 1855, preceding the ceremonies marking the 100th anniversary of founding of Moscow University, Nicholas gave an audience to a delegation of university professors, and in greeting them he said: "I want to tell you now what I think should be the goal of education in our time. I respect and highly appreciate scholarship; however, I appreciate morality even more. Without morality, instruction is useless and might be dangerous. The basis of morality is holy religion. It is necessary that the cultivation of religious feeling be a part of instruction. This is my view on education. This is what I expect from you. Many peoples have lost religion; in Russia it lives as it has always lived. It is necessary to preserve in Russia that which has been here from time immemorial. In many countries the people have accepted differences of opinion, so that nobody can understand anybody else, and no person knows what he wants. Such is not the case among us. My will is known to you; I am convinced that you will carry it out."[8]

Some thirty years earlier, Golitsyn and Magnitskii had tried to achieve exactly the same thing, and it took more than a decade to repair the damage wrought by their ill-considered actions. Nicholas's counselors, fortunately less hasty, dissuaded him from undertaking any radical reforms, and the educational system was not seriously disturbed, but the new reaction left its sorry mark. The curriculum suffered particularly, yet not, oddly enough, in the natural and exact sciences. The social sciences, law, and the humanities were considered to be the most open to ideological distortions. On October 24, 1849, the Minister of National Education assigned the university rectors and deans broad powers over the teaching of "constitutional law, political economy, finances, and in general all historical sciences susceptible to even the slightest abuse."[9] The rectors and deans were charged with the responsibility of seeing that the professors conformed to "the basic principle of our state system." "This principle," the instruction specified, "is based on the idea that, by its geographical position, national rights, estate needs, and history . . . Russia cannot and must not have any other form of government than monarchical autocracy, in which the ruler, as the guardian of the Church and the father of the homeland, embodies at the same time a concentration and a unification of the three branches of government: legislative, judicial, and executive."[10]

Opinions favorable to the republican and constitutional forms of government or pointing out the national advantages of the equality of all estates were considered particularly dangerous. Special measures were aimed at preventing the spread of dangerous "political-economic schemes, mostly of French origin," among which the best known were those of "Saint-Simonists, Fourierists, Socialists, and Communists." The rectors and deans were also ordered to prevent professors from expressing any sympathy for Russia's millions of enserfed peasants.

In 1850 philosophy was removed altogether from the university curriculum, and the teaching of logic and psychology was assigned to clerics. Philosophy was replaced in the curriculum by two military courses, both of which combined theory with regular drills. Moscow University, one writer commented, took on a military character, and one of its buildings looked like a fortress.[11] A similar fate came to other universities.

As in the latter days of Alexander I, professors were required to submit the full texts of their lectures for official approval. The lectures were carefully scrutinized for the expression of any ideas differing from official ideology or the hallowed teachings of the Orthodox Church. This was the time when Minister of National Education Platon Shirinskii-Shikhmatov visited S. M. Solov'ev's opening lecture in Russian history at Moscow University and reprimanded him for "disloyal" statements. A circular of December 13, 1850, ruled that no dissertations for higher degrees could contain statements which did not conform to the official political philosophy or could be variously interpreted.[12]

Unlike the dark epoch of Magnitskii and Runich, which had attacked science in general and rationalism, humanism, and experimentation in particular, the 1848–52 period was concerned chiefly with ideology. The term republicanism embraced the key targets of the new repression. Republicanism, indeed, was a concept covering a wide field of dangerous ideas, from unfavorable opinions of the ancient Russian monarchs to a matter-of-fact recognition of the growing movement in favor of an emancipation of the Russian serfs. It was because of the fear of republicanism that the constitutional law of Western European countries was dropped from the university curriculum. For the same reason, the Greek language and Greek literature were retained in only a few gymnasiums and instruction in Latin was drastically curtailed.

Natural science, being more or less neutral ideologically, was less affected by these repressive policies than were humanistic subjects. Imported books in the natural sciences were generally given fairly lenient treatment by the censors, although manuscripts were supposed to be perused for "unverified ideas" such as biological transformism, the physiological basis of human thought, and the basic postulates of historical geology. This ordinance was too vague to be strictly applied, however, especially by censors who were not sophisticated in matters of modern science.

Nevertheless, the nationalist hysteria which swept St. Petersburg in the wake of the tightening of thought control was a disturbing influence in the field of the natural sciences. An incident recorded by A. V. Nikitenko provides one telling example of how the influence worked. In 1848, N. A. Varnek defended his dissertation in embryology at St. Petersburg University. His research material "was very interesting and was presented with great skill," but one professor objected to Varnek's use of Latin, German, and French technical names, though this was the customary style at the time. Giving vent to his highly emotional nationalism, the professor accused Varnek of not loving his fatherland and of hating his native language, and, even worse, of having "materialistic leanings." In the spirit of the time, as Nikitenko commented, an academic discussion was transformed into a police denunciation.[13]

After 1848, university professors were rarely permitted to give public lectures. Granovskii's last series ended abruptly after the fourth lecture.

Contact between the university and the community fell far below the level of the mid-1840's. Popular journals like *Contemporary* continued to devote special sections to scientific articles, but articles on obscure and ideologically innocent themes from ancient Russian history were far more numerous.

Magnitskii, Runich, and Golitsyn undertook their antiscientific crusades at a time when the Academy of Sciences was weak and when many of the national universities were still in their infancy. In 1848, on the other hand, the universities were well established as scientific institutions, and, as organic components of their respective communities, the Academy of Sciences enjoyed the reputation of a great intellectual center recognized by Western scholarship as well as the growing ranks of native intellectuals, and fifteen learned societies were solidly entrenched in a number of cities. The inner momentum of scientific thought was clearly much too formidable a force to be seriously affected by restrictive legislation. The attack on science in 1848 was accordingly less harmful than the attack mounted during the closing years of Alexander's reign. Indeed, the official campaign against the republicanism and paganism of classical education allowed a certain expansion in the teaching of the natural and exact sciences. Nicholas was not ignorant of the limitless potentialities of applied science, for all his mistrust of scientific theory. Wittingly or unwittingly, he embraced O. I. Senkovskii's idea that in order to be fruitful science must divorce itself completely from philosophy, and Shevyrev's thought that in order to be socially beneficial science must work in concordance with religious thought.

Nicholas's attempts to introduce a religious spirit into education and science were in no way so ruthless or far-reaching as those of Magnitskii, but they met with a more formidable resentment owing to the existence of a larger group of patrons of science and secular knowledge in general. Science was no longer on trial, nor was it a German preoccupation incompatible with Orthodox Russia. The resentment was so great that all enlightened Russians greeted Nicholas's death with relief and anticipated the beginning of a new era, full of bright promises. Some indication of the national sentiment following Nicholas's death is given by a contemporary writer: "Although the [Crimean] war was still going on, the general feeling during the first days of the new Tsar's reign was one of joy and great hopes. Everybody felt that it was somehow easier to breathe; everybody was aware of the need for a change in internal policies and turned anxious eyes toward the throne."[14]

Resentment at Nicholas's repressions also accounts to a great extent for the widespread criticism of the scientific contributions of the 1850's by the new generation of the 1860's, who received a part of their education during the waning days of Nicholas's regime. Ivan Sechenov, who entered Moscow University in 1851 and subsequently gained prominence as a physiologist of great originality, contended that the development of the natural sciences in Russia before the 1860's was "generally poor."[15] Kliment Timiriazev, a St. Petersburg University graduate who became an eminent plant physiologist, was lavish in his praise of the scientific achievements of the 1860's and contemptuous of those of the preceding decade. "The generation whose conscious life began during the 1860's was no doubt the luckiest of all Russian generations," he said. "The springtime of its personal life coincided with the coming of a national springtime, which reached every part of the country, awakening it from the intellectual numbness which had kept it in chains for over a quarter of a century."[16] Neither Sechenov nor Timiriazev saw the better side of the 1840's and 1850's. They ignored the impressive range of scholarship in both the humanities and the sciences, dismissing the Academy of Sciences as a German institution and the learned societies as nonexperimental—and therefore quasi-scientific—organizations.

The historian and sociologist of science Afanasii Shchapov, on the other hand, both exaggerated the development of the humanities during Nicholas's era and overlooked the great strides made in the natural sciences. His interpretation was partly determined by his belief that Russian scientific capabilities were largely empirical rather than theoretical.[17] It was this national empiricism, according to Shchapov, that determined the two great Russian scientific traditions, the study of the physical features of Russia and the study of Russian history, both of which were part of Russia's national need for "self-understanding." The geographical tradition developed first, out of the work of Messerschmidt, Gmelin, Krasheninnikov, Falk, Georgi, Pallas, and Lepekhin. The "ethnohistorical" tradition did not begin to crystallize until the 1830's and after, mainly because, lacking theoretical strength, it could not effectively oppose Magnitskii's mysticism, Uvarov's official nationalism, and Nicholas I's moral and religious views.

Writing in 1859, Shchapov conceded that at the beginning of the century mathematical thought in Russia had begun to make noticeable progress, and that mathematics had since become "the most highly developed science in our society."[18] He was aware that Russia had had great mathematicians in the past, and he knew about Ostrogradskii and Somov; but he failed to see their work as a part of the Russian mathematical tradition and had not yet heard of Lobachevskii's and Chebyshev's revolutionary theories, which were what gave this tradition a commanding place in Russian scientific inquiry. The diversity, power, and intellectual daring exhibited by nineteenth-century Russian mathematicians belied Shchapov's assessment of the "Russian mind" as basically "sensualistic" and not given to abstractions of a higher order. Had he been up to date in his knowledge of the growth of chemistry and the biological sciences in Russia, he would have been more cautious with his generalizations.

Shchapov thought that the Russian disinclination for theoretical thought was the reason why undue emphasis was placed on philology, archaeology, classical history, and literature as school subjects and research fields during the first half of the nineteenth century. His assessment invites challenge on two accounts. In the first place, his interpretation of the Russian nontheoretical ("sensualistic") mind lacked historical reference. He did not explain, for example, the relationship of "archaeologism"—his term for the exaggerated academic concern with the national past—to the expanding national consciousness and its versatile cultural affirmation. Was not the "archaeologism" a great and dynamic source of inspiration for literature, music, philosophy, and social thought?

In the second place, Shchapov allowed the "archaeological-classicist" orientation in Russian science and education too broad a scope by overlooking real developments in the natural sciences and mathematics, the rise of a Russian "school" in chemistry, and the many contributions of the Academy of Sciences, the learned societies, and the growing ranks of university scholars.

From 1859, when he gave the first hints of his sensualistic theory, Shchapov wrote voluminously on the question of the intellectual attributes of the Russian mind, going far beyond the first narrow limits of his theory into what could be called a broad sociological analysis of Russian science, the first such in Russia. Not only are his essays a rich source of information on the development of scientific thought and the scientific attitude in Russia, but in their wide scope and generally high quality they are an impressive summation of the scientific achievements in Russia until the early 1850's.*

Shchapov knew that science had many sources, ranging from the folk

---

* Although written in 1859, Shchapov's first sociological-historical study of Russian science was not published until 1863; censorship authorities were responsible for the delay.

inventors at one extreme to the erudite Academicians at the other, and he examined them all in some detail. He was particularly alert to the relationship of science to ideology, philosophy, and religion, and devoted much attention to it (often contradicting his sensualistic theory). His analyses of the attitudes of various estates and classes toward science are perceptive and solidly documented.

Shchapov was not a good prophet, however—chiefly because he allowed his concept of "sensualism" as the basic trait of the Russian mind to prevail over objective evaluation. He was much too concerned with the past to scrutinize what was going on around him. He obviously did not understand why the St. Petersburg Academy of Sciences elected Pafnutii Chebyshev a regular member in 1859 or why in 1860 the French Academy of Sciences honored him as a corresponding member. Much less could he have realized that Chebyshev was working on the foundations of a great Russian school in abstract mathematics and that Aleksandr Korkin, the first disciple of the great mathematician to acquire international stature, was already making new contributions of his own. If by chance Shchapov had looked into the first volumes of Nikolai Koksharov's *Materials for Russian Mineralogy,* he would have been impressed with the author's familiarity with the theoretical and methodological foundations of contemporary crystallography. Koksharov was not a slave of Russian "sensualism"; he was a vital link between the early mineralogists who relied primarily on personal observation as a source of scientific knowledge and the great crystallographers of the end of the century.

Shchapov failed to see that in 1859 and 1860 Russian chemists were entering the modern period in the history of their science. The electrochemical ("dualistic") views of Berzelius and Liebig ceased to be the theoretical backbone of chemistry as taught in universities. Most chemists, including Academician Zinin, subscribed now to the "unitary theory" of Laurent and Gerhardt and were ready to cope with the intensive growth of structural organic chemistry. The momentum was strong enough to make it possible for N. N. Sokolov and A. N. Engelhardt to start Russia's first chemical journal and a chemical laboratory, both of which lasted for two years. Sokolov's lead article in the first number of the new journal discussed various current efforts of chemists to give their discipline a comprehensive theoretical basis. It not only presented Sokolov's keen theoretical insights but was also instrumental in making Gerhardt's and Laurent's ideas an integral part of the teaching of chemistry in Russian universities.

One wonders whether Shchapov would have become a champion of the sensualist theory if in 1859 he had decided to spend a year at Heidelberg University instead of writing his essay on the intellectual growth of Russia. If he had had the good fortune to go to Heidelberg as a student, a scholar, or even a mere visitor, he would have been pleasantly surprised to find there a typical *kruzhok* of youthful Russians, some working at the University on their own research projects or enrolled as graduate students, others visiting for a time, temporarily away from other leading universities in Western Europe where they were engaged in similar work. During the course of the year he would have become acquainted with no small number of the future leaders of Russian science.

He would have had little difficulty in spotting the truly original minds, for they stood out either as established scholars or as serious, dedicated men of knowledge engaged in the great theoretical problems of the day. Here he would have met Aleksandr Butlerov, a young professor of chemistry from Kazan University, who was engaged in a research project that led him within a few years to formulate a new theory of the structure of chemical compounds and to be immediately acknowledged as one of the founders of structural chemistry. Another acquaintance would undoubtedly have been Aleksandr Borodin, who before becoming famous as one of Russia's leading composers was a chemist of considerable accomplishment; soon after completing his studies at Heidelberg, he undertook fruitful research in the polymerization and condensation of aldehydes.

Shchapov would have been particularly attracted to the serious young man sitting on the other side of Borodin. He, too, was a chemist, likely to embark at any moment on a discussion of Gerhardt's "formal types" and Kolbe's "real types" as conceptual devices in modern chemistry, but most enthusiastic of all about the ideas contained in the *Epitome of a Course in Philosophical Chemistry,* a monograph written by the Italian chemist Stanislao Cannizzaro in anticipation of the international congress of chemists held in Karlsruhe in 1860. According to another member of the *kruzhok,* this young man was "the head of the group" because "despite his youth . . . he was an accomplished chemist."[19] The name of this young scholar was Dmitrii Mendeleev. He was on leave from St. Petersburg University, where he taught theoretical chemistry (among other subjects); he could already show an impressive list of publications. But his rise to fame was not to come until 1869, when he published the periodic tables of atomic weights—one of the greatest feats in chemistry of the nineteenth century. In 1859, Shchapov would probably have had no inkling of the coming of these tables, but he would hardly have missed the excitement of Mendeleev's enthusiasm for Cannizzaro's profound insights into the perplexing areas of modern chemistry.

There were several other chemists in the Heidelberg *kruzhok*, but there were also representatives from other scientific fields. Ivan Sechenov had come here to work with Helmholtz and Bunsen. The attentive group heard from him about the new trends in physiology and about his rewarding visits to such other great natural scientists as Magnus, Ludwig, Johannes Müller, Rose, and Du Bois-Reymond. A serious and dedicated scholar, Sechenov accomplished enough within the next few years to deserve the title of Father of Russian Physiology given him by Ivan Pavlov. For his part, however, Sechenov awarded this title to Ludwig of Berlin University, who trained and inspired six of Russia's most eminent physiologists of the second half of the nineteenth century.

There were many other regular and visiting members of the *kruzhok* in 1859 and thereabouts. One of them was Lev Tsenkovskii, a professor of zoology at St. Petersburg University and an established expert in the study of microfauna. A far cry from the old-fashioned natural historian, he found zoology particularly valuable as a discipline contributing to theoretical biology. In 1860, a noted member of the group was Aleksandr Kovalevskii, who told his friends of the great new ideas contained in Darwin's *The Origin of Species,* published the preceding year, and who had already started to study individual species of invertebrates. As a mature scholar, concentrating on the lanceolate organisms and ascidia, he formulated a general theory which accounted for the embryonic development of all animals and for a bridge between the kingdoms of plants and animals. His contributions were one of the cornerstones of biological evolutionism.

The Heidelberg *kruzhok* was only one of several similar aggregations of young Russian scholars. Their existence at the end of the 1850's marked the beginning of a new phase in the history of scientific thought in Russia —a phase of an accelerated and rich growth of science as a body of knowledge, a method of inquiry, a system of values, and a world outlook.

During the 1850's, history and the social sciences manifested a pronounced tendency to rise above archaeologism's principal tenet —the pure description of historical events or social details with no theoretical refinement or integration. The humanities became a battleground for ideological warfare, and this led to new conflicts engendered by diverse interpretations of general historical processes, rather than of individual events. The impulse for historical and social generalization was present everywhere. It gathered particular momentum with the publication of August von Haxthausen's *Studien über die inneren Zustände, das Volksleben und insbesondere die ländliche Einrichtungen Russlands*. Haxthausen, a dedicated German monarchist, traveled extensively in Russia in 1842–44 under the patronage of Nicholas I. His two-volume book was published in Hanover and Berlin in 1847, but the publication was financed by the Russian government. This work is remembered chiefly for its "discovery" of the *obshchina* as a unique village community, but it also contained detailed information on the basic forms of tenancy in northern Russia and rich ethnographic material on various Russian religious sects. Although Haxthausen impressed some historians with his search for a central theme in Russian history, he angered his liberal contemporaries with his recommendation that the *obshchina* be preserved to forestall the growth of a proletariat and that no legal measures be aimed at the abolition of serfdom.

The Slavophils were quick to endorse Haxthausen's interpretation of the *obshchina* as a survival of the ancient Russian society. They saw in the *obshchina* the bulwark of ancient Slavic democracy and an embodiment of Russia's true social philosophy. Chicherin, Kavelin, and other critics of the Slavophil interpretation were forced to re-examine the ancient historical documents and—as in the case of Granovskii—to search for comparative material by studying the early medieval social organization of Western Europe. Some scholars contended that the *obshchina* and the *mir* were actually the creations of feudalism, and considered the *rod*—a larger kin group—the oldest and most fundamental Russian social organization. Chicherin argued that the *obshchina* was only a specific form of local community present in all European countries at a given stage of social development. He thought—and many scholars of the succeeding generation agreed with him—that serfdom was the only reason why the *obshchina* was still in existence. In the West, he said, village communities of the *obshchina* type disappeared with the passing of feudalism.[20]

The controversy forced the legal historians to rise above a mere recapitulation of archival material, and it stimulated the ethnographers, the linguists, and even the archaeologists to look for historical and cultural generalizations.

K. D. Kavelin, who during the 1840's impressed Moscow University students with his unique and eloquently presented sociological interpretation of Russian legal history, added the concept of personality to Karamzin's state, Ewers's clan, the Slavophils' *obshchina*, and Polevoi's people. Society in ancient Russia, he thought, was dominated by kin groups—"natural" rather than "consciously formed" units—which provided no room for the realization of "the boundless and limitless dignity of man and the human personality." Russian history, according to him, was a gradual liberation of the individual from the fetters of kin-bound society. It was only when the individual began to assert himself that Russia's history was steered by the same ideas and principles as that of Western Europe. Before Peter I, Western European history and Russian history were noncomparable. The post-Petrine period, on the other hand, was dominated by Russia's concerted efforts to emulate the West. History, as treated by Kavelin, has a philosophical bent and a sociological meaning, but it is also programmatic. In the institution of serfdom he saw the last gigantic social force inimical to the positive affirmation of personality; and, faithful to his philosophy of history, he acquired wide reputation as an advocate of the liberation of serfs during the 1850's.

In 1854, Solov'ev declared that historiography was on its way to becoming scientific: "In the course of time, science matures and it becomes necessary . . . to show how events are interrelated, how the new emerges from the old, and how the organic wholeness rises above historical fragments. It becomes indispensable to substitute a physiological approach for the traditional anatomical approach."[21] In his provocative and competent essay "The Anthropological Principle in Philosophy" (1860), Chernyshevskii wrote: "The natural sciences have attained such heights that now they can offer plenty of material for the solution of moral [social] questions. Among the scholars engaged in the moral sciences, all the progressive ones have begun to apply exact methods, similar to those that are used in the natural sciences."[22]

THE EXPANDING CULTURAL BASE OF SCIENCE

During the 1850's stronger and more diversified bonds were established between science and society. Numerous regional branches of the Geographical Society became the nuclei of serious scholarly interest far from the cultural centers of European Russia, and scholarly questionnaires issued in quantity by some of the learned societies reached even the lowliest priests and teachers in every corner of the country, making them integral parts of the gigantic move to achieve a national "self-understanding." Instead of studying the past as a form of escape from the present, as earlier historians had often done, the new generation of historians looked on the study of the past as a means for acquiring a better understanding of the present. This was the important lesson of Granovskii.

One of the first decrees of Alexander II called for the improvement of the existing agricultural societies, among which the Free Economic Society was chief in importance, and for the establishment of new ones. These societies were now recognized as the most effective institutions for collecting the information the government needed before it could formulate the legal measures which were to lay the foundations for the socio-economic and technological modernization of rural Russia.

After 1852 the popular journals gradually began to assume new importance as effective disseminators of scientific knowledge. In 1852, for example, *Contemporary* carried translations of Alexander von Humboldt's *Views of Nature*, Arago's historical survey of the scientific studies of the physical composition of the sun, D. M. Perevoshchikov's essay on new historical materials relevant to Newton's *Principia*, and N. P. Barbot de Marni's long survey of geological investigations in Russia during the preceding ten years. Many of these popular journals had particularly wide circulation among persons interested in applied science.

In addition to the regular bulletins of the learned societies, there were many serious journals published by various government agencies or government-supported institutions. Such periodicals as the *Journal of the Institute of Communication Media and Public Buildings*, the *Military Journal*, the *Engineering Notes*, the *Mining Journal*, the *Moscow Medical Journal*, the *Companion of Health*, the *Military Medical Journal*, the *Agricultural Journal*, the *Journal of Manufacturing and Trade*, and the *Journal of the Ministry of State Properties* had a wide circulation and had not been adversely affected by the wave of repressive legislation. They helped to generate scientific interest among the uninitiated and to increase the effectiveness of university graduates employed in positions requiring scientific knowledge. It also provided those who had a bent for experimentation with an opportunity to share their findings with comparatively large groups.

The *Journal of the Ministry of National Education*, circulated among gymnasium teachers, continued its lengthy, systematic summaries of "the most important discoveries, experiments, and observations in the mathematical, physical, and natural sciences," an impressive feature started in

1848 by M. S. Khotinskii, a dedicated popularizer of the natural sciences. It also printed valuable summaries of the scientific activities of the universities and the learned societies and occasional translations of articles originally published by the Academy of Sciences in foreign languages. Thus it contributed tangibly to establishing a closer contact between the Academy and the larger body of science teachers. A supplement to this method of reaching a wider audience was the *Messenger of the Natural Sciences*, a weekly published from 1854 on under the sponsorship of the Moscow Society of Naturalists. The editor was the venerable and tireless Professor Rouillier.

The Academy of Sciences also took measures to bolster its ties with society at large. In 1856, Count D. N. Bludov, speaking as president of the Academy, recommended that the Academy make plans to bring scientific knowledge to persons who for various reasons did not receive adequate scientific grounding during their school years. He was aware of the current efforts of popular journals to disseminate modern scientific theory, but he reasoned that the Academy could do a better job because it was not dependent on unpredictable private donations and because it provided a better guaranty for an officially acceptable blending of science and ideology. However, the Academy's decision to publish a scientific journal in Russian was premature. The journal lasted only two years, partly because there was little demand among people speaking only the Russian language for a periodical of such high scientific caliber, and partly because even the Russian Academicians, aside from those in the historical and philological fields, preferred to write in foreign languages so as to reach Western scholars. When the journal was revived in 1862 the country was ready for it, and it became a successful and long-lasting publishing venture.

The new government of Alexander II also made its contribution to the rising awareness of the importance of science as a pillar of modern life. When in 1851 Shirinskii-Shikhmatov ordered that Greek be replaced by the natural sciences in thirty-one gymnasiums, he commented that "the implementation of this measure will ensure a more complete education for future civil servants and will give a more versatile and profound grounding in the natural sciences to students planning to enroll in the physico-mathematical and medical faculties."[23] In 1855, several months after the death of Nicholas, Avraam Norov, the new Minister of National Education, told a group of school administrators: "Science, gentlemen, has always been one of our most important needs, but today it is our first need. If our enemies are superior to us, it is only because of the power of their knowledge."[24] This pronouncement marked a turning point in the history of Russian science. "Until this time," said Timiriazev, "science developed despite government-erected barriers. . . . From this point on, it benefited from the government's cooperation. The new developments affected every branch of intellectual endeavor—the arts as well as the sciences—but none so much as the natural sciences."[25]

The Crimean debacle in 1855 was widely interpreted as being a result of Russia's technological underdevelopment. It demonstrated that by their overemphasis on classicism—and underemphasis on the natural sciences—the gymnasiums had given an unbalanced education to a whole generation of young Russians. In reaction, many so-called real gymnasiums which stressed the natural and exact sciences began to replace the old "classical" gymnasiums, in most instances by a change in curriculum. The number of students specializing in mathematics and physics increased astoundingly after Alexander became Tsar. In 1853, a total of twenty-two students were graduated in the natural and exact sciences from all universities; in 1855, the number had grown to 328. In 1856 there were 357, and by 1860 there were 508. The number of publications in the natural sciences and the number of visitors to scientific museums also increased.

The intellectual proclivities and aspirations of the new generation provided a special impetus for the growing emphasis on scientific thought. The "superfluous man" who dominated the intellectual life of the 1830's and the 1840's and was a product of Moscow and St. Petersburg salons and literary circles did not disappear, but he was greatly overshadowed by a new intellectual-realist who was intent on the massive job of paving the way for the great reforms of the 1860's. These were the people who discovered the natural sciences as a source of cures for Russia's chronic ills. Pisarev made a good summation of their views: "Strictly speaking, only the mathematical and natural sciences have the right to be called sciences. Only in them hypotheses do not remain hypotheses; they alone show us the truth and enable us to recognize the genuine truth."[26]

A special stimulus for the development of the new and widespread scientific outlook in Russia came from Western Europe, where scientific thought was arriving daily at new frontiers. The chemists of the 1850's prepared the way for the establishment of definitive valences and atomic weights of elements, which in turn led modern chemistry—both organic and inorganic—to construct structural models of the compounds of elements and to rise to a higher level of theoretical integration and consistency. In 1858 Kekulé and Archibald Scott Couper recognized the quadrivalence of carbon, and Kekulé formulated the fundamental principle of the linking of carbon atoms with one another; it was on this basis that only a few years later Aleksandr Butlerov formulated his theory of the structure of chemical compounds.*

In physics, the study of the velocity of electricity received strong stimulus from the work of Fizeau in France and Kirchhoff in Germany. The dynamic theory of heat set forth by Kelvin removed the main obstacle to the formulation of the law of the conservation of energy. Physical chemistry and modern spectroscopy emerged as great and challenging fields of scientific work. Spectroscopy, in turn, gave birth to spectrochemical analysis and astrophysics. The decade greeted the triumphant appearance of Wallace's study "On the Law Which Has Regulated the Introduction of New Species," Darwin's *The Origin of Species*, and the initial volumes of Helmholtz's *Physiological Optics*.

In the 1850's the young James Clerk Maxwell was beginning to build the foundations for his grand mathematical synthesis of "the very different orders of physical phenomena," and Louis Pasteur was well on his way to establishing the germ theory of disease. In this decade a new non-Euclidean geometry was born and subsequently came to be known as elliptic geometry, in contrast to Lobachevskii's and Bolyai's hyperbolic geometry. Riemann, the founder of elliptic geometry, belongs to the line of direct ancestors of the theory of relativity. Dedekind's concept of group foreshadowed the rise of mathematics to a higher level of abstraction.

The clustering of great scientific talent, the opening of numerous new areas to scientific inquiry, and the great and challenging new scientific ideas were not the only characteristics of this period. The method of teaching the natural sciences underwent revolutionary changes. Liebig's chemical laboratory at Giessen University in Germany became a model for similar "scientific workshops" which sprang up in all the leading Western European universities and in conjunction with the teaching of all the natural sciences, but particularly chemistry, physics, and physiology.

Laboratories, by enabling teachers to give concrete demonstrations of

---

* According to Henry M. Leicester: "A. M. Butlerov espoused the cause of the new theory with great enthusiasm and worked out many of the consequences. He stressed strongly the fact that there was but one formula for a given compound, instead of the various formulas that Gerhardt and others had used, depending on the various reactions of compounds. Butlerov introduced the term 'chemical structure' in 1861 at a chemical meeting at Speyer in Germany. His textbook of organic chemistry, published in Russian in 1864 and translated into German in 1868, was the first book that actually used the new formulas throughout. It did much to popularize the new theory." (Leicester, *The Historical Background*, p. 185.)

theoretical concepts, made teaching easier as well as more attractive to the growing numbers of gymnasium and university students. And as young Russian scholars began again to enroll in Western European universities, they acquired not only advanced theoretical ideas but also new and effective ways of showing the practical application of even the most abstract sciences.

The word "science" was now everywhere. Even the Slavophils, whose basic philosophy was hardly compatible with the scientific method of inquiry, found it imperative to make known their opinions on the "nationality of science."[27] Dobroliubov acknowledged that "the natural sciences have made gigantic progress by reconciling philosophical judgments about natural forces with the results of experimental studies of matter." He noted: "At the present time, the natural sciences have accepted the positive method based on experiments and factual knowledge instead of on nebulous theories squeezed out of thin air, or on dubious guesswork, which in the old days went hand in hand with ignorance and half-knowledge."[28] The journal *Contemporary* published a poem by Iakov Polonskii dedicated to the limitless powers of "the kingdom of science." Science alone, the poet said, offered the way to understanding "the living truth"; it alone was the true repository of wisdom.

The growing emphasis on the natural sciences in both the secondary and the higher schools also had its critics, a good many of whom were forward-looking persons who recognized the great importance of scientific thought but feared its overemphasis at the expense of other cultural forces. Granovskii believed that even history should become a science, but he was extremely critical of the new trend which favored the broadening of the natural science curriculum at the expense of humanistic subjects. Turgenev felt that Russia did not need highly specialized scholars as much as it needed broadly educated persons, dedicated as much to the humanistic equation of science as to the scientific facts, and who freely cross the boundaries separating individual sciences in search of pure models of higher morality.[29] To Granovskii and Turgenev science was considerably more than a body of differentiated and specialized knowledge; it was also a special embodiment of moral values. Both Granovskii and Turgenev thought that at that moment in Russian history it would be better if the natural and exact sciences were taught more as valuable parts of a rounded education than as highly professional subjects involving strict discipline.

The most determined and consistent spokesman of this group was the anatomist Nikolai Pirogov. "I know very well," he said in 1856 in an article published in the widely circulated *Naval Symposium,* "that the gigantic scientific achievements of our century have made specialization an essential social need; but, at the same time, never before this century have specialists stood so much in need of a general humanistic education. A one-sided specialist is either a crude empiricist or a street charlatan."[30] Pirogov was not opposed to specialized education; his main argument was that specialized training must be preceded by a general humanistic education. All these adherents of the philosophy of general education—including Chernyshevskii—were in favor of the natural sciences; what they were pleading for was essentially a new kind of scientist who was aware of his moral obligations to society and of the values which comprise the ethos of science.

During the 1850's it became obvious that the end was in sight for the foreign domination of the leading Russian scientific institutions. The traditional conflict between Russian and foreign professors was succeeded by an ephemeral conflict between two kinds of Russians: those of native parentage and a smaller group born in Russia but not of Russian ancestry (the same quarrel that took place in the Geographical Society). Beginning in 1851, most new Academicians in all fields were native Russians.

The leading intellects of the time were not only concerned with the educational and social attributes of science; they also sought to answer the vexing question of the national characteristics of science. What was "national science," and how was it related to "universal science"? Roughly speaking, there were three major types of answers.

Some persons viewed "Russian science" or "national science" as a specific branch of universal science, dedicated to the study of natural and cultural phenomena associated specifically with Russia. In 1849, Izmail Sreznevskii, a philologist, stated that every society has an exclusive right to its own national science, as a part of universal science. The main duty of every national science, he believed, was to study a specific people, "its nationality, its past and present, its physical and moral powers, its significance and destiny." He concluded that "national science in this sense is a confession of a people to itself and to the whole world."[31] The peculiarities of "national science" are found in the specific emphases of its subject matter, but not in its methodology.

The second view was expressed by the Slavophils Aleksei Khomiakov, Iurii Samarin, and Ivan Kireevskii, who maintained that the element of nationality was the quintessence of the science of every people. Whereas the first group viewed national science as a tributary of universal science, the second group regarded the science of each nation as a cultural phenomenon *sui generis*. As Khomiakov explained it, unless science is deeply embedded in the living culture of a society and filled with its spirit, it consists only of lifeless forms.[32] Science is universal as a cognitive *analysis* of reality, but as a *synthesis*—as an integral, functioning part of culture— it is strictly national. It must have a "heart," which it receives not from any universal principles of humanity but from the national spirit. Khomiakov was skeptical of the value of borrowed scientific ideas because they tend to obscure the difference between science as an "analysis" and as a "synthesis." He argued that Peter I in his efforts to import Western scientific ideas had also opened the gates to the influx of Western mores and values, which were incompatible with the Russian national character.

The third view held that science was one and undivided, consisting of a body of objective facts, and that the universal validity of its knowledge was its basic attribute. Chicherin, perhaps the outstanding holder of this view, considered any nationalism as a force inimical to the growth of scientific thought. He said: "To speak in our times about the national orientation of science not only is useless but can produce unfavorable consequences for our education."[33] Different peoples can make different contributions to the same fund of scientific knowledge, but the contributions of individual nations—or even individual social classes—to human knowledge enter the domain of science only when "they cease to bear a nationalist character and become the property of humanity."[34] Another expression of this idea was offered by Odoevskii, who during the 1850's abandoned his Schellingian idealism and became a staunch supporter of the scientific point of view: "There is only one science, just as there is only one sun and only one truth. The generations of thankful posterity refer to French chemistry, English techniques, German physiology—but all these sciences are the common heritage of all mankind."[35]

In his Introduction to the Russian translation of parts of Karl Ritter's *Erdkunde* dealing with agriculture in various Asian countries, published in 1856, Petr Semenov stated: "Science is a universal human value, and scientific ideas, whatever their origin, belong to mankind." He added that the nationalist orientation in science should signify only the dutiful aspiration of modern scholars to help in spreading scientific knowledge among the masses. "This is necessary," he said, "because in our realistic century science is no longer a hazy speculation of scholastic minds; science is self-understanding and knowledge of the objects and natural forces outside oneself.

Science is able to subject these objects and forces to human control and to exploit them for the benefit of man. Neither the intellectual progress of man nor the advancement of material culture and welfare is possible without science. Therefore, unless he wants to become a cold cosmopolite, every scholar is obliged not only to expand the boundaries of human knowledge, but also to make knowledge an integral part of his society."[36]

Symptomatic of the mood of this age was the fact that the scholars—who viewed science as a "universal value" and to whom the phrase "nationality in science," a topic of heated journalistic debate from 1856 to 1859, meant the duty of scholars to help in bringing the benefits of science to their people—were liberal social activists dedicated to the cause of the emancipation of Russian serfs. During the phase of his identification with the Society of the Lovers of Wisdom and Schelling's metaphysics and mysticism, Odoevskii showed no interest in social problems; during the 1850's he became a dedicated champion of the natural sciences and of the emancipation of the serfs. At the time when Semenov wrote his Introduction to Ritter's book he was a member of the Committee for the Emancipation of the Peasants from the Bonds of Serfdom.

The differences between the various philosophical and ideological interpretations of the social foundations of science were quantitative rather than qualitative: Khomiakov's and Samarin's idea of the historical individuality and cultural relativity of the scientific thought of each society was criticized by Chicherin and other Westerners not because it was patently untrue but because it accorded too little importance to the universal properties of science.

The emergence of diverse views on the relationship of science to the national character was accompanied by an expression of views favoring the essential compatibility of science and religion. This scientific attitude played an interesting part in an episode involving K. F. Rouillier, the much respected professor of Moscow University. In 1851 Rouillier, a pioneer ecologist, delivered a public lecture on the relationship of animals to their external environment. It was received with much enthusiasm by a large audience, and subsequently portions of it were reprinted in the *Moscow News*, which was sponsored by Moscow University. Despite its slight evolutionary slant, the article had no trouble passing the lax censors. The Minister of National Education, however, read the article, recognized its antibiblical tone, and warned Mikhail Katkov, the editor, not to publish similar materials in the future. But the case did not end there.

Rouillier's article was defended by two persons, both using the same line of argument. Stepan Shevyrev, the first defender, was a "government man," a staunch adherent of official nationalism who had been appointed dean of Moscow University's Faculty of Philosophy in 1851 by the Minister of National Education in place of Granovskii, who had been elected by the teaching staff. As a new dean, Shevyrev saw fit to defend Rouillier. He claimed that the accused professor "placed the truths of Providence above truths based on empirical knowledge," and that he accepted only those scientific truths which were compatible with biblical truths. In his memorandum, Shevyrev relied on passages from Basil the Great's *Hexaëmeron*, written in the fourth century, and Metropolitan Filaret's *Notes on the Genesis*, published in 1816, to show the basic compatibility of science and Eastern Orthodoxy. He ended his comment with Lomonosov's statement that "truth and religion are blood-sisters, the daughters of one supreme parent, which can never come in conflict with each other."[37]

The second defense came from Katkov. He also stressed the compatibility of Professor Rouillier's ideas with the theological wisdom of Filaret, Metropolitan of Moscow, who claimed that there were two kinds of truth—divine and human—one requiring no proofs and the other totally dependent on proofs. The function of science, according to him, was to combat ignorance and "to reveal the omnipotence, omniscience, and goodness of God, as revealed in his creations."[38]

Both Shevyrev and Katkov knew well that the antirationalism of Russian Orthodoxy was intrinsically incompatible with science as a mode of inquiry, and they resorted to this philosophical defense simply to help a colleague in distress. But there was more to their defense. The great reception accorded to Rouillier's public lectures by Moscow's most enlightened citizens was a vivid reminder to them of their moral obligation to protect men of knowledge in the pursuit of their professional duties; and if they expected religion to win the battle, it was because this was the expedient thing to do at a time when Christian morality was being stressed by Tsar Nicholas and his immediate counselors. Shevyrev, indeed, was one of the outstanding conservatives who realized that science was indispensable for Russia's progress and that in its cumulative power it was bigger than government edicts.

Significantly, the contemporary Russian theologians did not accept Katkov's and Shevyrev's statements on the compatibility of science and the Russian Orthodox religion. Led by Fedor Golubinskii—called the "Russian Hegel" by some of his contemporaries—they continued to marshal logical arguments against "the rationalist movement in philosophy." Although Golubinskii professed a philosophical view combining "the clear rationalism of the intellect" with "the true exaltation of the heart,"[39] he was basically a metaphysicist, who combined the idealism of Wolff and Schelling into a larger preoccupation with the mysticism of Jacobi and Claudius and the "speculative theology" of Baader. All his favored philosophers underscored the inadequacy of human rational faculties as a source of knowledge. N. P. Giliarov-Platonov, another influential cleric-philosopher, published an article in *Russian Conversation* (1859) in which he dissected the philosophical thoughts of Kant, Fichte, Schelling, and Hegel, all guilty of a rationalist bias. Despite the transparency of his logic, he was content to announce that rationalism had died a self-inflicted death and that the vacuum created by its demise was filled by a new orientation which he called "instinctualism." He did not explain this term but he made it unmistakably clear that it denoted the orientation of contemporary science, which was concerned with the study of man's place in nature and tended to explain "the totality of human life in terms of chemico-physiological processes" and to adopt a "historical" point of view.[40] As Giliarov-Platonov saw it, rationalist philosophy—the source of natural science—was an error of the past rather than a guidepost of the future.

The new antirationalism received a masterly endorsement in an essay written by Ivan Kireevskii, the leading Slavophil philosopher. The Slavophils had no official connections with the Church, but they were at the moment primarily bent on formulating a religious philosophy of culture. Kireevskii agreed with Giliarov-Platonov that rationalism had reached the highest possible level of development in the philosophies of Schelling and Hegel, and that in the future there would be no new *system* of rationalism—the philosophy which "broke the wholeness of man's intellectual self-consciousness and placed the source of man's spiritual life not in the moral and aesthetic sphere but in the abstract consciousness of deliberative reason."[41] Rationalism—and science as a form of it—was a philosophy which, because of its sole dependence on the power of reason, achieved only limited and relative truth. In placing reason as "the highest form of cognition" it overlooked more accurate sources of truth which transcended man's power of "abstract and rational thinking." Science as a repository of truth shrank to insignificance when compared with the truths that lay in Orthodox belief.

The antirationalist philosophy of the theologians and Slavophils was a great deal more than a simple academic exercise. The real goal of the antirationalists was to define the attributes of the Russian "national character," for ideological, not scientific, reasons. Their interest was not in objective knowledge but in human values, and in their writings they mercilessly attacked ideas incompatible with what they believed to be the values that gave Russian culture its "holiness" and uniqueness. To them Eastern Orthodoxy, in a state unchanged by the edicts of successive Church Councils and shorn of theological systematization, was at the same time the quintessence of the Russian "soul" and an uncompromising enemy of rationalism and science. In truth, neither the theologians nor the Slavophils sought to eliminate the study of the natural sciences in Russia, nor did they endeavor to subordinate it to strict religious control: their aim was to show that Russia's national genius and "world mission" derived their strength from the Russian "religious mind" untouched by and only slightly cognizant of the world of reason and science. They appreciated the power of scientific experiment and theory, but they thought the wisdom of the saints infinitely more powerful as well as more congenial to the Russian mind.

The opposing camps of rationalists (and science) and antirationalists (and Eastern Orthodoxy) did not confront each other head-on, and neither really gave way. On the contrary, both continued to marshal their forces. The next generation produced great scientists—headed by Mendeleev—but it also produced great religious philosophers—headed by Dostoevskii, Vladimir Solov'ev, and Nikolai Fedorov—the likes of whom had been quite unknown in pre-Reform Russia.

The 1850's marked the end of the formative stage of Russian scientific thought. This does not mean that the universal and buoyant growth of Russian science during the 1860's was in any sense a quantum jump. One epoch was gradually and painlessly transformed into another; the 1860's, contrary to popular opinion, did not suddenly arise from cultural stagnation and an almost moribund condition of scientific thought. The flowering of scientific thought during the 1860's had, in fact, two main sources, both of them considerably antedating 1860.

In the first place, it was a response to the exhilarating spirit of libertarianism which shook the country to its foundations and left its impression on every part of culture. Conditions were favorable for the sharpening of the scientific mind: the new critical spirit opened wide new areas to scientific inquiry, but also made it incumbent upon science to sharpen its defenses against formidable criticisms coming from the contending cultural forces. In the early 1860's Turgenev's *Fathers and Sons,* which espoused science as the epitome of modern progress, was matched by Dostoevskii's *Notes from the Underground,* which stingingly ridiculed the mathematical precision of science. The wave of libertarianism produced its most impressive fruits during the 1860's, but the winds of freedom had begun to blow in the middle of the 1850's. It was Timiriazev who said significantly that the 1860's actually began in 1855.

In the second place, the great scientific progress of the 1860's was nourished on and firmly anchored to the cumulative wisdom of the past. Solov'ev, who had established himself as a national historian of the first rank during the 1850's, and perhaps earlier, had no peer in the 1860's. The scholarly erudition of the mathematician Chebyshev was unchallenged during the 1860's, and he, too, came from the earlier period, as did Zinin in chemistry, Pirogov in anatomy, Kavelin in legal history, and Tsenkovskii in zoology. A fortunate coalescence of the great scientific minds of two generations meeting in an atmosphere conducive to scientific inquiry was the magic of the remarkable successes of the 1860's.

Notes

Notes

Complete authors' names, titles, and publication data are given in
the Bibliography, pp. 421–49.

CHAPTER ONE

1. Constantine Porphyrogenitus, the great master of political administration, arithmetic, astronomy, and geometry, was unknown in Russia before modern times. Emperor Manuel I Comnenus, who wrote a defense of "astronomic science" against the attacks made on it by learned clergymen, sent Ptolemy's *Almagest* as a present to the King of Sicily; the knowledge contained in this book came to Russia only by way of occasional citations in theological writings. Photius' *Bibliotheca,* an encyclopedic history of eminent grammarians, orators, historians, and students of nature and medicine, had no impact whatever on the Russian intellectual tradition. In the thirteenth century, Nicephorus Blemmydes' *Abridged Physics* (based mostly on Aristotle), *A History of the Earth,* and *General Geography* exercised a profound influence on Western scientific thought but found no echo in Russia. In the first half of the fifteenth century, Gemistus Plethon stimulated the Italian humanists with his analyses of the Aristotelian and Platonic philosophies, and generated the idea of founding the Platonic Academy in Florence; his thoughts, however, bypassed contemporary Russia. For brief statements on the scholarly work of these men see A. A. Vasiliev, I, 297; II, 490–91, 552, 699.

2. V. V. Bobynin, "Sostoianie matematicheskikh znanii," p. 200. An opposite view is held by V. P. Zubov. Referring to a fifteenth-century Slavic translation of a part of al-Ghazzāli's *Maqasid al-falasifa,* which contained a discussion of continuum as a philosophical and mathematical concept, Zubov claims that Bobynin's assertion that all Russian mathematics prior to the eighteenth century was practical in nature can no longer stand unchallenged. (Zubov, "Vopros," pp. 407–30. For a more general survey see Iushkevich, "Matematika i ee prepodavanie," No. 1, 1947, pp. 26–39.)

3. The leading man of "the golden age of Bulgarian literature," John the Exarch of Bulgaria, was at the same time "a theologian, an orator, a philosopher, a philologist, a poet, and a natural scientist." (Kristanov and Duichev, eds., p. 32.) For the ideas on natural science contained in his work see *ibid.,* pp. 58–157.

4. Ikonnikov, *Opyt issledovaniia,* pp. 512–13.

5. Immanuel ben-Iacob is better known as Immanuel Bonfils of Tarascon. George Sarton borrowed the title of this writer's book for his own *Six Wings.* Sarton states (p. x) that he was made aware of this title "thanks to a medieval writer, Immanuel Bonfils of Tarascon, who flourished c. 1340–77, and was best known because of his astronomical tables entitled *Kanfe nesharim* (wings of eagles, Exodus 19:4); as these

tables were divided into six parts they were more generally called *Shesh Kenafayim*. This was an allusion to the six wings of the seraphim (Isaiah 6:2), and Immanuel himself was called *Ba'al Kenafayim* (master of the wings)." Sarton also states that "Immanuel Bonfils was a very distinguished mathematician, one of the pioneers of the decimal and the exponential calculus" (p. 239). For more details see Sarton, *Introduction,* III, 1517–20.

6. For an interesting and provocative survey of the "scientific" ideas contained in the Russian *Six Wings* see Sviatskii, pp. 63–78. The author of this article claims that *Six Wings* was translated from the Hebrew.

7. A. S. Orlov, *Drevnaia russkaia literatura XI–XVII vv.,* pp. 249–50.

8. Sarton, *Introduction,* III, 1517.

9. Burckhardt, p. 206.

10. A. A. Vasiliev, I, 165. For excerpts from an Old Slavic translation of *The Christian Topography,* see Kristanov and Duichev, pp. 440–64. For a critical review of Slavic translations and their discrepancies with the Greek originals, see I. Sreznevskii, "Svedeniia i zametki," IX, 1–19.

11. Berdyaev, p. 86.

12. A. Arkhangel'skii, "Obrazovanie i literatura," LXVII, 93; Pypin, "Voprosy," pp. 330ff.

13. Whitehead, p. 39.

14. Hall, p. 195.

15. Lazarev, *Tochnye nauki,* p. 3.

16. Miliukov, *Ocherki,* Vol. II, Part 2, p. 272.

17. Solov'ev, *Istoriia,* I, 6.   18. Kliuchevskii, *Sochineniia,* III, 274.

19. Zabelin, *Opyty,* I, 120.   20. Shchapov, III, 21.

21. Rainov, *Nauka v Rossii,* p. 7.

22. Kliuchevskii, *Skazaniia inostrantsev,* pp. 209–10.

23. Platanov, *Ocherki po istorii smuty,* p. 120.

24. Platanov, *Moskva i zapad,* p. 15.

25. Georgii Florovskii, *Puti,* p. 49.

26. Pekarskii, *Nauka i literatura,* I, 2.

27. Sobolevskii, *Perevodnaia literatura,* pp. 60–63; B. E. Raikov, *Ocherki,* 120–24; Perel', *Razvitie,* p. 151.

28. B. E. Raikov, *Ocherki,* p. 128.

29. Fesenkov, "Ocherk istorii astronomii," p. 4.

30. Sarton, *Six Wings,* p. 178.

31. Solov'ev, *Istoriia,* III, 771–72; Kliuchevskii, *Sochineniia,* III, 276.

32. Solov'ev, *Istoriia,* III, 772.

33. Smentsovskii, *Brat'ia Likhudy,* pp. 24–25.

34. In the tenth century, John the Exarch of Bulgaria wrote his own *Hexaëmeron,* but he borrowed substantial sections from Basil the Great's book of the same title. At the end of the tenth or the beginning of the eleventh century John's work found its way to Russia, and with it selected fragments from Aristotelian physics.

35. Krizhanich, Supplement 6, pp. 251ff.

36. Picheta, *Iurii Krizhanich* (1914), p. 15.

37. Solov'ev, *Istoriia,* III, 782.

38. Krizhanich, Supplement 5, pp. 176–77; Supplement 1, p. 43.

39. Bulich, "Russkii iazyk," p. 825.

40. Pares, p. 174.   41. Sergei Smirnov, *Istoriia* (1855), p. 12.

42. *Ibid.,* pp. 61–62.   43. Shcherbatov, pp. 25–26.

44. Smentsovskii, "Likhudy, Ioannikii i Sofronii," p. 502.

45. Zabelin, "Pervoe vodvorenie," p. 13.

46. Arkhangel'skii, "Obrazovanie i literatura," LXV, 133–34.

47. Ikonnikov, "Blizhnii boiarin," pp. 298ff.

48. Samuel Kollins, p. 34. The English title of the original is *The Present State of Russia, in a Letter to a Friend at London.*

49. Kliuchevskii, *Sochineniia*, III, 339.   50. Solov'ev, *Istoriia*, III, 387.

51. Kliuchevskii, *Sochineniia*, III, 357.   52. Karamzin, *Istoriia*, XI, 45.

53. Platonov, *Boris Godunov*, pp. 90–91. See also Pekarskii, "Izvestie o molodykh liudiakh," p. 93; N. V. Golitsyn, pp. 3–4.

54. Park Benjamin, p. 338.

55. Malin, "Anglo-russkie kul'turnye i nauchnye sviazi," pp. 103–4; Bestuzhev-Riumin, ed., "Pamiatniki," pp. 264–65.

56. For a survey of foreign physicians in Russian service during the Romanov part of the seventeenth century, see W. M. Richter, Vol. II.

57. Platonov, *Boris Godunov*, p. 137.

58. Sobol', *Istoriia mikroskopa*, p. 15.

59. Figurovskii, ed., *Istoriia*, Vol. I, Part 1, p. 59.

60. Pekarskii, *Nauka i literatura*, I, 4; Eingorn, pp. 18–19.

61. "Predislovie k istoricheskoi knige, sostavlennoi po poveleniiu tsara Fedora Alekseevicha," in Zamyslovskii, pp. xxxv–xlii; Lappo-Danilevskii, "Ocherk razvitiia russkoi istoriografii," pp. 16–17; Peshtich, I, 45–52.

62. Lappo-Danilevskii, "Ocherk razvitiia russkoi istoriografii," pp. 20–21.

63. Figurovskii, ed., Vol. I, Part 1, p. 131.

64. Zmeev, p. 260; B. Raikov, "Estestvoznanie," p. 11.

65. Shchapov, II, 528.   66. Bobynin, "Matematika," p. 724.

67. Zabelin, *Opyty*, I, 75.   68. Pekarskii, *Nauka i literatura*, I, 263.

69. [Olearius], p. 578.

70. Shchapov, II, 562–66; Nikitin, *Khozhdenie*; Bartol'd, pp. 173–74. For a brief survey of Russian explorations in the Pacific area, see L. Berg, "Russian Discoveries in the Pacific," pp. 1–26. For the exploration of the Siberian coast, see Wrangel, pp. xvii–cxxxii.

71. V. V. Danilevskii, *Russkaia tekhnika*, p. 448.

72. Manshtein, *Zapiski*, II.

73. A. Florovskij, pp. 5–6.

74. Georges Florovsky, "The Problem of Old Russian Culture," p. 15.

75. Ikonnikov, *Opyt russkoi istoriografii*, Vol. II, Part 1, p. 668.

CHAPTER TWO

1. Lappo-Danilevskii, *Petr Velikii*, pp. 4–5.   2. *Ibid.*, pp. 5–6.

3. Zabelin, *Opyty*, I, 19ff.   4. Bogoslovskii, II, 124.

5. Grot, "Petr Velikii," pp. 31, 71–78; O. Miller, "Lomonosov," p. 377.

6. Grot, "Petr Velikii," p. 31.

7. Lappo-Danilevskii, *Petr Velikii*, pp. 6–7.

8. For a general discussion of the relationship of Protestantism to science during the seventeenth century, see Robert K. Merton, *Social Theory and Social Structure*, pp. 329–40. According to Charles C. Gillispie: "The correlation of Calvinist behavior patterns—hostility to tradition, utilitarianism, calculating self-denial, a calling to work

in this world, rationality, and the individual interpretation of experience—the correlation of these qualities with practical business and science (it is less notable when it comes to speculative and theoretical science) is a very general feature of Western cultural history. There can simply be no doubt that Protestant and bourgeois milieux have encouraged talent and ambition to rise through science." (Gillispie, p. 114.)

9. Pekarskii, *Istoriia*, I, xxviii.

10. Kliuchevskii, *Sochineniia*, III, 251–52.

11. Krizhanich, Supplement 4, pp. 35ff., 49–51.

12. *Ibid.*, pp. 19–20.

13. Zertsalov and Belokurov, pp. iii–xiii; Kniaz'kov, "Russkaia shkola," pp. 42–45.

14. Schuyler, I, 301.

15. Bogoslovskii, II, 168.

16. Hans, "The Moscow School of Mathematics and Navigation," pp. 532–33; John Perry, pp. 212–14.

17. Bogoslovskii, II, 378–79.

18. Guerrier, ed., p. 27.

19. Liselotte Richter, p. 18.

20. Guerrier, ed., p. 15.

21. Lappo-Danilevskii, *Petr Velikii*, pp. 17–18; L. Richter, pp. 14–15.

22. Chuchmarev, "G. V. Leibnits," pp. 127–28.

23. *Ibid.*, p. 128.

24. Pekarskii, *Istoriia*, I, xxii.

25. Leibnitz, p. 268 (as quoted by Chuchmarev, "G. V. Leibnits," p. 121).

26. Fontenelle, *Oeuvres choisies*, II, 226.

27. Andreev, "Osnovanie," p. 287. See also Pavlov-Sil'vanskii, *Proekty*, pp. 20–24; Miliukov, *Gosudarstvennoe khoziaistvo*, pp. 541–43, 573.

28. Pekarskii, *Nauka i literatura*, I, 5.

29. Grot, "Petr Velikii," p. 42.

30. Shchapov, II, 537.

31. Mel'gunova *et al.*, eds., I, 194.

32. Shchapov, II, 157.

33. Nikol'skii, "Dukhovnyia uchebnyia zavedeniia," pp. 204–5.

34. L. V., "Farvarson, Andrei Danilovich," p. 23. For more details on Farquharson's work in Russia, see Bobynin, *Russkaia fiziko-matematicheskaia bibliografiia*, Vol. I, Part 1, pp. 55–56; Pekarskii, *Nauka i literatura*, I, 271, and II, 74; Iushkevich, "Matematika i ee prepodavanie," No. 2, 1947, pp. 11–12.

35. For a detailed study of the contents of this work, see Bobynin, *Russkaia fiziko-matematicheskaia bibliografiia*, Vol. I, Part 1, pp. 15–17.

36. Bobynin, "Magnitskii (Leontii Filipovich, 1669–1736)," p. 328.

37. Pekarskii, *Nauka i literatura*, I, 269–71; II, 72–74.

38. *Ibid.*, I, 11.

39. N. A. Smirnov, *Zapadnoe vlianie*, pp. 4–11.

40. Pekarskii, *Nauka i literatura*, I, 283.

41. Bobynin, *Russkaia fiziko-matematicheskaia bibliografiia*, Vol. I, Part 1, pp. 67–69; Vorontsov-Vel'iaminov, *Ocherki*, p. 5. In 1707 a huge wall map, printed in Moscow for a wide distribution, showed graphically the universe as viewed by Copernicus, Ptolemy, Tycho Brahe, and Descartes.

42. P. M., "Feofan (Prokopovich)," pp. 929–30.

43. Chistovich, *Feofan Prokopovich*, pp. 627–28.

44. Pypin, *Istoriia russkoi literatury*, III, 193. It was primarily because of his rationalist orientation that Prokopovich has been usually treated with great disfavor by Russian theologians. G. Florovskii sums up the theological criticism of Prokopovich by stating that he did not feel "the mystical reality of the [Orthodox] Church." (*Puti*, p. 92.)

45. R. Sementkovskii, "Kantemir," p. 315.

46. Pekarskii, *Nauka i literatura*, I, 48.

47. Lappo-Danilevskii, *Petr Velikii*, pp. 17ff.

48. Ostrovitianov, ed., *Istoriia*, I, 28.

49. Ptashitskii, p. 271. A government decree of February 13, 1718, enumerated the materials of embryological, paleontological, and archaeological significance which should be delivered to local authorities for dispatch to St. Petersburg. The same decree also specified the fines for persons failing to turn in these materials. (*Polnoe sobranie zakonov Rossiiskoi Imperii s 1649 goda*, V, 1830, 541–42.)

50. Lebedev, *Geografiia v Rossii petrovskogo vremeni*, p. 42.

51. Pypin, "Russkaia nauka," p. 225.

52. V. I. Grekov, *Ocherki*, p. 16.

53. Efimov, pp. 70–72.

54. For a summary of cartographic activities during Peter's reign, see K. E. von Baer, *Peter's des Grossen Verdienste*, pp. 247–56.

55. G. Delisle l'Aîné, "Détermination géographique," p. 382.

56. "Addition à l'Histoire de MCCXX," *Histoire de l'Académie Royale des Sciences*, 1720, pp. 131–32.

57. G. Delisle l'Aîné, "Remarques," pp. 245–54.

58. According to Karl von Baer, although Peter I was an honorary member of the Académie, this learned body considered him an active and direct contributor to scientific knowledge. K. von Baer, p. 248.

59. O. V. Struve, "Ob uslugakh," p. 15.

60. Bulich, *Ocherk istorii*, I, 192.

61. Ikonnikov, *Opyt russkoi istoriografii*, Vol. II, Part 2, p. 1470.

62. Peshtich, I, 109.

63. Solov'ev, *Sobranie sochinenii*, p. 1328. This view is also shared by Peshtich (I, 103–9) and Lappo-Danilevskii ("Ocherk razvitiia russkoi istoriografii," pp. 24–29).

64. Pufendorf wrote that "nothing praiseworthy" could be said about the Muscovites, that reading and writing were "the highest degree of learning among them," that they were "jealous, cruel, and blood-minded," and that they had no military skill. (Pufendorf, pp. 363–64.)

65. Pekarskii, *Nauka i literatura*, I, 369; Skabichevskii, *Ocherki*, p. 6.

66. Bliakher, p. 10.

67. *The Record of the Royal Society of London for the Promotion of Natural Knowledge*, 4th edition, p. 393.

68. Vavilov, *Isaak N'iuton*, 2nd edition, pp. 212–13, the facsimile of Newton's letter following page 216; Vavilov, *Sobranie sochinenii*, III, 454–55.

69. Andreev, "Osnovanie," p. 294.

70. Chistovich, *Feofan Prokopovich*, p. 617.

71. *Briefe von Christian Wolff*, p. 9.

72. *Ibid.*, pp. 19–20; Lappo-Danilevskii, *Petr Velikii*, p. 30.

73. Pekarskii, *Istoriia*, I, lix–lx.

74. For a description of the three informal groups dedicated to scientific inquiry which served as the nuclei of the Royal Society, see Thomas Sprat, pp. 65–67; see also Dorothy Stimson, pp. 46–47.

75. Joseph Bertrand, p. 5.

76. Flourens, p. 353.

77. Pypin, *Istoriia russkoi etnografii*, I, 114.

78. Tatishchev, "Razgovor," pp. 110–11; Kliuchevskii, *Sochineniia*, VIII, 341–42.

79. *Polnoe sobranie zakonov Rossiiskoi Imperii s 1649 goda*, VII (1830), Item 4443, pp. 220ff.

80. Satkevich, p. 472.
81. D. A. Tolstoi, "Akademicheskii universitet," p. 3.
82. *Materialy dlia istorii,* I, 47, 57–58; Andreev, "Osnovanie," pp. 324–25.
83. Fontenelle, "Eloge du Czar Pierre I," pp. 105, 128.
84. Prokopovich, *Sochineniia,* pp. 135–36.
85. Zagoskin, *Istoriia,* I, vi.
86. John Perry, pp. 211–12.
87. K. S. Veselovskii, "Petr Velikii," p. 28.
88. Lappo-Danilevskii, *Petr Velikii,* p. 13.

CHAPTER THREE

1. Kravets, "N'iuton," pp. 314–15; Radovskii, "N'iuton i Rossiia," pp. 98–99.
2. *Materialy dlia istorii,* I, 301–24.
3. *Polnoe sobranie zakonov Rossiiskoi Imperii s 1649 goda,* VII (1830), Item 4443, pp. 222–23.
4. Zubov, *Istoriografiia,* p. 19.
5. D. A. Tolstoi, "Akademicheskaia gimnaziia," p. 10.
6. Zagoskin, *Istoriia,* I, vii.   7. Maksimov, *Ocherki,* pp. 24–25.
8. Pekarskii, *Istoriia,* I, 719.   9. *Materialy dlia istorii,* V, 981–82.
10. S. N. Chernov, p. 169.
11. Pekarskii, *Istoriia,* II, xiv–xv. See also Pekarskii, "O perepiske," p. 12.
12. *Materialy dlia istorii,* V, 506; Gnucheva, *Geograficheskii department,* p. 60.
13. *Materialy dlia istorii,* V, 634ff.
14. Pekarskii, *Istoriia,* I, lxvi.
15. Manshtein, II, 305. See also [Vockerodt], pp. 1412–14.
16. Shchapov, III, 155.   17. Ivanov, "Sledstvennoe delo," p. 84.
18. Pekarskii, *Istoriia,* II, xlv.   19. Maksimov, *Ocherki,* pp. 26–27.
20. Shchapov, III, 155.   21. Tatishchev, "Razgovor," pp. 116–17.
22. Solov'ev, *Istoriia,* IV, 1457.   23. Tatishchev, "Razgovor," pp. 110–11.
24. Lazarev, *Tochnye nauki,* p. 3.
25. S. N. Chernov, p. 165.
26. Pypin, "Russkaia nauka," Part 1, p. 220.
27. *Ibid.,* Part 2, p. 549.
28. Kniazev and Kol'tsov, pp. 13–14.
29. Svenske, "Materialy," p. 55.
30. For detailed biographical information on the members of the Bernoulli family who spent some time in St. Petersburg, see Bobynin, "Bernulli, Daniil, Iakov i Nikolai," pp. 92–115.
31. *Letters of Euler,* I, xl.
32. Lavrent'ev *et al.,* eds., *Leonard Eiler,* p. 14.
33. Pekarskii, *Istoriia,* I, 254.
34. Nicolaus Fuss, "Lobrede," pp. lvi–lvii.
35. Pekarskii, *Istoriia,* I, lx–lxi.
36. *Letters of Euler,* I, xliii.
37. Otto Spiess, p. 78.   38. Pekarskii, *Istoriia,* I, 265.
39. Satkevich, pp. 478–80.   40. Pekarskii, *Istoriia,* I, 258.
41. *Materialy dlia istorii,* pp. 572–73, 612–13.
42. *Letters of Euler,* I, xxxix.
43. Satkevich, p. 484. The wide scope of Euler's service as a link between the sci-

entists in Russia and Germany is discussed in Winter, "Euler und die Begegnung der deutschen mit der russischen Aufklärung," pp. 1–18; and in P. Hoffmann, "Zur Verbindung Eulers mit der Peterburger Akademie während seiner Berliner Zeit," pp. 150–56. Euler's very extensive correspondence with G. F. Müller and other members and officials of the St. Petersburg Academy is presented in Iushkevich and Winter, eds., *Die Berliner und die Petersburger Akademie der Wissenschaften im Briefwechsel Leonhard Eulers.*

44. Satkevich, p. 483.

45. Pasquier, p. 114.

46. For a detailed study of Euler's versatile interests in the St. Petersburg Academy's scholarly pursuits, see Winter and Iushkevich, "O perepiske Eilera i Millera," pp. 465–97.

47. *Letters of Euler*, I, lv.

48. For a full list of his works connected with the Great Northern Expedition, see Gnucheva, ed., *Materialy*, pp. 68–69.

49. Pekarskii, *Istoriia*, I, 456–57.

50. *Ibid.*, 448–49.

51. Chistovich, *Feofan Prokopovich*, p. 623.

52. Gurevich, "Steller, Georg-Vil'gel'm," p. 375.

53. Pekarskii, *Istoriia*, I, 404; Zubov, *Istoriografiia*, p. 61.

54. Pekarskii, *Istoriia*, I, 351–52.

55. *Ibid.*, lxvi.

56. Gnucheva, *Geograficheskii department*, p. 60.

57. Bestuzhev-Riumin, *Biografii i kharakteristiki*, p. 183.

58. Pypin, *Istoriia russkoi etnografii*, IV, 339.

59. Kosven, p. 181.

60. The first two volumes were published in 1937 and 1941 respectively, and the remaining two have been prepared for publication. For a Soviet appraisal of Müller's contributions, see M. N. Tikhomirov, ed., *Ocherki*, I, 191–93, and M. Tikhomirov, "Russkaia istoriografiia XVIII veka," pp. 69–99. The *History of Siberia* was originally published in German (Vol. I in 1761 and Vol. II in 1763). A part of Müller's study was published in Russian in 1750. For a detailed study of Müller's contributions to Siberian ethnography, see Kosven, pp. 178–94.

61. Müller's survey, entitled *Zur Geschichte der Akademie der Wissenschaften zu S.-Petersburg,* was used extensively by Pekarskii in the preparation of his *Istoriia Imperatorskoi Akademii nauk.* The full text of the survey was published for the first time in *Materialy dlia istorii*, VI, 1890. Pekarskii, while recognizing the richness of material presented by Müller, noted that the latter showed more the "partiality of a contemporary than the judiciousness of a historian." (Pekarskii, *Istoriia*, I, 428–29.)

62. Kunik, ed., *Sbornik materialov*, Part 1, xxxv–xxxvi. See also *Materialy dlia istorii*, III, 576.

63. Solov'ev, *Istoriia*, IV, 1466. The first printing presses using the secular script are described in Sopikov, I, lviii–lix.

64. For a summary of his linguistic work, see Bulich, *Ocherk istorii*, I, 205–9.

65. P. A. Novikov, "Akademik S. P. Krasheninnikov," pp. 262–96.

66. M. I. Belov, "O rodine Lomonosova," p. 245.

67. Menshutkin, *Russia's Lomonosov*, p. 52.

68. For Lomonosov's version of his transfer to the Academic University and subsequent developments, see Kunik, Part 2, pp. 371–72, and Pekarskii, *Istoriia*, II, 287.

69. Menshutkin, *Russia's Lomonosov*, p. 186.

70. Lomonosov, *Izbrannye filosofskie proizvedeniia*, pp. 156–57, 341; T. I. Rainov, "N'iuton i russkoe estestvoznanie," pp. 330–33.

71. Lomonosov, *Izbrannye filosofskie proizvedeniia*, p. 187; Menshutkin, "M. V. Lomonosov kak fiziko-khimik," pp. 77–78; L. B. Modzalevskii, ed., *Rukopisi Lomonosova*, p. 4.

72. Lomonosov, *Izbrannye filosofskie proizvedeniia*, pp. 168–69; Menshutkin, *Mikhailo Vasil'evich Lomonosov*, pp. 65–67.

73. Leicester, *The Historical Background*, p. 146.

74. Menshutkin, *Russia's Lomonosov*, p. 117; Menshutkin, "Lomonosov, Mikhail Vasil'evich," p. 620.

75. Lomonosov, *Izbrannye filosofskie proizvedeniia*, pp. 284ff.; Grigor'ian and Polak, eds., p. 206.

76. For a Soviet effort to give Lomonosov a significant place in the mainstream of scientific development of his age, see Grigor'ian and Polak, eds., pp. 206–16. For a succinct Soviet interpretation of Lomonosov's philosophy of science, see Vasetskii and Kedrov, pp. 119–71. See also Zvorikine, "Remarques," pp. 185–87.

77. Lomonosov, *Izbrannye filosofskie proizvedeniia*, pp. 137–54.

78. Lockemann, *The Story of Chemistry*, p. 122; Leicester, *The Historical Background*, p. 143. For a collection of Lomonosov's studies in chemistry and physics, see *Physikalisch-chemische Abhandlungen M. W. Lomonosows, 1741–1752*, translated from the Latin and the Russian with commentaries by B. N. Menshutkin and Max Speter (Leipzig, 1910). For a summary review of Lomonosov's main works and scientific undertakings, see "M. V. Lomonosov," in Vavilov *et al.*, eds., *Nauchnoe nasledstvo*, I, 11–62.

79. Solov'ev, *Sobranie sochinenii*, p. 1351. According to Koialovich: "Undoubtedly, historiography was far removed from Lomonosov's specialties. He began to study history quite late and did not produce satisfactory results." (Koialovich, p. 100.)

80. Kliuchevskii, *Sochineniia*, VIII, 410.

81. *Ibid.*, 409. For a laudatory assessment of Lomonosov's historical contributions, see B. D. Grekov, "Lomonosov-istorik," pp. 404–21. Grekov thinks that Solov'ev, as a Westerner, reacted unfavorably to the tendency of Slavophil circles to give full endorsement to Lomonosov's interpretation of Russian history. The Slavophil N. V. Savel'ev-Rostislavich praised Lomonosov as a fighter for the purity of Russian language and history. He commended Lomonosov particularly for his single-handed fight against the distortions of Russian history perpetrated by the adherents of "the German theory."

82. Sobolevskii, *Lomonosov*, pp. 6ff.

83. Ivanov-Razumnik, I, 26.

84. Lomonosov, *Polnoe sobranie sochinenii*, I, 427.

85. Pypin, *Istoriia russkoi etnografii*, I, 116; Grot, "Ocherk," p. 255; Sipovskii, p. 18; Menshutkin, *Mikhailo Vasil'evich Lomonosov*, pp. 119–20; Budilovich, No. 7–8, p. 293.

86. Katkov, "Apologiia," pp. 30–31; Bacon, *The Advancement of Learning*, p. 8.

87. Pekarskii, *Istoriia*, II, 326.

88. In 1760, for example, he submitted a memorandum to the Senate urging government sponsorship of a systematic gathering of samples of "sands, rocks, and clay" which would (*a*) facilitate the surveillance of deposits of gold, various precious stones, and marbles; and (*b*) enable him to write a general survey of Russian minerals to be used by young scholars engaged in surveying the country's resources. (P. Ivanov, "Donoshenie Professora Lomonosova," pp. 167–68.)

89. Lomonosov, *Izbrannye filosofskie proizvedeniia*, p. 598.

90. Sipovskii, p. 19.

91. Pekarskii, *Istoriia*, II, 847.

92. *Ibid.*, 599–602; Chenakal, "Eiler i Lomonosov," pp. 458–59; P. Pekarskii, "Dopolnitel'nyia izvestiia," pp. 74–78. For additional information on relations between Lomonosov and Euler, see Biliarskii, "Otzyv," pp. 104–10.

93. M. I. Sukhomlinov expressed an opposite view on Lomonosov's influence. He said: "Rumovskii, Kotel'nikov, and Protasov received their scientific education under the guidance of Lomonosov; Lepekhin and Inokhodtsev were the students of Rumovskii and Kotel'nikov; Ozeretskovskii, Sokolov, and Severgin formed their views under the favorable influence of Lepekhin, etc. These generations of scholars from Lomonosov to Severgin were united by the fundamental principles of their scientific work and by the literary tradition which grew from the living conditions of their time and from the historical stage of development of Russian education." (Sukhomlinov, *Istoriia*, IV, 2.) T. I. Rainov states that Sukhomlinov, in making the above statements, was concerned more with the literary tradition than the scientific work with which the names of these scholars were identified. (T. I. Rainov, "Russkoe estestvoznanie," p. 319.)

94. Kunik, Part 1, p. xlix.

95. Radishchev, *A Journey*, pp. 229, 235–36.

96. *Ibid.*, p. 236.

97. *Ibid.*, p. 237.

98. Maksimov, *Ocherki*, p. 60. The growth of Lomonosov's reputation as a towering force in Russia's intellectual history was gradual and subject to qualitative changes. During the first half-century after his death he was firmly established as "the legislator of poetry, rhetoric, and language." (Grot, "Ocherk," p. 221.) With the downfall of the antiquated pseudoclassical language as the vehicle of literary communication, this first view rapidly began to lose ground. During the next fifty years—the period of rising national consciousness—Lomonosov was hailed primarily as "a progressive fighter for Russian thought and Russian science." The emphasis was not now on his scientific achievements but on his work in favor of indigenous Russian thought. According to Gogol, Lomonosov's ability to sense Russia's great future was the source of his "miraculous power." A reassessment of Lomonosov's work in the natural sciences was undertaken at the time of the first centennial celebrations of Moscow University, but no agreement was reached as to his contribution. N. A. Liubimov, Professor of Physics, stated: "The name of Lomonosov is not connected with any significant discoveries. . . . The diversity of subjects with which he concerned himself with unlimited inquisitiveness shifted his attention from one topic to another and did not allow him enough time for detailed study of any single phenomenon." (Pekarskii, *Istoriia*, II, 447–48.) On the other hand, N. Liaskovskii, Professor of Chemistry, insisted that Lomonosov's chemical studies showed that he was "a natural scientist who endeavored to resolve chemical problems by relying on all the methods of delicate and precise research," and "a foremost interpreter of chemical phenomena." (Pekarskii, *Istoriia*, II, 451–52.)

During the 1860's Lomonosov's work became a challenging topic of historical research based mostly on the Academy's archival material. (Lamanskii, *Mikhail Vasil'evich Lomonosov* and "Lomonosov i Peterburgskaia Akademiia nauk"; Biliarskii, *Materialy dlia biografii Lomonosova*; Kunik, ed., *Sbornik materialov*; Grot, "Ocherk"; and Pekarskii, "Dopolnitel'nyia izvestiia.") This research was the product of a new and extensive scholarly interest in Russia's intellectual history. It unearthed a mass of material on Lomonosov as a public figure, as an advocate of science and rationalism, and as a poet and historian; it paid very little attention to his work in natural science, partly because his work in that field was thought to be outdated and partly because the writers feared that an account of it would make dull reading. The only exception was A. S. Budilovich's "Ob uchenoi deiatel'nosti Lomonosova," which contained several of Lomonosov's papers in physics and chemistry. In 1873 Pekarskii published the second and last volume of his highly regarded *Istoriia*, which gave over six hundred pages to a biography of Lomonosov. This detailed study has shown some of the less flattering features of Lomonosov's personality without detracting from his great talents and versatility; yet it, too, failed to give sufficient space to his contributions in the natural sciences. Lamanskii, a great admirer of Lomonosov, criticized his hero for his free bestowal of divine attributes upon the members of the ruling dynasty. Lamanskii claimed that Lomonosov's "government and official odes" placed Russian enlightenment on the wrong path and widened the gap that separated the people from the ruling class. "In theory, [Lomonosov] was a courageous fighter for freedom of thought and speech; in practice, he demanded censorship and permanent government tutelage over society. He often gave his social and moral struggle an official and coercive character and thus undermined his own work." (Lamanskii, *Mikhail Vasil'evich Lomonosov*, pp. 19–20.) A similar criticism of Lomonosov was voiced by Plekhanov, who also objected to Lomonosov's claim that science and religion "are two blood sisters, the daughters of the divine parent." (Plekhanov, II, 19–25.)

In 1877 the St. Petersburg Academy decided to publish Lomonosov's complete works and appointed Academician M. I. Sukhomlinov to serve as the editor. The result of this effort was the *Sochineniia M. V. Lomonosova* in five volumes (1891–1902). The fourth and fifth volumes contained Lomonosov's papers on natural science, supplemented by lengthy comments from a select group of modern Russian scholars.

In 1904 a completely new trend was begun in the scholarly interpretation of the Lomonosovian legacy; in that year B. N. Menshutkin published a lengthy study—and a model of scientific biography—entitled "M. V. Lomonosov kak fiziko-khimik." Based on a whole series of previously unpublished essays by Lomonosov on various topics in physics and chemistry, this study threw a completely new light on "the father of Russian science." It showed him to be a scientist of great originality, intuition, and intellectual daring. When Menshutkin's book appeared in a German translation in 1911, Lomonosov was reintroduced to the West, this time not as a poet and historian but as a natural scientist.

In the Soviet Union Lomonosov has become a cultural hero of the first rank. Every facet of his scholarly and public activity has been the subject of detailed studies and the most laudatory interpretations. The Academy of Sciences of the U.S.S.R. published all his works in ten volumes (1951–59), and during the 1950's alone there appeared over fifty full-length books dealing with his general or specific contributions. Most of the new source material is presented in L. B. Modzalevskii, ed., *Rukopisi Lomonosova v Akademii nauk SSSR: Nauchnoe opisanie* (Leningrad-Moscow, 1937). For a recent Soviet general interpretive study, see B. G. Kuznetsov, *Tvorcheskii put* (Leningrad, 1961).

99. Pypin, *Istoriia russkoi literatury*, III, 353–55.

100. Kantemir, *Sobranie stikhotvorenii*, pp. 200–202.

101. Ehrhard, pp. 187–88; Radovskii, *Antiokh Kantemir*, pp. 39–62.

102. "Materialy dlia izucheniia Tatishcheva," in Tatishchev, *Dukhovnaia*, p. 58.

103. For a detailed summary of Tatishchev's views on science, see Bestuzhev-Riumin, *Biografii i kharakteristiki*, pp. 99–140.

104. Pypin, *Istoriia russkoi literatury*, III, 360.

105. Tatishchev, "Razgovor," p. 123.

106. Tatishchev, *Dukhovnaia*, p. 65.

107. Nil Popov, *V. N. Tatishchev*, p. 444.

108. Nearly all his works were published posthumously. His *Dukhovnaia moemu synu* was first published in 1773, the *Lexicon* in 1793, and "Razgovor o pol'ze nauk i uchilishch" in 1887. For a well-rounded essay on Tatishchev's versatile interests in Russian history, see Andreev, "Trudy V. N. Tatishcheva," pp. 5–38.

109. Tatishchev, *Dukhovnaia*, pp. 65–66.

110. Peshtich, I, 223.

111. Solov'ev, *Sobranie sochinenii*, pp. 1349–50.

112. Pypin, *Istoriia russkoi literatury*, III, 363ff.

113. Bestuzhev-Riumin, *Biografii i kharakteristiki*, p. 175.

114. Peshtich, I, 196.

115. Nil Popov, *V. N. Tatishchev*, p. 531. See also Epifanov, pp. 50–51.

CHAPTER FOUR

1. Zagoskin, *Istoriia*, I, vii.

2. Kliuchevskii, *Sochineniia*, VIII, 234–35; Belozerskaia, p. 509.

3. Zagoskin, *Istoriia*, I, vii. 4. Shevyrev, *Istoriia*, p. 326.

5. Shchapov, II, 537. 6. Kazarin, "Didro," p. 91.

7. Haumant, p. 43.

8. *Ibid.*; N. I. Novikov, *Izbrannye pedagogicheskie sochineniia*, p. 53.

9. Mel'gunova *et al.*, eds., II, 43.

10. Haumant, p. 41. 11. Mel'gunova *et al.*, eds., II, 44.

12. Radishchev, *A Journey*, p. 211. 13. Solov'ev, *Istoriia*, VI, 258.

14. Kliuchevskii, *Sochineniia*, V, 178.

15. *Ibid.*, p. 20.

16. Cobban, p. 156. In 1762 Catherine made an unsuccessful appeal to Diderot to transfer the publication of the underfinanced *Encyclopédie* to Russia. (Shugurov, p. 260.)

17. Sukhomlinov, *Istoriia*, II, 215. •

18. Mel'gunova *et al.*, eds., I, 389–91.

19. Some Soviet historians of science have tended to minimize the role played by Shuvalov in establishing Moscow University as a really national institution of higher learning. A. F. Kononkov, for example, claims that while "Lomonosov strove to transform the newly founded Moscow University into a center of Russian national culture and science, Shuvalov, who was the first head of Moscow University, used his power . . . to appoint German professors and lecturers who had very little in common with science." Statements like these, designed primarily to add to the stature of Lomonosov as a greater fighter for "Russian science," have no basis in fact and their authors make no effort to document them. (A. F. Kononkov, p. 35.) For a candid biographical sketch of Shuvalov by one of his younger contemporaries, see [Timkovskii, I. F.], pp. 1439–66.

20. Shevyrev, *Istoriia*, p. 10. 21. *Ibid.*; Ferliudin, Part 1, p. 41.

22. Shevyrev, *Istoriia*, p. 11. 22. Shevyrev, *Istoriia*, p. 11.

24. Gnedenko, *Ocherki*, pp. 84–85; Iushkevich, "Matematika i ee prepodavanie," No. 1, 1948, p. 14.

25. Wilhelm Michael Richter, III, 480.

26. Penchko, p. 133. 27. Kliuchevskii, *Sochineniia*, V, 166.

28. Rozhdestvenskii, *Ocherki*, I, 348. 29. Maikov, "Betskoi," p. 10.

30. Rozhdestvenskii, *Istoricheskii obzor*, p. 31.

31. Konstantinov and Struminskii, p. 56.

32. *Ibid.*, p. 68; N. Hans, "F. I. Iankovich de Miriievo," p. 92.

33. Herzen, *O razvitii*, p. 47.   34. Sukhomlinov, *Istoriia*, II, 215.

35. Solov'ev, *Istoriia*, VI, 225.   36. *Ibid.*

37. Pekarskii, *Istoriia*, II, 789.

38. Bell, p. 143. For a full account of the relations between Catherine and Euler, see Pekarskii, "Ekaterina II i Eiler," pp. 59–92.

39. For the full text of his "Plan d'un rétablissement de l'Académie Impériale des sciences," see Pekarskii, *Istoriia*, I, 303–8.

40. Stählin, p. 298.

41. Sukhomlinov, "Piatidesiatiletnii i stoletnii iubilei," pp. 5–6. See also *Zapiski kniagini E. Dashkovoi*, p. 165.

42. Sukhomlinov, "Piatidesiatiletnii i stoletnii iubilei," p. 8.

43. *Zapiski kniagini E. Dashkovoi*, p. 171. In her first speech before the Academicians, Dashkova stated that once the sciences had taken deep root in the Academy they should become common property, since this would be the best assurance for the future development of scientific thought. (Sukhomlinov, *Istoriia*, I, 29.)

44. Lang, p. 198.

45. *Ibid.* For a detailed biography of Dashkova, see Sukhomlinov, *Istoriia*, I, 20–57.

46. K. S. Veselovskii, "Poslednie gody," p. 245.

47: Rozhdestvenskii, *Istoricheskii obzor*, p. 99; S. Smirnov, "Tsenzurnaia vedomost," p. 425.

48. K. S. Veselovskii, "Otnosheniia imp. Pavla k Akademii nauk," pp. 237–38.

49. *Polnoe sobranie zakonov Rossiiskoi Imperii s 1649 goda*, Vol. XXVI (1830), Item 19387, p. 133; No. 19, p. 378.

50. Gnucheva, *Geograficheskii department*, p. 93.

51. T. I. Rainov, relying exclusively on V. V. Bobynin's *Russkaia fiziko-matematicheskaia bibliografiia*, I and II (Moscow, 1886–92), gives the following data on the number of the Academy's scientific publications during the second half of the eighteenth century (T. I. Rainov, "Russkoe estestvoznanie," pp. 324–25):

Years	Number of Studies
1747–57	137
1758–67	146
1768–77	280
1778–87	356
1788–98	366

52. Euler, *Elements of Algebra*, p. xxiii.

53. *Letters of Euler*, I, lxvii.

54. Struve, "Obzor," p. 45.

55. For an excellent biography of Rumovskii, see Bobynin, "Rumovskii," pp. 441–50. See also Sukhomlinov, *Istoriia*, II, 3–157 and 389–451.

56. For an outline of the tasks assigned to the expeditionary teams, see *Polnoe sobranie uchenykh puteshestvii po Rossii*, I, x–xii.

57. Zubov, *Istoriografiia*, pp. 68–69.

58. Putnam, ed., pp. 270–71.

59. For a complete list of his unusually diverse publications, see F. Keppen, pp. 386–437.

60. "Pallas (Petr'-Simon)," p. 641.

61. B. E. Raikov, "Evoliutsionnaia ideia," pp. 37–38; F. Keppen, pp. 388–89.

62. Nordenskiöld, p. 263.

63. See, for example, many references to Pallas in Charles Darwin, *The Variation of Animals and Plants Under Domestication,* and Charles Lyell, *The Principles of Geology,* Vol. I. See also Cuvier, 377–400.

64. Grot, "Filologicheskiia zaniatiia," p. 426. Pallas' *Comparative Lexicons* was immediately recognized as a great pioneering work in general linguistics. It was used extensively by the American naturalist Benjamin Smith Barton in the preparation of his *New Views of the Origin of the Tribes and Nations of America* (Philadelphia, 1797), "the most ambitious American effort in comparative linguistics before 1815." (Greene, p. 511.)

65. I. V. Kuznetsov, ed., *Liudi russkoi nauki: geologiia, geografiia,* p. 377. See also Sukhomlinov, *Istoriia,* II, 250ff.

66. For Zuev's ideas on philosophy, see Zuev, p. 281.

67. Shchapov, III, 265ff.

68. Bliakher, pp. 21–68; Detlaf, pp. 282–87.

69. B. E. Raikov, "Evoliutsionnaia ideia," pp. 40–41.

70. Shevyrev, *Istoriia,* p. 93.

71. Tikhonravov, "Istoriia izdaniia 'Opyta o cheloveke,' " pp. 1312–15.

72. Ikonnikov, "Russkie universitety," p. 498.

73. Shevyrev, *Istoriia,* p. 141. 74. *Ibid.,* p. 142.

75. Sukhomlinov, "Materialy," p. 150. 76. [Lubianskii], pp. 115–16.

77. See, for example, his "Slovo o vseobshchikh i glavnykh zakonakh prirody," pp. 377–83.

78. Shevyrev, *Istoriia,* p. 303.

79. Khodnev, p. 5. 80. Putnam, ed., p. 272.

81. Sukhomlinov, *Istoriia,* I, 1. 82. *Ibid.,* II, 336–40.

83. *Ibid.,* III, 234, 243, 247–51. 84. Solov'ev, *Sobranie sochinenii,* p. 1351.

85. *Ibid.,* p. 1360. 86. Tikhomirov, ed., *Ocherki,* I, 210.

87. For a detailed biography of Boltin, see Sukhomlinov, *Istoriia,* V, 2–296, 317–432; also Pypin, "Russkaia nauka," Part 2, pp. 586–600.

88. Solov'ev, *Sobranie sochinenii,* pp. 1371–72.

89. Mil'kov, pp. 22–23.

90. Shchapov, II, 552.

91. For details on his education, see A. G. Kozlov, "Podlinnye dokumenty," pp. 185–86.

92. Michatek, against the opinion of most Russian scholars, thinks that Polzunov should be honored not as the inventor of the steam engine but as the man who built the first steam engine in Russia. (Michatek, p. 533.) For a Soviet interpretation, see V. V. Danilevskii, "I. I. Polzunov," pp. 79–83.

93. Voeikov, "Ivan Ivanovich Polzunov," p. 407. For Polzunov's description of every detail of the projected engine see Voeikov, pp. 631–44. Polzunov's inventions are listed in V. V. Danilevskii, *I. I. Polzunov,* pp. 443–44.

94. Virginskii, *Zamechatel'nye russkie izobretatelei Frolovy,* pp. 64–65, 82ff.

95. S. Kulibin, "Frolov," pp. 237–38.

96. For an autobiographical sketch, see [Kulibin], "Materialy," pp. 182–86. See also I. Andreevskii, "Ivan Petrovich Kulibin," pp. 734–37.

97. N. N. P., "Kulibin," p. 540. For blueprints of Kulibin's projects, see Raskin and Mal'kevich, *Rukopisnye materialy,* pp. 163–78, and Virginskii, *Tvortsy,* pp. 138–65.

98. Pekarskii, *Istoriia*, I, 118–19.

99. Michatek, p. 532.

100. Virginskii, *Zamechatel'nye russkie izobretatelei Frolovy*, pp. 67–68.

101. Sukhomlinov, "Materialy," p. 57.

102. Iu. Ia. Kogan, *Prosvetitel' XVIII veka*, p. 41.

103. Zubov, *Istoriografiia*, p. 80; Shchipanov, ed., *Izbrannye proizvedeniia*, I, 415–18.

104. Kozel'skii, p. 414.

105. *Ibid.*, p. 427.

106. Zubov, *Istoriografiia*, p. 80.

107. Kliuchevskii, *Sochineniia*, VIII, 249. For a similar statement, see Herzen, *O razvitii*, pp. 53–54.

108. N. I. Novikov, "Stat'i i zametki," p. 774.

109. N. I. Novikov, "Koshelek," p. 214.

110. Kliuchevskii, *Sochineniia*, VIII, 237.

111. N. I. Novikov, *Izbrannye pedagogicheskie sochineniia*, p. 54.

112. Kliuchevskii, *Sochineniia*, VIII, 230.

113. Zubov, *Istoriografiia*, pp. 47–48. 114. Makogonenko, *Nikolai Novikov*, p. 420.

115. *Ibid.*, p. 172. 116. Zubov, *Istoriografiia*, p. 49.

117. Pypin divides the articles in Novikov's publications expressing a "mystic orientation" into three types: (1) those that had nothing in common with Freemasonry but displayed a kind of early Christian asceticism and mysticism; (2) those that were Masonic in spirit and were written by Masons; and (3) those dominated by extreme Rosicrucianism and its emphasis on alchemy. (Pypin, *Russkoe masonstvo*, pp. 233–42.)

118. G. V. Vernadskii contends that in 1779 Novikov rented Moscow University's press for a ten-year period for the primary purpose of publishing books approved by Russia's Rosicrucian leaders, but that because of his contractual obligations to the University he also published books "completely alien to the aims of the order." (G. V. Vernadskii, *Russkoe masonstvo*, pp. 120–21. See also Olga Balashova, "Pismo neizvestnogo litsa," pp. 1039–40.)

119. Makogonenko, *Nikolai Novikov*, pp. 347ff.

120. Shchapov, III, 358–59.

121. *Ibid.*, p. 359.

122. V. V. Miakovskii, "Gody ucheniia A. N. Radishcheva," pp. 31ff; Radishchev, "Zhitie," pp. 319–20.

123. Radishchev, *A Journey*, p. 165.

124. *Ibid.*, p. 236.

125. Ivanov-Razumnik, I, 56.

126. Semennikov, *Radishchev*, p. 220; Babkin, ed., *Biografiia*, p. 53. For a more detailed analysis of Radishchev's interests in chemistry, see Luk'ianov, "A. N. Radishchev," pp. 158–67.

127. Radishchev, *A Journey*, p. 31.

128. For a succinct presentation of Radishchev's social and political ideas, see his "Opyt o zakonodavstve," in Radishchev, *Polnoe sobranie sochinenii*, pp. 5–27.

129. Because of Radishchev's great popularity in the Soviet Union—he is considered not only the first intellectual rebel against serfdom and absolutism but also the founder of Russian materialistic philosophy—a considerable literature has grown on his relationship to and concern with science. See A. V. Petrovskii, pp. 355–59; Luk'ianov, "A. N. Radishchev," pp. 158–67; Figurovskii, ed., *Istoriia*, Vol. I, Part 1, pp.

489–90; M. Plisetskii, pp. 178–82; Zubov, *Istoriografiia,* pp. 90–97; Pashkov, ed., *Istoriia,* Vol. I, Part 1, pp. 606–99. For a general Soviet interpretation of Radishchev's literary work, see Makogonenko, *Radishchev i ego vremia.*

130. Brunet, p. 123.
131. T. I. Rainov, "Russkoe estestvoznanie," p. 352.

CHAPTER FIVE

1. Pipes, *Karamzin's Memoir,* p. 135.
2. *Ibid.,* p. 136.
3. Shil'der, "Aleksandr I," p. 144. La Harpe impressed upon young Alexander the didactic importance of natural science. (Sukhomlinov, *Fridrikh-Tsezar Lagarp,* pp. 27ff.)
4. Sukhomlinov, "Materialy," pp. 18–19.
5. Ikonnikov, "Russkie universitety," pp. 523–24.
6. Pypin, "Russkaia otnosheniia Bentama," pp. 813ff.
7. Ikonnikov, *Graf N. S. Mordvinov,* p. 75.
8. Halévy, p. 296.
9. *Polnoe sobranie zakonov Rossiiskoi Imperii s 1649 goda,* XXVI (1830), Item 19807, p. 599.
10. Pypin, *Obshchestvennoe dvizhenie,* pp. 109–10; M. I. Bogdanovich, "Pervaia epokha," pp. 158–59.
11. V. Orlov, *Russkie prosvetiteli,* p. 181.
12. Sukhomlinov, "Materialy," pp. 12–13.
13. "Materialy dlia istorii i statistiki nashikh gimnazii," pp. 134–35.
14. Ferliudin, Part 1, Appendix Table I; A. K. Timiriazev, ed., *Ocherki,* p. 53.
15. Condorcet, "Report," p. 342. 16. *Ibid.,* p. 340.
17. Diderot, p. 204. 18. Condorcet, "Report," p. 326.
19. "Pervoe pisanie V. N. Karazina," p. 76.
20. Lavrovskii, "Vospominanie," p. 296.
21. Miliukov, "Universitety v Rossii," p. 789.
22. Sukhomlinov, "Materialy," p. 48.
23. Tarasov, pp. 195–96. According to autobiographical notes left by Aleksandr Turgenev, who attended Göttingen University in 1802–04, Schlözer was also popular among Russian students because of his "philosophical" interpretation of history and his political liberalism. (Istrin, pp. 131–34.)
24. Sukhomlinov, "Materialy," p. 134.
25. I. N. Borozdin, p. 355; Rozhdestvenskii, "Universitetskii vopros," p. 41.
26. Shevyrev, *Istoriia,* p. 350. 27. Sukhomlinov, "Materialy," p. 117.
28. Shevyrev, *Istoriia,* p. 380. 29. *Ibid.,* p. 335.
30. Sukhomlinov, "Materialy," p. 132.
31. *Ibid.,* p. 134; Korolivskii *et al.,* eds., p. 14; Shugorov, p. 285.
32. Shevyrev, *Istoriia,* p. 372.
33. S. T. Aksakov, *Sobranie sochinenii,* II, 162.
34. Shtorkh and Adelung, I, 340; II, 204. 35. Bodianskii, ed., pp. 1–56.
36. Shchapov, III, 306. 37. *Ibid.,* III, 680.
38. Sukhomlinov, *Istoriia,* III, 365–66; Gnedenko, *Mikhail Vasil'evich Ostrogradskii,* p. 96.
39. *Polnoe sobranie zakonov Rossiiskoi Imperii s 1649 goda,* XXVII (1830), Item 20803, p. 790.

40. "Staraia zapisnaia knizhka," pp. 262–63.
41. *Polnoe sobranie zakonov Rossiiskoi Imperii s 1649 goda,* XXVII (1830), Item 20803, p. 787.
42. Sukhomlinov, "Piatidesiatiletnii i stoletnii iubilei," pp. 16–17.
43. Iushkevich, "Akademik S. E. Gur'ev," p. 250.
44. *Ibid.,* p. 244.
45. Robert Grant, p. 504; Perel', "Vikentii Karlovich Vishnevskii," pp. 133–48.
46. Tarasevich, p. 294.
47. Bokii and Shafranovskii, pp. 86–87.
48. B. Modzalevskii, "Severgin, Vasilii Mikhailovich," p. 274.
49. Ioffe, ed., pp. 15–16; Bobynin and Kul'bin, "Petrov, Vasilii Vladimirovich," pp. 662–67; G. Tovey, pp. 287–90.
50. B. E. Raikov, "Evoliutsionnaia ideia," p. 43. Detlaf, pp. 288–91; Mechnikov, "Sovremennoe sostoianie," pp. 158ff.
51. *Polnoe sobranie zakonov Rossiiskoi Imperii s 1649 goda,* XXVII (1830), Item 20803, p. 788.
52. B. G. Kuznetsov, *Ocherki istorii russkoi nauki,* p. 42.
53. Pypin, *Obshchestvennoe dvizhenie,* p. 107. The diversity of scientific interests among foreign scholars was well illustrated by the specialties and academic backgrounds of professors hired by Murav'ev in 1804 to serve on the staff of Moscow University. Ido, an expert in higher geometry, was already known in Europe for his explanations of Laplace's theory of the solar system. Professor Reiss, also from Göttingen University, was known for his biochemical and galvanic experiments. Professor Hoff-mann, from the same school, was a recognized expert in cryptogamous plants and was particularly known for his book on German flora and *Plantae lichenosae*. Goldbach, an astronomer from Leipzig, published a celestial atlas and was a collaborator of J. E. Bode, a famous Berlin astronomer. Murav'ev reported in 1804 that all these men were known in the learned world and were enthusiastic about the prospect of teaching Russian youth. (S. Shevyrev, *Istoriia,* p. 337.)
54. Shchapov, III, 82.
55. Osipovskii, "O prostranstve," pp. 45–46.
56. A. V. Vasil'ev, "Lobachevskii," p. 562.
57. For a brief survey of the main proponents of Schelling's philosophy in Russia, see Chizhevskii, *Gegel' v Rossii,* pp. 36–49; Wsewolod Setschkareff, *Schellings Einfluss.*
58. Miliukov, *Glavnyia techeniia,* p. 255.
59. A statement made by Ivan Kireevskii (Ivanov-Razumnik, II, 172).
60. Osipovskii, "Rassuzhdenie o dinamicheskoi sisteme Kanta," p. 50.
61. Bacon, *The New Organon,* pp. 7–8; Lobachevskii, "Rech'," p. 383.
62. Ikonnikov, *Graf N. S. Mordvinov,* p. 75.
63. Pashkov, ed., *Istoriia,* Vol. I, Part 2, pp. 98ff.
64. Luchinskii, "Teoriia rodovogo byta," p. 908.
65. A. S. Pushkin, "Zapiska o narodnom vospitanii," p. 215.
66. Sukhomlinov, "Materialy," p. 86. For a stimulating analysis of Karamzin's political philosophy, see Pipes, "Karamzin's Conception of the Monarchy," pp. 35–58.
67. Miliukov, "Istochniki russkoi istorii," p. 437. Belinskii called Karamzin's *History* "the cornerstone of historical studies in and of Russia." He added: "*The History of the Russian State* is not a history of Russia but of the Muscovite state, erroneously treated as the highest ideal of every state. Its style is not historical but that of a poem, the type of which belongs to the eighteenth century. As the first effort of the gifted author, *The History of the Russian State* is a great work of permanent value and sig-

nificance." (Belinskii, *Sochineniia*, Vol. III, 1911, p. 316.) In his *Letters of a Russian Traveler,* Karamzin spelled out his idea of history writing. He said: "It grieves me to say this, but in fairness it must be said that till now we have had no good history of Russia, that is, one written with philosophical understanding, a critical spirit, and noble eloquence. . . . All that one needs is intelligence, taste, and talent. One can select, enliven, color, and the readers will be surprised how, from Nestor, Nikon, and others, there can emerge something attractive, powerful, deserving of the interest not only of Russians, but of foreigners as well." (Karamzin, *Letters,* p. 218.)

68. Bestuzhev-Riumin, "Karamzin," p. 508.
69. Miliukov and Kirpichnikov, "Karamzin," p. 445.
70. Miliukov, "Istochniki russkoi istorii," p. 437.
71. Bestuzhev-Riumin, *Biografii i kharakteristiki,* pp. 206–7.
72. Karamzin, *Istoriia,* I, xxiv.
73. Zubov, *Istoriografiia,* p. 219.
74. Miliukov and Kirpichnikov, "Karamzin," p. 443.
75. Maikov, "Rumiantsev," p. 516.
76. Semevskii, *Krestianskii vopros,* I, 390–91.
77. Semevskii, "Turgenev (Nikolai Ivanovich)," p. 107.
78. Semevskii, *Krestianskii vopros,* I, 391.
79. Charnoluskii, p. 69.
80. Tarasevich, p. 290.
81. Ferliudin, Part 1, p. 64.
82. Ikonnikov, "Russkie universitety," p. 549.
83. Zagoskin, *Istoriia,* II, 207; Tarasevich, p. 290.
84. Zagoskin, *Istoriia,* II, 207.
85. Sukhomlinov, "Materialy," p. 100; Bagalei, pp. 155, 187–89.
86. "Materialy dlia istorii i statistiki nashikh gimnazii," p. 147. Actually, in gymnasiums alone there were only 2,826 students, the remainder of students being mostly gentry enrolled in private schools.
87. "Materialy dlia istorii i statistiki nashikh gimnazii," pp. 150–51.
88. Rozhdestvenskii, *Istoricheskii obzor,* p. 132.
89. Sukhomlinov, "Materialy," p. 130.
90. Rozhdestvenskii, *Istoricheskii obzor,* p. 61.
91. I. N. Borozdin, p. 355.
92. Sukhomlinov, "Materialy," p. 67.
93. Rozhdestvenskii, *Istoricheskii obzor,* p. 61; V. V. Grigor'ev, p. 29: Aleshintsev, "Zapiska," p. 729; Lavrovskii, "Iz pervonachal'noi istorii," pp. 243–44.
94. Shchapov, III, 63.
95. Aleshintsev, "Zapiska," pp. 730–35.
96. Rozhdestvenskii, *Istoricheskii obzor,* p. 61; Rozhdestvenskii, "Soslovnyi vopros," p. 93; "Iz zapisok barona (v posledstvii grafa) M. A. Korfa," p. 43.
97. Peter I made sporadic efforts to encourage formal schooling by granting educated persons higher ranks at the beginning of their government careers. (Rozhdestvenskii, "Soslovnyi vopros," p. 87.)
98. *Oeuvres complètes de Mme la Baronne de Staël,* XV, 308.
99. Rozhdestvenskii, *Materialy,* p. 375.
100. Joseph de Maistre, "Cinq lettres," pp. 299–362; Ikonnikov, "Russkie universitety," p. 73; Dovnar-Zapol'skii, *Iz istorii,* p. 27. For a detailed analysis of Jesuit activities in Russia from 1772 to 1820, see Winter, "Die Jesuiten in Russland," pp. 167–191.
101. Sukhomlinov, "Materialy," p. 34.

102. Putiata, p. 481. See also Morley, p. 193.
103. Rozhdestvenskii, "Soslovnyi vopros," p. 96.
104. In 1833–34 one-half of all students at St. Petersburg University were enrolled in the Faculty of Law.
105. Shevyrev, *Istoriia*, pp. 442ff.
106. "Materialy dlia istorii i statistiki nashikh gimnazii," pp. 156–57.
107. Potez, ed., pp. xxxii–xxxiii.
108. Shevyrev, *Istoriia*, pp. 333–35.
109. Pipes, *Karamzin's Memoir*, pp. 158–61.
110. M. I. Bogdanovich, "Padenie Speranskogo," pp. 496–99; Pogodin, "Speranskii," p. 1133.
111. Putiata, p. 479.
112. N. A. Popov, "Obshchestvo," pp. 81–82.
113. Pypin, *Religioznyia dvizheniia*, pp. 154–55.
114. "Pis'mo (grafa) Sergeia Semenovicha Uvarova," p. 0130.
115. For a contemporary description of various religious currents in Russia during the epoch of Alexander I, see Barsov, pp. 270ff.
116. Dovnar-Zapol'skii, *Iz istorii*, pp. 33–34.　　117. Petukhov, p. 339.
118. Zagoskin, *Istoriia*, III, 258.　　　　　　　119. *Ibid.*
120. Rozhdestvenskii, *Istoricheskii obzor*, pp. 117–18.
121. Zagoskin, *Istoriia*, III, 303.
122. *Ibid.*, p. 311.
123. *Ibid.*, pp. 316ff.
124. "Mnenie deistvitel'nogo statskogo sovetnika Magnitskogo," p. 157.
125. Zagoskin, *Istoriia*, III, 317.
126. Rozhdestvenskii, *Istoricheskii obzor*, p. 119.
127. Zagoskin, *Istoriia*, III, 350–51.
128. Rozhdestvenskii, ed., *S.-Peterburgskii universitet*, pp. xl ff.; Ikonnikov, "Russkie universitety," pp. 80–81; Skabichevskii, *Ocherki*, pp. 131, 140ff.; Kamenskii, "I. Kant," p. 55; Koyré, pp. 79–80.
129. Chirikov, p. 478.
130. Sukhomlinov, "Materialy," p. 85.
131. I. N. Borozdin, p. 367.　　　　　132. Skabichevskii, *Ocherki*, p. 130.
133. *Ibid.*, pp. 130–31.　　　　　　　134. Bagalei, p. 298.
135. Ikonnikov, "Russkie universitety," p. 79.
136. Skabichevskii, *Ocherki*, p. 171.
137. Rozhdestvenskii, *Istoricheskii obzor*, p. 166.
138. Shevyrev, *Istoriia*, pp. 469–70.　　　139. Pirogov, *Sochineniia*, III, 375ff.
140. *Ibid.*　　　　　　　　　　　　　　　141. *Katalog izdanii.*
142. Mazour, *The First Russian Revolution*, pp. 53ff.
143. Pavlov-Sil'vanskii, *Ocherki*, p. 56.
144. For a sample of titles of articles published in the *New Journal*, see Kononkov, pp. 284–86; A. K. Timiriazev, *Ocherki*, p. 88.
145. Zubov, *Istoriografiia*, pp. 198–99; Iu. I. Solov'ev and Ushakova, pp. 20–21.
146. Cauchy, p. 2.
147. Kliuchevskii, *Sochineniia*, V, 240.
148. A. V. Vasil'ev, "Lobachevskii," p. 554; Lobatschewskij, *Zwei geometrische Abhandlungen*, p. 368.
149. Somov, pp. 6–7.
150. Baranskii *et al.*, eds., pp. 157–61. Among the members of Krusenstern's crew

were Wilhelm Tilesius, a natural scientist, and J. C. Hörner, an astronomer, both hired by Alexander I to form the expedition's scientific staff. (M. Bogdanovich, "Pervaia epokha," pp. 159–60.) Tilesius was subsequently elected a member of the St. Petersburg Academy of Sciences. In 1813 he published *Naturhistorische Früchte der unter Krusensterns volbrachten Erdumsegelung.*

151. I. V. Kuznetsov, ed., *Liudi russkoi nauki: geologiia, geografiia,* p. 447.

152. Rozhdestvenskii, "Soslovnyi vopros," p. 98.

153. *Ibid.,* p. 103.

154. Rozhdestvenskii, *Istoricheskii obzor,* p. 198.

155. Shchapov, *Sochineniia,* III, 315–16.

CHAPTER SIX

1. Poliakov, p. 313.

2. Skabichevskii, *Ocherki,* p. 214.

3. "Iz bumag kniaza V. F. Odoevskogo," No. 7, p. 12.

4. Skabichevskii, *Ocherki,* p. 215.

5. Rozhdestvenskii, *Istoricheskii obzor,* p. 336.

6. Ikonnikov, "Russkie universitety," p. 95.

7. Shchapov, III, 187.

8. Rozhdestvenskii, *Istoricheskii obzor,* pp. 334–35.

9. *Ibid.,* p. 337; Skabichevskii, *Ocherki,* pp. 344ff.; Lemke, pp. 175ff.; Nifontov, p. 230.

10. "Materialy dlia istorii i statistiki nashikh gimnazii," p. 160.

11. Ikonnikov, "Russkie universitety," p. 108.

12. Rozhdestvenskii, *Istoricheskii obzor,* pp. 253–54; Aleshintsev, *Soslovnyi vopros,* p. 36.

13. Rozhdestvenskii, *Istoricheskii obzor,* pp. 259–60.

14. Ikonnikov, "Russkie universitety," p. 105.

15. Rozhdestvenskii, *Istoricheskii obzor,* p. 257.

16. Sechenov, *Avtobiograficheskii zapiski,* p. 70.

17. Ikonnikov, "Russkie universitety," p. 105.

18. V. V. Grigor'ev, p. 306.

19. Shchapov, II, 551.

20. "Materialy dlia istorii i statistiki nashikh gimnazii," pp. 140–41.

21. [Afanas'ev], p. 828; Rudakov, "Gimnaziia," p. 700.

22. Kovalenskii, "Srednaia shkola," p. 148.

23. Tikhonravov, *Sochineniia,* Vol. III, Part 1, p. 592.

24. Ikonnikov, "Russkie universitety," p. 107; Stasiulevich, p. 14.

25. Stasiulevich, p. 17.

26. "T. N. Granovskii o klassitsizme i realizme," pp. 3–4.

27. Pogodin, "Shkol'niya vospominaniia," p. 619.

28. "Materialy dlia istorii i statistiki nashikh gimnazii," pp. 168–69.

29. For the curriculum, see Ferliudin, Part 1, Appendix I.

30. Miliukov, "Universitety v Rossii," p. 791.

31. Rozhdestvenskii, *Istoricheskii obzor,* p. 245.

32. Shchedrin, XIV, 514.

33. K. S. Aksakov, *Vospominanie studentstva,* p. 39.

34. "Materialy dlia istorii i statistiki nashikh gimnazii," p. 162.

35. Miliukov, "Universitety v Rossii," p. 791.

36. Shchapov, II, 545–46; Ikonnikov, "Russkie universitety," p. 94.

37. Ferliudin, Part 1, p. 90; Sakharov and Shelestov, p. 37; I. N. Borozdin, p. 372; Rozhdestvenskii, *Istoricheskii obzor*, p. 245.

38. I. N. Borozdin, p. 372.

39. Nikitenko, I, 179.

40. Petukhov, I, 487–88.

41. Pirogov, *Sochineniia*, III, 425.

42. Rozhdestvenskii, *Istoricheskii obzor*, p. 188.

43. *Ibid.*, p. 251.

44. Poliakov, p. 314.

45. Pypin, "Istoriia russkoi literatury," p. 615.

46. Dostoevskii, *The Dream*, p. 34.

47. Chaadaev, II, 117ff.; Schelting, pp. 26–36; Miliukov, *Glavnyia techeniia*, pp. 330–33; Mazour, "Petr Jakovlevič Čaadaev," p. 16.

48. Skabichevskii, *Istoriia*, p. 6.

49. *Zapiski Sergeia Mikhailovicha Solov'eva*, p. 139.

50. Chicherin, *Vospominaniia. Moskva*, p. 122.

51. Miliukov, "Istochniki russkoi istorii," p. 439.

52. Pirogov, *Sochineniia*, III, 154.

53. Chicherin, *Vospominaniia. Moskva*, p. 260.

54. Khomiakov, *Polnoe sobranie sochinenii*, I, 76–77.

55. Samarin, "Dva slova," pp. 35–36, 43.

56. Chicherin, *Vospominaniia. Moskva*, p. 261.

57. *Ibid.*, p. 224.

58. Belinskii, *Izbrannye filosofskie sochineniia*, II, 291–92.

59. Chicherin, *Vospominaniia. Moskva*, p. 27. Another author identified the 1840's as "the golden age of Moscow University." (Shestakov, "Moskovskii universitet," p. 641.) He, too, had nothing to say about the natural sciences.

60. *Zapiski Sergeia Mikhailovicha Solov'eva*, pp. 25ff.; N. Speranskii, pp. 22–24.

61. Nicholas V. Riasanovsky, "Pogodin and Shevyrev," p. 150.

62. Bestuzhev-Riumin, *Biografiii i kharakteristiki*, p. 249.

63. For a comprehensive list of his writings, see Korsakov, "Pogodin," pp. 156–58; also Mazour, *Modern Russian Historiography*, pp. 77ff. Pogodin's "mathematical method"—the counting of how frequently individual facts appeared in the ancient chronicles without any effort to unravel their deeper significance—was the target of a biting attack by Pypin ("Kharakteristiki," Part 5, pp. 164–65).

64. Shevyrev, *Istoriia*, pp. 469–70.

65. Miliukov, "Istochniki russkoi istorii," p. 439.

66. Tikhomirov, ed., *Ocherki*, I, 330–31.

67. Koialovich, p. 183.

68. Polevoi, "Kriticheskiia issledovaniia," p. 77.

69. Kozmin, "Polevoi," pp. 300–301.

70. Vinogradov, "Granovskii," p. 563.

71. Ger'e, *Timofei Nikolaevich Granovskii*, pp. 2–3.

72. *Ibid.*, pp. 5ff.; Stankevich, *Timofei Nikolaevich Granovskii*, p. 294.

73. *Ibid.*, pp. 240, 242; also Shchapov, III, 109.

74. Granovskii, *Sochineniia*, I, 378, 392.

75. Passek, II, 361–62.

76. Chicherin, *Vospominaniia. Moskva*, p. 14. See also Schelting, p. 95.

77. *Zapiski Sergeia Mikhailovicha Solov'eva*, p. 102.

78. Dovnar-Zapol'skii, *Iz istorii*, p. 283.

79. Kliuchevskii, *Sochineniia*, VIII, 390–91.

80. *Zapiski Sergeia Mikhailovicha Solov'eva*, p. 102.

81. Kliuchevskii, *Sochineniia*, VIII, 259–60; VII, 131.

82. Solov'ev, *Istoriia*, I, 2.

83. Solov'ev wrote a comprehensive and rather sympathetic study of Karamzin's place in Russian historiography. However, he compared Karamzin with his predecessors and deliberately left out a comparison with his successors. (Solov'ev, *Sobranie sochinenii*, pp. 1389–1539.)

84. Shmurlo, "Solov'ev," p. 802; Korsakov, "Solov'ev," p. 90; Bestuzhev-Riumin, *Biografii i kharakteristiki*, pp. 266ff.

85. Miliukov, "Istochniki russkoi istorii," p. 442.

86. Ivanov-Razumnik, II, 168.

87. Odoevskii, *Russkie nochi*, p. 56. For a cogent analysis of Odoevskii's intellectual role in the 1820's and the 1830's and of his connections with Slavophilism, see Christoff, pp. 35–40.

88. "Iz bumag kniaza V. F. Odoevskogo," No. 2, p. 317.

89. Sakulin, *Iz istorii russkogo idealizma*, Vol. I, Part 1, pp. 117–19.

90. Mikulinskii and Rybkin, "Borba materializma," pp. 341–42.

91. M. G. Pavlov, "O vzaimnom otnoshenii," p. 97; Koyré, pp. 133–34.

92. Herzen, *Byloe i dumy*, II, 134, 137.

93. Miliukov, *Glavnyia techeniia*, p. 259.

94. Sakulin, *Iz istorii russkogo idealizma*, Vol. I, Part 1, p. 139.

95. Chernyshevskii, *Polnoe sobranie sochinenii*, XVI, 78.

96. *Ibid.*, pp. 78, 174. Nordenskiöld, p. 277.

97. V. Kuzen, p. 50. A year earlier (1838) the official journal of the Ministry of National Education carried an unfavorable article on Kant. The author of this article defined Kant's philosophy as a combination of *"deism,* which widens the distance between God and man, and *naturalism,* which does not allow for anything endowed with supernatural powers and recognizes only the practical reason." (I. S., "Kriticheskoe obozrenie," p. 98.) In another article the same journal stated: "In the final analysis, philosophy is national self-understanding: therefore, it should express the true spirit of a people. The spirit of Russia is known to everybody: exemplary devotion and profound loyalty to the Fatherland and the Tsar—these are the dominant features of its character and spirit." (Orest Novitskii, pp. 328–29.)

98. Chernyshevskii, *Polnoe sobranie sochinenii*, III, 179.

99. Ivanov-Razumnik, II, 201.

100. Belinskii, *Sochineniia*, III, 273–78.

101. Malia, p. 236.

102. Herzen, *Byloe i dumy*, II, 143.

103. Herzen, *Izbrannye filosofskie proizvedeniia*, I, 304.

104. Herzen, *Sochineniia*, II, 44. For his views on mathematics, see Maistrov, pp. 481–88.

105. Herzen, *Sochineniia*, II, 9. 106. *Ibid.*, p. 47.

107. *Ibid.*, p. 78. 108. *Ibid.*, p. 103.

109. Herzen, *Izbrannye filosofskie sochineniia*, II, 304–14; Herzen, *O razvitii*, p. 32.

110. Herzen, *Sochineniia*, II, 10.

111. *Ibid.*, p. 51.

112. Herzen, *Izbrannye filosofskie sochineniia*, II, 304.

113. As quoted by Lampert, p. 205.

114. Zubov, *Istoriografiia*, p. 352.
115. V. V. T-va (O. Pochinkovskaia), p. 500.

CHAPTER SEVEN

1. *Pamiatnaia knizhka*, p. 142.
2. *Ibid.*, pp. 161–62.
3. "Uvarov (graf Sergeia Semenovich)," p. 419.
4. M. Stepanov, "Zhozef de Mestr," pp. 678, 681.
5. Platova, "Razvitie ucheniia o kletke," p. 343; Meyer, *Human Generation*, p. 55. According to Sarton: "The anti-Darwinian von Baer was not simply the founder of modern embryology, he was one of the pioneers of the evolutionary philosophy." (Sarton, "The Discovery of the Mammalian Egg," p. 329.)
6. Radlov, "K. E. fon Ber," pp. 63–114.   7. Anuchin, "Beglyi vzgliad," p. 35.
8. Levin, *Ocherki*, pp. 18–38.   9. Newcomb, *The Reminiscences*, p. 309.
10. Clerke, *A Popular History*, p. 55.
11. Newcomb, *A Compendium*, p. 345.
12. Vorontsov-Vel'iaminov, "Istoriia astronomii," p. 42.
13. Ioffe, ed., pp. 66–70.
14. A. Savel'ev, "O trudakh akademika Lentsa," pp. 28–29.
15. For a particularly interesting cooperative project of Lenz and Jacobi, see Lezhneva and Rzhonsnitskii, pp. 79–95.
16. R. Hinton Thomas, p. 28. In 1808 N. P. Rumiantsev met Humboldt in Paris and suggested that he accompany an official Russian delegation to Kashgar and Tibet. Inspired by this invitation, Humboldt prepared a detailed plan for prolonged and extensive expeditionary studies in Russia. He submitted his plan to the Russian government in 1812, but Napoleon's invasion of Russia prevented an immediate realization of his ambition. It was not until 1827 that he again expressed a desire to visit the Urals, Mt. Ararat, and Lake Baikal. The Russian government approved his plan and undertook to pay all the expenses incurred by his team. (Shcherbakov, ed., p. 8.)
17. From 1830 to 1864 the Academy published 324 studies based partly or completely on materials collected by various expeditionary teams. (Brandt, p. 21.) Pypin, *Istoriia russkoi etnografii*, IV, 287–91; Bartol'd, *Istoriia*, p. 235.
18. Brandt, p. 21.
19. Kollins never completed university studies. As a young man he was very much interested in mathematics and was conversant with the contributions of contemporary French mathematicians. He was a great-grandson of Euler and an offspring of the Fuss family, whose influence was most probably responsible for his election into the ranks of Academicians.
20. A. K. Timiriazev, *Ocherki*, pp. 90–91.
21. Prudnikov, *P. L. Chebyshev*, p. 20; Gnedenko, *Ocherki*, p. 103; Tarasevich, pp. 319–20.
22. Panaev, "Vospominaniia," p. 407.
23. Sechenov, *Avtobiograficheskiia zapiski*, p. 17.
24. Panaev, "Vospominaniia," p. 78–80.
25. Gnedenko, *Mikhail Vasil'evich Ostrogradskii*, p. 98.
26. Bobynin, "Ostrogradskii," p. 453. For Ostrogradskii's teaching activities, see Maron, pp. 197–340.
27. Remez, pp. 9–98.

28. Maxwell, I, 117.
29. Todhunter, pp. 111–39.
30. Lobachevskii, *Polnoe sobranie sochinenii,* I, 410.
31. A. V. Vasil'ev, "Lobachevskii," p. 555.
32. Lobatschewskij, *Zwei geometrische Abhandlungen,* p. 420.
33. Clifford, p. 553.
34. Helmholtz, pp. 27–28.
35. Kline, pp. 428, 431.
36. Nagel, *The Structure of Science,* p. 266. See also P. S. Aleksandrov, "Russkaia matematika," pp. 7–8. For a brief summary of the interpretation by Poincaré, Minkowski, and Klein of the internal consistency of Lobachevskii's geometry, see Nut, pp. 7–8, 299.
37. Lobatschewskij, *Zwei geometrische Abhandlungen,* pp. 354–55; A. V. Vasil'ev, "Lobachevskii," p. 530; A. Vasiliev, *Nicolai Ivanovich Lobachevsky,* p. 4.
38. Bell, pp. 222–23. A different view is held by Depman, who cites a letter of the astronomer O. Struve to show that when the word of Lobachevskii's non-Euclidean geometry reached Bartels, the latter rejected it as unscientific. Depman thinks that if Bartels had been familiar with Gauss's efforts to construct a new geometry, he would not have been so quick to oppose Lobachevskii's ideas. (Depman, "M. F. Bartels," p. 478.)
39. Gauss was full of praise for the conciseness and precision of the *Geometrische Untersuchungen.* (Dunnington, p. 208.)
40. Zagoskin, ed., *Za sto let,* I, 407.
41. *Ibid.,* p. 408.
42. On the basis of new documentary material, B. L. Laptev shows that as early as 1822 Lobachevskii was convinced of the futility of all efforts to adduce proofs for the parallel postulate and that most probably by 1824 he was preoccupied with constructing a new geometry. (Laptev, "Teoriia parallel'nykh linii," p. 114.)
43. L. B. Modzalevskii, ed., *Materialy dlia biografii N. I. Lobachevskogo,* pp. 202–3.
44. Faidel' and Shafranovskii, p. 128. For a view not implicating Ostrogradskii, see Depman, "Novoe o N. I. Lobachevskom," p. 561.
45. Lobachevskii, *Polnoe sobranie sochinenii,* I, 410. Gauss, who read Lobachevskii's Russian studies in the original, compared them with "a confused forest through which it is difficult to find a passage and perspective, without having first gotten acquainted with all the trees individually." (Dunnington, p. 186.)
46. In 1837 Crelle's famous *Journal für reine und angewandte Mathematik* carried Lobachevskii's "Géométrie imaginaire." Three years later Lobachevskii presented his ideas in a book written in German and published in Berlin (*Geometrische Untersuchungen zur Theorie der Parallellinien*). In 1855, on the occasion of the fiftieth anniversary of the founding of Kazan University, an article by Lobachevskii entitled "Pangeometry" appeared in the *Scientific Journal of Kazan University.* For a chronological review of his studies, see Lobachevskii, *Polnoe sobranie sochinenii,* I, 14–23.
47. L. B. Modzalevskii, ed., *Materialy dlia biografiii N. I. Lobachevskogo,* p. 339.
48. Kamenskii, "I. Kant," pp. 59–60.
49. Lobachevskii, *Polnoe sobranie sochinenii,* I, 186.
50. Osipovskii, "O prostranstve," p. 49.
51. Lobachevskii, *Polnoe sobranie sochinenii,* II, 159.
52. L. B. Modzalevskii, ed., *Materialy dlia biografii N. I. Lobachevskogo,* p. 204.
53. Lobachevskii, *Polnoe sobranie sochinenii,* II, 164.
54. Lobachevskii, "Rech'," p. 383.

55. Lobachevskii, "Nastavleniia uchiteliam," p. 556.

56. Lobachevskii, *Polnoe sobranie sochinenii*, II, 147.

57. Lobachevskii, "Rech'," p. 383.

58. Zubov, *Istoriografiia*, p. 152.

59. Osipovskii, "Rassuzhdenie," p. 50.

60. L. B. Modzalevskii, *Materialy dlia biografii N. I. Lobachevskogo*, p. 434.

61. Lobachevskii, "Rech'," p. 382.

62. Nagaeva, "Pedagogicheskie vzgliady," p. 101.

63. Kagan, *Lobachevskii*, p. 214.

64. Clemens Schaeffer, ed., p. 668; Rybkin and Fedorenko, pp. 105–10.

65. Faidel' and Shafranovskii, p. 128.

66. Zubov, *Istoriografiia*, p. 380.

67. *Ibid.*, p. 381; Faidel' and Shafranovskii, p. 129.

68. Zubov, *Istoriografiia*, p. 381.

69. Faidel' and Shafranovskii, pp. 129–30.

70. Bell, p. 292.

71. Prudnikov, *P. L. Chebyshev*, p. 37. Together with Dirichlet and Riemann, he laid the foundations for the analytical theory of numbers—a mathematical discipline that studies ordinal integers by methods of mathematical analysis. (P. S. Aleksandrov, "Russkaia matematika," pp. 12–13.) Chebyshev's principal contributions are succinctly reviewed in Kolmogorov, "Rol' russkoi nauki," p. 56; Delone, "Razvitie teorii chisel," pp. 78–79; and Prudnikov, "Akademik P. L. Chebyshev," pp. 117–35.

72. Posse, pp. 21–22.

73. *Ibid.*, p. 2.

74. Petukhov, I, 399.

75. Ikonnikov, "Russkie universitety," p. 110.

76. Sechenov, "Nauchnaia deiatel'nost," pp. 331–32.

77. Afanas'ev, "Moskovskii universitet," pp. 358ff.

78. Zagoskin, ed., *Za sto let*, I, 340.

79. Butlerov, *Sochineniia*, III, 98.

80. Anuchin, *O liudiakh russkoi nauki*, p. 187. He has also been called the founder of Russian ecology. (Davitashvili and Mikulinskii, p. 530.)

81. Odoevskii, *Russkaia nochi*, p. 175.

82. Tarasevich, p. 299.

83. "Iz bumag kniaza V. F. Odoevskogo," No. 2, pp. 316–17.

84. Khotinskii, p. 129.

85. Pavlov-Sil'vanskii, *Ocherki*, p. 271.

86. As quoted by Kedrov, *Klassifikatsiia nauk*, I, 245.

87. *Ivan Sergeevich Aksakov v ego pis'makh*, III, 290.

88. Belinskii, *Polnoe sobranie sochinenii*, X, 26–27.

89. Dobroliubov, *Izbrannye filosofskie sochineniia*, I, 344–45.

90. Dobroliubov, *Izbrannye filosofskie proizvedeniia*, I, 193–202.

91. Zagoskin, ed., *Za sto let*, II, 129.

92. Mikulinskii, *Razvitie obshchikh problem biologii*, p. 86.

93. Pirogov, *Sochineniia*, III, 397.

94. *Ibid.*, pp. 494–95.

95. Engelhardt, p. 299; Iu. G. Malis, p. 30.

96. Tarasevich, p. 304.

97. *Ibid.*, p. 303.

98. "Iz bumag kniaza V. F. Odoevskogo," No. 7, p. 22.

99. Gel'mersen, "Sovremennoe sostoianie," p. 8.

100. Gel'mersen, "Sir Roderik," pp. 183–84. Murchison regarded Fischer von Waldheim, Pander, Eichwald, Kutorga, and J. F. Parrot as the pioneers in Russian geological studies. (Murchison, II, vi.)

101. B. E. Raikov, *Russkie biologi-evoliutsionisty,* II, 309. For a summary of Sokolov's scientific work, see Figurovskii, ed., Vol. I, Part 2, pp. 225–28.

102. Anuchin, *O liudiakh russkoi nauki,* pp. 172–73. Physics was the last major science to be adequately represented in the universities despite the fact that the St. Petersburg Academy of Sciences boasted of such illustrious physicists as Lenz, Jacobi, Kupffer, Ostrogradskii, and G. F. Parrot. University professors concentrated primarily on the preparation of textbooks (I. A. Dvigubskii, N. P. Shchegelov), or on such "empirical" disciplines as meteorology and earth magnetism (M. F. Spasskii, I. M. Simonov, E. Knorr). In physics, as in biology, Schelling's philosophy was a lasting, and rather disturbing, influence. For over two decades, D. M. Vellanskii taught "physics" at the St. Petersburg Medical and Surgical Academy. In 1831 he completed a volume entitled *Experimental and Speculative Physics,* the first part of a projected *Encyclopedia of Physical Knowledge,* of which he was to be the sole writer. He submitted his manuscript to the Academy of Sciences in hope of receiving the Demidov Prize, one of the highest awards in the field of scholarship. As was expected, the Academicians expressed a very unfavorable opinion about Vellanskii's study; a special committee labeled it "a novel about nature" and took the opportunity to warn about the contaminating influences of the *Naturphilosophie* on Russian higher education. (K. S. Veselovskii, "Russkii filosof D. M. Vellanskii," pp. 16–17.) Lenz directed a similar criticism at M. G. Pavlov's *Foundations of Physics.* (Figurovskii, ed., *Istoriia,* Vol. I, Part 2, p. 151.) Pavlov, another Schellingian, taught "physics" at Moscow University from 1827 to 1838. He inspired his students to ponder about the great metaphysical problems without giving them much substantive knowledge in physics or an appreciation of its experimental and mathematical foundations. The Academicians were particularly disturbed about the negative and antiscientific effects of the Schellingian idea of physics as a special derivation from the ontological principles of subjective idealism. Lenz was vehement in his insistence that the laws of nature are the laws of mechanics, free of human intuition and idealistic metaphysics. In an article written at the end of the 1830's, Academician Kollins censored the proponents of the *Naturphilosophie* for their attacks on Newton and on mathematics as a methodological basis of physics. (E. A. Kollins, pp. 340–41.)

103. Pirogov, *Sochineniia,* III, 154.

104. Val'ter, pp. 250–51.

105. Review of *Otchet Imperiatorskoi Publichnoi Biblioteki,* p. 7.

106. Review of *Vestnik estestvennykh nauk,* pp. 7–8.

107. Lipshits, *Moskovskoe obshchestvo,* p. 21.

108. Berg, *Vsesoiuznoe geograficheskoe obshchestvo,* p. 48.

109. *Ibid.,* p. 44; Pypin, *Istoriia russkoi etnografii,* I, 266ff. An early and distinguished member of the Society noted that while von Baer favored an ethnographic study of small Siberian tribes that were gradually dying out, Nadezhdin stressed an ethnographic study of Russian rural life. Semenov inferred that von Baer was guided primarily by the interests of scientific theory and Nadezhdin by the urgency for a fuller understanding of the pressing needs of the common people. (Semenov, *Istoriia,* I, 51.)

110. N. I. Veselovskii, *Istoriia,* p. 13.

111. "Arkheologicheskiia obshchestva v Rossii," p. 232.

112. N. I. Veselovskii, *Istoriia,* pp. 75–76, 207.

113. "Lichnji sostav Imperatorskoi Akademii nauk v kontse 1852 goda," pp. 580–89.
114. Anuchin, *O liudiakh russkoi nauki*, pp. 253, 179.
115. Khodnev, p. 139.
116. Tarasevich, p. 305.
117. K. A. Timiriazev, "Probuzhdenie estestvoznaniia," p. 7.
118. Pypin, *Istoriia russkoi etnografii*, IV, 291.
119. Butlerov, *Sochineniia*, III, 86.
120. B. E. Raikov, *Russkie biologi-evoliutsionisty*, II, 221.
121. Figurovskii, ed., *Istoriia*, Vol. I, Part 2, p. 244.
122. Gel'mersen, "Sovremennoe sostoianie," p. 10.
123. *Ibid.*, p. 11.

CHAPTER EIGHT

1. K. A. Timiriazev, "Probuzhdenie estestvoznaniia," p. 1.
2. Ikonnikov, "Russkie universitety," p. 103.
3. P. E. Pavlov, p. 1051; Buslaev, *Moi vospominaniia*, p. 307.
4. *Zapiski Sergeia Mikhailovicha Solov'eva*, p. 122.
5. Herzen, *Byloe i dumy*, III, 289–90.
6. Nikitenko, I, 384.
7. Shil'der, "Imperator Nikolai I," pp. 186–87.
8. Rozhdestvenskii, "Posledniaia stranitsa," pp. 42–43.
9. Skabichevskii, *Ocherki*, p. 342.
10. *Ibid.*
11. Buslaev, *Moi vospominaniia*, p. 313.
12. I. V. Kuznetsov, ed., *Liudi russkoi nauki—geologiia, geografiia*, p. 139.
13. Nikitenko, I, 381; Platova, "N. A. Varnek," pp. 317–62.
14. Chicherin, *Vospominaniia. Moskva*, p. 160. For similar views expressed by K. D. Kavelin and E. M. Feoktistov, see Vinogradov, ed., pp. 607–12.
15. Sechenov, "Nauchnaia deiatel'nost," p. 331.
16. K. A. Timiriazev, "Probuzhdenie estestvoznaniia," p. 1.
17. Shchapov, III, 286–91, 314–15. Ironically, the censors did not pass Shchapov's study and it was not published until 1863.
18. Shchapov, III, 290.
19. Sechenov, *Avtobiograficheskii zapiski*, p. 103; Figurovskii, *Dmitrii Ivanovich Mendeleev*, pp. 42–43.
20. Chicherin, *Vospominaniia. Moskva*, pp. 262–63.
21. Solov'ev, *Istoriia*, I, 1339.
22. Chernyshevskii, *Izbrannye filosofskie sochineniia*, III, 208.
23. "Materialy dlia istorii i statistiki nashikh gimnazii," p. 169.
24. K. A. Timiriazev, "Probuzhdenie estestvoznaniia," p. 2.
25. *Ibid.*
26. Pisarev, *Sochineniia*, II, 226.
27. Samarin, "Dva slova," p. 47; Khomiakov, *Polnoe sobranie sochinenii*, I, 180–82.
28. Dobroliubov, *Izbrannye filosofskie sochineniia*, I, 194.
29. I. S. Turgenev, "Dva slova o Granovskom," pp. 85–86.
30. Pirogov, *Izbrannye pedagogicheskie sochineniia*, p. 61. See also Chernyshevskii, "Zametki o zhurnalakh, 1856, iul'," pp. 215–21.
31. Sreznevskii, *Mysli*, p. 16.

32. Khomiakov, *Polnoe sobranie sochinenii*, I, 180–82.

33. Chicherin, "O narodnosti v nauke," p. 71.

34. K. A. Timiriazev, "Probuzhdenie estestvoznaniia," p. 68.

35. Zubov, *Istoriografiia*, p. 540.

36. I. V. Kuznetsov, ed., *Liudi russkoi nauki—geologiia, geografiia,* pp. 462–66.

37. Katkov, "Apologiia," pp. 30–31.

38. *Ibid.*, p. 33.

39. G. Florovskii, *Puti*, p. 238.

40. Giliarov-Platonov, *Sbornik sochinenii*, I, 365.

41. I. V. Kireevskii, "O neobkhodimosti i vozmozhnosti novykh nachal," p. 17. Minor differences and basic similarities between Khomiakov's and Kireevskii's theories of knowledge are discussed in Radlov, "Teoriia znaniia," pp. 153–65.

Bibliography

The Bibliography includes only sources that have been consulted. Because of the relatively broad scope of this study, the source material is of all sorts, and all degrees of scholarly merit. However, most items fall into five categories.

(1) Histories of scientific institutions, chiefly universities and learned societies. This category includes such richly documented sources as Pekarskii's study of the Academy of Sciences, Sukhomlinov's of the Imperial Russian Academy, Shevyrev's of Moscow University, Zagoskin's of Kazan University, Grigor'ev's of St. Petersburg University, Khodnev's of the Free Economic Society, Veselovskii's of the Russian Archaeological Society, and Semenov's of the Russian Geographical Society.

Many institutional histories, notably those written to commemorate anniversaries, systematically overstate the past achievements of the institution concerned. However, the works of Pekarskii, Sukhomlinov, and Zagoskin, which avoid this distortion, are models of thorough and dispassionate research. Of the recent institutional histories the most useful is *Istoriia Akademii nauk SSSR* (the first volume of a planned series), edited by Ostrovitianov. Much relevant material is also available in the journals *Vestnik Evropy, Russkaia starina, Russkii arkhiv, Russkii vestnik,* and *Zhurnal Ministerstva narodnogo prosveshcheniia.* Two useful primary sources are *Polnoe sobranie zakonov Rossiiskoi imperii s 1649 goda,* and the ten-volume *Materialy dlia istorii Imperatorskoi Akademii nauk.* Rozhdestvenskii's *Istoricheskii obzor deiatel'nosti Ministerstva narodnogo prosveshcheniia* provides valuable analytical summaries of the principal laws and decrees of the Ministry of National Education.

(2) Autobiographical and biographical writings. Von Baer, Pogodin, Solov'ev, Busliaev, Butlerov, Sechenov, Markovnikov, and a few other scholars have left extensive autobiographical notes, and the vast majority of Russian scholars seem to have left at least a few autobiographical fragments. Some of the leading institutional studies, notably those by Pekarskii and Sukhomlinov, are written in the form of detailed biographies of the members of learned bodies. Pekarskii's *Istoriia,* for example, contains one of the most detailed and objective biographies of Lomonosov ever written, and Sukhomlinov's *Istoriia* is the best source of information on Lepekhin, Kotel'nikov, Rumovskii, Ozeretskovskii, and Severgin. The *Zapiski Akademii nauk,* published from 1862

to 1895, contains an impressive number of biographical essays on famous Academicians.

The *Russkii biograficheskii slovar'* and the Brockhaus-Efron *Entsiklopedicheskii slovar'* are rich and valuable sources of biographical information on Russian scholars, both major and minor. As a rule, the biographical essays in these encyclopedias are written by scientific experts and highly qualified scholars. The *Russkii biograficheskii slovar'*, for example, contains biographies of Lomonosov and Zinin written by Menshutkin, of Rumovskii by V. V. Bobynin, of Lobachevskii by A. V. Vasil'ev, and of Severgin by B. Modzalevskii; the Brockhaus-Efron encyclopedia has biographies of Voskresenskii by Mendeleev, of Granovskii by P. Vinogradov, and of Ostrogradskii by Bobynin.

Soviet historians of science have written at length about all Russian scientists of any consequence. Some Soviet works are straightforward, careful, thoroughly documented narratives (such as Kagan's biography of Lobachevskii, Menshutkin's of Lomonosov, Iushkevich's of Gur'ev, Gnedenko's of Ostrogradskii, Prudnikov's of Chebyshev, and Dezhneva and Rzhonsnitskii's of Lenz); others are marred by Marxist philosophical excesses and nationalist bias.

Extensive biographical information is also contained in the separate volumes of *Nauchnoe nasledstvo*; in Modzalevskii's collection of biographical material on Lobachevskii; in *Lomonosov: Sbornik statei i materialov*, by Andreev and Modzalevskii (a continuing publication started in 1940); and in individual volumes of the *Trudy Instituta istorii estestvoznaniia* and its successor, the *Trudy Instituta istorii estestvoznaniia i tekhniki,* published by the Academy of Sciences.

(3) Histories of individual sciences. The most impressive pre-Soviet histories of Russian scientific thought appear in the Brockhaus-Efron encyclopedia (Vol. XXVIII, 1900, pp. 720–859) and in the *Istoriia XIX veka* published by the Granat brothers (particularly the articles by Borozdin, Kagan, and Timiriazev). V. V. Bobynin's *Ocherki istorii razvitiia fiziko-matematicheskikh znanii v Rossii*, containing detailed summaries of Old Russian "scientific" information, has not been available to me.

After World War II, in response to the Communist Party's emphasis on the indigenous nature of the Russian intellectual heritage, the various institutes of the Academy of Sciences published a great many histories of individual sciences in Russia. At first these were mostly perfunctory studies marked by the exaggerated nationalist bias stimulated by Stalin's anti-cosmopolitan campaigns. But when the Stalinist hysteria subsided, the quality of published material began to improve. Worth mentioning are the works by Bliakher in the history of embryology; by Gnedenko, Iushkevich, and Delone in the history of mathematics; by Koshtoiants in the history of physiology; by Mikulinskii in the history of theoretical biology; by Fesenkov, Perel', and Vorontsov-Vel'iaminov in the history of astronomy; by D. M. Lebedev in the history of geography; and by M. G. Levin in the history of physical anthropology. These works vary in quality and depth, but all of them contain useful historical material. In particular, Bliakher's *Istoriia embriologii* is an excellent study, a model of thorough and careful historiography. Another very useful study is V. P. Zubov's *Istoriografiia estestvennykh nauk v Rossii*, although unfortunately the author is concerned more with the minutiae in his sources than with their broader cultural significance. Valuable information is also contained in the *Trudy* of the Academy's Institute of the History of Natural Sciences and its successor, the Institute of the History of Natural and Applied Sciences.

(4) General studies of Russian science. Here belong B. G. Kuznetsov's *Ocherki istorii russkoi nauki*, T. I. Rainov's *Nauka v Rossii XI–XVII vekov*, and such pre-Soviet studies as Sechenov's "Nauchnaia deiatel'nost russkikh universitetov po estestvoznaniiu za polednee dvadtsatipiatiletie" and Timiriazev's "Probuzhdenie estestvoznaniia v tret'ei chetverti veka." The Soviet Academy of Sciences has published a collection of essays entitled *Istoriia estestvoznaniia v Rossii*, of which the first volume (in two parts) covers the pre-Reform period. Each essay traces the contributions of various Russian scholars to a specific science or group of sciences. Although the essays are informative, no broad historical and cultural analysis is attempted; and the extensive coverage of the work of minor figures tends to obscure the greater contributions of the leading scholars.

(5) Histories of nonscientific modes of inquiry—notably religion, literature, and philosophy. Sociologically oriented works in these fields have been of particular value for this study. In theology, the excellence of G. Florovskii's *Puti russkogo bogosloviia* is unsurpassed, mostly because it treats Russian theology within a larger context of philosophical and social thought. The work of Berdyaev, an "unofficial" philosopher of Russian Orthodox religious thought, particularly *The Russian Idea*, gives concise expression to the traditional incompatibility of Russian theology and science. Among the histories of literature written with a definite sociological orientation, Pypin's *Istoriia russkoi literatury* and Skabichevskii's *Istoriia noveishei russkoi literatury* are outstanding. Both of them pay a great deal of attention to the growth of rationalism in Russian culture.

The best Russian philosophizing (and most of it) has come from poets and novelists, scientists and historians, social critics, and men of religion. Their ideas have been treated historically in several special studies written in Russia and abroad, notably Sakulin's *Iz istorii russkogo idealizma*, Chizhevskii's *Gegel' v Rossii*, Koyré's *La philosophie et le problème national en Russie*, Setschkareff's *Schellings Einfluss*, Christoff's *Xomjakov*, Malia's *Alexander Herzen*, and Schelting's *Russland und Europa*.

Among the most useful general works on the humanities are Koialovich's *Istoriia russkogo samosoznaniia*, and Ivanov-Razumnik's *Istoriia russkoi ob-*

shchestvennoi mysli. Pypin's *Istoriia russkoi etnografii,* despite its narrow title, offers excellent documentation on the development of conditions conducive to the advancement of scientific thought and the general growth of secular knowledge in Russia.

The following abbreviations are used in the Bibliography:

AIN-T. Arkhiv istorii nauki i tekhniki.

Brockhaus-Efron. Entsiklopedicheskii slovar'. F. A. Brockhaus and I. A. Efron, eds. 41 vols. St. Petersburg: 1894–1904.

Chten. Chteniia v Imperatorskom Obshchestve istorii i drevnostei rossiiskikh pri Moskovskom universitete.

Granat-Ents. Entsiklopedicheskii slovar'. 53 vols. Moscow: The Granat Institute. N.d.–1937 (7th edition).

Granat-Ist. Istoriia Rossii v XIX veke. 9 vols.

IMI. Istoriko-matematicheskie issledovaniia.

IV. Istoricheskii vestnik.

PSZ. Polnoe sobranie zakonov Rossiiskoi Imperii s 1649 goda.

RA. Russkii arkhiv.

RB. Russkaia beseda.

RBS. Russkii biograficheskii slovar'. 25 vols. St. Petersburg: 1896–1913.

RIZ. Russkii istoricheskii zhurnal.

RS. Russkaia starina.

RV. Russkii vestnik.

SRIO. Sbornik Russkogo istoricheskogo obshchestva.

TIIE. Trudy Instituta istorii estestvoznaniia.

TIIE-T. Trudy Instituta istorii estestvoznaniia i tekhniki.

VAN. Vestnik Akademii nauk SSSR.

VE. Vestnik Evropy.

VF. Voprosy filosofii.

VI. Voprosy istorii.

VIMK. Vestnik istorii mirovoi kul'tury.

ZAN. Zapiski Imperatorskoi Akademii nauk.

ZMNP. Zhurnal Ministerstva narodnogo prosveshcheniia.

Afanas'ev, A. N. "Moskovskii universitet, 1843–1849," *RS,* LI (1886), 357–94.

[———.] "Iz vospominanii A. N. Afanas'eva," *RA,* 1872, No. 3-4, 805–52.

A. Ia. "Desnitskii (Semen Efimovich)," *Brockhaus-Efron,* X (1893), 485–86.

[Aksakov, Ivan S.] Ivan Sergeevich Aksakov v ego pis'makh. Vol. III, Moscow, 1892.

Aksakov, K. S. Vospominanie studentstva 1832–1835 godov. St. Petersburg, 1911.

Aksakov, S. T. Sobranie sochinenii. Vol. II. Moscow, 1955.

Aleksandrov, P. S. "Russkaia matematika XIX i XX vv. i ee vlianie na mirovoiu nauku," Rol' russkoi nauki v razvitii mirovoi nauki i kul'tury, Vol. I, Part 1. (*Uchenye zapiski Moskovskogo universiteta,* XCI, 1947, 3–33.)

Aleksandrov, P. S., *et al.,* eds. Istoriia Moskovskogo universiteta. Vol. II. Moscow, 1955.

Aleshintsev, I. Soslovnyi vopros i politika v istorii nashikh gimnazii v XIX veke: Istoricheski ocherk. St. Petersburg, 1908.

———. "Zapiska grafa Speranskogo 'Ob usovershenii obshchego narodnogo vospitaniia'," *RS,* CXXXII (1907), 729–35.

Andreev, A. I., ed. Petr Velikii: Sbornik statei. Vol. I. Moscow-Leningrad, 1947.

———. "Osnovanie Akademii nauk v Peterburge," in A. I. Andreev, ed., Petr Velikii, I, 284–333.

———. "Petr I v Anglii v 1698 g.," in A. I. Andreev, ed., Petr Velikii, I, 63–103.

———. "Trudy V. N. Tatishcheva po istorii Rossii," in Tatishchev, Istoriia Rossiiskaia, I, 5–38.

Andreev, A. I., and L. B. Modzalevskii, eds. Lomonosov: Sbornik statei i materialov. 4 vols. Moscow-Leningrad, 1940–60.

Andreevich. Opyt filosofii russkoi literatury. St. Petersburg, 1909.

Andreevskii, Iv. "Ivan Petrovich Kulibin, 1735–1818," RS, VIII (1873), 734–37.

Anuchin, D. N. "Beglyi vzgliad na proshloe antropologii i na eia zadachi v Rossii," Russkii antropologicheskii zhurnal, No. 1 (1900), 25–42.

——. O liudiakh russkoi nauki i kul'tury. Moscow, 1950.

Arkhangel'skii, A. "K istorii drevne-russkogo lutsidariusa," Uchenyia zapiski Imperatorskogo Kazanskogo universiteta, LXV–LXVI (1898–99), Section: Unofficial papers.

——. "Obrazovanie i literatura v Moskovskom gosudarstve kon. XV–XVII vv.," Uchenyia zapiski Imperatorskogo Kazanskogo universiteta, LCV–LCVIII (1898–1901), Section: Unofficial papers.

"Arkheograficheskiia kommissii," Brockhaus-Efron, II (1891), 221–25.

"Arkheologicheskiia obshchestva v Rossii," Brockhaus-Efron, II (1891), 230–43.

Babkin, D. S. "Biografii M. V. Lomonosova, sostavlennye ego sovremennikami," in Andreev and Modzalevskii, eds., Lomonosov (Moscow-Leningrad, 1946), II, 5–70.

——. ed. Biografiia A. N. Radishcheva napisannaia ego synov'iami. Moscow-Leningrad, 1959.

Bacon, Francis. The Advancement of Learning. London: J. M. Dent, 1950.

——. The New Organon and Related Writings. New York: The Liberal Arts Press, 1960.

Baer, K. E. von. Peter's des Grossen Verdienste um die Erweiterung der geographischen Kentnisse. St. Petersburg, 1872.

——. Reden gehalten in wissenschaftlichen Versammlungen und kleinere Aufsätze vermischten Inhalts. 3 vols. St. Petersburg, 1864–76.

——. "Vzgliad na razvitie nauk," in Vasteskii and Mikulinskii, Izbrannye proizvedeniia, 216–35.

Bagalei. D. I. Prosvita: Ocherki po istorii ukrainskoi kul'tury. (Sbornik Khar'kovskogo Istoriko-Filologicheskogo Obshchestva, XX.) Khar'kov, 1911.

Balashova, Olga. "Pismo neizvestnogo litsa o moskovskom masonstve XVIII veka," RA, 1874, No. 4, 1031–42.

Baranov, P. I. "Arkheologiia. Rasporiazhenie Petra I o voznagrazhdenii za arkheologicheskiia nakhodki," RS, VI (1872), 474.

Baranskii, N. N., et al., eds. Otechestvennye fiziko-geografy i puteshestvenniki. Moscow, 1859.

Barbashev, N. I. K istorii morekhodnogo obrazovaniia v Rossii. Moscow, 1959.

Barsov, N. I. "O sudbe pravoslavnoi tserkvi russkoi v tsarstvovanie imperatora Aleksandra I-go (Iz zapisok A. S. Sturdzy)," RS, XV (1876), 266–88.

Bartenev, Petr, ed. Deviatnadtsatyi vek: Istoricheskii sbornik. 2 vols. Moscow, 1872.

——. Osmnadtsatyi vek: Istoricheskii sbornik. 4 vols. Moscow, 1868–69.

Bartol'd, V. Istoriia izucheniia Vostoka v Evrope i Rossii. 2nd ed. Leningrad, 1925.

Beliavskii, S. I., ed. Sto let Pulkovskoi observatorii. Moscow-Leningrad, 1945.

Belinskii, V. G. Sochineniia. 4th edition. Vol. IV. Kiev, 1911.

——. Polnoe sobranie sochinenii. Vol. X. Moscow, 1956.

——. Izbrannye filosofskie sochineniia. Vol. II. Moscow, 1948.

Bell, E. T. Men of Mathematics. New York: Simon and Schuster, 1961.

Belokurov, Sergei. O biblioteke moskovskikh gosudarei v XVI stoletii. Moscow, 1899.

Belov, M. I. "O rodine Lomonosova po novym materialam. (K biografii Lomonosova)," in Andreev and Modzalevskii, eds., Lomonosov, III, 1951, 226-45.

Belozerskaia, N. A. "Rossiia v shestidesiatykh godakh proshlogo veka," *RS*, LV (1887), 499–522.

Benjamin, Park. A History of Electricity. New York: John Wiley, 1898.

Berdyaev, Nicolas. The Russian Idea. New York: Macmillan, 1948.

Berg, L. "Russian Discoveries in the Pacific," in A. Fersman, ed., The Pacific (Leningrad, 1926), 1–26.

———. Vsesoiuznoe geograficheskoe obshchestvo za sto let. Moscow-Leningrad, 1946.

———. Dostizheniia sovetskoi geografii (1917–1947). Leningrad, 1948.

Bertrand, Joseph. L'Académie des Sciences et les académiciens de 1666 à 1793. Paris, 1869.

Bestuzhev-Riumin, B. "Karamzin, Nikolai Mikhailovich," *RBS*, VIII (1897), 500–514.

Bestuzhev-Riumin, K. N. Biografii i kharakteristiki. St. Petersburg, 1882.

———, ed. "Pamiatniki diplomaticheskikh snoshenii Moskovskogo gosudarstva s Anglieiu," Part 2, *SRIO*, XXVIII (1883).

Bil'basov, V. A. Didro v Peterburge. St. Petersburg, 1884.

Biliarskii, P. S. Materialy dlia biografii Lomonosova. St. Petersburg, 1865.

———. "Otzyv Eilera o Lomonosove," *ZAN*, V (1864), 104–10.

Bliakher, L. Ia. Istoriia embriologii v Rossii (s serediny XVIII do serediny XIX veka). Moscow, 1955.

Bobynin, V. V. "Ostrogradskii, Mikhail Vasil'evich," *RBS*, XII (1905), 452–57.

———. "Sostoianie matematicheskikh znanii v Rossii do XVI veka," *ZMNP*, CCXXXII (1884), Section: Science, 183–209.

———. "Rumovskii, Stepan Iakovlevich," *RBS*, XVII (1918), 441–50.

———. "Bernulli, Daniil, Iakov i Nikolai," in S. A. Vengerov, ed., Kritiko-biograficheskii slovar russkikh pisatelei i uchenykh (St. Petersburg, 1892), III, 92–115.

———. Russkaia fiziko-matematicheskaia bibliografiia. 2 vols., 6 parts. Moscow, 1886–92.

———. "Magnitskii (Leontii Filipovich, 1669–1739)," *Brockhaus-Efron*, XVIII (1896), 327–28.

———. "Matematika," *Brockhaus-Efron*, XXVIII (1900), 724–28.

——— and N. Kul'bin. "Petrov, Vasilii Vladimirovich," *RBS*, XIII (1902), 662–67.

Bodianskii, O. M., ed. "Fizika, vybrannaia iz luchshikh avktorov, raspolozhennaia i dopolnennaia Nevskoi Seminarii Filosofii i Fiziki Uchitelem Mikhailom Speranskim. V. Sanktpeterburge 1797 goda," *Chten*, 1871, No. 7–9, Section 2, 1–56.

Bogdanovich, M. I. "Padenie Speranskogo," *VE*, 1868, No. 12, 495–505.

———. "Pervaia epokha preobrazovanii imperatora Aleksandra I (1801–1805 g.): Narodnoe prosveshchenie," *VE*, 1866, No. 6, Section 1, 130–63.

Bogoslovskii, M. M. Petr I. Vol. II. Moscow, 1941.

Bokii, G. B., and I. I. Shafranovskii. "Russkie kristallografy," *TIIE*, I (1947), 81–120.

Borozdin, Aleksandr K. Protopop Avvakum: ocherk iz istorii zhizni russkogo obshchestva v XVII veke. St. Petersburg, 1898.

Borozdin, I. N. "Universitety v Rossii v pervoi polovine XIX veka," in *Granat-Ist.*, II, 349–79.

Botsianovskii, V. "Polevoi (Nikolai Alekseevich)," *Brockhaus-Efron*, XXIV (1898), 264–67.

Brandt, F. "Das zoologische und vergleichend-anatomische Museum," *Bulletin de l'Académie Imperiale des Sciences de St. Petersburg*, VII (1864), Supplement 2, 11–28.

Briantsev, A. M. "Slovo o vseobshchikh i glavnykh zakonakh prirody," in Shchipanov, ed., Izbrannye proizvedeniia, I, 377–83.

Brikner, A. G. "Russkie diplomaty-turisty v Italii v XVII stoletii," *RV*, CXXVIII–CXXX (1877).

Brunet, P. Les physiciens hollandais et la méthode experimentale en France au XVIII siècle. Paris, 1926.

Budilovich, A. "Ob uchenoi deiatel'nosti Lomonosova po estestvovedenii i filologii," *ZMNP*, CXLIV-CXLV (1869), Section 2, 272–333, 48–106.

Bulich, N. Iz pervykh let Kazanskogo universiteta, 1805–1819. 2 vols. 2nd ed. St. Petersburg, 1904.

Bulich, S. "Russkii iazyk i sravnitel'noe iazykoznanie," *Brockhaus-Efron*, XXVIII (1900), 823–33.

———. Ocherk istorii iazykoznaniia v Rossii. Vol. I. St. Petersburg, 1904.

Buniakovskii, V. "Parallel'nyia linii," *Uchenyia zapiski Imperatorskoi Akademii nauk po Pervomu i Tret'emu otdeleniiam*, II (1854), 337–411.

Burckhardt, Jacob. The Civilization of the Renaissance in Italy. 2 vols. New York: Harper, 1958.

Buslaev, F. I. Moi vospominaniia. Moscow, 1897.

Butlerov, A. M. Sochineniia. Vol. III. Moscow, 1958.

———. "Chetvertoe izmerenie prostranstva i mediumizm," *RV*, CXXXIII (1878), 945–71.

Butterfield, Herbert. Man on His Past. Boston: Beacon, 1960.

———. The Origins of Modern Science. New York: Macmillan, 1960.

Bykov, A. A. Patriarkh Nikon. St. Petersburg, 1891.

Chaadaev, P. Ia. Sochineniia i pis'ma. Edited by M. Gershenzon. 2 vols. Moscow, 1913–14.

Cauchy, Augustin-Louis. Mémoire sur les intégrales définies, prises entre des limites imaginaires. Paris, 1825.

Charnoluskii, V. I. "Nachal'noe obrazovanie v pervoi polovine XIX stoletiia," *Granat-Ist*, IV (n.d.), 68–128.

Chekanov, A. A. "M. V. Lomonosov i tekhnika," *TIIE-T*, XLV (1962), 3–18.

Chenakal, V. L. "Eiler i Lomonosov (k istorii ikh nauchnykh sviazei)," in Lavrent'ev *et al.*, eds., Leonard Eiler, 423–63.

Chernikov, A. "Rabota Akademii nauk po izdaniiu pervogo nauchnogo atlasa Rossii 1745 g.," *VAN*, 1936, No. 10, 69–72.

———. "Ekspeditsiia akademika Bera na Novuiu Zemliu," *VAN*, 1937, No. 9, 79–84.

Chernov, S. N. "Leonard Eiler i Akademiia nauk," in Deborin, ed., Leonard Eiler, 163–238.

Chernyshevskii, N. G. Izbrannye filosofskie sochineniia. Vol. III. Moscow, 1951.

———. Polnoe sobranie sochinenii. Vols. III and XVI. Moscow, 1947–53.

———. "Zametki o zhurnalakh, 1856, iul'," *Sovremennik*, LVIII (1856), Section: Smes', 205–21.

Chicherin, Boris N. Vospominaniia. Moskva sorokovykh godov. Moscow, 1929.

———. Vospominaniia. Moskovskii universitet. Moscow, 1929.

———. "O narodnosti v nauke," *RV*, III (1856), Section: Sovremennaia letopis', 62–71.

Chirikov, G. S. "Timofei Fedorovich Osipovskii, rektor Khar'kovskogo universiteta, 1820 g.," *RS*, XVII (1876), 463–90.

Chistovich, I. Feofan Prokopovich i ego vremia. St. Petersburg, 1868.

Chizhevskii, D. I. Gegel' v Rossii. Paris, 1939.

Christoff, Peter K. A. S. Xomjakov. 's-Gravenhage, 1961.

Chuchmarev, V. I. "G. V. Leibnits i russkaia kul'tura nachala 18 stoletiia," *VIMK*, 1957, No. 4, 120–32.

Clerke, Agnes M. A Popular History of Astronomy During the Nineteenth Century. 2nd ed. Edinburgh: Adam & Black, 1887.

Clifford, William Kingdon. "The Postulates of the Science of Space," in James R. Newman, ed., The World of Mathematics (New York: Simon and Schuster, 1956), I, 552–67.

Cobban, Alfred. In Search of Humanity. New York: Braziller, 1960.

Collins, Samuel. See Kollins, Samuel.

Condillac, Etienne. La logique, ou les premiers developpements de l'art de penser, in Oeuvres complètes de Condillac (Paris, 1822), XV, 319–463.

Condorcet, Marquis de. "Report on the General Organization of Public Instruction," in Fontainerie, French Liberalism (New York: McGraw-Hill, 1932), 323–78.

Cousin, Victor. See Kuzen, V.

Cuvier, Georges. Recueil des éloges historiques lus dans les séances publiques de l'Institut de France. Vol. I. Paris, 1861.

Danilevskii, V. V. I. I. Polzunov: Trudy i zhizn' pervogo russkogo teplotekhnika. Moscow-Leningrad, 1940.

———. "I. I. Polzunov—velikii russkii revoliutsioner v oblasti tekhniki," VAN, 1938, No. 7-8, 19–83.

———. Russkaia tekhnika. Leningrad, 1948.

[Dashkova, E.] Zapiski kniagini E. Dashkovoi. St. Petersburg, 1906.

Davitashvili, L. Sh., and S. R. Mikulinskii, "K. F. Rul'e—vydaiushchiisia russkii estestvoispytatel'-evoliutsionist," in S. I. Vavilov, ed., Nauchnoe nasledstvo, II, 529–69.

Deborin, A. M., ed. Leonard Eiler, 1707–1783: Sbornik statei i materialov k 150-letiiu so dnia smerti. Moscow-Leningrad, 1935.

Delisle l'Aîné. "Remarques sur la carte de la Mer Caspienne, envoyée à l'Académie par sa Majesté Czarienne," Mémoires de mathématique et de physique, tirés des registres de l'Académie Royale des Sciences. Paris, 1721, 245–54.

———. "Détermination géographique de la situation et de l'étendue des différentes parties de la terre," Mémoires de mathématique et de physique, tirés des registres de l'Académie Royale des Sciences. Paris, 1720, 365–84.

Delone, B. N. Matematika i ee razvitie v Rossii. Moscow, 1948.

———. Peterburgskaia shkola teorii chisel. Moscow-Leningrad, 1947.

———. "Razvitie teorii chisel v Rossii," in Rol' russkoi nauki v mirovoi nauki i kul'tury, Vol. I, Part 1. (Uchenye zapiski Moskovskogo universiteta, XCI, 1947, 77–96.)

———. "Geometriia N. I. Lobachevskogo i nekotorye ee primeneniia," in S. I. Vavilov et al., eds., Voprosy istorii otechestvennoi nauki, 113–41.

Denisov, A. P. "Nikolai Gavrilovich Kurganov (1725–1796)," TIIE-T, XXXIV (1960), 360–83.

Depman, I. Ia. "M. F. Bartels—uchitel' N. I. Lobachevskogo," IMS, III (1950), 474–85.

———. "Novoe o N. I. Lobachevskom (K voprosu o retsenzii v 'Syne otechestva')," TIIE, II (1948), 561–63.

Detlaf, T. A. "Otkrytie zarodyshevikh listkov K. F. Vol'fom i Kh. Panderom i uchenie o zarodyshevikh listkakh K. M. Bera," TIIE, V (1953), 280–316.

Diderot, Denis. "Plan for a University for the Russian Government Submitted to Her Imperial Majesty Catherine II," in Fontainerie, French Liberalism, 199–310.

Die Deutsche Universität Dorpat im Lichte der Geschichte und der Gegenwart. Eine historische Studie aus dem Gebiete östlicher Culturkämpfe. Leipzig, 1882.

Dobroliubov, N. A. Izbrannye filosofskie sochineniia. Vol. I. Moscow, 1945.

———. Izbrannye filosofskie proizvedeniia. Vol. I. Moscow, 1948.

Dostoevskii, Fedor. The Dream of a Queer Fellow and the Pushkin Speech. Tr. by S. Koteliansky and J. Middleton Murry. New York: Barnes and Noble, 1961.
Dovnar-Zapol'skii, M. V., ed. Russkaia istoriia v ocherkakh i stat'iakh. Vol. I. Moscow, n.d.
——. Iz istorii obshchestvennykh techenii v Rossii. Kiev, 1910.
Dunnington, G. Waldo. Carl Friedrich Gauss: Titan of Science. New York: Exposition Press, 1955.
Dvukhsotletie Akademii nauk SSSR, 1725–1925. Moscow, 1925.
Efimov, A. V. Iz istorii russkikh ekspeditsii na Tikhom Okeane: Pervaia polovina XVIII veka. Moscow, 1948.
Ehrhard, Marcelle. Le Prince Cantemir à Paris (1738–1744). Paris, 1938.
Eingorn, V. O. "O rasprostranenii v Moskve v tret'iu chetvert XVII v. knig kievskoi i l'vovskoi pechati," Chten, 1895, No. 2, Section 5, 18–19.
Engelhardt, Roderich von. Die deutsche Universität Dorpat in ihrer geistesgeschichtlichen Bedeutung. Munich, 1933.
Epifanov, P. P. " 'Uchenaia druzhina' i prosvetitel'stvo XVIII veka," VI, 1963, No. 3, 37–53.
Erman, Adolph. Travels in Siberia. Tr. by W. D. Cooley. Vol. I. London: Longman, Brown, Green, and Longmans, 1848.
Euler, Leonard. Elements of Algebra. Tr. from the French. 5th ed. London: Longman, Orme and Co., 1840.
[——.] Letters of Euler on Different Subjects in Physics and Philosophy. Addressed to a German Princess. Tr. from the French by H. Hunter. 2 vols. 2nd ed. London: Murray and Highle, 1802.
Faidel', E. P., and K. I. Shafranovskii. "Pechat' v Rossii o trudakh N. I. Lobachevskogo (1834–56)," VAN, 1944, No. 3, 127–31.
"Farvarson," Brockhaus-Efron, XXXV (1902), 303.
Ferliudin, P. Istoricheskii obzor mer po vysshemu obrazovaniiu v Rossii. Part 1: Akademiia nauk i universitety. Saratov, 1894.
Fersman, A., ed. The Pacific: Russian Scientific Investigations. Leningrad, 1926.
Fesenkov, V. G. "Ocherk istorii astronomii v Rossii v XVII i XVIII stoletiiakh," TIIE, II (1948), 3–25.
Figurovskii, N. A. Dmitrii Ivanovich Mendeleev, 1834–1907. Moscow, 1961.
——, ed. Istoriia estestvoznaniia v Rossii. Vol. I, 2 parts. Moscow, 1957.
Filomafitskii, A. M. "Pervaia lektsiia fiziologii," in Vasetskii and Mikulinskii, Izbrannye proizvedeniia, 335–41.
F. K. "Stempkovskii, Ivan Aleksandrovich," RBS, XIX (1909), 377–80.
Florinsky, Michael T. Russia: A History and Interpretation. 2 vols. New York: Macmillan, 1953.
Florovskij, A. Le conflit de deux traditions—la latine et la byzantine—dans la vie intellectuelle de l'Europe Orientale aux XVI–XVII siècles. Prague, 1937.
Florovsky, Georges. "The Problem of Old Russian Culture," Slavic Review, XXI (1962), 1–15.
——. Puti russkogo bogosloviia. Paris, 1937.
Flourens, Pierre. "Historical Sketch of the Academy of Sciences of Paris," translated from the French by C. A. Alexander, Annual Report of the Board of Regents of the Smithsonian Institution (Washington, 1863), 337–57.
Fomin, A. G., et al. Vystavka "Lomonosov i Elizavetinskoe vremia." Vol. VII. Petrograd, 1915.
Fontenelle, Bernard. Oeuvres choisies. Vol. II. Paris, 1883.

[————.] "Addition à l'Histoire de MCCXX," *Histoire de l'Académie Royale des Sciences,* Paris, 1720, 125–32.

[————.] "Eloge du Czar Pierre I," *Histoire de l'Académie Royale des Sciences,* Paris, 1727, 105–28.

[————.] "Eloge de M. Leibnitz," *Histoire de l'Académie Royale des Sciences,* Paris, 1718, 94–128.

Fountainerie, F. de la, ed. and tr. French Liberalism and Education in the Eighteenth Century. New York: McGraw-Hill, 1932.

Friche, V. M. "Vysshaia shkola v kontse veka," *Granat-Ist,* IX (n.d.), 145–63.

Fuss, Nicolaus. "Lobrede auf Herrn Leonhard Euler, in der Versammlung der Kaiserlichen Akademie der Wissenschaften zu St. Petersburg den 23 Octob. 1783 vorgelesen," in Leonhardi Euleri Opera Omnia, Series I, Vol. I. Leipzig, 1911, xliii–xcv.

[Gauss, C. F.] "Pis'ma K. F. Gaussa v S.-Peterburgskuiu Akademiiu nauk," *AIN-T,* 1934, No. 3, 209–38.

Gebel, A. "O katalogakh Mineralogicheskogo muzeia Akademii nauk, sostavlennykh Lomonosovym," *ZAN,* VIII (1866), 57–66.

Gel'mersen, G. P. "Sovremennoe sostoianie geologii v Rossii," *ZAN,* V (1864), Supplement 3.

————. "Sir Roderik Impei Murchison," *ZAN,* XX (1872), 176–90.

Ger'e, V. I. See Guerrier, V. I.

Gershenzon, M. O. Epokha Nikolaia I. Moscow, 1910.

Gertsen, A. I. See Herzen.

Giliarov-Platonov, N. P. Sbornik sochinenii. 2 vols. Moscow, 1899–1900.

Gillispie, Charles C. The Edge of Objectivity: An Essay in the History of Scientific Ideas. Princeton: Princeton University Press, 1960.

Gnedenko, B. V. Mikhail Vasil'evich Ostrogradskii: Ocherki zhizni, nauchnogo tvorchestva i pedagogicheskoi deiatel'nosti. Moscow, 1952.

————. Ocherki po istorii matematiki v Rossii. Moscow-Leningrad, 1946.

————. "O rabotakh N. I. Lobachevskogo po teorii veroiatnostei," *IMI,* II (1949), 129–36.

Gnucheva, V. F. Geograficheskii department Akademii nauk XVIII veka. Moscow-Leningrad, 1946.

————, ed. Materialy dlia istorii ekspeditsii Akademii nauk v XVIII i XIX vekakh: Khronologicheskie obzory i opysanie arkhivnikh materialov. Moscow-Leningrad, 1940.

Godichnyi torzhestvennyi akt v Imperatorskom Sankpeterburgskom universitete byvshii 8 fevralia 1854 goda. St. Petersburg, 1854.

Golitsyn, N. V. Nauchno-obrazovatel'nyia snosheniia Rossii s Zapadom v nachale XVII veka. Moscow, 1898.

Gorodetskii, B. P., ed. Istoriia russkoi kritiki. 2 vols. Moscow-Leningrad, 1958.

Granat, A. and I., publishers. Istoriia Rossii v XIX veke. 9 vols. St. Petersburg, n.d.

Granovskii, T. N. Sochineniia. Vol. I. Moscow, 1866.

[————.] "T. N. Granovskii o klassitsizme i realizme," *VE,* December 1866, Section 4, 1–8.

Grant, Robert. History of Physical Astronomy from the Earliest Ages to the Middle of the Nineteenth Century. London: Bohn, 1852.

Greene, John C. "Early Scientific Interest in the American Indian: Comparative Linguistics," *Proceedings of the American Philosophical Society,* CIV (1960), 511–17.

Grekov, B. D. "Deiatel'nost' Lomonosova v Akademii," in Izbrannye trudy, Vol. III (Moscow, 1960), 330–50.

———. "Lomonosov-istorik," in Izbrannye trudy, Vol. III (Moscow, 1960), 404–21.

Grekov, V. I. Ocherki iz istorii russkikh geograficheskikh issledovanii v 1725–1765 gg. Moscow, 1960.

Grigor'ev, V. V. Imperatorskii S. Peterburgskii universitet v techenie pervykh piati-desiati let ego sushchestvovaniia. St. Petersburg, 1870.

Grigor'ian, A. T., and L. S. Polak, eds. Ocherki razvitiia osnovnykh fizicheskikh idei. Moscow, 1959.

Grot, Ia. K. "Erik Laksman," ZAN, XL (1881), Part 1, 21–42.

———. "Filologicheskiia zaniatiia Ekateriny II-i," RA, 1877, No. 4, 425–42.

———. "Ocherk akademicheskoi deiatel'nosti Lomonosova," ZAN, VII (1865), 220–58.

———. "Petr Velikii, kak prosvetitel' Rossii," ZAN, XXI (1872), 31–86.

———. "Pis'ma Lomonosova i Sumarokova k I. I. Shuvalovu: Materialy dlia istorii russkogo obrazovaniia," ZAN, I (1862), Supplement 1.

Guerrier, V. I. Sbornik pisem i memorialov Leibnitsa otnosiashchikhsia k Rossii i Petru Velikomu. St. Petersburg, 1873.

———. Timofei Nikolaevich Granovskii. Moscow, 1914.

Gurevich, P. "Steller, Georg-Vil'gel'm," RBS, XIX (1909), 370–76.

Halévy, Elie. The Growth of Philosophical Radicalism. Tr. by M. Morris. Boston: Beacon, 1955.

Hall, A. R. The Scientific Revolution. Boston: Beacon, 1956.

Hans, Nicholas. "The Moscow School of Mathematics and Navigation (1701)," The Slavonic and East European Review, XXIX (1951), 532–36.

———. "F. I. Iankovich de Miriievo, organizator ruskog shkolskog sistema," Ruski arkhiv, Belgrade, 1930, No. 7, 86–95.

Haumant, Emile. La culture française en Russie, 1700–1900. Paris, 1910.

Helmersen. See Gel'mersen, G. P.

Helmholtz, Hermann von. Popular Lectures on Scientific Subjects. Tr. by E. Atkinson. London: Longmans, Green, 1895.

Herzen, A. I. Sochineniia. Vol. II. Moscow, 1955.

———. Izbrannye filosofskie proizvedeniia. 2 vols. Moscow, 1946.

———. O razvitii revoliutsionnykh idei v Rossii. Moscow, 1958.

———. Sobranie sochinenii v tridtsati tomakh. Vol. III. Moscow, 1954.

———. Byloe i dumy. 3 vols. London: Trübner, 1861.

———. Selected Philosophical Works. Tr. by L. Navrozov. Moscow, 1956.

Hoffmann, P. "Zur Verbindung Eulers mit der Petersburger Akademie während seiner Berliner Zeit," in Winter, ed., Die deutsch-russische Begegnung, 150–56.

[Humboldt, Alexander von.] See Shcherbakov, D. I.

Idel'son, N. I. "Lobachevskii-astronom," IMI, II (1949), 137–67.

Ikonnikov, V. S. Opyt russkoi istoriografii. 2 vols. Kiev, 1891–1908.

———. Opyt issledovaniia o kul'turnom znachenii Vizantii v russkoi istorii. Kiev, 1869.

———. "Blizhnii boiarin Afanasii Lavrent'evich Ordin-Nashchokin, odin iz pred-shestvennikov petrovskoi reformy," RS, XL (1883), 2–66, 273–308.

———. "Russkie universitety v sviazi s khodom obshchestvennogo obrazovaniia," VE, 1876, No. 9, 161–206; No. 10, 492–550; No. 11, 73–132.

———. Graf N. S. Mordvinov: Istoricheskaia monografiia. St. Petersburg, 1873.

Ioffe, A. F., ed. Ocherki po istorii Akademii nauk: Fiziko-matematicheskie nauki. Moscow-Leningrad, 1945.

I. S. "Kriticheskoe obozrenie Kantovoi religii v predelakh odnogo razuma," *ZMNP,*
    XVII (1938), Section 2, 44–98.
Istrin, V. "Russkie studenty v Gettingene v 1802–1804 gg.," *ZMNP,* New Series,
    XXVIII (1910), Section 2, 80–144.
Iushkevich, A. P. "Matematika i ee prepodavanie v Rossii v XVII–XIX vv.: Matemati-
    cheskiia znaniia v dopetrovskoi Rusi," *Matematika v shkole,* 1947, No. 1, 26–39.
——. "Matematika i ee prepodavanie v Rossii v XVII–XIX vv.: Matematicheskoe i
    voenno-tekhnicheskoe obrazovanie pri Petre I," *Matematika v shkole,* 1947, No. 2,
    11–21.
——. "Matematika i ee prepodavanie v Rossii v XVII–XIX vv.: Evoliutsiia prepo-
    davaniia matematiki v XVIII v.," *Matematika v shkole,* 1947, No. 3, 1–13.
——. "Matematika i ee prepodavanie v Rossii v XVII–XIX vv.: Uchebnaia litera-
    tura, 1730–1800 gg.," *Matematika v shkole,* 1947, No. 4, 17–30.
——. "Matematika i ee prepodavanie v Rossii v XVII–XIX vv.: Matematicheskie
    issledovaniia v XVIII v.," *Matematika v shkole,* 1947, No. 5, 23–33.
——. "Matematika i ee prepodavanie v Rossii v XVII–XIX vv.: Russkaia mate-
    matika na rubezhe XVII–XIX stoletii," *Matematika v shkole,* 1947, No. 6, 26–37.
——. "Matematika i ee prepodavanie v Rossii v XVII–XIX vv.: Reforma mate-
    maticheskogo obrazovaniia v pervoi polovine XIX v.," *Matematika v shkole,* 1948,
    No. 1, 14–23.
——. "Matematika i ee prepodavanie v Rossii v XVII–XIX vv.: Nikolai Ivanovich
    Lobachevskii," *Matematika v shkole,* 1948, No. 2, 1–14.
——. "Matematika i ee prepodavanie v Rossii v XVII–XIX vv.: Novye matemati-
    cheskie issledovaniia v Akademii nauk. M. V. Ostrogradskii i V. Ia. Buniakovskii,"
    Matematika v shkole, 1948, No. 3, 1–10.
——. "Akademik S. E. Gur'ev i ego rol' v razvitii russkoi nauki," *TIIE,* I (1947),
    219–68.
——. "Eiler i russkaia matematika v XVIII v. (Iz istorii pervoi peterburgskoi mate-
    maticheskoi shkoly)," *TIIE,* III (1949), 45–116.
—— and E. Winter, eds. Die Berliner und die Petersburger Akademie der Wissen-
    schaften im Briefwechsel Leonhard Eulers. 2 vols. Berlin, 1959–61.
Ivanov, P. I. "Donoshenie Professora Lomonosova Senatu o sposobakh k otyskaniiu
    v Rossii raznykh rud, metallov i mineralov," *Chten,* 1862, No. 4, Section 5, 167–68.
——. "Sledstvennoe delo o sovetnike Akademii nauk, Shumakhere," *Chten,* 1860,
    No. 3, Section 5, 64–122.
Ivanov-Razumnik. Istoriia russkoi obshchestvennoi mysli. 5 vols. 5th ed. Petrograd,
    1918.
Johnson, William H. E. Russia's Educational Heritage. Pittsburgh: Carnegie, 1950.
Kafengauz, B. B. I. T. Pososhkov: Zhizn' i deiatel'nost'. 2nd ed. Moscow, 1951.
Kagan, V. F. "Nauchnoe dvizhenie v Rossii v pervoi polovine XIX veka: Mate-
    matika," *Granat-Ist,* VI (n.d.), 308–27.
——. *Lobachevskii.* Moscow-Leningrad, 1944.
Kamenskii, Z. A. "I. Kant v russkoi filosofii nachala XIX veka," *VIMK,* 1960, No. 1,
    49–64.
Kant, Immanuel. Critique of Pure Reason. Tr. by Norman Kemp Smith. London:
    Macmillan, 1958.
Kantemir, Antiokh. Sobranie stikhotvorenii. Leningrad, 1956.
Kapustinskii, A. F. Ocherki po istorii neorganicheskoi i fizicheskoi khimii v Rossii
    ot Lomonosova do Velikoi Oktiabr'skoi sotsialisticheskoi revoliutsii. Moscow-
    Leningrad, 1948.

Karamzin, Nikolai. Istoriia gosudarstva Rossiiskogo. 12 vols. St. Petersburg, 1816–29.
———. Letters of a Russian Traveller, 1789–1790. Tr. and abridged by F. Jonas. New York: Columbia University Press, 1957.
[———.] Karamzin's Memoir on Ancient and Modern Russia. See Pipes, R.
[Karazin, Vasilii Nazarovich.] "Pervoe pisanie V. N. Karazina k imperatoru Aleksandru I-mu 22 marta 1801 goda," RS, IV (1871), 68–80.
[———.] "Vasilii Nazarovich Karazin: Osnovanie Khar'kovskogo universiteta," RS, XII (1875), 329–38; XIII (1875), 61–80; XIV (1875), 185–200, 470–77.
Karneev, A. Materialy i zametki po literaturnoi istorii Fiziologa. St. Petersburg, 1890.
Katalog izdanii Imperatorskoi Akademii nauk. St. Petersburg, 1912.
Katkov, M. N. "Apologiia publichnykh lektsii Professora K. F. Rul'e," RA, 1895, No. 5, 30–35.
Kazarin, A. I. "Didro i nekotorye voprosy russkoi kul'tury 18 veka," VIMK, 1958, No. 1, 83–102.
Kedrov, B. M. Klassifikatsiia nauk. Vol. I. Moscow, 1961.
Keppen, F. "Uchenye trudy P. S. Pallasa," ZMNP, CCXCVIII (1895), Section 2, 386–437.
Khmyrov, M. D. "Svedeniia o Vasilii Kiprianove, bibliotekare moskovskoi grazhdanskoi tipografii pri Petre I," RA, 1866, No. 8-9, 1291–1300.
Khodnev, A. I. Istoriia Imperatorskogo Vol'nogo ekonomicheskogo obshchestva s 1765 do 1865 goda. St. Petersburg, 1865.
Khomiakov, A. S. Polnoe sobranie sochinenii. Vol. I. Moscow, 1911.
Khotinskii, M. "Kurs fiziologicheskoi khimii, chitannyi v Khar'kovskom universitete adiunktom A. Khodnevym," ZMNP, LVII (1848), Section 6, 128–36.
Kireevskii, I. V. "O neobkhodimosti i vozmozhnosti novykh nachal dlia filosofii," RB, 1856, No. 2, Section: "Nauki," 1–48.
Kline, Morris. Mathematics in Western Culture. New York: Oxford University Press, 1953.
Kliuchevskii, V. O. Sochineniia. 8 vols. Moscow, 1956–59.
———. Skazaniia inostrantsev o moskovskom gosudarstve. Moscow, 1916.
Kniazev, G. A., and A. V. Kol'tsov. Kratkii ocherk istorii Akademii nauk SSSR. Moscow-Leningrad, 1957.
Kniaz'kov, S. A. "Russkaia shkola do poloviny XVIII veka," in Kniaz'kov and Serbov, Ocherk, 1–60.
——— and N. I. Serbov. Ocherk istorii narodnogo obrazovaniia v Rossii do epokhi reform Aleksandra II. Moscow, 1910.
Kogan, Iu. Ia. Prosvetitel' XVIII veka Ia. P. Kozel'skii. Moscow, 1958.
Koialovich, M. O. Istoriia russkogo samosoznaniia po istoricheskim pamiatnikam i nauchnym sochineniiam. St. Petersburg, 1893.
Kollins, E. A. "O vlianii matematiki na razvitie i uspekhi estestvennoi filosofii," ZMNP, XIX (1838), Section 2, 336–58.
Kollins, Samuel. "Nyneshnee sostoianie Rossii, izlozhenoe v pis'me k drugu zhivushchemu v Londone," tr. by Peter Kireevskii, Chten, 1846, No. 1, Section 3, 1–47.
Kol'man, E. Velikii russkii myslitel' N. I. Lobachevskii. Moscow, 1956.
Kolmogorov, A. N. "Rol' russkoi nauki v razvitii teorii veroiatnostei," Rol' russkoi nauki v razvitii mirovoi nauki i kul'tury, I, Part 1. (Uchenye zapiski Moskovskogo universiteta, XCI, 1947, 53–64.)
Kolubovskii, Ia. "Chaadaev, Petr Iakovlevich," RBS, XXII (1905), 3–5.
Kononkov, A. F. Istoriia fiziki v Moskovskom universitete s ego osnovaniia do 60-kh godov XIX stoletiia: 1755–1859. Moscow, 1955.

Konstantinov, N. A., and V. Ia. Struminskii. Ocherki po istorii nachal'nogo obrazo-vaniia v Rossii. Moscow, 1949.

Köppen, F. *See* Keppen, F.

[Korf, M. A.] "Iz zapisok barona (v posledstvii grafa) M. A. Korfa," Part 18, *RS,* CII (1900), 27–50.

Korolivskii, S. M., *et al.,* eds. Khar'kovskii gosudarstvennyi universitet im. A. N. Gor'kogo za 150 let. Khar'kov, 1955.

Korsakov, D. "Pogodin, Mikhail Petrovich," *RBS,* XIV (1905), 154–66.

———. "Senkovskii, Osip Ivanovich," *RBS, XVIII* (1914), 316–25.

———. "Solov'ev, Sergei Mikhailovich," *RBS,* XIX (1909), 82–92.

Koshtoiants, Kh. S. Ocherki po istorii fiziologii v Rossii. Moscow-Leningrad, 1946.

———. Russkaia fiziologicheskaia shkola i eia rol' v razvitii mirovoi nauki. Moscow, 1948.

Kostomarov, N. I. Russkaia istoriia v zhizneopisaniiakh eia glavneishikh deiatelei. Vol. III. St. Petersburg, n.d.

Kosven, M. O. "Etnograficheskie rezul'taty Velikoi Severnoi Ekspeditsii 1733–1743 gg.," *Sibirskii etnograficheskii sbornik,* III (1961), 167–212.

Kovalenskii, M. N. "Srednaia shkola," *Granat-Ist,* IV (n.d.), 128–85.

Kovalevskaia, S. "Vospominaniia detstva," *VE,* 1890, No. 7, 55–98.

Kovnator, R. A., ed. Moskovskii universitet v vospominaniiakh sovremennikov. Moscow, 1956.

Koyré, Alexandre. La philosophie et le problème national en Russie au début du XIXᵉ siècle. Paris, 1929.

Kozel'skii, Ia. P. "Filosoficheskiia predlozheniia," in Shchipanov, ed., Izbrannye proizvedeniia, I, 411–51.

Kozlov, A. G. "Podlinnye dokumenty ob Ivane Ivanoviche Polzunove," *TIIE-T,* III (1955), 184–89.

Kozmin, N. N. "Polevoi, Nikolai Alekseevich," *RBS,* XIV (1905), 295–303.

Krachkovskii, Ignatii. Izbrannye sochineniia. Vol. V. Moscow-Leningrad, 1958.

Kravets, T. P. "N'iuton i izuchenie ego trudov v Rossii," in S. I. Vavilov, ed., Isaak N'iuton, 312–28.

Krempol'skii, V. F. Istoriia razvitiia kartoizdaniia v Rossii i v SSSR. Moscow, 1959.

Kristanov, Tsv., and Iv. Duichev, eds. Estestvoznanieto v srednevekovna Bulgariia: Sbornik ot istoricheski izvori. Sofia, 1954.

Krizhanich, Iurii. Russkoe gosudarstvo v polovine XVII veka. Rukopis' vremen tsaria Alekseia Mikhailovicha. Discovered and published by P. Bezsonov. Special sup-plements to *RB,* 1859, Nos. 1–6.

Krylov, A. N. "Leonard Eiler," in Deborin, ed., Leonard Eiler, 1–28.

Kubasov, Iv. "Odoevskii, kniaz Vladimir Fedorovich," *RBS,* XII (1905), 124–52.

[Kulibin, I. P.] "Materialy o Kulibine," *Chten,* 1862, No. 1, Section 5, 178–87.

Kulibin, S. "Frolov, Kuz'ma Dmitrievich," *RBS,* XXI (1901), 237–38.

Kunik, A. "Izvestie o neizdannykh sochineniiakh Ivana Pososhkova," *ZAN,* V (1864), 62–64.

———, ed. Sbornik materialov dlia istorii Imperatorskoi Akademii nauk v XVIII veke. 2 parts. St. Petersburg, 1865.

Kuzen, V. "Kant i ego filosofiia," *Syn otechestva,* XII (1839), Section 4, 1–50.

Kuznetsov, B. G. "Iz akademicheskoi khroniki XVIII v.," *VAN,* 1940, No. 4-5, 131–45.

———. Patriotizm russkikh estestvoispytatelei i ikh vklad v nauku. Moscow, 1951.

———. Ocherki istorii russkoi nauki. Moscow-Leningrad, 1940.

———. Tvorcheskii put' Lomonosova. Moscow, 1961.

Kuznetsov, I. V., ed. Liudi russkoi nauki: ocherki o vydaiushchikhsia deiateliakh estestvoznaniia i tekhniki. 2 vols. Moscow-Leningrad, 1948.

————, ed. Liudi russkoi nauki—ocherki o vydaiushchikhsia deiateliakh estestvoznaniia i tekhniki: geologiia, geografiia. Moscow, 1962.

————, ed. Liudi russkoi nauki—ocherki o vydaiushchikhsia deiateliakh estestvoznaniia i tekhniki: matematika, mekhanika, astronomiia, fizika, khimiia. Moscow, 1961.

Lamanskii, V. I. Mikhail Vasil'evich Lomonosov: Biograficheskii ocherk. St. Petersburg, 1864.

————, ed. "Lomonosov i Peterburgskaia Akademiia nauk: Materialy k stoletii pamiati ego, 1765–1865," *Chten,* 1865, No. 1, Section 5, 37–102.

Lampert, E. Studies in Rebellion. London: Routledge, 1957.

Lang, David Marshall. The First Russian Radical: Alexander Radishchev, 1749–1802. London: Allen and Unwin, 1958.

Lappo-Danilevskii, A. S. Petr Velikii, osnovatel' Imperatorskoi Akademii nauk v S.-Peterburge. St. Petersburg, 1914.

————. "Ocherk razvitiia russkoi istoriografii," *RIZ,* 1920, No. 6, 5–29.

Laptev, B. L. "Teoriia parallel'nykh linii v rannykh rabotakh N. I. Lobachevskogo," in Norden, ed., Sto dvadtsat' piat let, 99–116.

Lavrent'ev, M. A. "Vstupitel'naia rech'," in Lavrent'ev *et al.,* eds., Leonard Eiler, 7–15.

————, A. P. Iushkevich, and A. T. Grigor'ian, eds. Leonard Eiler: Sbornik statei v chest' 250-letiia so dnia rozhdeniia, predstavlennykh Akademii nauk SSSR. Moscow, 1958.

Lavrovskii, N. A. "Vospominanie o Vasilii Nazaroviche Karazine," *ZMNP,* CLXV (1873), Section 2, 294–311.

————. "Iz pervonachal'noi istorii Khar'kovskogo universiteta," *ZMNP,* CXLV (1869), Section 2, 235–60.

Lazarev, P. P. Ocherki istorii russkoi nauki. Moscow-Leningrad, 1950.

————. Tochnye nauki v Rossii za dvesti let. Moscow-Leningrad, 1925.

Lebedev, D. M. Ocherki istorii geografii v Rossii XV i XVI vekov. Moscow, 1956.

————. Geografiia v Rossii XVII v. (dopetrovskoi epokhi). Ocherki po istorii geograficheskikh znanii. Moscow-Leningrad, 1949.

————. Geografiia v Rossii petrovskogo vremeni. Moscow-Leningrad, 1950.

Leicester, Henry M. The Historical Background of Chemistry. New York: Wiley, 1956.

Lemke, Mikh. Nikolaevskie zhandarmy i literatura 1826–1855 gg. St. Petersburg, 1909.

Levchenko, M. V. Ocherki po istorii russko-vizantiiskikh otnoshenii. Moscow, 1956.

Levin, M. G. Ocherki po istorii antropologii v Rossii. Moscow, 1960.

Lezhneva, O. A., and B. N. Rzhonsnitskii. Emilii Khristianovich Lents. Moscow-Leningrad, 1952.

"Lichnyi sostav Imperatorskoi Akademii nauk v kontse 1852 goda," *Uchenyia zapiski Imperatorskoi Akademii nauk po Pervomu i Tret'emu otdeleniiam,* I (1853), 580–89.

Lipshits, S. Iu. Moskovskoe obshchestvo ispytatelei prirody za 135 let ego sushchestvovaniia, 1805–1940. Moscow, 1940.

Liubimenko, I. I. "Ob osnovanii Rossiiskoi Akademii," *AIN-T,* 1935, No. 6, 97–116.

Lobachevskii, N. I. Polnoe sobranie sochinenii. Vols. I and II. Moscow-Leningrad, 1946–49.

——. Tri sochineniia. Moscow, 1956.

——. "Rech' o vazhneishikh predmetakh vospitaniia," in Vasetskii and Mikulinskii, Izbrannye proizvedeniia, 381–85.

——. "Nastavleniia uchiteliam matematiki v gimnaziakh," *TIIE*, II (1948), 554–60.

Lobatschewskij, Nikolaj Iwanowitsch. Zwei geometrische Abhandlungen. Tr. from the Russian by Friedrich Engel. Leipzig, 1898.

Lockemann, Georg. The Story of Chemistry. New York: Philosophical Library, 1959.

Lomonosov, M. V. Polnoe sobranie sochinenii. Vol. I. Moscow-Leningrad, 1950.

——. Izbrannye filosofskie proizvedeniia. Moscow, 1950.

[——.] "V Pravitel'stvuiushchii Senat nizhaishee donoshenie ot kollezhskogo sovetnika i professora Mikhaila Lomonosova," *Chten*, 1862, No. 4, Section 5, 169–72.

[——.] Physikalisch-chemische Abhandlungen M. W. Lomonosows, 1741–1752. Tr. from Latin and Russian, with commentaries by B. N. Menshutkin and Max Speter. Leipzig, 1910.

[Lubianskii, F. P.] "Vospominaniia Fedora Petrovicha Lubianskogo," *RA*, 1872, No. 1, 98–185; No. 3-4, 449–533.

Luchinskii, G. "Teoriia rodovogo byta v russkoi istorii," *Brockhaus-Efron*, XXXII (1901), 908–11.

Luk'ianov, P. M. Kratkaia istoriia khimicheskoi promyshlennosti SSSR. Moscow, 1959.

——. "A. N. Radishchev i khimiia," *TIIE-T*, II (1954), 158–67.

Lunts, G. L. "O rabotakh N. I. Lobachevskogo po matematicheskom analizu," *IMI*, II (1949), 9–71.

Luppol, I. K. "Pol' Gol'bakh—russkii akademik (k 150-letiiu so dnia smerti)," *VAN*, 1939, No. 4-5, 163–67.

L. V. "Farvarson, Andrei Danilovich," *RBS*, XXI (1901), 22–23.

Lysenko, V. I. "Iz istorii pervoi Peterburgskoi matematicheskoi shkoly," *TIIE-T*, XLIII (1961), 182–205.

[Magnitskii, Mikhail L.] "Mnenie deistvitel'nogo statskogo sovetnika Magnitskogo o nauke estestvennogo prava," *Chten*, 1861, No. 10-12, Section 5, 157–59.

Maikov, P. "Rumiantsev, graf Nikolai Petrovich," *RBS*, XVI (1913), 493–520.

——. "Betskoi, Ivan Ivanovich," *RBS*, III (1905), 5–12.

[Maistre, Joseph de.] Lettres et opuscules inédits du comte Joseph de Maistre précédés d'une Notice Biographique par son fils le comte Rodolphe de Maistre. Vol. II. Paris, 1851.

Maistrov, L. I. "A. I. Gertsen o matematike," *IMI*, VIII (1955), 481–88.

Makogonenko, G. P. Radishchev i ego vremia. Moscow, 1956.

——. Nikolai Novikov i russkoe prosveshchenie XVIII veka. Moscow-Leningrad, 1952.

Maksimov, A. A. Ocherki po istorii borby za materializm v russkom estestvoznanii. Moscow, 1947.

Maksimovich, K. I. "Ocherk zhizni i trudov Frantsa Ivanovicha Ruprekhta," *ZAN*, XX (1872), 1–49.

Malia, Martin. Alexander Herzen and the Birth of Russian Socialism, 1812–1855. Cambridge, Mass.: Harvard University Press, 1961.

Malin, M. "Anglo-russkie kul'turnye i nauchnye sviazi (do osnovaniia Peterburgskoi Akademii nauk)," *VIMK*, 1957, No. 3, 98–107.

Malis, Iu. G. N. I. Pirogov: Ego zhizn i nauchno-obshchestvennaia deiatel'nost'. St. Petersburg, 1893.

Manshtein, Kristofor G. Zapiski istoricheskiia, grazhdanskiia i voennyia o Rossii s 1727 po 1744 god. Tr. from the French by T. Mal'gin. 2 vols. Moscow, 1823.

Markovnikov, V. V. Izbrannye trudy. Moscow, 1955.

Maron, I. A. "Akademik M. V. Ostrogradskii kak organizator prepodavaniia matematicheskikh nauk v voenno-uchebnykh zavedeniiakh Rossii," *IMI*, III (1950), 197–340.

Materialy dlia istorii Imperatorskoi Akademii nauk. 10 vols. St. Petersburg, 1885–1900.

"Materialy dlia istorii i statistiki nashikh gimnazii," *ZMNP*, CXXI (1864), Section 2, 129–71, 353–90, 492–571.

Mavrodin, V. V., *et al*. Leningradskii universitet (kratkii ocherk). Leningrad, 1957.

Maxwell, James Clerk. A Treatise on Electricity and Magnetism. Vol. I. 2nd ed. Oxford: Clarendon Press, 1881.

Mazour, Anatole G. Modern Russian Historiography. Princeton, N.J.: Van Nostrand, 1958.

——. The First Russian Revolution, 1825: The Decembrist Movement. Berkeley, Calif.: University of California Press, 1937.

——. "Petr Jakovlevič Čaadaev (1796–1856)," *Le Monde Slave*, IV (1937), 1–24.

——. Russia: Tsarist and Communist. Princeton, N.J.: Van Nostrand, 1962.

McConnell, Allen. "Helvétius' Russian Pupils," *Journal of the History of Ideas*, XXIV (1963), 373–86.

McLean, Hugh, M. E. Malia, and G. Fischer. Russian Thought and Politics (Harvard Slavic Studies, Vol. IV). 's-Gravenhage, 1957.

Mechnikov, I. I. Stranitsy vospominanii: Sbornik avtobiograficheskikh statei. Moscow, 1946.

——. "Sovremennoe sostoianie nauki o razvitii zhivotnykh," *ZMNP*, CXLII (1869), Section 2, 158–86.

Mel'gunova, P. E., K. V. Sivkov, and N. P. Sidorov. Russkii byt po vospominaniiam sovremennikov. XVIII vek. 2 vols. Moscow, 1914–18.

Mel'nikova, N. N. Izdaniia Moskovskogo universiteta, 1756–1779. Moscow, 1955.

Mendeleev, D. Review of E. Hofman, ed., Severnyi Ural, Vol. 2, St. Petersburg, 1856, in *ZMNP*, XCIII (1857), Section 6, 119–26.

——. "Voskresenskii (Aleksandr Abramovich)," *Brockhaus-Efron*, VII (1895), 243–44.

——. Sochineniia. Vol. XV. Moscow-Leningrad, 1949.

Menshutkin, B. N. Trudy M. V. Lomonosova po fizike i khimii. Moscow, 1936.

——. "Lomonosov, Mikhail Vasil'evich," *RBS*, X (1914), 596–628.

——. Russia's Lomonosov: Chemist, Courtier, Physicist, Poet. Tr. from the Russian by J. E. Thal and E. J. Webster. Princeton, N.J.: Princeton University Press, 1952.

——. Mikhailo Vasil'evich Lomonosov: Zhizneopisanie. St. Petersburg, 1911.

——. "M. V. Lomonosov kak fiziko-khimik: k istorii khimii v Rossii," *Zhurnal Russkogo fiziko-khimicheskogo obshchestva*, XXXVI (1904), Section 2, 77–304.

Merton, Robert K. Social Theory and Social Structure. Glencoe, Ill.: The Free Press, 1949.

Meyer, Arthur William. Human Generation: Conclusions of Burdach, Döllinger, and von Baer. Stanford, Calif.: Stanford University Press, 1956.

Miakovskii, V. V. "Gody ucheniia A. N. Radishcheva," *Golos minuvshego*, 1914, No. 3, 5–45; No. 5, 83–104.

Michatek, N. "Polzunov, Ivan Ivanovich," *RBS*, XIV (1905), 532–33.

Mikulinskii, S. R. "Iz istorii biologii v Rossii v 20-30e gody XIX veka," *Voprosy istorii estestvoznaniia i tekhniki*, I (1956), 98–115.

——. Razvitie obshchikh problem biologii v Rossii. Moscow, 1961.

—— and G. F. Rybkin. "Borba materializma protiv idealizma v estestvoznanii v Rossii (pervaia polovina XIX v.)," in Vasetskii *et al.*, eds., Ocherki, I, 338–73.

Miliukov, P. Gosudarstvennoe khoziaistvo Rossii v pervoi chetverti XVIII stoletiia i reforma Petra Velikogo. St. Petersburg, 1892.

———. Ocherki po istorii russkoi kul'tury. 3 vols. Paris, 1930–37.

———. Glavnyia techeniia russkoi istoricheskoi mysli. 3rd ed. St. Petersburg, 1913.

———. "Universitety v Rossii," *Brockhaus-Efron*, XXXIX (1902), 788–800.

———. "Istochniki russkoi istorii i russkaia istoriografiia," *Brockhaus-Efron*, XXVIII (1900), 430–46.

——— and A. Kirpichnikov. "Karamzin (Nikolai Mikhailovich)," *Brockhaus-Efron*, XIV (1895), 440–47.

Mil'kov, F. N. P. I. Rychkov. Moscow, 1953.

Miller, O. "Lomonosov i reforma Petra Velikogo," *VE*, March 1866, Section 1, 373–92.

"Ministerskiia rasporiazheniia," *ZMNP*, I (1834), Section 1, xlix–lxxx.

Modzalevskii, B. L. "Severgin, Vasilii Mikhailovich," *RBS*, XVIII (1904), 272–76.

———. Spisok chlenov Imperatorskoi Akademii nauk, 1725–1907. St. Petersburg, 1908.

Modzalevskii, L. B. "M. N. Lomonosov," in S. I. Vavilov, ed., Nauchnoe nasledstvo, I, 11–62.

———. "Pushkin—chlen Rossiiskoi Akademii," *VAN*, 1937, No. 2-3, 245–50.

———, ed. Rukopisi Lomonosova v Akademii nauk SSSR: Nauchnoe opisanie. Moscow-Leningrad, 1937.

———, ed. Materialy dlia biografii N. I. Lobachevskogo. Moscow-Leningrad, 1948.

Morley, John Viscount. Biographical Studies. London: Macmillan, 1923.

Murchison, Roderick Impey, Edouard de Verneuil, and Alexander von Keyserling. The Geology of Russia in Europe and the Ural Mountains. 2 vols. London: John Murray, 1845.

Musabekov, Iu. S. Iustus Libikh, 1803–1873. Moscow, 1962.

Nagaeva, V. M. "Pedagogicheskie vzgliady i deiatel'nost' N. I. Lobachevskogo," *IMI*, III (1950), 76–153.

Nagel, Ernest. The Structure of Science. Problems in the Logic of Scientific Exploration. New York: Harcourt, Brace, 1961.

Nalivkin, D. V. "Nachalo russkoi geologii," in S. I. Vavilov, ed., Voprosy istorii otechestvennoi nauki, 384–93.

Newcomb, Simon. The Reminiscences of an Astronomer. Boston: Houghton, Mifflin, 1903.

———. A Compendium of Spherical Astronomy. New York: Macmillan, 1906.

Nifontov, A. S. Rossiia v 1848 godu. Moscow, 1949.

Nikitenko, A. V. Moia povest': Zapiski i dnevnik (1804–1877 gg.). 2 vols. 2nd ed., St. Petersburg, 1904–5.

Nikitin, Afanasii. Khozhdenie za tri moria. Moscow, 1950.

Nikol'skii, N. "Dukhovnyia uchebnyia zavedeniia," in *Granat-Ents*, XIX (n.d.), 202–9.

N. N. P., "Kulibin, Ivan Petrovich," *RBS*, IX (1903), 539–43.

Norden, A. P., ed. Sto dvadtsat' piat' let neevklidovoi geometrii Lobachevskogo: 1826–1951. Moscow-Leningrad, 1952.

Nordenskiöld, Erik. The History of Biology. Transl. from the Swedish by L. B. Eyre. New York: Tudor, 1935.

Novikov, M. M. Velikany rossiiskogo estestvoznaniia. Posev, 1960.

Novikov, N. I. "Stat'i i zametki iz satiricheskogo zhurnala 'Zhivopisets,' " in Shchipanov, ed., Izbrannye proizvedeniia, II, 166–210.

———. "Koshelek," in Shchipanov, ed., Izbrannye proizvedeniia, II, 214–16.

———. Izbrannye pedagogicheskiia sochineniia. Moscow, 1959.

Novikov, P. A. "Zoologicheskie issledovaniia Ia. Shamisso i I. Eshshol'tsa vo vremia krugosvetnoi ekspeditsii O. E. Kotsebu na 'Riurike' (1815–1818)," TIIE-T, XL, 1962, 248–82.

———. "Akademik S. P. Krasheninnikov kak pervyi issledovatel' zhivotnogo mira Kamchatki," TIIE, III (1949), 262–96.

Novitskii, Orest. "Ob uspekakh, delaemykh filosofii v teoreticheskom otnoshenii, ikh sile i vazhnosti," ZMNP, XVII (1838), Section 2, 229–329.

Novlianskii, M. G., ed. Boris Semenovich Iakobi: Bibliograficheskii ukazatel'. Moscow-Leningrad, 1953.

Nut, Iu. Iu. Geometriia Lobachevskogo v analiticheskom izlozhenii. Moscow, 1961.

Odoevskii, V. F. Russkie nochi. Moscow, 1913.

———. Izbrannye pedagogicheskie sochineniia. Moscow, 1955.

[———.] "Iz bumag kniaza V. F. Odoevskogo," RA, 1874, No. 2, 278–359; No. 7, 11–54.

[Olearius, Adam.] "Podrobnoe opisanie puteshestviia golshtinskogo posol'stva v Moskoviiu i Persiiu," translated from the German by P. P. Barsov, Book 4, Chten, 1869, No. 2, 531–692.

Orbeli, L. A., and Kh. S. Koshtoiants, eds. Ocherki po istorii Akademii nauk: Biologicheskie nauki. Moscow-Leningrad, 1945.

Orlov, A. S. Drevnaia russkaia literatura XI–XVII vv. Moscow-Leningrad, 1945.

Orlov, Vl. Russkie prosvetiteli 1790–1800-kh godov. Moscow, 1950.

Orlov-Davidov, Vladimir P. Biograficheskii ocherk grafa Vladimira Grigor'evicha Orlova. St. Petersburg, 1878.

Osipov, A. M., et al. Afanasii Nikitin i ego vremia. Moscow, 1951.

Osipovskii, Timofei Fedorovich. "O prostranstve i vremeni," in Vasetskii and Mikulinskii, eds., Izbrannye proizvedeniia, 45–49.

———. "Rassuzhdenie o dinamicheskoi sisteme Kanta," in Vasetskii and Mikulinskii, Izbrannye proizvedeniia, 49–54.

[Ostrogradskii, M. V.] "Mikhail Vasil'evich Ostrogradskii pod nadzorom politsii," RS, CVIII (1901), 341–42.

[———.] "Spisok sochinenii M. V. Ostrogradskogo," ZAN, I (1862), 46–50.

Ostrovitianov, K. V., ed. Istoriia Akademii nauk SSSR. Vol. I. Moscow-Leningrad, 1958.

"Pallas (Petr-Simon)," Brockhaus-Efron, XXII (1897), 641–42.

Pamiatnaia knizhka Imperatorskoi Akademii nauk na 1905 god. St. Petersburg, 1905.

Panaev, Valerian Aleksandrovich. "Vospominaniia," RS, LXXX (1893), 63–89, 395–412.

Pares, B. A History of Russia. New York: Knopf, 1947.

Pashkov, A. I., ed. Istoriia russkoi ekonomicheskoi mysli. Vol. I, 2 parts. Moscow, 1955–58.

Pasquier, L. Gustave du. Léonhard Euler et ses amis. Paris, 1927.

Passek, T. P. Iz dal'nykh let. Vospominaniia. Vols. I–II. St. Petersburg, 1878–79; Vol. III, 2nd ed., 1906.

Pavlov, M. G. "O vzaimnom otnoshenii svedenii umozritel'nykh i opytnykh," in Vasetskii and Mikulinskii, eds., Izbrannye proizvedeniia, 88–97.

Pavlov, P. E. "Stoletie pervogo russkogo istoricheskogo obshchestva," IV, XCV (1904), 1045–54.

Pavlov-Sil'vanskii, N. P. Ocherki po russkoi istorii XVIII–XIX vv. St. Petersburg, 1910.

———. Proekty reform v zapiskakh sovremennikov Petra Velikogo. St. Petersburg, 1897.

Pekarskii, Petr P. Nauka i literatura pri Petre Velikom. Vol. I: Vvedenie v istoriiu prosveshcheniia v Rossii XVIII stoletiia. Vol. II: Opisanie slaviano-russkikh knig i tipografii 1698–1725 godov. St. Petersburg, 1862.

———. Istoriia Imperatorskoi Akademii nauk. 2 vols. St. Petersburg, 1870–73.

———. "Dopolnitel'nyia izvestiia dlia biografii Lomonosova," *ZAN*, No. 7 (1865), Supplement 7.

———. "Ekaterina II i Eiler," *ZAN*, VI (1865), 59–92.

———. "Izvestie o molodykh liudiakh, poslannykh Borisom Godunovym dlia obucheniia naukam v Angliiu v 1602 godu," *ZAN*, XI (1867), 91–96.

———. "Materialy dlia istorii zhurnal'noi i literaturnoi deiatel'nosti Ekateriny II," *ZAN*, III (1863), Supplement 6.

———. "O perepiske akademika Shtelina, khranishcheisia v Imperatorskoi Publichnoi Biblioteke," *ZAN*, VII (1865), 117–33.

Penchko, N. A. Osnovanie Moskovskogo universiteta. Moscow, 1953.

Perel', Iu. G. "Vikentii Karlovich Vishnevskii," *Istoriko-astronomicheskie issledovaniia*, I (1955), 133–48.

———. Razvitie predstavlenii o vselennoi. Moscow, 1958.

———. Vydaiushchiesia russkie astronomy. Moscow, 1951.

Pereselenkov, S. A. "Zakonodatel'stvo i tsenzurnaia praktika v Rossii v 1-iu chetvert' 19-go veka," in Opisanie del Arkhiva Ministerstva Narodnogo Prosveshcheniia (Petrograd, 1921), II, xi–xxxii.

Peretts, V. N. "Obrazovannost'," in Dovnar-Zapol'skii, ed., Russkaia istoriia, I, 461–79.

Peretts, Varvara P. Khozhdenie za tri moria Afanasiia Nikitina, 1466–1472 gg. Leningrad, 1958.

Perry, John. The State of Russia Under the Present-Day Tsar. London, 1716.

Peshtich, S. L. Russkaia istoriografiia XVIII veka. Vol. I. Leningrad, 1961.

Petrovskii, A. V. "O vyskazyvaniiakh A. N. Radishcheva po voprosam estestvoznaniia," *VF*, 1949, No. 1, 355–59.

Petukhov, E. V. Imperatorskii Iur'evskii, byvshii Derptskii, universitet za sto let ego sushchestvovaniia (1802–1902). Vol. I. Iur'ev, 1902.

Piatkovskii, A. P. "S.-Peterburgskii Vospitatel'nyi dom pod upravleniem I. I. Betskogo," *RS*, XII (1875), 146–59, 359–80, 665–80; XIII, 177–253, 532–53; XIV, 421–43.

Picheta, V. I. "Iurii Krizhanich i ego otnosheniia k russkomu gosudarstvu (1618–1683)," Slavianskii sbornik, Moscow, 1947, 202–40.

———. Iurii Krizhanich: Ekonomicheskie i politicheskie ego vzgliady. St. Petersburg, 1914.

Pipes, Richard. "Karamzin's Conception of the Monarchy," in McLean, Malia, and Fischer, Russian Thought and Politics, 35–58.

———. Karamzin's Memoir on Ancient and Modern Russia. Cambridge, Mass.: Harvard University Press, 1959.

Pirogov, N. I. Sochineniia. Vol. III. Kiev, 1910.

———. Izbrannye pedagogicheskie sochineniia. Moscow, 1953.

———. Sobranie sochinenii. Vol. VIII. Moscow, 1957.

Pisarev, D. I. Sochineniia. Vol. II. Moscow, 1955.

Platonov, S. F. Moskva i zapad. Berlin, 1926.

———. Ocherki po istorii smuty v Moskovskom gosudarstve XVI–XVII vv. (Opyt izucheniia obshchestvennogo stroia i soslovnykh otnoshenii v Smutnoe vremia). St. Petersburg, 1899.

————. Boris Godunov. Petrograd, 1921.

Platova, T. P. "N. A. Varnek i Moskovskii universitet srediny XIX veka," *TIIE,* V (1953), 317–62.

————. "Razvitie ucheniia o kletke v Rossii v 40–50-kh godakh XIX veka," *TIIE,* IV (1952), 332–72.

Plekhanov, G. V. Literatura i estetika. Vol. II. Moscow, 1958.

Plisetskii, M. "Ob antropologicheskikh vzgliadakh A. N. Radishcheva," *Sovetskaia etnografiia,* 1949, No. 3, 178–82.

P. M. "Feofan (Prokopovich)," *Brockhaus-Efron,* XLI-A (1904), 929–30.

Pl. V. "Krizhanich, Iurii Gasparovich," *RBS,* IX (1903), 441–43.

Pogodin, M. P. "Shkol'nyia vospominaniia, 1814–1820 gg.: Iz moikh zapisok," *VE,* 1868, No. 8, 604–30.

————. "Speranskii (Posviashchaetsia Baronu Modestu Andreevichu Korfu)," *RA,* 1871, No. 6-7, 1098–252.

————. "Predislovie" in Sochineniia Ivana Pososhkova, Part 2, Moscow, 1863, iii–xlv.

Polevoi, N. "Kriticheskiia issledovaniia kasatel'no sovremennoi russkoi literatury," *Syn otechestva,* VI (1839), Section 4, 75–83.

Poliakov, M. "Studencheskie gody Belinskogo," Literaturnoe nasledstvo, LVI (1950), 303–436.

Polievktov, M. Nikolai I: Biografiia i obzor tsarstvovaniia. Moscow, 1918.

Polnoe sobranie uchenykh puteshestvii po Rossii. 7 vols. St. Petersburg, 1818–25.

Poludenskii, M. "Petr Velikii v Parizhe," *RA,* 1865, No. 6, 675–702.

Popov, Nil. V. N. Tatishchev i ego vremia. Moscow, 1861.

————. "Obshchestvo liubitelei otechestvennoi slovesnosti i periodicheskaia literatura v Kazani, s 1805 po 1834 god," *RV,* XXIII (1859), 52–98.

Posse, K. "Chebyshev, Pafnuti L'vovich," in S. A. Vengerov, ed., Kritiko-biograficheskii slovar' russkikh pisatelei i uchenykh, VI (St. Petersburg, 1904), 1–23.

Potez, Henry, ed. Pages choisies des grands écrivains: Joseph de Maistre. Paris, 1901.

Predtechenskii, A. V. Ocherki obshchestvenno-politicheskoi istorii Rossii v pervoi chetverti XIX veka. Moscow-Leningrad, 1957.

"Proekt Ukaza, sostavlennyi v kontse 1725," *Uchenyia zapiski Imperatorskoi Akademii nauk po Pervomu i Tret'emu otdeleniiam,* II (1854), Section: "Istoriko-Literaturnaia Letopis'," 173–85.

Prokopovich, Feofan. Sochineniia. Moscow-Leningrad, 1961.

Prudnikov, V. E. "Akademik P. L. Chebyshev i russkaia shkola," *TIIE,* III (1949), 117–35.

————. P. L. Chebyshev: uchenyi i pedagog. Moscow, 1950.

Ptashitskii, S. L. "Peterburg v 1720 godu; zapiski poliaka-ochevidtsa," *RS,* XXV (1879), 263–90.

Pufendorf, Samuel. An Introduction to the History of the Principal Kingdoms and States of Europe. London, 1695.

Pushkin, A. S. "Zapiska o narodnom vospitanii," in Bartenev, ed., Deviatnadtsatyi vek. Vol. II. Moscow, 1872, 209–18.

Putiata, N. "Obozrenie zhizni i tsarstvovaniia imperatora Aleksandra Pervogo," in Bartenev, ed., Deviatnadtsatyi vek. Vol. I. Moscow, 1872, 426–94.

Putnam, Peter, ed. Seven Britons in Imperial Russia, 1698–1812. Princeton, N.J.: Princeton University Press, 1952.

Pypin, A. N. "Istoriia russkoi literatury," *Brockhaus-Efron,* XXVIII (1900), 581–634.

————. Istoriia russkoi etnografii. 4 vols. St. Petersburg, 1890–92.

————. Istoriia russkoi literatury. 4 vols. St. Petersburg, 1898–99.

————. "Russkiia otnosheniia Bentama," *VE,* 1869, No. 2, 784–819.

------. "Rossiiskoe Bibleiskoe obshchestvo, 1812–26," *VE*, 1868, No. 8, 639–712; No. 9, 231–97; No. 11, 222–85; No. 12, 708–68.

------. "Voprosy drevne-russkoi pis'mennosti. II. Maksim Grek i kniaz Kurbskii," *VE*, 1894, No. 7, 313–67.

------. Religioznyia dvizheniia pri Aleksandre I. Petrograd, 1916.

------. Obshchestvennoe dvizhenie v Rossii pri Aleksandre I. St. Petersburg, 1900.

------. "Russkaia nauka i natsional'nyi vopros v XVIII-m veke," *VE*, 1884, No. 5, 212–56; No. 6, 548–600; No. 7, 72–117.

------. Russkoe masonstvo: XVIII i pervaia chetvert' XIX v., St. Petersburg, 1919.

------. "Kharakteristiki literaturnykh mnenii ot dvadtsatykh to piatidesiatikh godov," Part 4, *VE*, 1872, No. 5, 145–206.

Radishchev, A. N. "Zhitie Fedora Vasil'evicha Ushakova," in Bartenev, ed., Osmnad-tsatyi vek: Istoricheskii sbornik. Vol. II. Moscow, 1869, 296–361.

------. Polnoe sobranie sochinenii. Moscow-Leningrad, 1952.

------. Izbrannye filosofskie sochineniia. Moscow, 1949.

------. A Journey from St. Petersburg to Moscow. Tr. from the Russian by Leo Wiener. Cambridge, Mass.: Harvard University Press, 1958.

Radlov, E. L. "Teoriia znaniia Slavofilov," *ZMNP*, New Series, LXI (1916), Section 3, 153–65.

------. "K. E. fon Ber kak filosof," in V. Vernadskii, ed., Pervyi sbornik pamiaty Bera, II, Leningrad, 1927, 60–71.

Radovskii, M. I. "Materialy k izucheniiu tvorchestva I. P. Kulibina," *AIN-T*, 1934, No. 2, 227–46.

------. Antiokh Kantemir i Peterburgskaia Akademiia nauk. Moscow-Leningrad, 1959.

------. "N'iuton i Rossiia," *VIMK*, 1957, No. 6, 96–106.

------. "Angliiskii naturalist XVIII v. Gans Sloan i ego nauchnye sviazi s Peterburg-skoi Akademii nauk," *TIIE-T*, XXIV (1958), 311–30.

Raikov, B. E. Russkie biologi-evoliutsionisty do Darvina. 4 vols. Moscow-Leningrad, 1951–59.

------. "Evoliutsionnaia ideia v trudakh russkikh akademikov XVIII i pervoi poliviny XIX veka," *VAN*, 1946, No. 3, 37–46.

------. "Estestvoznanie v umstvennom obikhode i shkol'nom prosveshchenii drevnei Rusi," *ZMNP*, New Series, LXVI (1916), Section: "Narodnoe obrazovanie," 1–34.

------. Ocherki po istorii geliotsentricheskogo mirovozreniia v Rossii: Iz proshlogo russkogo estestvoznaniia. Moscow-Leningrad, 1947.

Rainov, T. I. "Russkoe estestvoznanie vtoroi poloviny XVIII v. i Lomonosov," in Andreev and Modzalevskii, eds., Lomonosov, I, 1940, 301–88.

------. "N'iuton i russkoe estestvoznanie," in S. I. Vavilov, ed., Isaak N'iuton, 329–44.

------. "Russkie akademiki 2-i poloviny XVIII v. i Buffon," *VAN*, 1939, No. 10, 126–47.

------. Nauka v Rossii XI–XVII vekov. Moscow-Leningrad, 1940.

------. "Daniil Bernulli e ego rabota v Peterburgskoi Akademii nauk (k 200-letiiu 'Gidrodinamiki')," *VAN*, 1938, No. 7-8, 84–93.

Raskin, N. M., ed. Rukopisnye materialy khimikov vtoroi poloviny XVIII v. v Arkhive Akademii nauk. Moscow-Leningrad, 1957.

------ and B. A. Mal'kevich. Rukopisnye materialy I. P. Kulibina v Arkhive Aka-demii nauk SSSR. Moscow-Leningrad, 1953.

The Record of the Royal Society of London for the Promotion of Natural Knowledge. 4th ed. London: The Royal Society, 1940.

Remez, E. Ia. "O matematicheskikh rukopisiakh akademika M. V. Ostrogradskogo," *IMI*, IV (1951), 9–98.

Review of *Otchet Imperatorskoi Publichnoi Biblioteki* za 1854 god (St. Petersburg, 1855), in *Sovremennik*, LI (1855), Section 4, 5–7.

Review of *Vestnik estestvennykh nauk*, in *Sovremennik*, XLIX (1855), Section 4, 6–11.

Riasanovsky, Nicholas V. "Pogodin and Shevyrev in Russian Intellectual History," in McLean, Malia, and Fischer, eds., Russian Thought and Politics, 149–67.

——. Russia and the West in the Teaching of the Slavophiles: A Study of Romantic Ideology. Cambridge, Mass.: Harvard University Press, 1952.

Riazanovskii, V. A. Razvitie russkoi nauchnoi mysli v XVIII–XX st. st. (Nauki o prirode). New York: Rausen, 1949.

Richter, Liselotte. Leibniz und sein Russlandbild. Berlin, 1946.

Richter, Wilhelm Michael. Geschichte der Medizin in Russland. 3 vols. Moscow, 1813–17.

Rober, A. I. "Korennoi nedostatok srednikh uchebnykh zavedenii v Rossii," *RV*, XXIII (1859), 577–602.

Rogozhin, V. N. Ukazatel' k "Opytu rossiiskoi bibliografii" V. S. Sopikova. St. Petersburg, 1908.

Rotsen, I. P. "Mikhail Vasil'evich Lomonosov," *VAN*, 1936, No. 11-12, 5–28.

Rouillier, K. F. "Somneniia v zoologii kak nauke," in Vasetskii and Mikulinskii, Izbrannye proizvedeniia, 479–89.

Rozhdestvenskii, S. V. Ocherki po istorii sistem narodnogo prosveshcheniia v Rossii v XVIII–XIX vekakh. Vol. I. St. Petersburg, 1912.

——. Materialy dlia istorii uchebnykh reform v Rossii v XVIII–XIX vekakh. St. Petersburg, 1910.

——. Istoricheskii obzor deiatel'nosti Ministerstva narodnogo prosveshcheniia, 1802–1902. St. Petersburg, 1902.

——. "Posledniaia stranitsa iz istorii politiki narodnogo prosveshcheniia imperatora Nikolaia I (Komitet grafa Bludova, 1849–1856)," *RIZ*, 1917, No. 3-4, 37–59.

——. "Soslovnyi vopros v russkikh universitetakh v pervoi chetverti XIX veka," *ZMNP*, New Series, IX (1906), Section 2, 83–108.

——. "Universitetskii vopros v tsarstvovanie imp. Ekateriny II-oi i sistema narodnogo prosveshcheniia po ustavam 1804 goda," *VE*, 1907, No. 7, 5–46; No. 8, 437–57.

——, ed. S.-Peterburgskii universitet v pervoe stoletie ego deiatel'nosti 1819–1919: Materialy po istorii S.-Peterburgskogo universiteta. Vol. I. Petrograd, 1919.

Rudakov, V. "Studencheskiia nauchnyia obshchestva," *IV*, LXXVIII (1899), 1143–56.

——. "Gimnaziia," *Brockhaus-Efron*, VIII (1893), 694–707.

Ruprecht, J. F. "Das Botanische Museum," *Bulletin de l'Académie Imperiale des Sciences de St. Petersbourg*, VII (1864), Supplement 2.

Rybkin, G. F., and B. V. Fedorenko, eds. "Gettingenskoe obshchestvo nauki i N. I. Lobachevskii," *IMI*, IX (1956), 105–10.

Sakharov, A. A., and D. K. Shelestov. Moskovskii universitet za 200 let. Moscow, 1955.

Sakulin, P. N. Iz istorii russkogo idealizma. Kniaz V. F. Odoevskii—myslitel', pisatel'. Vol. I, Part 1. Moscow, 1913.

Samarin, F. Iu. "Dva slova o narodnosti v nauke," *RB*, 1856, No. 1, Section: "Nauka," 35–47.

Sarton, George. Introduction to the History of Science. Vol. III. Baltimore: Carnegie, 1948.

——. Six Wings. Bloomington: Indiana University Press, 1957.

———. "The Discovery of the Mammalian Egg and the Foundation of Modern Embryology," *Isis,* XVI (1931), 315–30.

Satkevich, A. "Leonard Eiler (V dvukhsotuiu godovshchinu dnia ego rozhdeniia)," *RS,* CXXXII (1907), 467–506.

Savel'ev, A. "O trudakh akademika Lentsa v magnito-elektrichestve," *ZMNP,* LXXXII (1854), Section 5, 1–48.

Sbornik postanovlenii po Ministerstvu narodnogo prosveshcheniia. 2 vols. 2nd ed. St. Petersburg, 1875.

Sbornik rasporiazhenii po Ministerstvu narodnogo prosveshcheniia. Vol. I. 2nd ed. St. Petersburg, 1898. Vol. II, 1866.

Schaeffer, Clemens, ed. Briefwechsel zwischen Carl Friedrich Gauss und Christian Ludwig Gerling. Berlin, 1927.

Schelting, Alexander von. Russland und Europa im russischen Geschichtsdenken. Bern, 1948.

Schlözer, August Ludwig. Offentliches und Privat-Leben, von ihm selbst beschrieben. Vol. I. Göttingen, 1802.

Schuyler, Eugene. Peter the Great, Emperor of Russia. 2 vols. New York: Charles Scribner's Sons, 1884.

Sechenov, Ivan Mikhailovich. Avtobiograficheskiia zapiski. Moscow, 1907.

———. "Nauchnaia deiatel'nost' russkikh universitetov po estestvoznaniiu za poslednee dvadtsatipiatiletie," *VE,* 1883, No. 11, 330–42.

Semennikov, V. P. Radishchev: Ocherki i issledovaniia. Moscow-Petrograd, 1923.

———. Sobranie staraiushcheesia o perevode inostrannykh knig, uchrezhdennoe Ekaterinoi II, 1768–1783 gg. St. Petersburg, 1913.

Semenov, P. P. Istoriia poluvekovoi deiatel'nosti Imperatorskogo Russkogo geograficheskogo obshchestva, 1845–1895. 3 vols. St. Petersburg, 1896.

Sementkovskii, R. "Kantemir (kn. Antiokh Dmitrievich)," *Brockhaus-Efron,* XIV (1895), 314–17.

Semevskii, V. "Turgenev (Nikolai Ivanovich)," *Brockhaus-Efron,* XXXIV (1902), 106–13.

———. Krest'ianskii vopros v Rossii v XVIII i pervoi polovine XIX veka. 2 vols. St. Petersburg, 1888.

Serbina, K. I. " 'Kniga Bol'shogo chertezha' i ee redaktsii," *Istoricheskie zapiski,* XIV (1945), 129–47.

Serbov, N. I. "Shkola v tsarstvovanie Aleksandra I i Nikolaia I," in Kniaz'kov and Serbov, Ocherk, 161–238.

———. "Shkola v tsarstvovanie Ekateriny II," in Kniaz'kov and Serbov, Ocherk, 61–160.

Setschkareff, Wsewolod. Schellings Einfluss in der russischen Literatur der 20er und 30er Jahre des XIX. Jahrhunderts. Berlin, 1939.

Shchapov, A. P. Sochineniia. 3 vols. St. Petersburg, 1906–8.

Shchedrin, N. (M. E. Saltykov). Polnoe sobranie sochinenii. Vol. XIV. Leningrad, 1936.

Shcherbakov, D. I., ed. Perepiska Aleksandra Gumbol'dta s uchenymi i gosudarstvennymi deiateliami Rossii. Moscow, 1962.

Shcherbatov, M. M. "Sostoianie Rossii do Petra Velikogo," *Chten,* 1860, No. 1, Section 2, 23–28.

Shchipanov, I. Ia., ed. Ibzrannye proizvedeniia russkikh myslitelei vtoroi poloviny XVIII veka. 2 vols. Moscow, 1952.

Shestakov, P. D. "Moskovskii universitet v 40-kh goda," *RS,* LV (1887), 641–62.

Shevyrev, Stepan. Istoriia Imperatorskogo Moskovskogo universiteta, 1755–1855. Moscow, 1855.

Shil'der, N. "Aleksandr I," *RBS*, I (1896), 141–384.

———. "Imperator Nikolai I v 1848 i 1849 godakh," *IV*, LXXVIII (1899), 173–93.

Shmurlo, E. "Solov'ev (Sergei Mikhailovich)," *Brockhaus-Efron*, XXX (1900), 798–803.

Shpet, Gustav. Ocherk razvitiia russkoi filosofii. Vol. I. Petrograd, 1922.

Shtorkh, A., and F. Adelung. Sistematicheskoe obozrenie literatury v Rossii v techenie piatiletiia, s 1801 po 1806 god. 2 vols. St. Petersburg, 1810–11.

Shtrange, M. M. Russkoe obshchestvo i Frantsuzskaia Revoliutsiia, 1789–1794 gg. Moscow, 1956.

Shugurov, M. F. "Didro i ego otnosheniia k Ekaterine II-i," in Bartenev, ed., Osmnadtsatyi vek: Istoricheskii sbornik. Vol. I. Moscow, 1868, 257–305.

Sipovskii, V. V. Literaturnaia deiatel'nost' Lomonosova. St. Petersburg, 1911.

Skabichevskii, A. M. Istoriia noveishei russkoi literatury: 1848–1908 gg. 7th ed. St. Petersburg, 1909.

———. Ocherki istorii russkoi tsenzury (1700–1863). St. Petersburg, 1892.

Smentsovskii, Mikh. "Likhudy, Ioannikii i Sofronii," *RBS*, X (1914), 499–510.

———. Brat'ia Likhudy. St. Petersburg, 1899.

Smirnov, N. A. Zapadnoe vlianie na russkii iazyk v petrovskuiu epokhu. St. Petersburg, 1910.

Smirnov, S. "Tsenzurnaia vedomost 1786–1788 godov," in Bartenev, ed., Osmnadtsatyi vek: Istoricheskii sbornik. Vol. I, 425–52.

———. Istoriia Moskovskoi Slaviano-Greko-Latinskoi akademii. Moscow, 1855.

———. Istoriia Moskovskoi dukhovnoi akademii do eia preobrazovaniia (1814–1870). Moscow, 1879.

Sobol', S. L. Istoriia mikroskopa i mikroskopicheskikh issledovanii v Rossii v XVIII veke. Moscow-Leningrad, 1949.

Sobolevskii, A. I. Perevodnaia literatura Moskovskoi Rusi XIV–XVII vekov. Bibliograficheskie materialy. St. Petersburg, 1903.

———. "Iz perevodnoi literatury Petrovskoi epokhi. Bibliograficheskie materialy," Sbornik Otdeleniia russkogo iazyka i slovesnosti, LXXXIV (1908), No. 3, vii–47.

———. Lomonosov v istorii russkogo iazyka. St. Petersburg, 1911.

Solov'ev, Iu. I., and N. N. Ushakova. Otrazhenie estestvennonauchnykh trudov M. V. Lomonosova v russkoi literature XVIII i XIX vv. Moscow, 1961.

Solov'ev, Sergei M. Istoriia Rossii s drevneishikh vremen. Vols. I–III, 3rd ed.; Vols. IV–VI, 2nd ed.; n.d.

[———.] Zapiski Sergeia Mikhailovicha Solov'eva. Petrograd, n.d.

———. "Disput v Moskovskom universitete 25 avgusta 1769 goda: Donoshenie Sinodu Amvrosiia arkhiepiskopa moskovskogo," *RA*, 1875, No. 11, 312–13.

———. Sobranie sochinenii. St. Petersburg, n.d.

Somov, Osip. "Ocherk zhizni i uchenoi deiatel'nosti Mikhaila Vasil'evicha Ostrogradskogo," *ZAN*, III (1863), 1–29.

Sopikov, V. S. Opyt rossiiskoi bibliografii. Edited and supplemented by V. N. Rogozhin. 5 vols. St. Petersburg, 1904–6.

Speranskii, N. Krizis russkoi shkoly. Moscow, 1914.

Spiess, Otto. Leonhard Euler. Ein Beitrag zur Geistesgeschichte des XVIII Jahrhunderts. Leipzig, 1929.

Sprat, Thomas. History of the Royal Society. Edited by Jackson I. Cope and Harold Whitmore Jones. St. Louis: Washington University Studies, 1958.

Sreznevskii, I. I. Mysli ob istorii russkogo iazyka. Moscow, 1959.

————. "Svedeniia i zametki o maloizvestnykh i neizvestnykh pamiatniakh," *ZAN*, IX (1866), Supplement 3.

Sreznevskii, Vsevolod I., ed. Sbornik pisem I. T. Pososhkova k mitropolitu Stefanu Iavorskomu. St. Petersburg, 1900.

[Staël.] Oeuvres complètes de M-me la Baronne de Staël. Vol. XV. Paris, 1821.

Stähhlin, Karl. Aus den Papieren Jacob von Stählins: Ein biographischer Beitrag zur deutsch-russischen Kulturgeschichte des 18. Jahrhunderts. Leipzig, 1926.

Staniukovich, T. V. Kunstkamera Peterburgskoi Akademii nauk. Moscow-Leningrad, 1953.

Stankevich, A. Timofei Nikolaevich Granovskii. 3rd ed. Moscow, 1914.

"Staraia zapisnaia knizhka, nachataia v 1813 godu, neizvestnogo sochinitelia," in Bartenev, ed., Deviatnadtsatyi vek. Vol. II. Moscow, 1872, 219–96.

Stasiulevich, M. "O 'Zapiske' i 'Programme uchebnika vseobshchei istorii,' sostavlennykh v 1850 g. T. N. Granovskim," *VE*, September 1866, Section 4, 13–28.

Stepanov, M. "Zhozef de Mestr v Rossii," *Literaturnoe nasledstvo*, Vols. XXIX–XXX, Moscow, 1937, 577–726.

Stepanov, N. N. "M. V. Lomonosov i russkaia etnografiia (k 250-letiiu dnia rozhdeniia)," *Sovetskaia etnografiia*, 1961, No. 5, 107–23.

Sternberg, Leo. "Ethnography," in Fersman, ed., The Pacific, 161–88.

Stimson, Dorothy. Scientists and Amateurs: A History of the Royal Society. New York: Henry Schuman, 1948.

Stolipianskii, P. "Odin iz nezametnykh deiatelei Ekaterinenskoi epokhi. II. Iakov Pavlovich Kozel'skii," *RS*, CXXVIII (1906), 567–84.

Struve, O. V. "Ob uslugakh, okazannykh Petrom Velikim matematicheskoi geografii Rossii," *ZAN*, XXI (1872), 1–19.

Struve, V. I. "Obzor geograficheskikh rabot v Rossii," *Zapiski Russkogo Geograficheskogo obshchestva*, I (1846).

Suchowa, N. G. Alexander von Humboldt in der russischen Literatur. Leipzig, 1960.

Sukhomlinov, M. I. Istoriia Rossiiskoi Akademii. 8 vols. St. Petersburg, 1874–88. (Individual volumes appeared as Supplements to *ZAN*, XXIV, XXVII, XXIX, XXXII, XXXVIII, XLII, XLIX, and LVIII.)

————. Issledovaniia i staty po russkoi literature i prosveshcheniiu. 2 vols. St. Petersburg, 1889.

————. "Materialy dlia istorii obrazovaniia v Rossii v tsarstvovanie imperatora Aleksandra I," *ZMNP*, CXXVIII (1865), Section 2, 9–172.

————. Fridrikh-Tsezar Lagarp, vospitatel' imperatora Aleksandra I. St. Petersburg, 1871.

————. "Piatidesiatiletnii i stoletnii iubilei S.-Peterburgskoi Akademii nauk: 1776 i 1826 gg.," *RS*, VIII (1877), 1–20.

Sukhov, A. D. "A Russian Forerunner of Darwin," *VIMK*, 1958, No. 4, 198–201.

Svenske, Karl. "Materialy dlia istorii sostavleniia Atlasa Rossiiskoi Imperii, izdannogo Imperatorskoi Akademiei nauk v 1745 godu," *ZAN*, XIX (1866), Supplement 2.

Sviatskii, D. O. "Astronomicheskaia kniga 'Shestokryl' na Rusi XV veka," *Mirovedenie*, XVI (1927), 63–78.

Tarasevich, L. A. "Nauchnoe dvizhenie v Rossii v pervoi polovine XIX veka: Estestvoznanie i meditsina," *Granat-Ist*, VI (n.d.), 285–327.

Tarasov, E. "Russkie 'gettingentsy' pervoi chetverty XIX veka i vliianie ikh na razvitie liberalizma v Rossii," *Golos minuvshego*, 1914, No. 7, 195–209.

Tatishchev, V. N. Istoriia Rossiiskaia. Vol. I. Moscow-Leningrad, 1962.

————. "Razgovor o pol'ze nauk i uchilishch," *Chten*, 1887, No. 1, Section 1, 1–171.

————. Dukhovnaia moemu synu. St. Petersburg, 1896.

Thomas, R. Hinton. Liberalism, Nationalism and the German Intellectuals, 1822–1847. Cambridge: W. Hepper, 1951.

Tikhomirov, M. N., ed. Ocherki istorii istoricheskoi nauki v SSSR. Vol. I. Moscow, 1955.

————, ed. Istoriia Moskovskogo universiteta. Vol. I. Moscow, 1955.

————. "Russkaia istoriografiia XVIII veka," VI, 1948, No. 2, 94–99.

Tikhonravov, N. S. Sochineniia. Vol. III, Part 1. Moscow, 1898.

————. "Istoriia izdaniia 'Opyta o cheloveke' v perevode Popovskogo," RA, 1872, No. 7–8, 1311–22.

Timiriazev, A. K., ed. Ocherki po istorii fiziki v Rossii. Moscow, 1949.

Timiriazev, K. A. "Nauka," Granat-Ents, XXX (n.d.), 2–53.

————. "Probuzhdenie estestvoznaniia v tret'ei chetverti veka," Granat-Ist, VII (n.d.), 1–30.

[Timkovskii, I. F.] "Zapiski Il'i Fedorovicha Timkovskogo," RA, 1874, No. 6, 1377–1466.

Todhunter, I. A History of the Progress of the Calculus of Variations. Cambridge (England): Macmillan, 1861.

Tolstoi, D. A. "Vzgliad na uchebnuiu chast' v Rossii v XVIII stoletii do 1782 goda," ZAN, XLVII (1884), Supplement 2.

————. "Akademicheskaia gimnaziia v XVIII stoletii, po rukopisnym dokumentam Arkhiva Akademii nauk," ZAN, LI (1885), Supplement 2.

————. "Akademicheskii universitet v XVIII stoletii, po rukopisnym dokumentam Arkhiva Akademii nauk," ZAN, LI (1885), Supplement 3.

Tovey, G. "A Forgotten Electrician," Science Progress, XXXI (1936–37), 287–90.

Tsetlin, L. S. Iz istorii nauchnoi mysli v Rossii (Nauka i uchenye v Moskovskom universitete vo vtoroi polovine XIX veka). Moscow, 1958.

Turgenev, I. S. "Dva slova o Granovskom," Sovremennik, LIV (1855), Section 2, 83–86.

T-va, V. V. (O. Pochinkovskaia). "God raboty s znamenitym pisatelem (posviashchaetsia pamiati Fedora Mikhailovicha Dostoevskogo)," IV, XCV (1904), 488–542.

"Ustav Akademii nauk," PSZ, XXVII (1830), 20863, 786–800.

"Ustav Imperatorskoi Sanktpeterburgskoi Akademii nauk," PSZ, second series, XI (1837), Section 1, 8765, 14–25.

Ustrialov, N. G. Istoriia imperatora Petra Velikogo. Vol. III. St. Petersburg, 1858.

[Uvarov, Sergei Semenovich.] "Pis'mo (grafa) Sergeiia Semenovicha Uvarova k baronu Shteinu," RA, 1871, No. 1, 0129–34.

"Uvarov (graf Sergei Semenovich)," Brockhaus-Efron, XXXIV (1902), 419–20.

Val'ter, A. "Shkoly i stremleniia v russkoi meditsine," RV, XXIII (1859), Section: "Sovremennaia letopis'," 247–52.

Varsanof'eva, V. A. Moskovskoe obshchestvo ispytatelei prirody i ego znachenie v razvitii otechestvennoi nauki. Moscow, 1955.

Vasetskii, G. S., et al., eds. Ocherki po istorii filosofskoi i obshchestvenno-politicheskoi mysli narodov SSSR. 2 vols. Moscow, 1955–56.

———— and S. R. Mikulinskii, eds. Izbrannye proizvedeniia russkikh estestvoispytatelei pervoi poloviny XIX veka. Moscow, 1959.

———— and B. M. Kedrov. "M. V. Lomonosov—osnovopolozhnik materialisticheskoi filosofii i peredovogo estestvoznaniia v Rossii," in Vasetski et al., eds., Ocherki, I, 119–71.

Vasiliev, A. A. History of the Byzantine Empire. 2 vols. Madison: University of Wisconsin Press, 1958.
Vasiliev, A. V. Nicolai Ivanovich Lobachevsky. Tr. from the Russian by G. B. Halsted. Austin, Texas: The Neoman, 1894.
——. "Lobachevskii, Nikolai Ivanovich," *RBS*, X (1914), 528–65.
——. Matematika. Vol. I. Petrograd, 1921.
Vavilov, S. I. "Fizicheskaia optika Leonarda Eilera," in Deborin, ed., Leonard Eiler, 29–38.
—— et al., eds. Voprosy istorii otechestvennoi nauki. Moscow-Leningrad, 1949.
——. Sobranie sochinenii. Vol. III. Moscow, 1956.
——. Isaak N'iuton. 2nd ed. Moscow-Leningrad, 1945.
—— et al., eds. Nauchnoe nasledstvo. Vols. I and II. Moscow, 1946–51.
Vernadskii, G. V. Russkoe masonstvo v tsarstvovanie Ekateriny II. St. Petersburg, 1917.
Vernadskii, V. I. Mysli o sovremennom znachenii istorii znanii. Leningrad, 1927.
——, ed. Pervyi sbornik pamiati Bera (Trudy Komissii po istorii znanii, Vol. II). Leningrad, 1927.
Veselovskii, K. S. "Russkii filosof D. M. Vellanskii," *RS*, CV (1901), 6–19.
——. "Otnosheniia imp. Pavla k Akademii nauk," *RS*, XCIV (1898), 5–18, 225–46.
——. "Petr Velikii, kak uchreditel' Akademii nauk," *ZAN*, XXI (1872), 2–30.
——. "Poslednie gody proshlogo stoletiia v Akademii nauk," *RS*, XCIII (1898), 225–45.
——. Istoricheskoe obozrenie trudov Akademii nauk na pol'zu Rossii v proshlom i tekushchem stoletiiakh. St. Petersburg, 1865.
[——.] "Vospominaniia K. S. Veselovskogo. Vremia prezidentstva grafa D. N. Bludova v Akademii nauk, 1855–1864," *RS*, CVIII (1901), 495–528.
Veselovskii, N. I. Istoriia Imperatorskogo Russkogo arkheologicheskogo obshchestva za pervoe piatidesiatiletie ego sushchestvovaniia, 1846–1896. St. Petersburg, 1910.
Vinogradov, P. "Granovskii (Timofei Nikolaevich)," *Brockhaus-Efron*, IX (1893), 561–63.
Vinogradov, V. V., ed. Literaturnoe nasledstvo. Vol. LXVII. Moscow, 1959.
Virginskii, V. S. Tvortsy novoi tekhniki v krepostnoi Rossii. Moscow, 1962.
——. Zamechatel'nye russkie izobretateli Frolovy. Moscow, 1952.
[Vockerodt, Johann G.] "Rossiia pri Petre Velikom (Zapiski Vockerodta)," *RA*, 1873, No. 8, 1360–1434.
Voeikov, A. N. "Pervaia parovaia mashina v Evrope v opisanii eia izobretatelia Iv. Iv. Polzunova, 1763 god," *RS*, XL (1883), 631–44.
——. "Ivan Ivanovich Polzunov, izobretatel' pervoi v Evrope parovoi mashiny v 1763–1766 gg.," *RS*, XL (1883), 407–14.
Vorontsov-Vel'iaminov, B. A. Ocherki istorii astronomii v SSSR. Moscow, 1956.
——. "Istoriia astronomii v Rossii v XIX stoletii," *TIIE*, II (1948), 26–70.
Voskresenskii, A. A. "Ob uspekakh khimii v noveishee vremia," in Vasetskii and Mikulinskii, Izbrannye proizvedeniia, 396–402.
Vucinich, Alexander. "Mathematics in Russian Culture," *Journal of the History of Ideas*, XXI (1960), 161–79.
——. "Nikolai Ivanovich Lobachevskii: The Man Behind the First Non-Euclidean Geometry," *Isis*, LIII (1962), 465–81.
Vvedenskii, Aleksandr. Filosofskie ocherki. Prague, 1924.
Vysheslavtsev, B., et al. Problemy russkogo religioznogo soznaniia. Berlin, 1924.
Whitehead, Alfred N. Science in the Modern World. New York: Monitor Books, 1948.

Winter, E., and A. P. Iushkevich. "O perepiske Leonarda Eilera i G. F. Millera," in Lavrent'ev *et al.*, eds., Leonard Eiler, 465–97.

Winter, E., ed. Die deutsch-russische Begegnung und Leonhard Euler. Beiträge zu den Beziehungen zwischen der deutschen und der russischen Wissenschaft und Kultur im 18. Jahrhundert. Berlin, 1958.

——. Halle als Ausgangspunkt für deutsche Russlandkunde im 18. Jahrhundert. Berlin, 1953.

——. "Die Jesuiten in Russland (1772 bis 1820). Ein Beitrag zur Auseinandersetzung zwischen Aufklärung und Restauration," in: Forschen und Wirken: Festschrift zur 150-Jahr-Feier der Humboldt-Universität zu Berlin, 1810–1960. Vol. III. Berlin, 1960, 167–91.

——. "Euler und die Begegnung der deutschen mit der russischen Aufklärung," in Winter, ed., Die deutsch-russische Begegnung, 1–18.

[Wolff, Christian.] Briefe von Christian Wolff aus den Jahren 1719–1753. Ein Beitrag zur Geschichte der Kaiserlichen Academie der Wissenschaften zu St. Petersburg. St. Petersburg, 1866.

Wrangel, Ferdinand von. Narrative of an Expedition to the Polar Sea, in the Years 1820, 1821, 1822, and 1823. Tr. by E. Sabine. London: James Madden, 1840.

Zabelin, I. E. "Pervoe vodvorenie v Moskve grekolatinskoi i obshchei evropeiskoi nauki," *Chten,* 1886, No. 4, Section 4, 1–24.

——. Opyty izucheniia russkikh drevnostei i istorii. 2 vols. Moscow, 1872–73.

Zagoskin, N. P. Istoriia Imperatorskogo Kazanskogo universiteta za pervyia sto let ego sushchestvovaniia, 1804-1904. 4 vols. Kazan, 1902–6.

——, ed. Za sto let: Biograficheskii slovar' professorov i prepodavatelei Imperatorskogo Kazanskogo universiteta (1804–1904). 2 vols. Kazan, 1904.

Zamyslovskii, E. Tsarstvovanie Fedora Alekseevicha. Vol. I. St. Petersburg, 1871.

"Zapiski Imperatorskogo Russkogo geograficheskogo obshchestva, knizhka V," book review in *Sovremennik,* XXVII (1851), Section 5, 26–33.

Zertsalov, A. N., and S. A. Belokurov, eds. "O nemetskikh shkolakh v Moskve v pervoi chetverti XVIII v. (1701–1715 gg.); Dokumenty moskovskikh arkhivov," *Chten,* 1907, No. 1, i–xli, 1–244.

Zhigalova, L. V., and M. I. Radovskii. "Nauchnye sviazi russkikh i angliiskikh biologov," *TIIE-T,* XLI, 1961, 94–111.

Zhmuds'kii, O. Z., ed. Istoriia Kiivs'kogo universiteta. Kiev, 1859.

Zinin, N. N. "Vzgliad na sovremennoe napravlenie organicheskoi khimii," in Vasetskii and Mikulinskii, Izbrannye proizvedeniia, 403–14.

Zmeev, L. F. Russkie vrachebniki; issledovanie v oblasti nashei drevnei vrachebnoi pis'mennosti. St. Petersburg, 1896.

Zubov, V. P. "Lomonosov i Slaviano-greko-latinskaia akademiia," *TIIE-T,* I (1954), 5–52.

——. "Vopros o 'nedelimykh' i beskonechnom v drevne-russkom literaturnom pamiatnike XV veka," *IMI,* II (1950), 407–30.

——. Istoriografiia estestvennykh nauk v Rossii (XVIII v.—pervaia polovina XIX v.). Moscow, 1956.

Zuev, Vasilii. "Teoriia prevrashcheniia nasekomykh, primenennaia drugim zhivotnym," *TIIE-T,* IV (1955) 281–89.

Zviagintsev, O. E. "Razvitie teorii khimicheskogo stroeniia A. M. Butlerova v neorganicheskoi khimii," *Voprosy istorii estestvoznaniia i tekhniki,* I (1956), 70–81.

Zvorikine, A. A. "Remarques sur l'histoire des inventions et de la pensée scientifique et technique russes des XVIIIe et XIXe siècles," *Cahiers d'Histoire Mondiale,* special number (Contributions à l'histoire Russe), 1958, 183–211.

Index